Fiber & Fabric Mania! A Travel Guide

2019

Published by Direction Press

A quick guide to using our book.

All needle arts shops are listed by state. On each state map, you can see all the cities that have needle arts shops. The cities are listed alphabetically, and under each city are the needle arts shops in the city.

We mark each shop by the type of goods they carry:

Q = Quilting	M = Machines	C = Cross Stitch
Y = Yarn	N = Needlepoint	E = Embroidery
S = Spinning	W = Weaving	**Unconfirmed Shops*

We hope this makes it easier for you to find what you are looking for!

A Note from the Publisher:

Welcome to NeedleTravel.com
Fiber and Fabric Mania! A Travel Guide

I'm so excited and grateful on the arrival of our precious grandson, Aden, 9 months ago. My travels take me to Boston more than anywhere else to visit him. Proudly, this is our 16th year publishing the only complete and confirmed needle arts travel guide. Our dedicated staff has scoured the country from coast to coast to find every brick and mortar store. They have made thousands of phone calls in an effort to speak to each owner to confirm the information we have provided. We appreciate your input as well. Please let us know if you have any updates or suggestions for us.

We want to express our special thanks to those in the industry that help support us. Please be sure to continue supporting our sponsors as they make this book possible.

Download our free NeedleTravel app for the Ipone and Android. We continue to update and improve it. Check out our companion website NeedleTravel.com. Both are more important than ever and we are working on updating them.

My personal thanks to Juli, Carol, Jessie, Cathy, Lisa, Rossya, Dani, Pam, Betty and the other members of our wonderful team of dedicated people who have made this book so successful.

Kudos to Kay and Lisa who join me in traveling to shows where we meet many shop owners. They are the friendly, smiling faces in our booth. Be sure to stop by and say "hi".

Special thanks to our customers for all the wonderful comments we've received on our past editions. You have helped make us a tremendous success. Look for new and exciting things to come.

Safe Travels.
Creatively yours,

Michele Merin, Publisher

Follow us on Twitter, Facebook and Pinterest

Table of Contents

Listings by State

Alabama

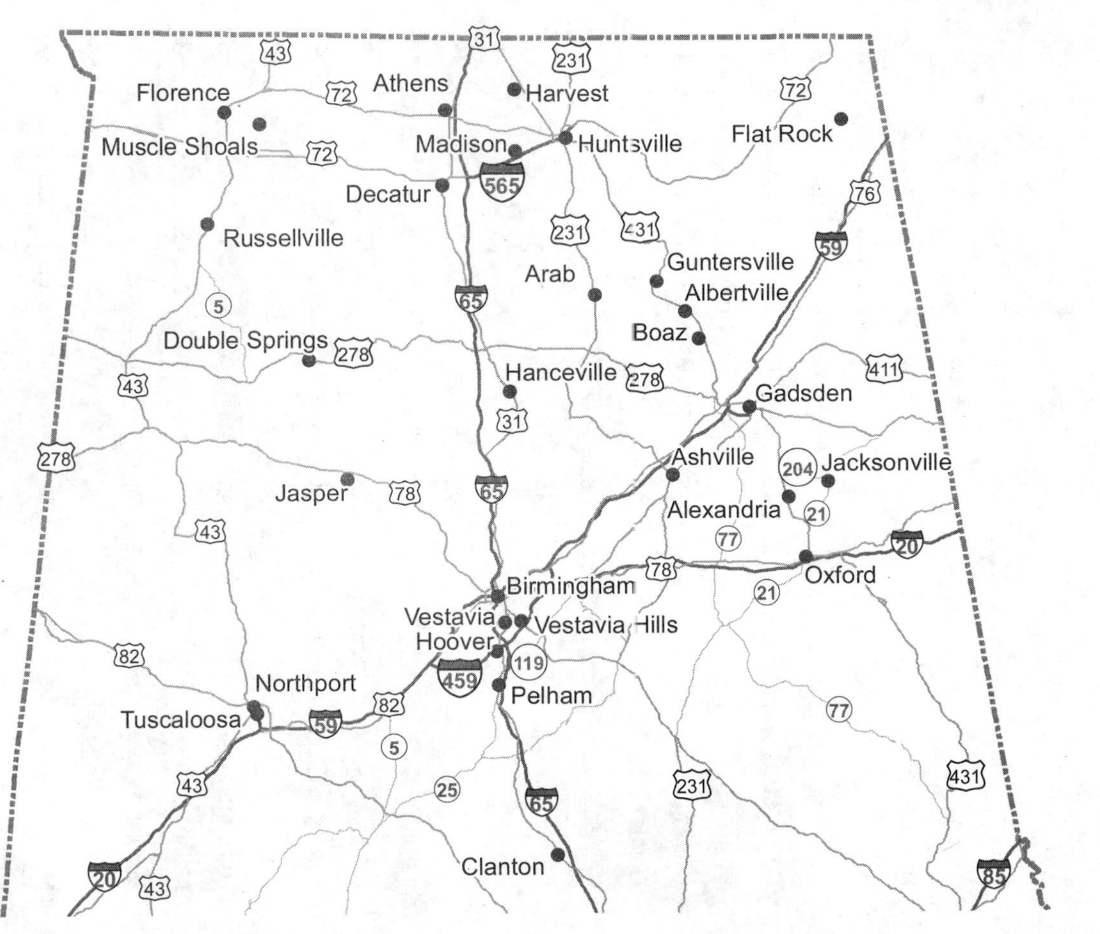

Florence
Athens
Harvest
Muscle Shoals
Madison
Huntsville
Flat Rock
Decatur
Russellville
Arab
Guntersville
Albertville
Boaz
Double Springs
Hanceville
Gadsden
Ashville
Jacksonville
Jasper
Alexandria
Oxford
Birmingham
Vestavia
Vestavia Hills
Hoover
Pelham
Northport
Tuscaloosa
Clanton

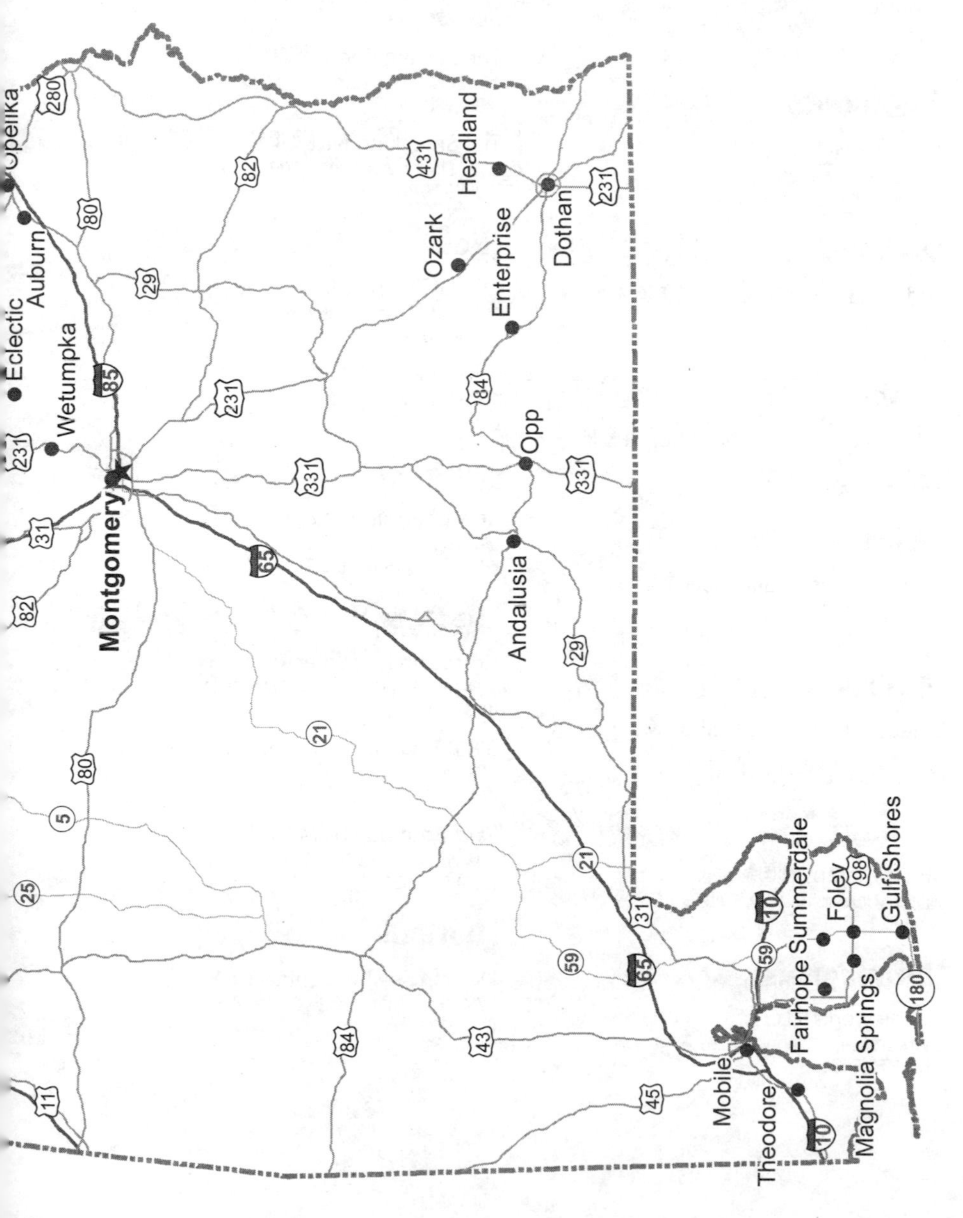
Opelika
Auburn
Eclectic
Wetumpka
Montgomery
Ozark
Headland
Enterprise
Dothan
Opp
Andalusia
Mobile
Theodore
Fairhope
Summerdale
Foley
Magnolia Springs
Gulf Shores
280
80
82
29
85
231
431
84
331
31
65
21
5
25
59
43
45
11
10
98
180

Alabama

Albertville

Sew Irresistible Q E M
212 N. Broad Street, Suite B, 35950
(256) 878-0023

Alexandria

Yvie's Y W S
7534 US Highway 431, 36250
(256) 225-7986

Andalusia

Andalusia Sewing Center Q E C M
900 Westgate Plaza, 36420
(334) 222-4124

Arab

Patrick's One Stop Fabric Shop Q Y N
155 N. Main Street, 35016
(256) 586-1901

Ashville

Ashville House Quilt Shop Q
35 Third Street, 35953
(205) 594-7046

Athens

3 Hens & A Chick Quilt Shop Q
1114 US Highway 31S, 35611
(256) 771-2040

Auburn

Stitch Therapy Q E M
2140 E. University Drive, Suite B, 36830
(334) 821-7781

Birmingham

Needleworks, LLC N
2810 Crescent Avenue, 35209
(205) 870-5191

Robin's Sewing Shoppe E M
5886 Trussville Crossing Blvd, 35173
(205) 655-3388

Sewing Machine Mart E M
1722 28th Avenue, Suite C, 35209
(205) 870-1931

The Sewing Room Q E M
1040 Inverness Corners, 35242
(205) 980-1112

The Smocking Bird Q E M
2831 Linden Avenue, 35209
(205) 879-7662

Boaz

Out Of The Box Q C
103 S. Main Street, 35957
(256) 840-0059

Wilson's Fabric Outlet, Inc. Q E N C
1524 US Highway 431N, 35957
(256) 593-6501

Clanton

Sew Charming, LLC Q E
213 7th Street N, 35045
(205) 903-4133 or (205) 294-4747

Decatur

Cross Stitch Peddler C
124 14th Street SW, Suite D1, 35601
(256) 350-7780

S & R Sewing & Vacuum Center Q E M
628 14th Street SE, 35601
(256) 350-0444

Yarn Boutique by Mitsie Y
302 2nd Avenue SE, 35601
(256) 580-5510

Dothan

Dothan Sewing Center Q E M
2797 Ross Clark Circle, 36301
(334) 794-3177

Double Springs

Fine Yarns on Main Y
25215 Highway 195, 35553
(205) 489-8009

Eclectic

Strickland Cloth Barn Inc. Q
8 Claud Road, 36024
(334) 541-3214

Enterprise

Enterprise Sewing Q M
732 Glover Avenue, 36330
(334) 347-8797

Fairhope

In The Making Q Y
314 De La Mare Avenue, Suite A, 36532
(251) 270-7028

Flat Rock

Moore's Discount Fabric and Quilt Shop Q
19093 AL Highway 71, 35966
(256) 632-2340

Florence

Calico Rose Quilt Shop Q E
1707 Darby Drive, 35630
(256) 760-8227

Thread Fabric Store Q E Y
1609 Darby Drive, 35630
(256) 275-7112

Foley

Clara's Loom / Coastal Textile Center Y W S
7518 Riverwood Drive, 36535
(251) 943-2960
W-Sa 10-4
www.clarasloom.com

Gadsden

Sew Irresistible Q E M
2104 Rainbow Drive, 35901
(256) 459-5355

The Taming of the Ewe Y W S
541 Broad Street, 35901
(256) 546-9090

Gulf Shores

SEA Quilt Shoppe Q
22131 Cotton Creek Drive (CR 4E), 36542
(251) 968-7327

Guntersville

S & R Sewing & Vacuum Center Q E M
2020 Gunter Avenue, 35976
(256) 486-3630

Stitchers Haven Q Y N C
1600 Gunter Avenue, 35976
(256) 582-8234

Hanceville

Sew Blessed Fabric and Embroidery Q E
445 Alabama Highway 69S, Suite C, 35077
(205) 790-7339

Harvest

Little Barn Inc. Y S
173 McKee Road, 35749
(256) 755-0129

Headland

Quilted Creations Q E
24 S. Main Street, 36345
(334) 693-5808

Hoover

Thimbles Q E M
181 Main Street, Suite 221, 35244
(205) 682-6008

Huntsville

Barb's Sewing Center Q E M
2310-A Whitesburg Drive S, 35801
(256) 539-2414

Creative Sewing Q
8415-S Whitesburg Drive, 35802
(256) 883-4414

Fiber Art Work Y S
817B Regal Drive SW, 35801
(256) 656-0163

Huntsville Sew and Vac Q E M
1847 University Drive NW, 35801
(256) 536-3757
Handi Quilter® Authorized Retailer
Designed by a Quilter, for Quilters.®

Just Add Needles C
602 Nightingale Circle, 35803
(256) 529-2766

Patches and Stitches Q E N C
603 Humes Avenue NE, 35801
(256) 533-3886 or (877) 743-7397

S & R Sewing & Vacuum Center Q E M
1407 Memorial Parkway NW, Suite #1, 35801
(256) 536-5696

Sparkle Studio Y W S
2211 Seminole Drive SW, Studio 103, 35805
(256) 651-9121

Threaded Needle Too Q M
1847 University Drive NW, 35801
(256) 585-1339

Jacksonville

Yarns by HomePlace Farm Y W S
402 Pelham Road N, Suite 4, 36265
(256) 282-8798

Jasper

Sew Simple Q E M
215 Highway 195N, 35503
(205) 295-2229

Madison

Hook a Frog Fiber and Fun Y W S
105 Church Street, Suite C, 35758
(256) 325-0572

Magnolia Springs

Magnolia Quilt Company Q
300 River Route, 36555
(251) 422-9437

The Nest at Magnolia Springs Q
14906 US Highway 98, 36555
(251) 965-1988

Mobile

Mobile Yarn Y W
4318 Downtowner Loop N., Suite M, 36609
(251) 308-2257
Tu-Sa 10-6, Th open late.
www.mobileyarn.com

All About Sewing Inc. Q E C
590 Schillinger Road S, Suite D, 36695
(251) 634-3133

American Sew and Vac E M
3454 Springhill Avenue, 36608
(251) 344-9430

Peanut Butter-n-Jelly Kids Q E
3300 Old Shell Road, 36607
(251) 479-8811

Montgomery

Sew Bernina Q E M
51 N. Burbank Drive, 36117
(334) 274-0887
Handi Quilter® Authorized Retailer
Designed by a Quilter, for Quilters.®

The Needle Bug N
7012 Vaughn Road, 36116
(334) 270-0064

Muscle Shoals

Ken's Sewing Center Q E M
912 East 2nd Street, 35661
(256) 381-0161

Northport

Faye's Fabric Sew and Vac Ⓠ Ⓜ
3617 McFarland Blvd., 35476
(205) 339-0444

Opelika

Opelika Sewing Center Ⓠ Ⓔ Ⓒ Ⓜ
3305 Pepperell Parkway, 36801
(334) 749-9522

Opp

Oh Sew Pretty LLC Ⓠ Ⓔ
600 Highway 52, 36467
(334) 208-4508
M-F 10-5, Sa 10-2
https://www.facebook.com/ohsewprettyembroidery/

Oxford

Wilson's Fabric Outlet Inc. Ⓠ
832 Snow Street, Suites E & F, 36203
(256) 831-8804

Ozark

Front Porch Quilt Shoppe Ⓠ
199 N. Highway 231, 36360
(334) 445-3521
M-F 10-5, Sa 10-3
www.frontporchquiltshoppe.com

Pelham

Zig Zag Sewing Studio Ⓠ Ⓔ Ⓜ
2156 Pelham Parkway, Suite C, 35124
(205) 624-4647

Russellville

Home Place Quilt Shop Ⓠ
865 E. Lawrence Street, 35654
(256) 324-1032

Summerdale

Fabrics by the Pound Ⓠ Ⓔ
102 State Highway 59S, 36580
(251) 989-6505

Theodore

Susan's Heirloom and Quilter's Fabric Ⓠ Ⓔ Ⓜ
6851 Old Pascagoula Road, 36582
(251) 653-7784

Tuscaloosa

General Sewing and Vacuum Ⓔ Ⓜ
1711 Hackberry Lane, 35401
(205) 752-3939

Vestavia

Knit Happenz at Memory Hagler Knitting Ⓨ
2126 Columbiana Road, 35216
(205) 822-7875

Vestavia Hills

In The Making Ⓠ Ⓨ
4232 Dolly Ridge Road, 35243
(205) 298-1309 or (877) 298-1309

Wetumpka

Beth's Heirloom Sewing Ⓠ Ⓔ
12 Cambridge Court, 36092
(334) 567-2448

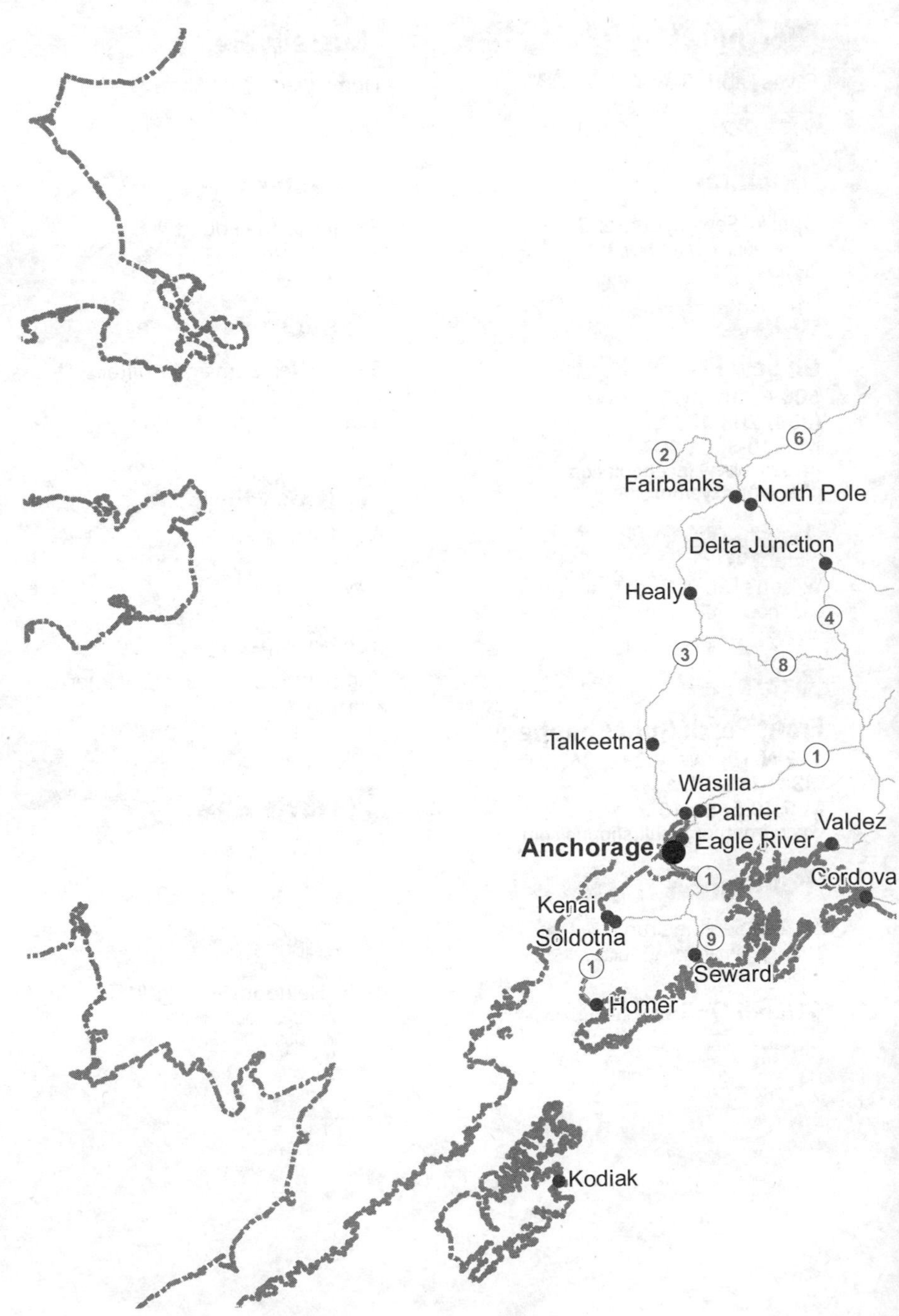

6
2
Fairbanks
North Pole
Delta Junction
Healy
4
3
8
Talkeetna
1
Wasilla
Palmer
Valdez
Anchorage
Eagle River
1
Cordova
Kenai
Soldotna
9
1
Seward
Homer
Kodiak

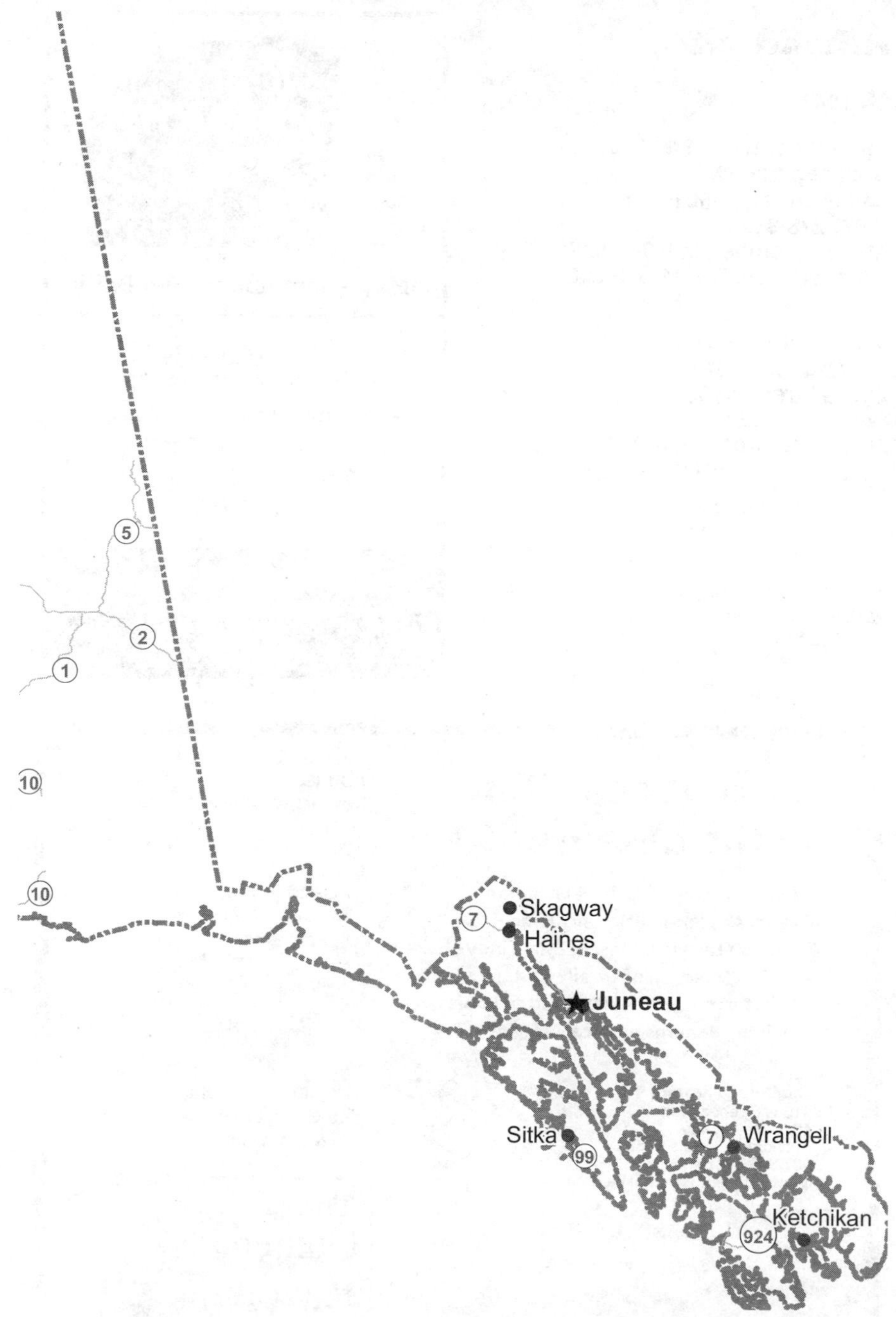

5
2
1
10
10
Skagway
7
Haines
Juneau
Sitka
99
7
Wrangell
Ketchikan
924

Alaska

Anchorage

The Quilted Raven Ⓠ Ⓒ

➡ **SEE AD BELOW**

415 G Street, 99501
(907) 278-3521
May-September: M-F 9-6, SaSu 10-6;
October-April: ThF 11-6, Sa 10-6
www.quiltedravenalaska.com

Wooly Mammoth Ⓨ

➡ **SEE AD AT RIGHT**

416 G Street, 99501
(907) 278-3524
May-September, 10-6 Daily
www.woolymammothalaska.com

Far North Fibers Ⓨ Ⓦ Ⓢ
3960 Doroshin Avenue, 99516
(907) 279-0332

Far North Yarn Co. Ⓨ
2636 Spenard Road, Suite 6, 99503
(907) 258-5648

Quilt Zone Ⓠ
510 W. Tudor Road, Suite 2, 99503
(907) 561-2020

Seams Like Home Quilt Shoppe ⓆⒺ
2153 E. 88th Avenue, 99507
(907) 677-8790

The Quilt Tree / Yarn Branch ⓆⓎ
341 E. Benson Blvd., Suite 5, 99503
(907) 561-4115

Cordova

Forget-Me-Not Fabrics & Crafts ⓆⒺⒸ
201 Breakwater Avenue, 99574
(907) 424-3656

The Net Loft ⒺⓎⓃⓌⓈⒸ
140 Adams Street, 99574
(907) 424-7337

Delta Junction

The Calico Cow ⓆⒺⓂ
1407 Grizzly Lane, 99737
(907) 895-5210

Eagle River

Twisted Sisters' Quilty Pleasures ⓆⒺ
➡ SEE AD BELOW
11401 Old Glenn Highway 101-A, 99577
(907) 694-8777
Tu-Sa 10-7, Su 12-5
www.twistedquilting.com

The Quilt Cache ⓆⒺ
12812 Old Glenn Highway, Unit A-2, 99577
(907) 622-7858

The Tangled Skein ⓎⓌⓈ
11753 Celestial Street, 99577
(907) 622-9276

Fairbanks

A Weaver's Yarn Ⓔ Ⓨ Ⓝ Ⓦ Ⓢ Ⓒ

➡ SEE AD BELOW

1810 Alaska Way, 99709
(907) 374-1995
Tu-F 10-6, Sa 10-4, also by appt.
www.aweaversyarn.com

Northern Threads Ⓠ Ⓜ

1875 University Avenue S, Suite 2, 99709
(907) 455-0299 or (877) 840-3237
M-Sa 10-6, Su 12-5
www.northernthreads.net

Inua Wool Shoppe Ⓨ Ⓢ
3677 College Road, Suite 3, 99709
(907) 479-5830

That Old Sew and Sew Ⓠ Ⓨ Ⓜ
519 1st Avenue, 99701
(907) 799-9031

Haines

Dalton City Yarn Emporium Ⓨ

312 Main Street, 99827
(907) 766-2779
M-Sa 11-5
www.daltoncityyarn.com

Healy

Granma's Quilt Shop Ⓠ
4 Coal Street, 99743
(907) 683-2200

Homer

Ulmer's Drug and Hardware Ⓠ Ⓔ Ⓨ Ⓝ Ⓦ Ⓢ Ⓒ
3858 Lake Street, Suite 5, 99603
(907) 235-8594

Juneau

Changing Tides Ⓠ Ⓔ Ⓨ Ⓝ Ⓒ

➡ SEE AD AT RIGHT

175 S. Franklin Street, Suite 203, 99801
(907) 523-6084
Winter: Tu-Thur 11-5:30, Fri - Sa 11-5;
Summer: Daily 8:30-7 and beyond;
http://www.facebook.com/pages/Changing-Tides/386487671401122

Ben Franklin Ⓠ Ⓔ Ⓨ Ⓝ Ⓒ
233 Front Street, 99801
(907) 586-6762

RainTree Quilting Ⓠ Ⓔ Ⓜ
2213 Dunn Street, 99801
(907) 789-7900

Kenai

Kenai Fabric Center Ⓠ Ⓔ Ⓨ Ⓜ
115 N. Willow Street, 99611
(907) 283-4595

Ketchikan

Soft Goods and Green Things Fabric Store Ⓠ Ⓒ
2417 Tongass Avenue, Suite 218, 99901
(907) 225-3222

The Hive on the Creek Ⓠ Ⓨ Ⓒ
716 Totem Way, #100, 99901
(907) 225-9161

The Whale's Tail Quilt Shop Ⓠ Ⓜ
5 Salmon Landing, Suite 204, 99901
(907) 225-5422

Kodiak

Flying Geese Fabric & Quilts Ⓠ Ⓒ
202 Center Avenue, Suite 320, 99615
(907) 486-8700

The Rookery Ⓠ Ⓔ Ⓨ Ⓝ Ⓦ Ⓢ Ⓒ
104 Center Avenue, Suite 100B, 99615
(907) 486-0052

North Pole

Ben Franklin Ⓠ Ⓔ Ⓨ Ⓝ Ⓒ
301 N. Santa Claus Lane, Suite 16, 99705
(907) 488-8544

Palmer

Just Sew Ⓠ Ⓨ
579 S. Alaska Street, 99645
(907) 745-3649

Musk Ox Farm Ⓨ Ⓢ
12850 E. Archie Road, 99645
(907) 745-4151

Seward

Sew'n Bee Cozy Ⓠ Ⓔ Ⓝ Ⓒ
211 4th Avenue, 99664
(907) 224-7647
Winter: Tu-Sa 10-6; Summer: Every Day 10- 6
www.sewnbeecozy.com

Sitka

Abby's Reflection Apparel & Quiltworks Ⓠ Ⓨ Ⓒ Ⓜ
231 Lincoln Street, 99835
(907) 747-3510
Winter: M-Sa 10:30-5:30; Summer: Every Day 9-6
www.abbysreflection.com

Ben Franklin Ⓠ Ⓔ Ⓨ Ⓝ Ⓒ
216 Lincoln Street, 99835
(907) 747-3336

Knitting With Class Ⓨ
106 Chirikov Drive, 99835
(907) 738-0957

Skagway

Aurora Yarns of Alaska Ⓨ Ⓢ
340 5th Avenue, 99840
(907) 983-3707 or (800) 981-5432

Rushin' Tailor's Quilt Alaska Ⓠ Ⓨ Ⓝ Ⓒ
370 Third Avenue, 99840
(907) 983-2397

Soldotna

Bearly Threaded Quilting Too Ⓠ Ⓔ Ⓜ
44332 Sterling Highway, Suite 8, 99669
(907) 262-3262

Top of the Whorl Ⓨ Ⓢ
105 Robin Place, 99669
(907) 260-9276

Talkeetna

Talkeetna Gifts and Collectables Ⓠ Ⓨ Ⓒ
22253 S. Talkeetna Spur, 99676
(907) 733-2710

Valdez

Salmonberry Quilting Ⓠ
204 Raven Drive, 99686
(907) 255-8955

Smiling Seal Sewing Ⓠ Ⓨ
354 Fairbanks Street, 99686
(907) 835-3222

Wasilla

Sylvia's Quilt Depot Ⓠ
1261 Seward Meridian Road, Suite E, 99654
(907) 376-6468

Wrangell

Haystack Ⓠ
1002 Case Avenue, 99929
(907) 874-3648

NeedleTravel

Download our App!

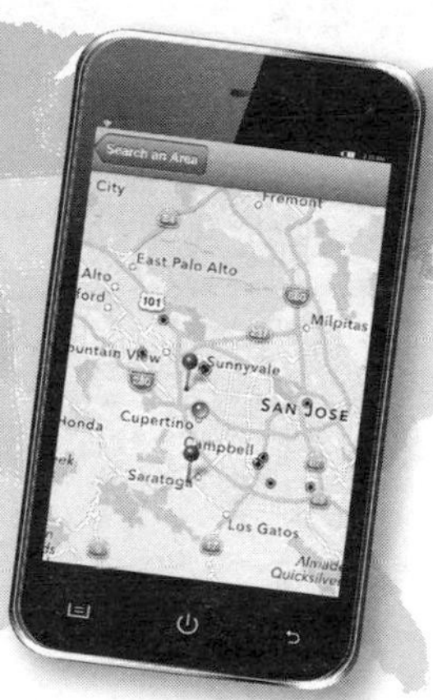

Find Shops From Your Phone

It's Free!

Check us out on:

www.facebook.com/Needletravel

http://www.pinterest.com/needletravel

https://twitter.com/Needletravel

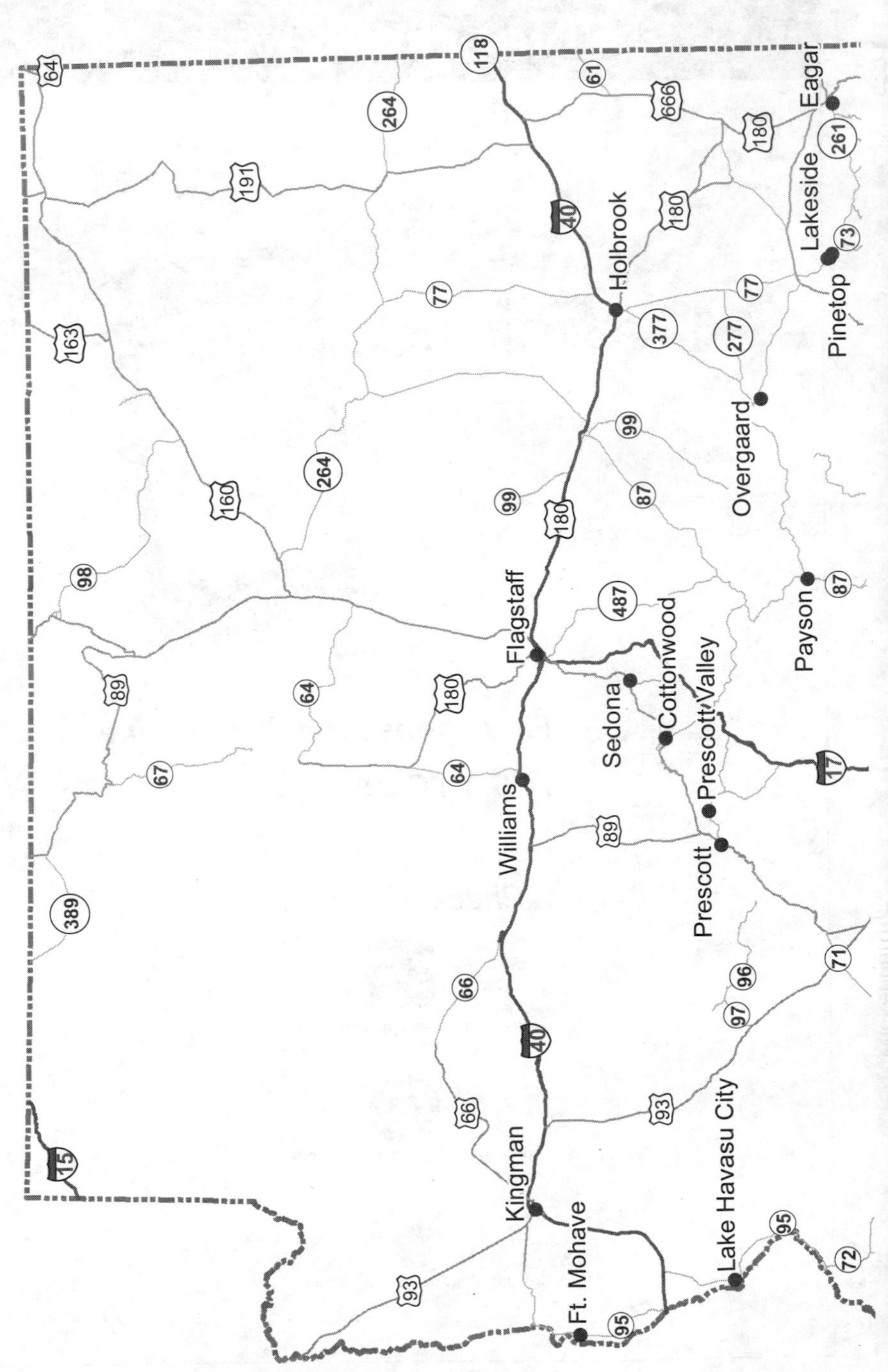
Holbrook
Flagstaff
Williams
Kingman
Ft. Mohave
Lake Havasu City
Sedona
Cottonwood
Prescott Valley
Prescott
Payson
Overgaard
Pinetop
Lakeside
Eagar
118
64
61
666
264
191
180
40
77
377
277
73
261
163
99
87
160
98
487
89
17
67
389
66
93
96
97
71
15
95
72

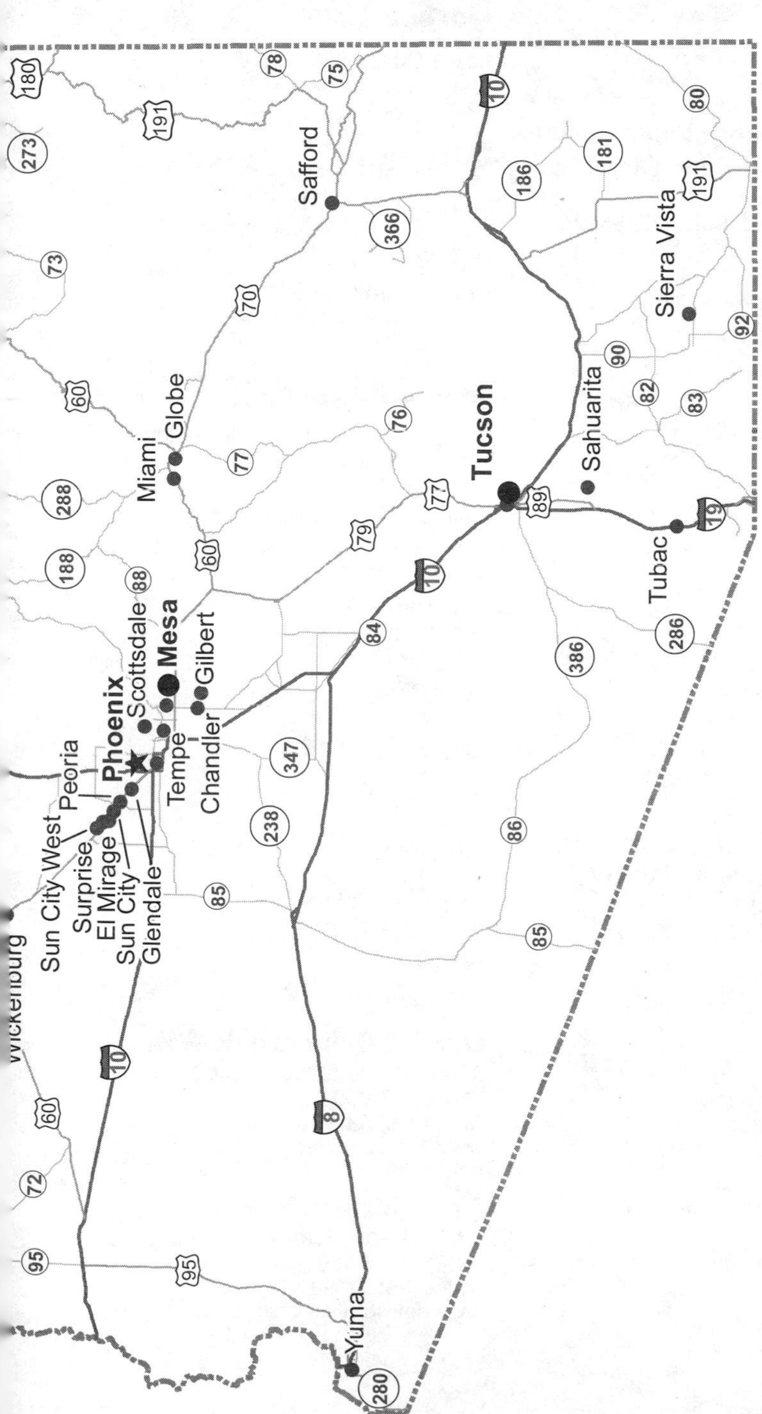
Safford
Globe
Miami
Tucson
Sahuarita
Sierra Vista
Tubac
Scottsdale
Mesa
Gilbert
Phoenix
Peoria
Tempe
Chandler
Sun City West
Surprise
El Mirage
Sun City
Glendale
Yuma

Arizona

Chandler

35th Avenue Fabric World (inside 35th Avenue Sew and Vac) Q M
➡ SEE AD AT RIGHT
4939 W. Ray Road, Suite 27, 85226
(480) 961-7363
M-F 9-6, Sa 9-5, Su 10-4
www.35thavesewandvac.com

Cutting Edge Quilts Q
64 S. San Marcos Place, 85225
(480) 857-3443

Cottonwood

Quilters Quarters & Bernina Too Q E M
51 Verde Heights Drive, 86326
(928) 634-8161

Eagar

Quilter's Haven, LLC Q E
41 W. 2nd Avenue, Suite A, 85925
(928) 333-2739

El Mirage

35th Avenue Fabric World (inside 35th Avenue Sew and Vac) Q M
➡ SEE AD AT RIGHT
12213 NW Grand Avenue, 85335
(623) 583-0070
M-F 9-5, Sa 9-3
www.35thavesewandvac.com

Flagstaff

Odegaard's Sewing Center Q M
2109 N. 4th Street, 86004
(928) 774-2331 or (800) 360-2331

Purl In The Pines Y W S
2544 N. 4th Street, 86004
(928) 774-9334

Fort Mohave

Roxy's Quilt & Sewing Q E N C
5221 Highway 95, Suites 6, 7 & 8, 86426
(928) 788-2400

Gilbert

Bolts and More Q E
3133 S. Lindsay Road, Suite 107, 85295
(480) 899-4611

Doro's Quiltworks & More Q
4502 E. Juanita Avenue, 85234
(623) 217-6081

Glendale

Mulqueen Sewing & Fabric Centers Q M
7838 N. 59th Avenue, 85301
(623) 934-0084

Quilted Country Bear LLC Q
5930 W. Greenway Road, Suite 21, 85306
(602) 368-2536 or (800) 889-9898

Sally Knits Y
6823 N. 58th Avenue, 85301
(623) 934-8367

Globe

Hill Street Mall Q E Y N C
383 S. Hill Street, 85501
(928) 425-0022

Holbrook

Painted Desert Quilts Q
206 Navajo Blvd., 86025
(928) 524-5600

Kingman

Connie's Quilters Hide-A-Way Q
310 E. Beale Street, 86401
(928) 753-9096
M-F 10-5, Sa 10-4
www.facebook.com/pages/Connies-Quilters-Hide-A-Way/141210895925218

The Spinster Y W S
624 E. Beale Street, 86401
(928) 753-3660
M-F 10-5:30, Sa 10-4
www.spinsterinkingman.com

Donna's Quilt Shop Q
310 E. Oak Street, 86401
(928) 718-5535

Handi Quilter® Authorized Retailer
Designed by a Quilter, for Quilters.®

Lake Havasu City

Copper Canyon Quilting Q
375 El Camino Way, 86403
(928) 855-0445
W-Sa 9-4
https://www.facebook.com/Copper-Canyon-Quilting-123619754980165/

Fabrics Unlimited Q M
2089 W. Acoma Blvd., Suite 1, 86403
(928) 733-6331

Handi Quilter® Authorized Retailer
Designed by a Quilter, for Quilters.®

Lakeside

Amazing Quilts Q
2964 W. White Mountain Blvd., 85929
(928) 368-5567

Handi Quilter® Authorized Retailer
Designed by a Quilter, for Quilters.®

Mesa

A Quilter's Oasis Q
9963 E. Baseline Road, Suite 105, 85209
(480) 354-4077

Attic Needlework & Collectibles E C
1837 W. Guadalupe, Suite 109, 85202
(480) 898-1838 or (888) 942-8842

Fiber Factory Inc. Y W S
216 W. Main Street, 85201
(480) 969-4346 or (888) 969-9276

Mad B's Quilt & Sew Q M
7415 E. Southern Avenue, #108, 85209
(480) 964-8914

Mulqueen Sewing & Fabric Centers Q M
3716 E. Main Street, 85205
(480) 545-0778

Handi Quilter® Authorized Retailer
Designed by a Quilter, for Quilters.®

Miami

Julie's Sewing Corner & Quilt Shop Q
600 W. Sullivan Street, 85539
(928) 473-7633

Overgaard

Rim Country Quilts & PaperCrafts Q Y
2361 Highway 260, Bison Ranch #4, 85933
(480) 271-4864 or (480) 271-4864

Payson

The Copper Needle Q M
201 W. Main Street, Suite B, 85541
(928) 363-4036

Peoria

You Can Quilt Q
9720 W. Peoria Avenue, Suite 108, 85345
(623) 594-2783

Phoenix

35th Avenue Fabric World (inside 35th Ave. Sew & Vac) Q M
➔ SEE AD BELOW
3548 W. Northern Avenue, 85051
(602) 841-5427 or (877) 242-6282
M-F 9-6, Sa 9-5, Su 10-4
www.35thavesewandvac.com

Handi Quilter® Authorized Retailer
Designed by a Quilter, for Quilters.®

Family Arts Needlework Shop (N)
➡ SEE AD BELOW
5555 N. 7th Street, Suite 144, 85014
(602) 277-0694
M-Sa 9:30-4
www.familyartsneedlework.com

Modern Quilting (Q)
4649 E. Cactus Road, 85032
(602) 710-1771

Phoenix Knits (Y)
5044 N. 7th Street, Suite B, 85014
(602) 277-1335

SAS Fabrics (Q)
1111 E. Indian School Road, 85014
(602) 279-2171

SAS TOO (Q)
1101 E. Indian School Road, 85014
(602) 248-4136

The Bernina Connection LLC (Q)(M)
4219 E. Indian School Road, Suite 103, 85018
(602) 553-8350

The Olde World Quilt Shoppe (Q)(E)
30855 N. Cave Creek Road, Suite 134, 85331
(480) 473-2171

The Other Quilt Shop (Q)
4233 W. Thunderbird Road, 85053
(602) 843-1554

Pinetop

Made at Nana's (Q)
1684 E. White Mountain Blvd., Suite 1, 85935
(928) 367-1929

Pinetop-Lakeside

Pinetop Star (Q)(Y)
103 W. Yeager Lane, 85929
(928) 367-1709

Prescott

Fiber Creek (Y)(W)(S)
➡ SEE AD BELOW
1046 Willow Creek Road, Suite 123, 86301
(928) 717-1774
MTuThFSa 10-5, W 10-8
www.fibercreekprescott.com

Studio Three (Y)(W)(S)
1440 W. Gurley Street, 86305
(928) 778-0307

Prescott Valley

ClothPlus Quilt Shop (Q)
6479 E. Copper Hill Drive, 86314
(928) 772-5010

Quilt n' Sew Connection (Q)(E)(M)
6546 2nd Street, Suite A, 86314
(928) 775-9580

Safford

Cotton Clouds, Inc. Ⓨ Ⓦ Ⓢ
5176 S. 14th Avenue, 85546
(928) 428-7000 or (800) 322-7888

Debbie's Ⓠ Ⓔ Ⓨ Ⓒ
411 W. Main Street, 85546
(928) 428-1105

The Jack of Arts Ⓠ Ⓜ
417 W. Main Street, 85546
(928) 428-5225

Sahuarita

Cathey's Sewing & Vacuum Ⓜ
18805 S. Frontage Road, Suite B103, 85614
(520) 300-5002

Scottsdale

BeStitched Needlepoint Ⓝ
6990 E. Shea Blvd., Suite 124, 85254
(480) 991-0706
Tu-Sa 10-4; Summer: please call ahead
www.bestitchedneedlepointshop.com

Quail Run Needlework Ⓝ
7704 E. Doubletree Ranch Road, Suite 125, 85258
(480) 551-1423
M-Sa 10-4
www.quailrunneedlework.com

Scottsdale Quilts Ⓠ Ⓔ Ⓝ
16459 N. Scottsdale Road, Suite C-117, 85254
(480) 951-8000
M-F 10-5, Sa 10-3
www.scottsdalequilts.com

Old Town Needlework Ⓝ Ⓒ
7128 E. 5th Avenue, 85251
(480) 990-2270

Sewing Nuts Ⓠ Ⓜ
4250 N. Scottsdale Road, 85251
(480) 659-1222

Sedona

Sedona Knit Wits Ⓨ Ⓦ
2370 W. Highway 89A, Suite 3, 86336
(928) 282-3389
M-F 10-5, Sa 10-3
www.sedonaknitwits.com

Quilter's Store Sedona Ⓠ Ⓔ
3075 W. State Route 89A, 86336
(928) 282-2057

Quilts LTD Gallery Ⓠ
313 State Route 179, 86336
(800) 255-2306

Sierra Vista

Sew Easy Sewing Ⓜ Ⓠ Ⓔ
1100 S Highway 92, Suite 3, 85635
(520) 224-5591
Tu-F 10 - 5, Sa 10-3, Su M by appt.
www.seweasysewing.com

Sun City

Sun Valley Quilts Ⓠ Ⓜ
9857 W. Bell Road, 85351
(623) 972-2091
M-F 9-5, Sa 9-4, Su 12-4
www.sunvalleyquilts.com

Sewin Asylum Ⓠ Ⓜ
10050 W. Bell Road, #1, 85351
(623) 398-6235

Sun City West

Quilts Plus Ⓠ Ⓔ Ⓨ Ⓝ Ⓒ
13583 W. Camino Del Sol, 85375
(623) 584-2448

Surprise

Arizona Quilts Ⓠ
12301 W. Bell Road, Suite A-109, 85378
(623) 566-8878

Tempe

SAS Fabrics Ⓠ
1700 E. Apache Blvd., 85281
(480) 966-7557

Tempe Yarn Ⓨ Ⓦ Ⓢ
1415 E. University Drive, Suite A102, 85281
(480) 557-9166

Tubac

Quilts LTD Gallery Q
7 Camino Otero, 85646
(800) 255-2306 or (520) 398-9190

Tucson

Birdhouse Yarns Y
2540 E. 6th Street, 85716
(520) 305-4187

Cactus Quilt Shop Q
7921 N. Oracle Road, 85704
(520) 498-4698 or (520) 498-4708

Fabrics That Go Q
3105 N. Campbell Avenue, 85719
(520) 881-4444

Grandma's Spinning Wheel Y W S
6544 E. Tanque Verde, Suite 150, 85715
(520) 290-3738

SAS Fabrics Q
5320 E. Speedway Blvd., 85712
(520) 326-7252

The Quilt Basket / Sewing Room Q E M
6538 E. Tanque Verde, Suite 130, 85715
(520) 722-8810

The Quilter's Market Q
7601 E. Speedway Blvd., 85710
(520) 747-8458

The West, Inc. E N C
5615 E. River Road, Suite 101, 85750
(520) 299-1044

Wickenburg

Isabelle's Parlour – A Yarn Boutique Y
51020 Highway 60/89, 85390
(928) 684-4937
Tu-Sa 10-4 (mid Sept.-June)
www.isabellesparlour.com

Wagons West Quilt Shop & Studio Q
1141 W. Wickenburg Way, 85390
(928) 684-1739

Williams

Quilts On Route 66 Q E N
221 W. Railroad Avenue, 86046
(928) 635-5221
Summer: 9-7:30 Daily;
Winter: check website for hours
www.quiltsonroute66.com

Yuma

Grandma Jo's Fabrics Q
5720 E. 32nd Street, 85365
(928) 314-0058
Winter: (Oct.-Apr.) M-Sa 9-5;
Summer: (May-Sept.) M-Sa 10-3
www.facebook.com/Grandma-Jos-463922043739087/

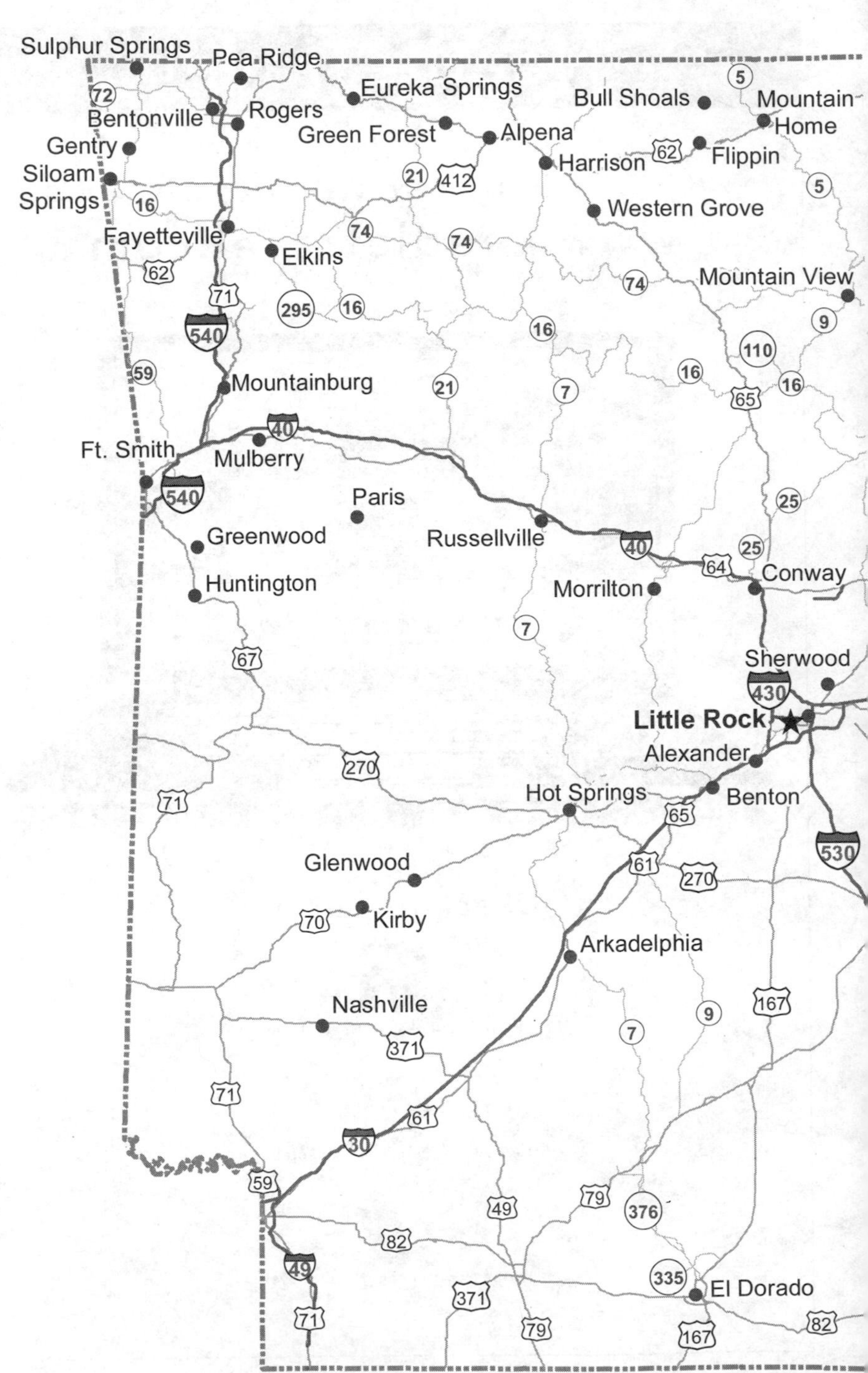

Sulphur Springs
Pea Ridge
Eureka Springs
Bull Shoals
Mountain Home
Bentonville
Rogers
Green Forest
Alpena
Flippin
Gentry
Harrison
Siloam Springs
Western Grove
Fayetteville
Elkins
Mountain View
Mountainburg
Ft. Smith
Mulberry
Paris
Russellville
Greenwood
Conway
Huntington
Morrilton
Sherwood
Little Rock
Alexander
Hot Springs
Benton
Glenwood
Kirby
Arkadelphia
Nashville
El Dorado

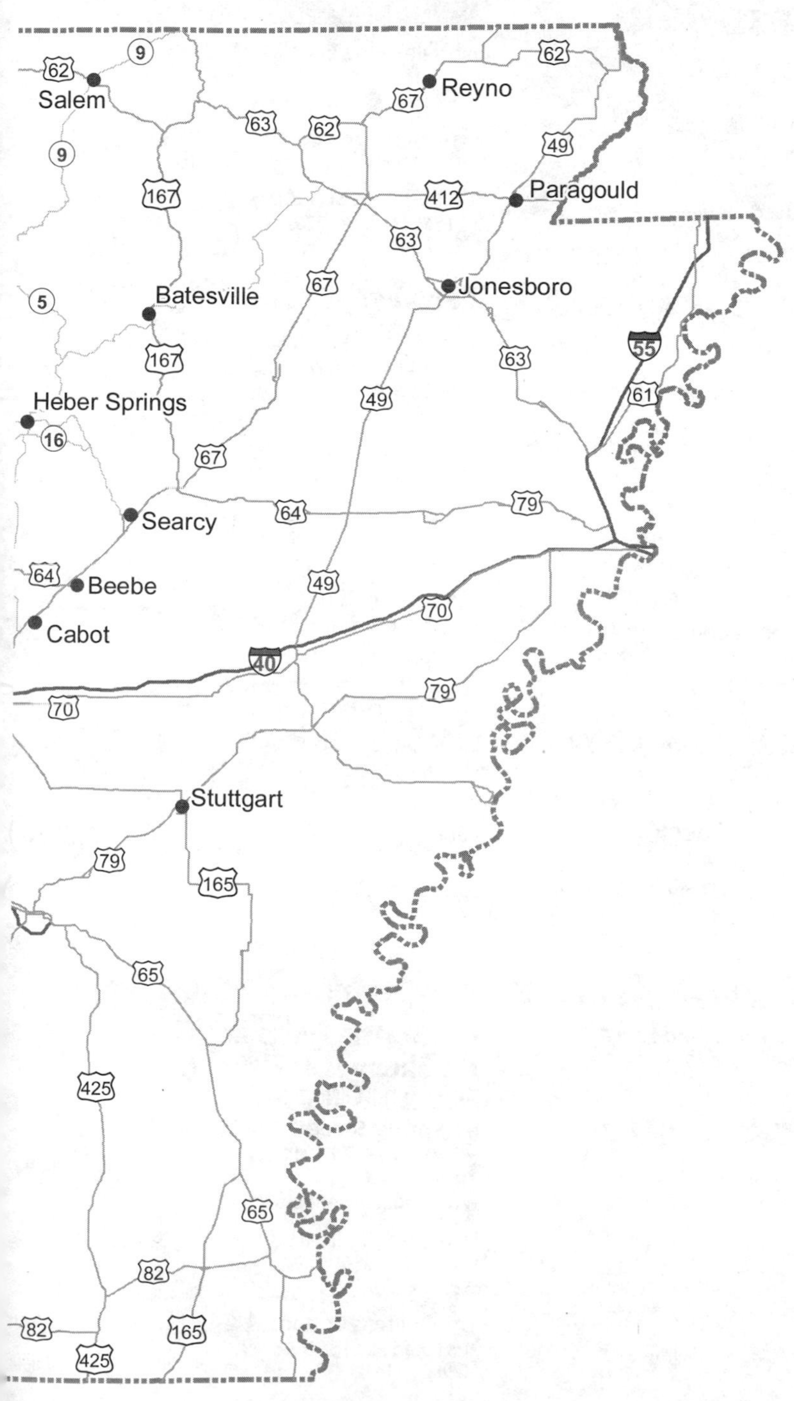

Salem
Reyno
Paragould
Jonesboro
Batesville
Heber Springs
Searcy
Beebe
Cabot
Stuttgart
62
9
67
63
49
412
167
5
55
61
16
64
79
70
40
165
65
425
82

Arkansas

Alexander

Pinwheel Fabrics Q M
7915 Highway 5 N, 72002
(501) 847-4177

Alpena

Rag Barn Q
307 E. Elm Street, 72611
(870) 437-2325

Arkadelphia

Knit Unto Others Y W S
323 Main Street, 71923
(870) 245-2552

Batesville

Marshall Dry Goods Company, Inc. Q E N C
310 W. Main Street, 72501
(870) 793-2405 or (888) 744-8277

Paper Chase Book and Yarn Shop Y S
136 W. Main Street, 72501
(870) 793-4276

Beebe

Calico Junction Fabrics and Quilting Q
210 W. Center Street, 72012
(501) 882-0333

Benton

The Bed-Warmer Quilt and Sew Q E M
17270 Interstate 30 N, Suite 9, 72019
(501) 860-6176

Bentonville

Village Quilting Q
13020 Frontage Road, Suite 105, 72712
(479) 855-3800

Bull Shoals

Gabriele's Flowers & Fibers Y
904 Central Blvd., 72619
(870) 445-4273

Cabot

Stitchery Sewist Shop Q
302 E. Main Street, 72023
(501) 286-8335

Conway

Grana's Front Porch Fabrics Q E M
803 5th Street, 72032
(501) 358-6807

Sewing Center, Etc. Q E M
813 Oak Street, Suite 4, 72032
(501) 205-1975

The Stitcher's Garden E N C
1026 Van Ronkle, 72032
(501) 513-1851

The Twisted Purl Y S
2850 Prince Street, Suite J, 72034
(501) 908-6724

El Dorado

MNM Quilt Shop Q
171 Pete Mason Road, 71730
(870) 862-0580

Elkins

Lonesome Pine Quilts Q
1910 Highway 16, 72727
(479) 601-6011

Eureka Springs

Red Scottie Fibers at the Shoppes at Fleece N Flax Q E Y N W S C
51 Spring Street, 72632
(479) 253-0711 or (479) 981-0832
Tu-Sa 10-4
www.redscottiefibers.com

Hardcastle Folk Art Y
508 Village Circle, 72632
(580) 235-2279

The Quilter's Cottage Q C
106 E. Van Buren, 72632
(479) 719-1412

Treasures From The Pacific Q E N C
435 W. Van Buren, 72632
(479) 981-0233

Fayetteville

B. Sew Inn Q E M
2910 N. McKee Circle, 72703
(479) 442-7808

Hand-Held-A Knitting Gallery Y
225 N. Block Avenue, 72701
(479) 582-2910

Sew In Heaven Q E M
3162 W. Martin Luther King Blvd., Suite 10, 72704
(479) 443-2444 or (479) 443-2445

Flippin

The Curiosity Shop Q
9084 Highway 62 E, 72634
(870) 656-6030 or (870) 453-5300

Fort Smith

Sewing Machine Center Q M
6700 Phoenix Avenue, 72903
(479) 484-5351 or (800) 928-7739

Gentry

Gentry Quilts Q
213 E. Main Street, 72734
(479) 736-0050

Glenwood

Fabric Creations by Tiffany Q
219 N. Bumble Bee Road, 71943
(870) 356-3142

Green Forest

McKee Sewing Center Q E M
64 Sparrow Road, 72638
(870) 437-2862 or (800) 533-4531

Greenwood

Crooked Creek Quilts Q
1736 W. Center Street, 72936
(479) 996-5808

Harrison

Country Corner Quilt Shop Q E M
10872 Highway 392, 72601
(870) 437-2299

Heart Quilt Shop Q
8874 Highway 62W, 72601
(870) 437-5400

Ozark Mountain Relics and Beads E Y C
910 Highway 65 N, 72601
(870) 688-4337

Heber Springs

Quilters Corner Fabric Q E M
207 W. Main Street, 72543
(501) 362-8612

Hot Springs

Cathy's Quiltin' Square and Monogrammin' Designs Q
3256 Albert Pike Road, 71913
(501) 760-6099

Hickory Hill Quilts Q E M
2998 Park Avenue, 71901
(501) 318-2739

Huntington

Mama's Log House Q
3715 E. Clarks Chapel Road, 72940
(479) 928-1600 or (479) 883-0254

Jonesboro

Jana's Quilting & Decor Q
2005 E. Highland Drive, 72401
(870) 972-5543

Kirby

Vickie's Quilting Shack Q
3049 Highway 70 W, 71950
(870) 398-4109

Little Rock

Shepherd's Needle E N C
11601 W. Markham, Suite D, 72211
(501) 221-6990

Stifft Station Gifts E Y W S
3009 West Markham, 72205
(501) 725-0209

Stitchin' Post Q E M
1501 Macon Drive, 72211
(501) 227-0288

Yarn Kandy Y W S
8201 Cantrell Road, Suite 120, 72227
(501) 508-5559

Morrilton

The Fabric Patch and More Q
204 W. Railroad Avenue, 72110
(501) 289-6512

Mountain Home

Remember Me Quilt Shop & Embroidery PLUS Q M
201 N. College Street, 72653
(870) 425-7670 or (419) 261-7812

Handi Quilter® Authorized Retailer
Designed by a Quilter, for Quilters.®

Sew Unique Q M
960 E. 9th Street, 72653
(870) 424-4739

Mountain View

Ritsy Rags Q E
112 Howard Avenue, 72560
(870) 269-2800

Mountainburg

Piece of Heaven Quilt Fabric Q
525 Highway 71 SW, 72946
(479) 369-4006

Mulberry

Cozy Quilts and Things Q
10017 Silver Maple Drive, 72947
(479) 997-8366

Nashville

Arkansas Emporium Q E Y N C
105 N. Main Street, 71852
(870) 451-9696
M-F 10-5
www.etsy.com/shop/ArkansasEmporium?ref=search_shop_redirect

Southern Belle Fabrics* Q
180 Harding Road, 71852
(470) 223-5532

Paragould

Hancocks Fabric and Tuxedo Q
421 W. Kings Highway, 72450
(870) 236-7536

Paris

PJ'S Fabric N More* Q E
2000 Greasy Valley Road, 72855
(479) 963-1399

Pea Ridge

Country House Quilting and Quilt Shop Q
16324 N. Highway 94, 72751
(479) 451-8978

Sew-n-Sew Quilt Shop Q
346 Leetown Road, 72751
(479) 451-1685

Reyno

Fabrics and Quilts Q
272 W. 2nd Street, 72462
(870) 810-1485

Rogers

Mockingbird Moon Yarn Y S
315 N. 2nd Street, 72756
(479) 202-5640

Rogers Sewing Center Q M
1802 S. 8th Street, 72756
(479) 636-8240

Sew A Stitch Q M
1311 W. Hudson, 72756
(479) 621-0000

Sew Graceful Quilting Q
14094 Pleasant Ridge Road, 72756
(479) 372-7403

Russellville

Knit 2 Together Y S
2300 W. Main Street, Suite 6, 72801
(479) 968-5648 or (479) 968-KNIT

Salem

The Quilted Heart Q Y
3022 Highway 289 S, 72576
(870) 670-4292

Searcy

Pins, Needles, & Sew Much More Q E Y N C M
2223 E. Race Avenue, 72143
(501) 268-2950

Sherwood

Sew Much More Q W
2001 Kiehl Avenue, 72120
(501) 753-6050

Siloam Springs

Sager Creek Quilts Q
304 E. Central Street, 72761
(479) 524-5244

Stuttgart

The French Seam Q M
2015 S. Buerkle Street, 72160
(870) 673-8156
M-F 9:30-5, Sa 10-2
www.frenchseam.com

Sulphur Springs

The Quilt Corner Q
110 S. Hibler Street, 72768
(479) 298-3006

Western Grove

White Chapel Fabrics Q E Y C M
813 US 65-B Highway, 72685
(870) 429-5454

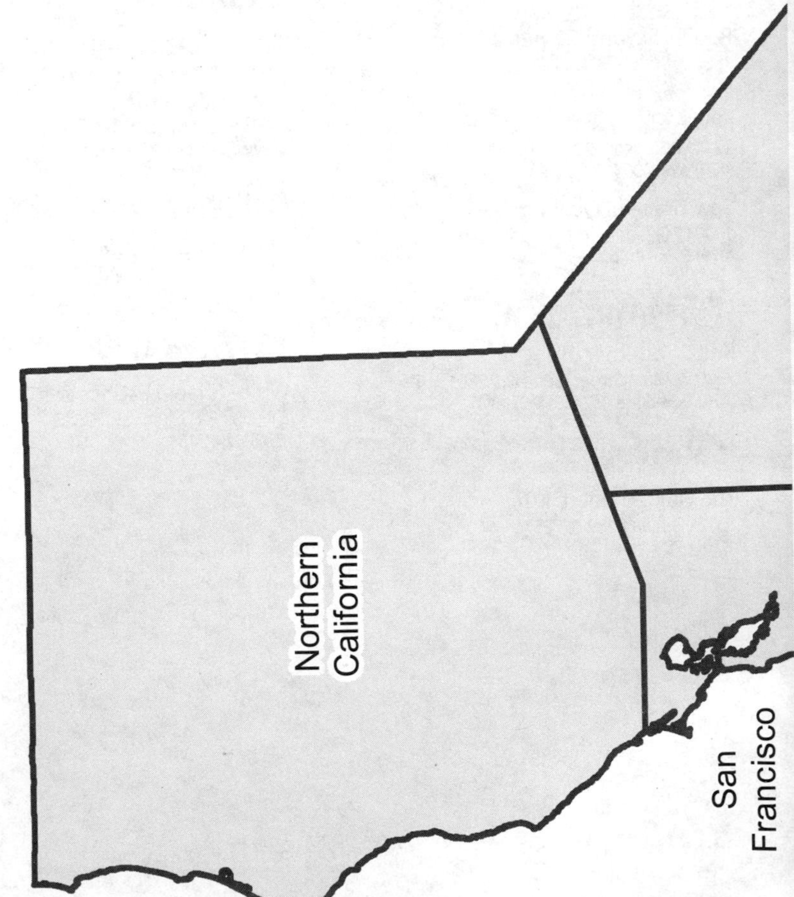
Northern California
San Francisco

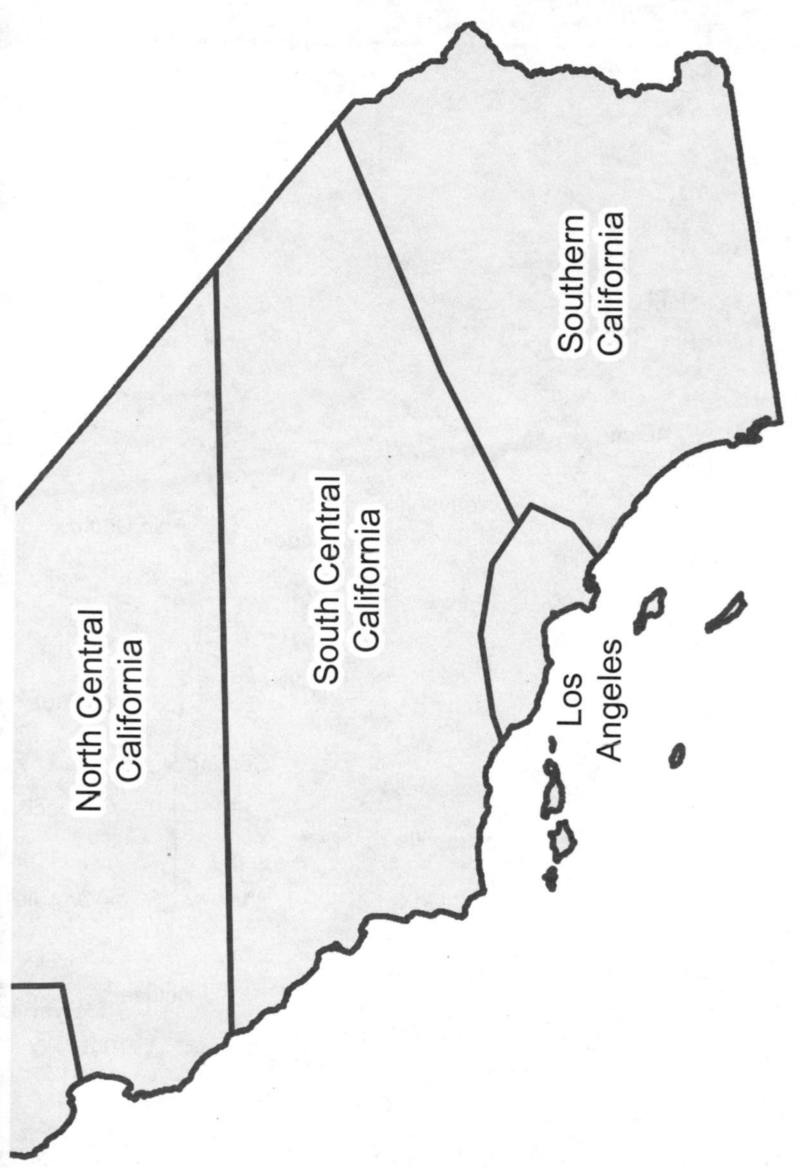
North Central California
South Central California
Southern California
Los Angeles

101
199
97
Mt. Shasta
101
3
89
299
Arcata
Eureka
5
299
Weaverville
299
Fortuna
Redding
Palo Cedro
Ferndale
36
36
36
44
211
211
36
Red Bluff
Los Molinos
101
Corning
99
32
32
Paradise
Chico
Laytonville
191
1
Willows
45
Oroville
Ft. Bragg
Little River
20
101
99
Colusa
Marysville
Ukiah
Yuba City
Lakeport
20
128
99
45
1
Gualala
Cloverdale
Healdsburg
29
505
1
80
Napa
Winters
Santa Rosa
Sebastopol
29
Vacaville
Petaluma
Sonoma

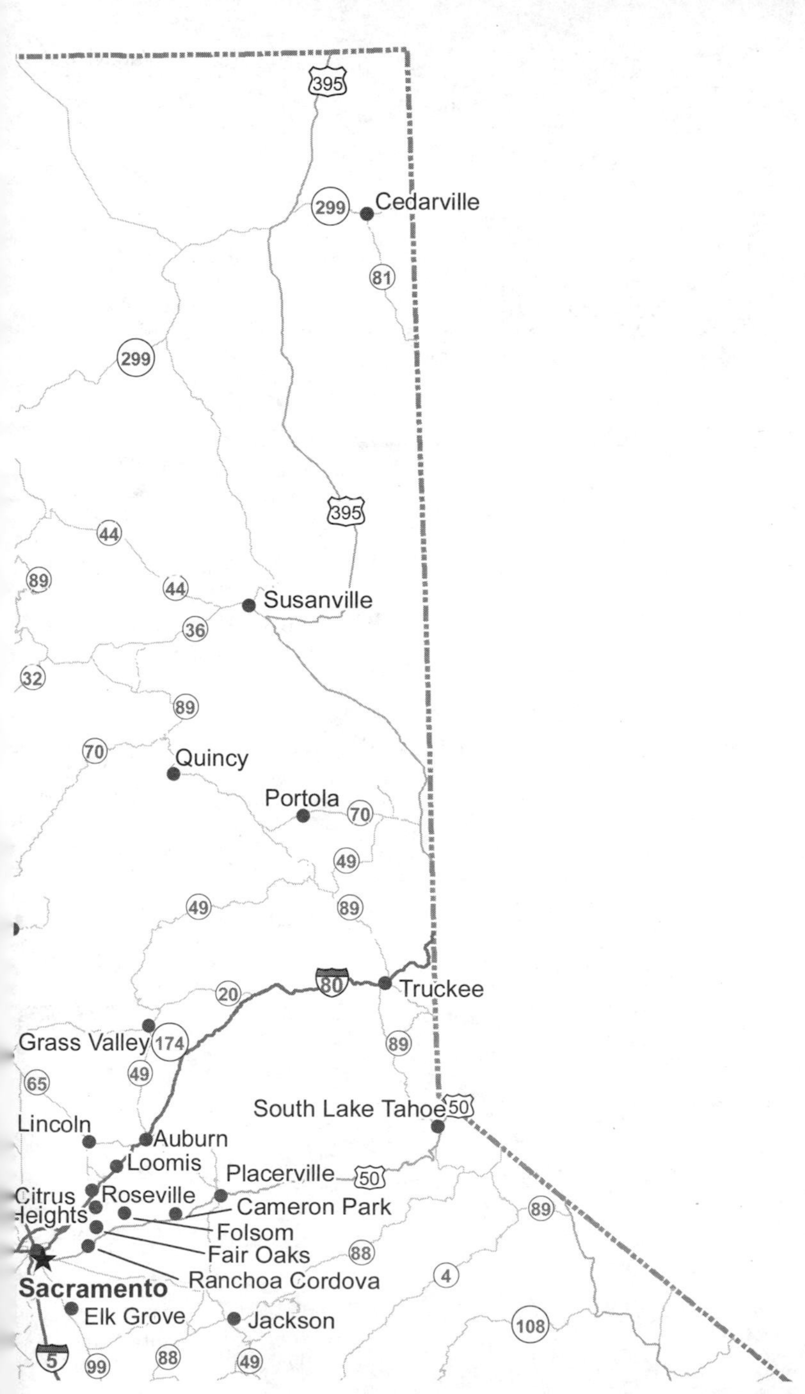
395
299
Cedarville
81
299
395
44
89
44
Susanville
36
32
89
70
Quincy
Portola
70
49
49
89
80
Truckee
20
Grass Valley
174
89
49
65
South Lake Tahoe
50
Lincoln
Auburn
Loomis
Placerville
50
Citrus Heights
Roseville
Cameron Park
89
Folsom
Fair Oaks
88
4
Sacramento
Ranchoa Cordova
Elk Grove
Jackson
108
5
99
88
49

116
12
29
121
Vacaville
80
Sonoma
101
12
12
Petaluma
116
1
12
121
680
Point Reyes Station
780
101
4
Fairfax
San Rafael
San Anselmo
Richmond
580
Walnut Creek
Mill Valley
1
Albany
24
Lafayette
Berkeley
13
Danville
Oakland
San Francisco
Alameda
580
280
South San Francisco
880
Pacifica
1
Fremont
San Mateo
280
1
Half Moon Bay
Menlo Park
Emerald Hills
Mountain View
Los Altos
Sunnyvale
85
9
1
9
Santa Cruz

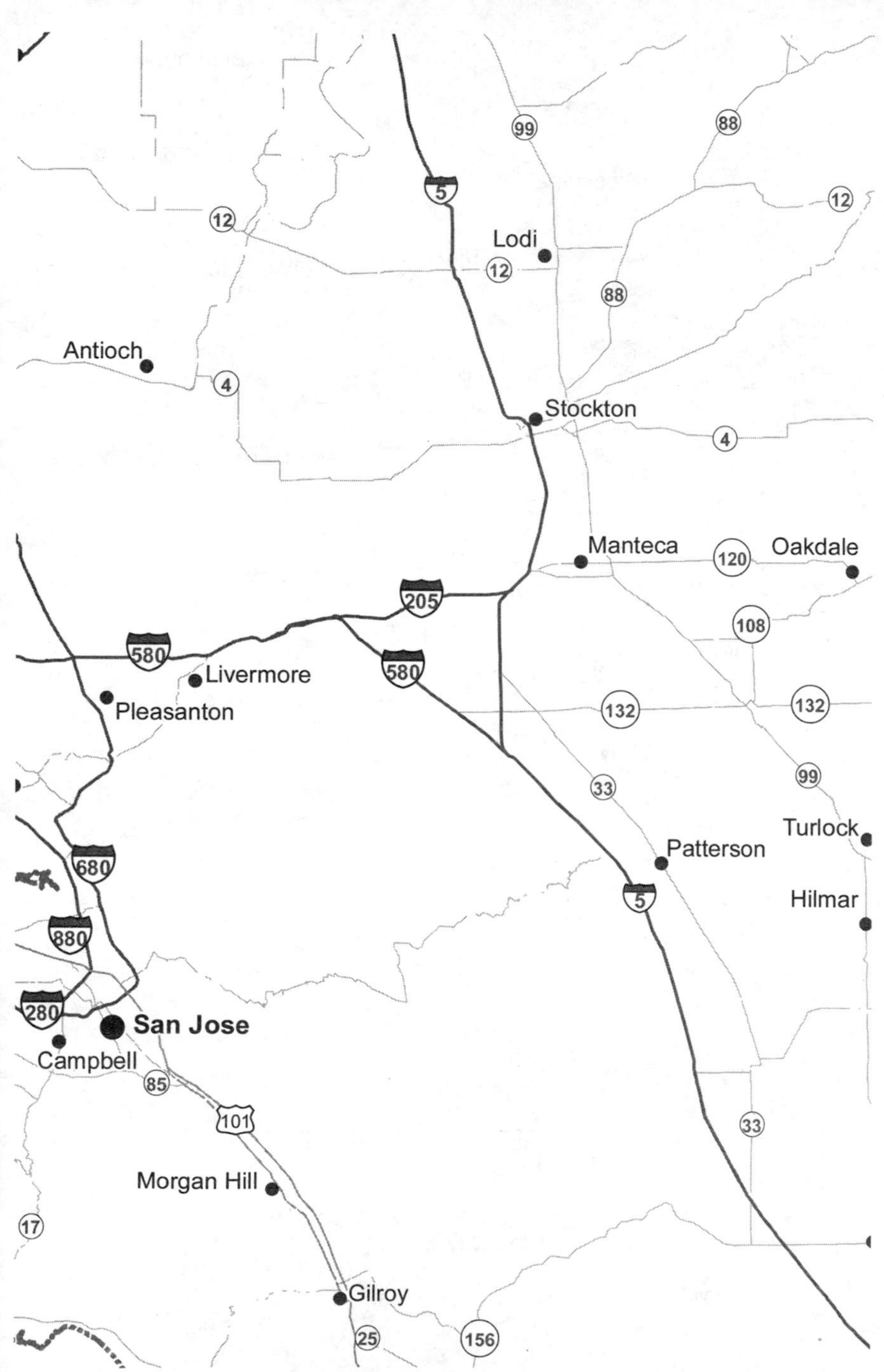

99
88
5
12
Lodi
12
12
88
Antioch
4
Stockton
4
Manteca
120
Oakdale
205
108
580
580
Livermore
Pleasanton
132
132
33
99
Turlock
Patterson
680
5
Hilmar
880
280
San Jose
Campbell
85
101
33
Morgan Hill
17
Gilroy
25
156

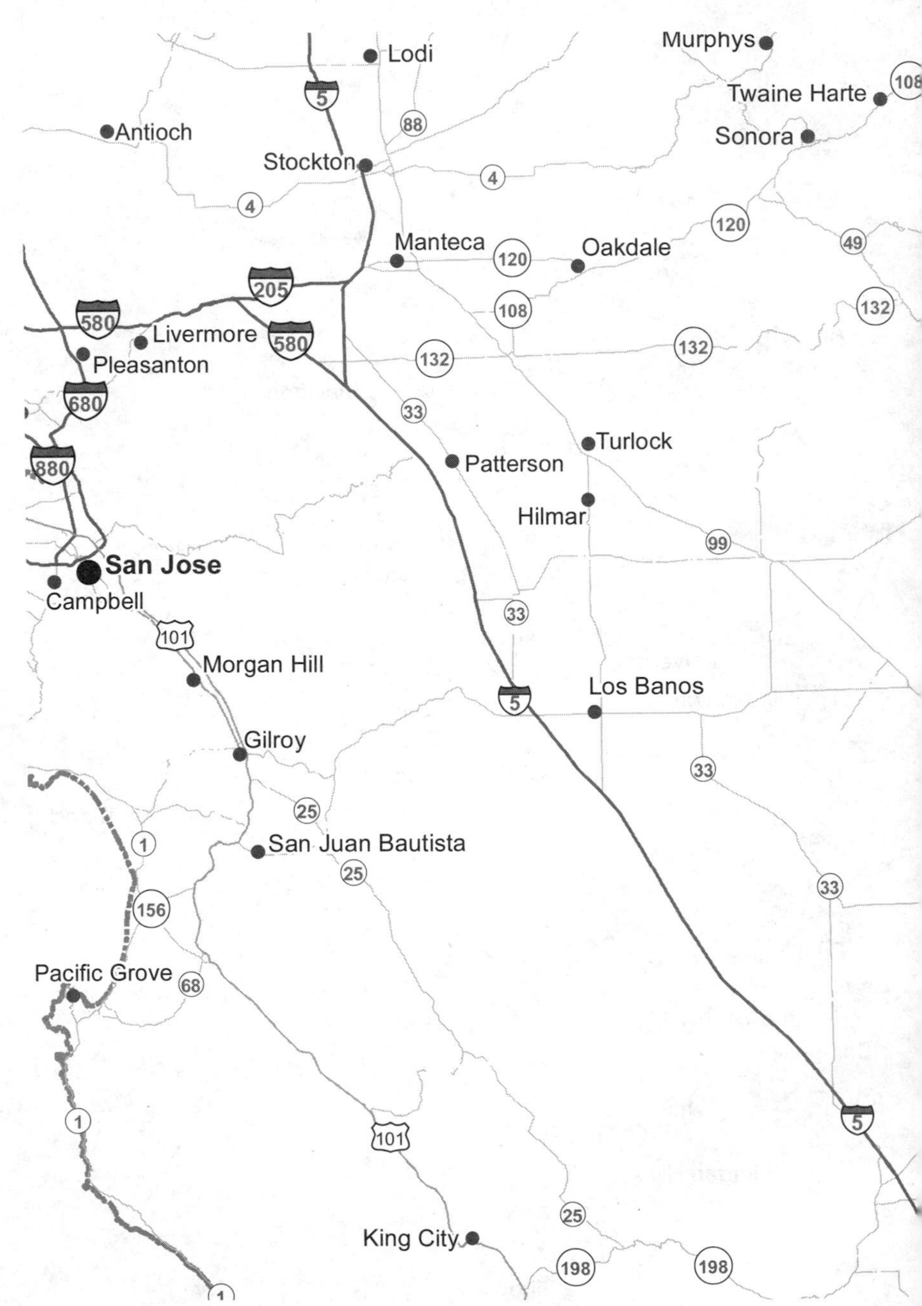

Lodi
Murphys
Twaine Harte
Sonora
Antioch
Stockton
Manteca
Oakdale
Livermore
Pleasanton
Turlock
Patterson
Hilmar
San Jose
Campbell
Morgan Hill
Los Banos
Gilroy
San Juan Bautista
Pacific Grove
King City
5
88
4
4
120
120
49
205
580
580
108
132
132
132
680
33
880
99
33
101
5
33
25
1
25
33
156
68
1
101
5
25
198
198
1
108

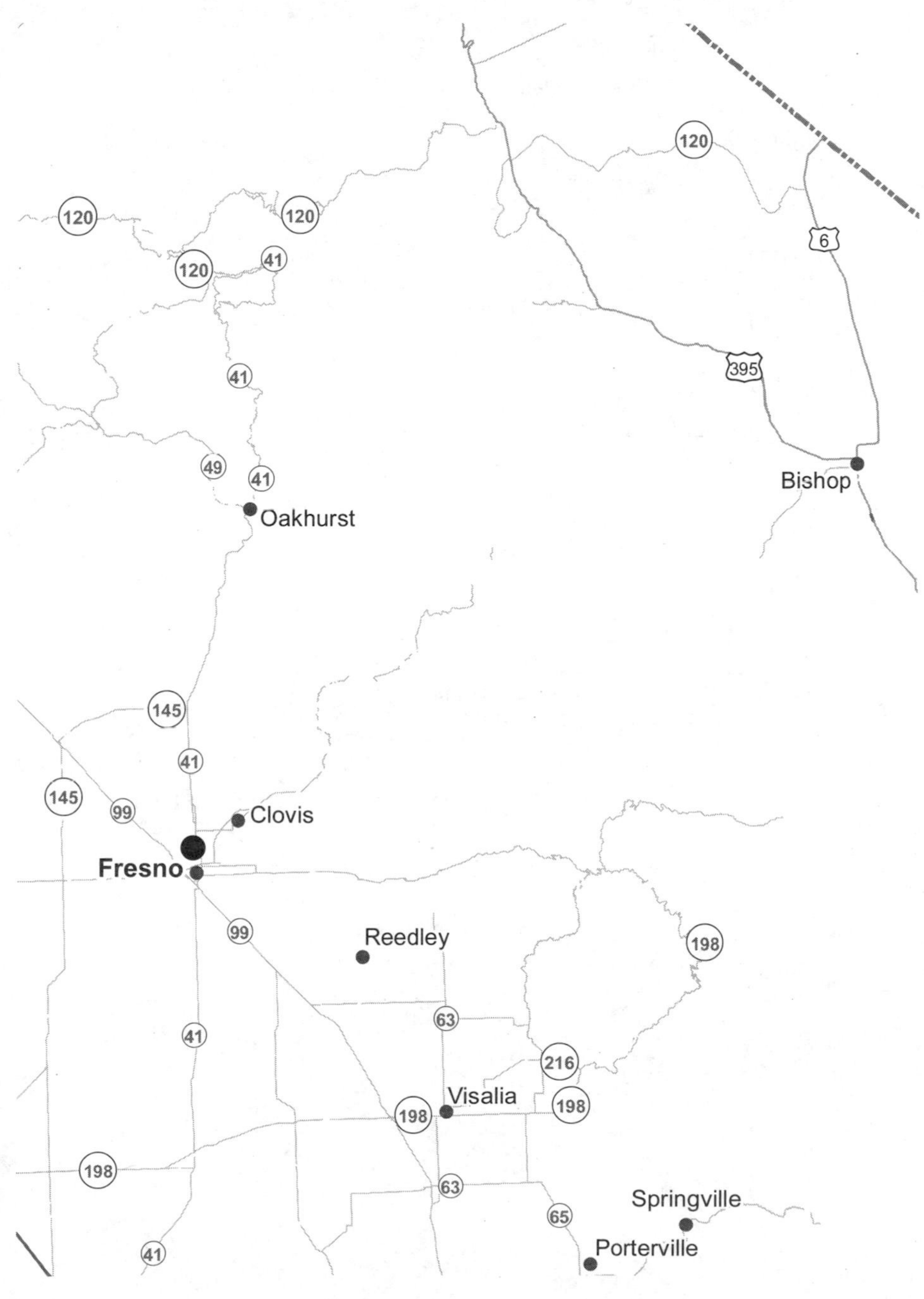
120
120
120
41
120
6
395
41
49
41
Oakhurst
Bishop
145
41
145
99
Clovis
Fresno
99
Reedley
198
63
41
216
Visalia
198
198
198
63
65
Springville
Porterville
41

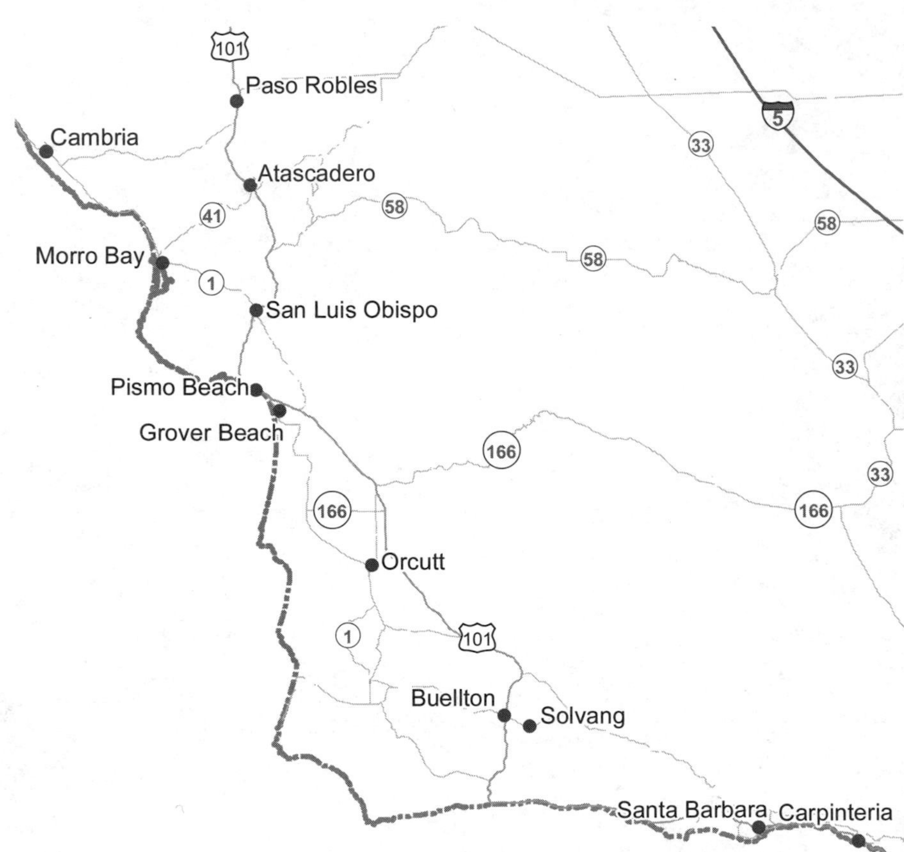
101
Paso Robles
Cambria
5
33
Atascadero
41
58
58
Morro Bay
58
1
San Luis Obispo
33
Pismo Beach
Grover Beach
166
33
166
166
Orcutt
1
101
Buellton
Solvang
Santa Barbara
Carpinteria

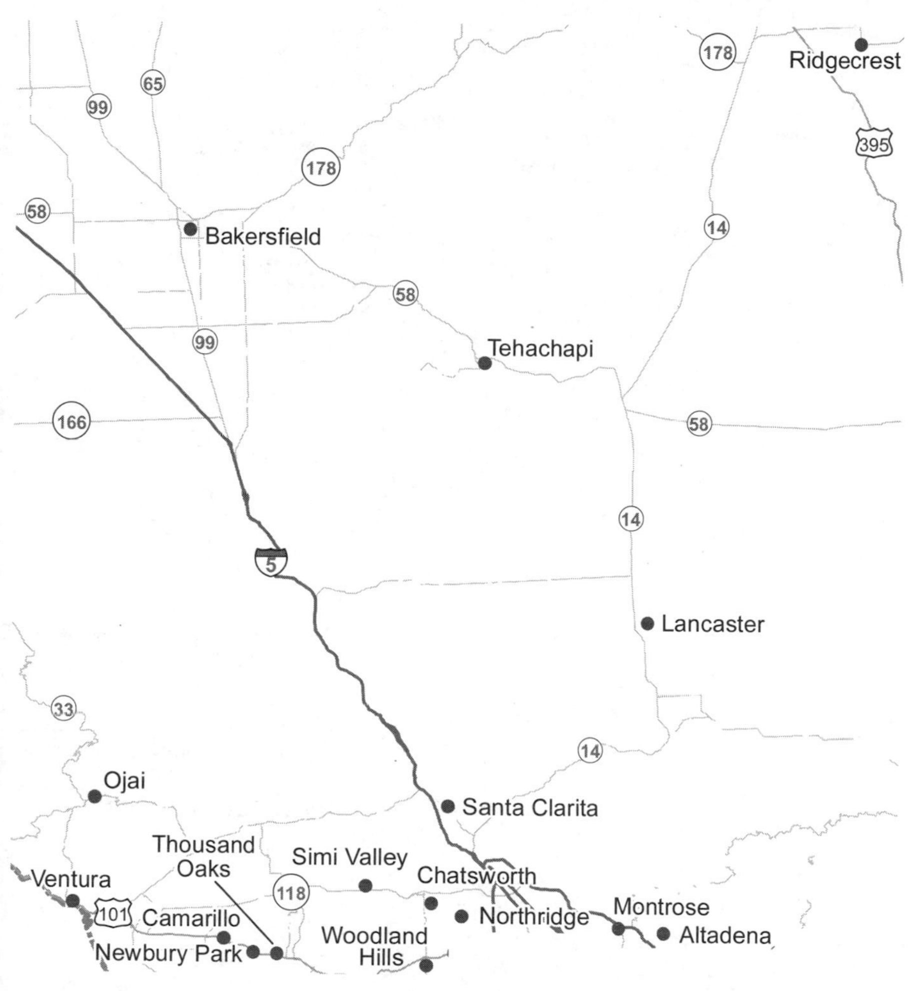
178
Ridgecrest
65
99
395
178
58
Bakersfield
14
58
99
Tehachapi
166
58
14
5
Lancaster
33
14
Ojai
Santa Clarita
Thousand
Oaks
Simi Valley
Chatsworth
Ventura
118
101
Camarillo
Northridge
Montrose
Altadena
Woodland
Hills
Newbury Park

Northridge
Montrose
Altadena
Van Nuys
Tarzana
Valley Village
Studio City
Pasadena
Arcadia
Glendora
San Marino
Covina
La Verne
Los Angeles
Beverly Hills
Chino Hills
Santa Monica
Inglewood
Yorba Linda
Manhattan Beach
Hawthorne
Bellflower
Anaheim
Redondo Beach
Stanton
Orange
Long Beach
Lomita
Garden Grove
Tustin
Santa Ana
Fountain Valley
Huntington Beach
Costa Mesa
Newport Beach
Corona del Mar

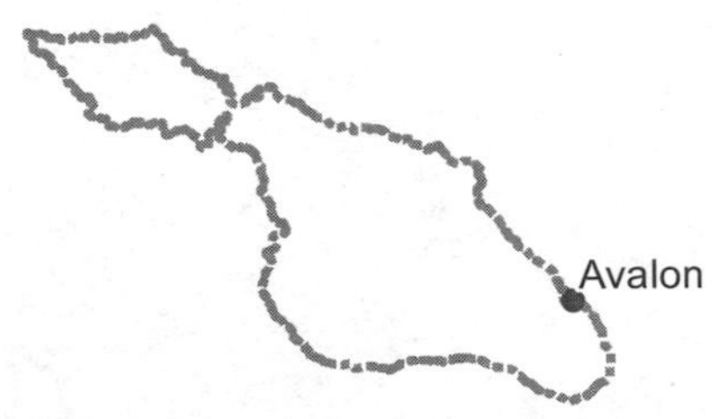

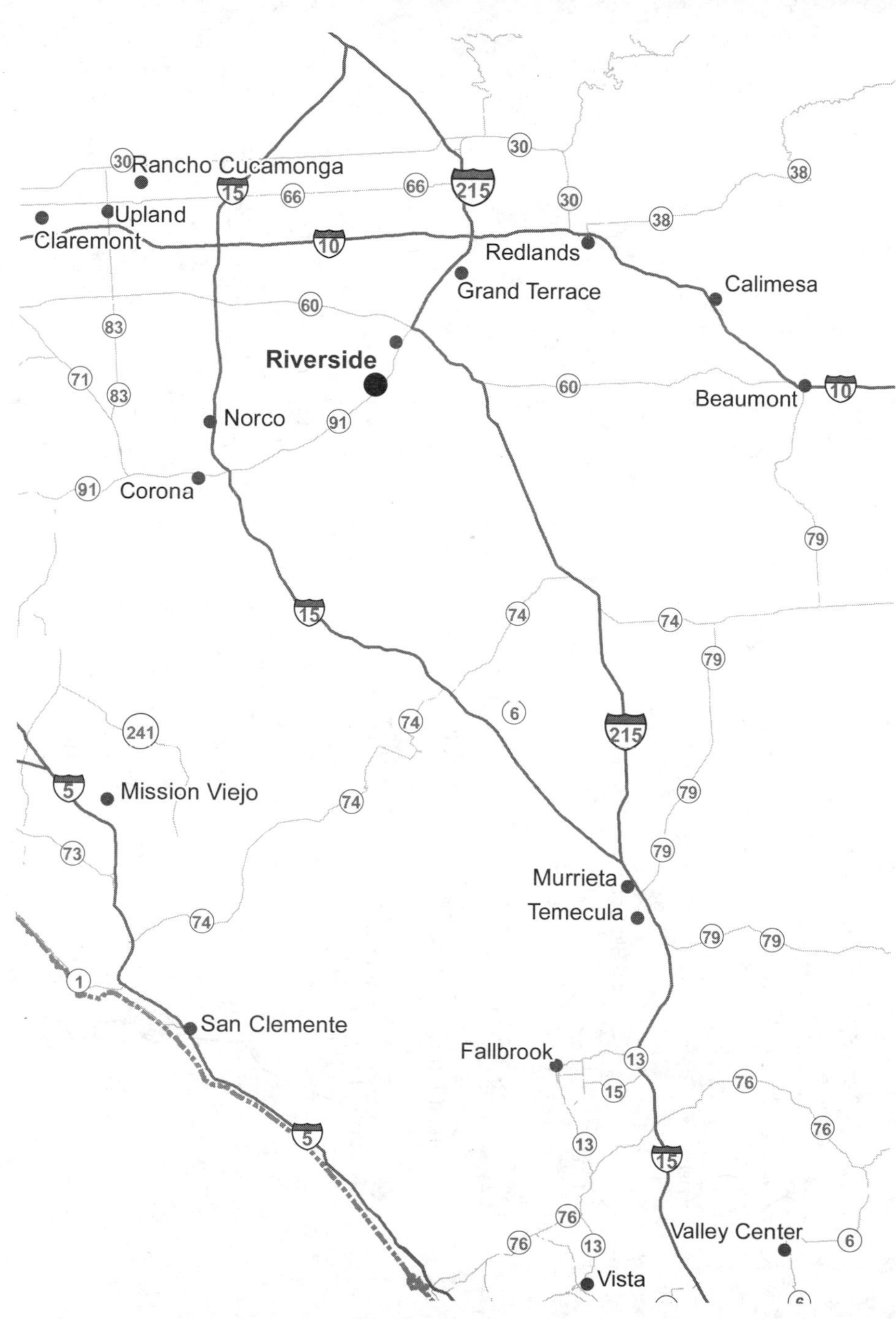
Rancho Cucamonga
Upland
Claremont
Redlands
Grand Terrace
Calimesa
Riverside
Norco
Beaumont
Corona
Mission Viejo
Murrieta
Temecula
San Clemente
Fallbrook
Valley Center
Vista
30
15
66
215
38
10
60
83
71
91
79
74
6
241
5
73
1
13
76

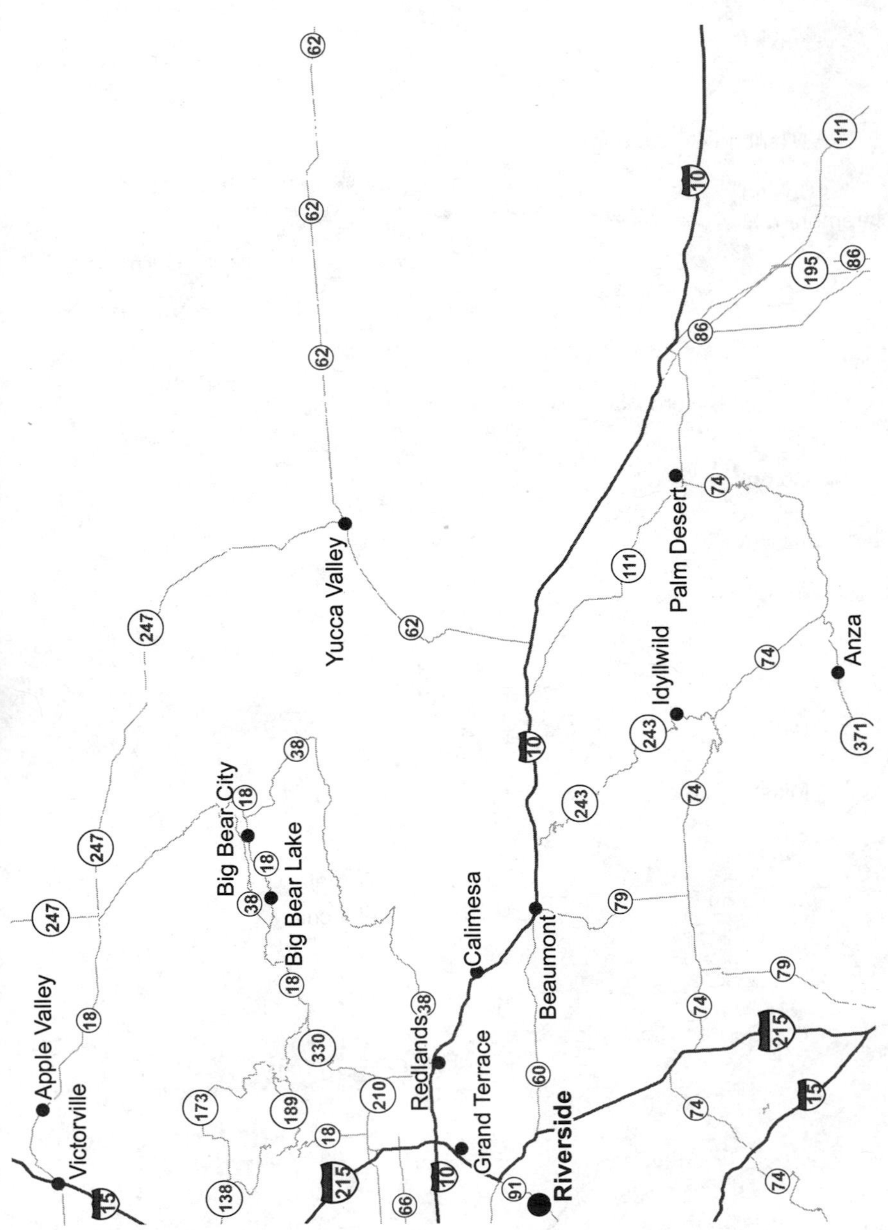
Apple Valley
Victorville
Big Bear City
Big Bear Lake
Yucca Valley
Redlands
Calimesa
Grand Terrace
Beaumont
Riverside
Palm Desert
Idyllwild
Anza
15
215
10
62
247
18
38
173
189
138
330
210
66
91
60
79
243
111
74
86
195
371

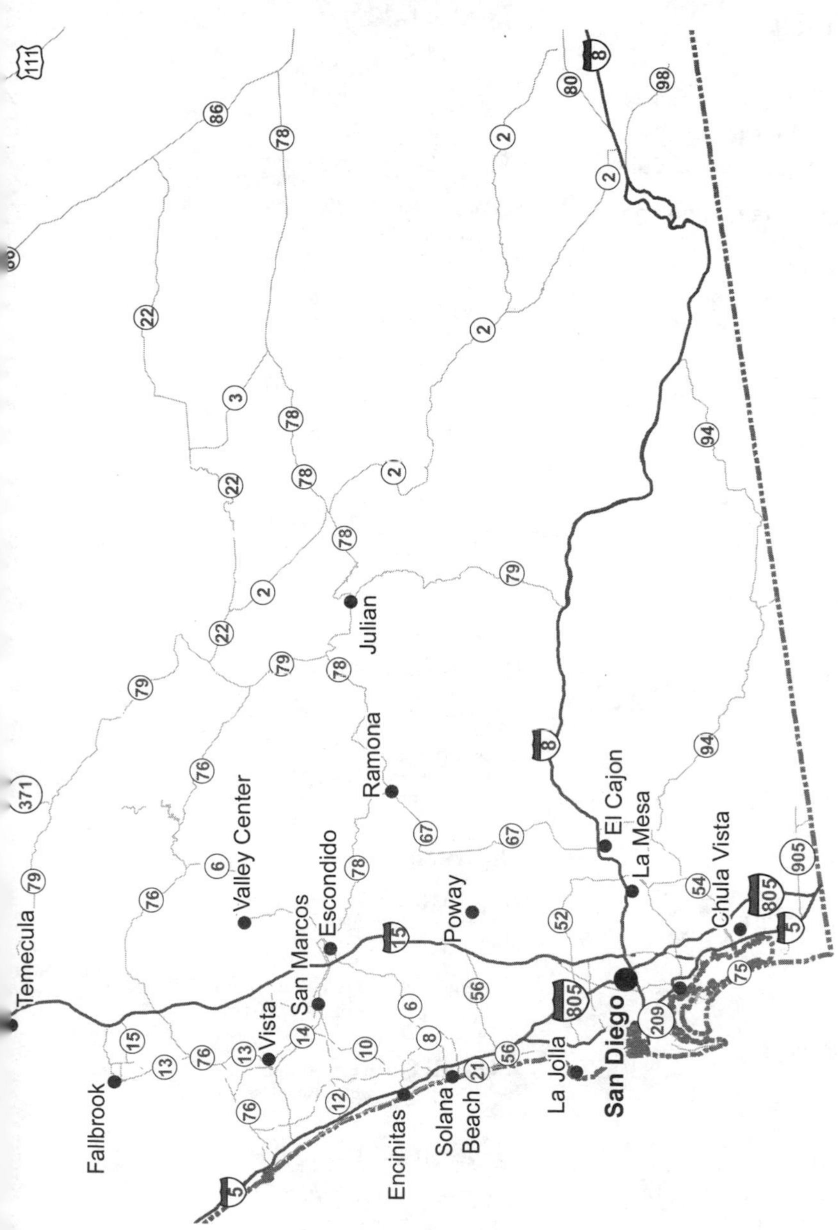
Temecula
Fallbrook
Vista
San Marcos
Valley Center
Escondido
Ramona
Julian
Poway
Encinitas
Solana Beach
La Jolla
San Diego
El Cajon
La Mesa
Chula Vista

California

Alameda

Needle In A Haystack E N C
2433 Mariner Square Loop, Suite 102, 94501
(510) 522-0404 or (877) 429-7822
Tu-F 11-5, Sa 11-4
www.needlestack.com

The Recrafting Co. Q E Y N
2449 Santa Clara Avenue, 94501
(510) 263-0249

Albany

Avenue Yarns Y W S
1325 Solano Avenue, 94706
(510) 526-9276 or (888) 722-9276

Altadena

Quilt 'n' Things Fiber Arts Q E Y M
2353 Lincoln Avenue, 91001
(626) 421-6243

Anaheim

M & L Fabrics Q
3430 W. Ball Road, 92804
(714) 995-3178

Mel's Sewing & Fabric Center Q E M
1189 N. Euclid Street, 92801
(714) 774-3460

Newton's Yarn Country Y W
1550 S. Sunkist Street, Suite 8, 92806
(714) 634-9116

Antioch

Queen B's Quilt Shop Q
720 W. 2nd Street, 94509
(925) 978-4587

Anza

Anza Valley Hardware & Variety Y
56350 State Highway 371, 92539
(951) 763-4668

Apple Valley

Fanciwerks Yarn Shoppe Y
21810 US Highway 18, Suite 2, 92307
(760) 961-0113

Arcadia

Pollard's Sew Creative Q M
27 S. First Avenue, 91006
(626) 795-9907

Arcata

Daisy Drygoods Q E Y N W S C
959 H Street, 95521
(707) 822-1893

Fabric Temptations Q E Y
942 G Street, 95521
(707) 822-7782

Atascadero

Never Not Knitting Q Y
5990 Entrada Avenue, 93422
(805) 703-4010

Quilter's Cupboard Q
5275 El Camino Real, 93422
(805) 466-6996

Sew Fun Q M
8775 El Camino Real, 93422
(805) 462-9739

Auburn

Auburn Needleworks Y N W
13344 Lincoln Way, 95603
(530) 888-0202

Howell's Sewing & Vacuum Q E
13555 Bowman Road, Suite 300 & 400, 95603
(530) 885-9624

Avalon

Catalina Crafters Q E Y N C
115 Sumner Avenue, 90704
(310) 510-3590

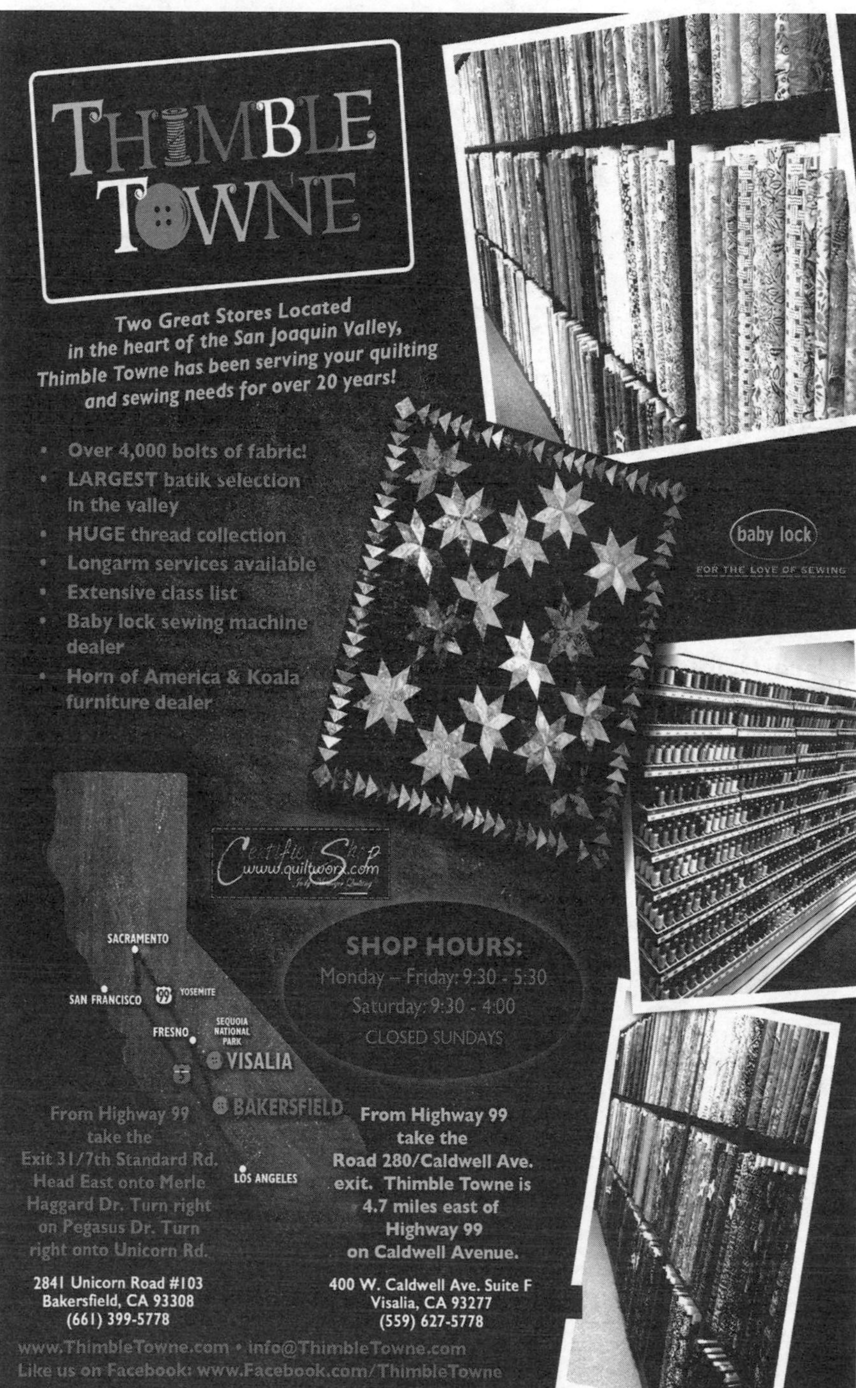
THIMBLE TOWNE
Two Great Stores Located in the heart of the San Joaquin Valley, Thimble Towne has been serving your quilting and sewing needs for over 20 years!
• Over 4,000 bolts of fabric!
• LARGEST batik selection in the valley
• HUGE thread collection
• Longarm services available
• Extensive class list
• Baby lock sewing machine dealer
• Horn of America & Koala furniture dealer
baby lock
FOR THE LOVE OF SEWING
Certified Shop
www.quiltworx.com
SACRAMENTO
SAN FRANCISCO
99
YOSEMITE
SEQUOIA NATIONAL PARK
FRESNO
VISALIA
5
BAKERSFIELD
LOS ANGELES
SHOP HOURS:
Monday – Friday: 9:30 - 5:30
Saturday: 9:30 - 4:00
CLOSED SUNDAYS
From Highway 99 take the Exit 31/7th Standard Rd. Head East onto Merle Haggard Dr. Turn right on Pegasus Dr. Turn right onto Unicorn Rd.
2841 Unicorn Road #103
Bakersfield, CA 93308
(661) 399-5778
From Highway 99 take the Road 280/Caldwell Ave. exit. Thimble Towne is 4.7 miles east of Highway 99 on Caldwell Avenue.
400 W. Caldwell Ave. Suite F
Visalia, CA 93277
(559) 627-5778
www.ThimbleTowne.com • info@ThimbleTowne.com
Like us on Facebook: www.Facebook.com/ThimbleTowne

Bakersfield

Thimble Towne Q
➡ SEE AD ON PAGE 43
2841 Unicorn Road #103, 93308
(661) 399-5778
M-F 9:30-5:30, Sa 9:30-4
www.thimbletowne.com

Cherry Berry Quilts Q M
6433 Ming Avenue, 93309
(661) 282-8300

The Twisted Skein Y W S
4609 New Horizon Blvd., Suite 3, 93313
(661) 398-9276

Beaumont

Georgia's Quilting Obsession Q
1390 E. 6th Street, Suite 2, 92223
(951) 845-8009

Susan's Quilt Paradise Q
851 E 6th Street
Suite A-4, 92223
(951) 845-8445

Bellflower

Stitches In Time Yarn Y
16525 Bellflower Blvd., 90706
(562) 804-9341

Berkeley

Stonemountain & Daughter Fabrics Q
➡ SEE AD BELOW
2518 Shattuck Avenue, 94704
(510) 845-6106
M-F 10-6:30, Sa 10-6, Su 11-5:30
www.stonemountainfabric.com

Lacis Museum Of Lace And Textiles E Y N W S C
2982 Adeline Street, 94703
(510) 843-7290

New Pieces Quilt Store & Gallery Q
766 Gilman Street, 94710
(510) 527-6779

The Black Squirrel Q Y
651 Addison Street, Suite B, 94710
(805) 441-3886

Beverly Hills

Knitting House Y
260 S. Beverly Drive, Suite 203, 90212
(310) 275-6438

Big Bear City

Yarn Designers Boutique Q E Y N W S C
439 W. Big Bear Blvd., 92314
(909) 584-9715

Big Bear Lake

Bear Country Quilts & Gifts Q
42139 Big Bear Blvd., 92315
(909) 567-8766

Patchworks Q
42124 Big Bear Blvd., Suite H, 92315
(909) 866-9695

Bishop

Sierra Cottons & Wools Q E Y
117 E. Line Street, 93514
(760) 872-9209

Buellton

The Creation Station Fabric & Quilt Shop Q
252 E. Highway 246, Unit A, 93427
(805) 693-0174

Handi Quilter® Authorized Retailer
Designed by a Quilter, for Quilters.®

Calimesa

Cherry Berry Quilts Q M
1096 Calimesa Blvd., Suite B, 92320
(909) 795-9090

Handi Quilter® Authorized Retailer
Designed by a Quilter, for Quilters.®

Camarillo

The Fabric Shoppe Q M
642 Las Posas Road, 93010
(805) 383-7183

Handi Quilter® Authorized Retailer
Designed by a Quilter, for Quilters.®

Cambria

Ball & Skein & More Y N W S
4210 Bridge Street, #6, 93428
(805) 927-3280

Cameron Park

Brother's Sewing and Vacuum Q M
4100 Cameron Park Drive, 95685
(530) 676-9966

Campbell

Golden State Quilting Q
2435 S. Winchester Blvd., 95008
(408) 866-1181
M-F 10-6, Sa 10-5, Su 12-4
www.goldenstatequilting.com

Carpinteria

Roxanne's, A Wish And A Dream Q E Y M
919 Maple Avenue, 93013
(805) 566-1250

Cedarville

Warner Mountain Weavers & Lani's Lana Y W S
459 S. Main Street, 96104
(530) 279-2164

Chatsworth

Patches Fabrics Q
Call For New Location, 91311
(818) 709-2678

Chico

HeartStrings Yarn Studio Y
1909 Esplanade, 95926
(530) 894-1434

Honey Run Quilters / Cathy's Sew & Vac Q E N M
2418 Cohasset Road, 95926
(530) 342-5464

The Yarn Basket E Y N W S C
2015 Palm Avenue, 95926
(530) 345-2187

Chino Hills

We, of the Needle E C
Call for address, 91709
(909) 444-8325
Call for hours
www.weoftheneedle.com

Chula Vista

Border Leather Corp. Ⓨ
261 Broadway, 91910
(619) 691-1657

Citrus Heights

Runs With Scissors Quilt Shop Ⓠ
7130 Auburn Blvd., 95610
(916) 722-2500

Claremont

Phebie's Needleart ⒺⓎ
532 W. 1st Street, Unit 210, 91711
(909) 624-5250

Cloverdale

Bolt Fabric + Home Ⓠ
219 N. Cloverdale Blvd., 95425
(707) 894-2658

Clovis

D & J Sewing Center ⓆⒺⓂ
2700 Clovis Avenue, Suite 101, 93612
(559) 225-4927

Colusa

Friends Around The Block Ⓠ
211 8th Street, 95932
(530) 458-7467

Corning

Quilt'n Thyme Sew & Vac ⓆⓂ
955 Highway 99 W, Suite 115, 96021
(530) 824-4240

Corona

Moore's Sewing Center ⓆⓂ
591 N. McKinley Street, Suite 105, 92879
(951) 688-6254 or (951) 736-5457

Corona del Mar

Jebba Needlepoint Design Ⓝ
2628 East Coast Highway, 92625
(949) 644-7904

Costa Mesa

Knit Schtick Ⓨ
2915 Red Hill Avenue, Suite C108, 92626
(714) 557-4220

Newport Needlepoint Ⓝ
369 E. 17th Street, Suite 24, 92627
(949) 650-8022

Pal's Sewing and Vacuum Center Ⓜ
2299 Harbor Blvd., 92626
(949) 645-7257

Piecemakers Country Store ⓆⒺⓎ
1720 Adams Avenue, 92626
(714) 641-3112

Covina

Garden Gate Needlepoint, Inc. Ⓝ
236 N. Citrus Avenue, 91723
(626) 966-4141

Danville

A Yarn Less Raveled ⓎⓌ
730 Camino Ramon, Suite 186, 94526
(925) 263-2661

Wooden Gate Quilts ⓆⒺ
125-F Railroad Avenue, 94526
(925) 837-8458

El Cajon

A Simpler Time - Alpacas & Mill ⓎⓌⓈ
1802 Alta Place, 92021
(619) 579-9114

Cozy Creative Center ⓆⓂ
756 Jamacha Road, 92019
(619) 670-0652

Memory Lane Quilt Shop ⓆⓂ
1626 N. Magnolia Avenue, 92020
(619) 562-2288

Elk Grove

Elk Grove Sewing and Vacuum Center Q M
8705 Elk Grove Blvd., 95624
(916) 714-0904

Knitique Y
8739 Elk Grove Blvd., 95624
(916) 714-7719

Emerald Hills

Amazing Yarns Y W S
2559 Woodland Place, 94062
(650) 306-9218

Encinitas

Common Threads Y W S
191 N. El Camino Real, Suite 201, 92024
(760) 436-6119

Escondido

Annie's Quilting Den, LLC Q
1876 W. El Norte Parkway, 92026
(760) 747-4444

Dancing Bear Indian Trader Q
1313 Simpson Way, Suite A, 92029
(760) 747-2323

Eureka

Bunny Hop Quilt Shop Q
1809 Albee Street, 95501
(707) 497-6356

Eureka Fabrics Q
412 2nd Street, 95501
(707) 442-2646 or (888) 469-6799

Lavender Rose Fabrics & Notions Q
301 W. Harris Street, 95503
(530) 945-2770

Ocean Wave Quilts Q E
305 V Street, 95501
(707) 444-0252

Yarn Y S
518 Russ Street, 95501
(707) 443-9276

Fair Oaks

Babetta's Yarn Cafe Y W S
4400 San Juan Avenue, Suite 20, 95628
(916) 965-6043

Thistle Dew Quilt Shoppe Q E
10127 Fair Oaks Blvd., 95628
(916) 967-5479

Fairfax

Rainbow Fabrics Crafts And Things Q E Y
50 Bolinas Road, 94930
(415) 459-5100

Fallbrook

Quilter's Cottage Q M
131 E. Fig Street, Suite 6, 92028
(760) 723-3060

Ferndale

Stitch Q
385 Main Street, 95536
(707) 786-5007

Folsom

Meissner Sewing & Vacuum Centers Q M
98 Clarksville Road, Suite 130, 95630
(916) 984-7071

Fortuna

Fortuna Fabrics & Crafts Q E Y C
2045 Main Street, 95540
(707) 725-2501

Fountain Valley

Jenny's Fabrics Q
8984 Warner Avenue, 92708
(714) 847-2202

Fremont

Color Me Quilts Q E Y
37495 Niles Blvd., 94536
(510) 494-9940

Not Just QuiltZ, LLC Q E
37831 Niles Blvd., 94536
(510) 797-6579

Fresno

SWATCHES Y
➡ SEE AD BELOW
1764 W. Bullard Avenue, 93711
(559) 435-2813
W-Su call ahead, and by appt.
www.swatchesfresno.com

1764 W. Bullard Ave.
Fresno CA 93711
559-435-2813
SWATCHES
A Yarn Studio
swatches2008@aol.com
www.swatchesfresno.com
Like us on FACEBOOK: Swatches - Fresno

Sierra Fiber Arts Q E M
7462 N. Fresno Street, 93720
(559) 432-8900
M-F 10-6, Sa 10-5
www.sierrafiberarts.com

Authorized Vac & Sew Q E M
5233 N. Blackstone Avenue, 93710
(559) 439-2560

Janna's Needle Art Y N
1085 E. Herndon Avenue, Suite 104, 93720
(559) 227-6333

Kiki's Quilt Shack Q M
1732 W. Bullard Avenue, 93711
(559) 412-8233

Second Chance Fabrics Q
5322 W. Spruce Avenue, #110, 93722
(559) 365-0132

Ft. Bragg

Sew 'n Sew Fabrics Q E
890-A N. Franklin Street, 95437
(707) 964-4152

Garden Grove

Needlepoints, Ltd. E N C
12832 Valley View Street, Suite F, 92845
(657) 337-9445

The Sewing Escape Q
7713 Garden Grove Blvd., 92841
(714) 622-4551

Gilroy

The Nimble Thimble Q E M
7455 Monterey Street, 95020
(408) 842-6501

Glendora

Pollard's Sew Creative Q M
1008 E. Route 66, 91740
(626) 335-2770

The Purl Side Y
1200 E. Route 66, #109, 91740
(626) 914-3747

The Sew N Sew Q E N C M
160 N. Glendora Avenue, Suite E, 91741
(626) 852-2223

Grand Terrace

Bluebird Quilts & Gallery Q E
22320 Barton Road, Suite A, 92313
(909) 514-0333

Grass Valley

Villa Rosa Design Q
➡ SEE AD PAGE 343
12438 Loma Rica Drive, Ste. A, 95945
(530) 268-5355
Call for hours
www.villarosadesigns.com

Ben Franklin Crafts and Frames Q E Y N S C
598 Sutton Way, 95945
(530) 273-1348

Grover Beach

Yarn and Beads Ⓨ
225 W. Grand Avenue, 93433
(805) 668-2333
Tu-Sa 10-4
www.yarnandbeads.com

Gualala

The Loft ⓆⒺⓎⓃⓌⓈⒸ
39225 S. Highway 1, 95445
(707) 884-4424

Half Moon Bay

Fengari Ⓨ
415 Main Street, 94019
(650) 726-2550

Hawthorne

SAS Fabrics Ⓠ
13500 Hawthorne Blvd., 90250
(310) 978-8985

The Slipt Stitch Ⓨ
13737 Inglewood Avenue, Suite 104, 90250
(310) 322-6793

Healdsburg

Purls of Joy Ⓨ
461 Healdsburg Avenue, 95448
(707) 433-5697

Hilmar

Cloth and Quilts ⓆⓂ
19949 American Avenue, 95324
(209) 632-3225

Quilters Cabin Hilmar Ⓠ
8177 Lander Avenue, 95324
(209) 427-2100

Huntington Beach

Moore's Sewing Center ⓆⓂ
15041 Goldenwest Street, 92647
(714) 899-3222
M-F 10-6, Sa 10-5:30
www.moores-sew.com

Miki's California Yarn Sales ⓎⓃⓌ
9542 Hamilton Avenue, 92646
(714) 965-0018 or (714) 964-4059

Idyllwild

The Idyllwild Yarn Shop Ⓨ
54225 N. Circle Drive, 92549
(951) 659-4481

Inglewood

Sew Together Stitching Lounge Ⓠ
1031 W. Manchester Blvd, #1, 90301
(424) 393-4038

The Knitting Tree, LA ⒺⓎⓌⓈ
1031 W. Manchester Blvd., #2, 90301
(310) 395-3880

Jackson

MIY Studio Ⓠ
11990 Highway 88 Suite 2056, 95642
(209) 223-2002

Julian

Kat's Yarn & Craft Cottage ⓆⓎⓃⓌⓈⒸ
2000 Main Street, Suite 106, 92036
(619) 246-8585

King City

Meandering Threads Ⓠ
51460 White Oak Drive, 93930
(831) 385-3434

La Jolla

Fay's Needle Nook of La Jolla Ⓝ
7719 Fay Avenue, 92037
(858) 459-1711

La Mesa

Yarn & Thread Expressions [Y]
➡ **SEE AD BELOW**
7882 La Mesa Blvd., 91942
(619) 460-9276
Tu 11-8, W 1-7, Th 11-7, F 1-8, Sa 10-5
www.yarneshop.com

La Verne

Make One Yarn Company [Y]
2127 Foothill Blvd., Suite A, 91750
(909) 593-8790

Lafayette

Busy Stix [Y][N][W][S]
3409 Mt. Diablo Blvd., Suite D, 94549
(925) 284-1172

The Cotton Patch [Q][E][N][M]
1025 Brown Avenue, 94549
(925) 284-1177
Handi Quilter® Authorized Retailer
Designed by a Quilter, for Quilters.®

Lakeport

Kerrie's Quilting [Q][M]
1853 N. High Street, 95453
(707) 263-8555

Lancaster

Bolts in the Bathtub [Q][E][M]
723 W. Lancaster Blvd., 93534
(661) 945-5541

Laytonville

The Fat Quail Quilt Shop [Q]
44550 N. Highway 101, 95454
(707) 984-6966

Lincoln

Cherry Moose Quilts [Q][E]
603 Fifth Street, 95648
(916) 884-1832
W-F 10-4, Sa 10-2
https://cherry-moose-quilts.myshopify.com

AngelQuilters [Q][E]
6011 Nicolaus Road, 95648
(916) 645-8760 or (916) 825-8309

Little River

Mendocino Yarn Shop [Y][W][S][C]
7901 N. Highway One, 95456
(707) 937-0921 or (888) 530-1400

Livermore

In Between Stitches [Q][E]
2190 1st Street, 94550
(925) 371-7064

Lodi

Lodi Vacuum and Sewing Center [Q][E][M]
26 W. Lodi Avenue, 95240
(209) 369-5026 or (209) 333-2941

Lomita

AAA Sewing, Fabrics, & Vacuum Center Ⓠ Ⓔ Ⓜ
2365 Pacific Coast Highway, 90717
(310) 257-1744

Long Beach

Alamitos Bay Yarn Company Ⓨ Ⓦ
174 N. Marina Drive, 90803
(562) 799-8484

Mari Pat's Needlework Shop Ⓝ Ⓒ
3926 Atlantic Avenue, 90807
(562) 427-2880

SewVac Ltd. Ⓠ Ⓜ
1762 Clark Avenue, 90815
(562) 498-6684
Handi Quilter® Authorized Retailer
Designed by a Quilter, for Quilters.®

Loomis

The Tin Thimble Ⓠ Ⓢ
3750 Taylor Road, 95650
(916) 652-2134

Los Altos

Uncommon Threads Ⓨ Ⓦ
293 State Street, 94022
(650) 941-1815

Los Angeles

Jennifer Knits Ⓨ
108 Barrington Walk, 90049
(310) 471-8733
Tu 11-7, W-Sa 11-4
www.jenniferknits.com

Needlepoints West Ⓠ Ⓔ Ⓨ Ⓝ Ⓦ Ⓢ Ⓒ
6227 W. 87th Street, 90045
(310) 670-4847
Tu-F 11-5, Sa 11-4
http://www.needlepointswest.com

F & S Fabrics Ⓠ
10629 W. Pico Blvd., 90064
(310) 475-1637 or (310) 475-1637

Fabric Hotel Ⓠ
848 S. Wall Street, 90014
(213) 623-8081

Gather DTLA Ⓨ
453 S. Spring Street, #M1, 90013
(213) 908-2656

Michael Levine, Inc. Ⓠ Ⓨ
920 S. Maple Avenue, 90015
(213) 622-6259

The Little Knittery Ⓨ Ⓦ Ⓢ
1808 N. Vermont Avenue, 90027
(323) 663-3838

Los Banos

JMG Fabric And Crafts Ⓠ
1044 6th Street, 93635
(209) 827-1808

Los Molinos

Sew Smart Supplies Ⓠ Ⓔ Ⓜ
8064 Highway 99 E, 96055
(530) 576-3131

Manhattan Beach

Twist . . . Yarns of Intrigue Ⓨ Ⓦ Ⓢ
226 S. Sepulveda Blvd., 90266
(310) 374-7810

Manteca

Ladybug's Quilts Ⓠ Ⓔ
1236 N. Main Street, Suite A, 95336
(209) 824-0485

Marysville

Sew-n-Piece Ⓠ
410 Fourth Street, 95901
(530) 713-3822

Menlo Park

Old World Designs Ⓝ
727 Santa Cruz Avenue, 94025
(650) 321-3494

Mill Valley

Once Around ⓆⓎ
75 Throckmorton Avenue, 94941
(415) 326-5217

Mission Viejo

Moore's Sewing Center ⓆⓂ
25390 Marquerite Parkway, 92692
(949) 580-2520

Yarn del Sol ⓎⓌⓈ
24471 Alicia Parkway, #2, 92691
(949) 581-9276

Montrose

Needle In A Haystack ⒺⓎⓃⒸ
2262 Honolulu Avenue, 91020
(818) 248-7686

Morgan Hill

Continental Stitch Ⓨ
16375 Monterey Road, Suite J, 95037
(408) 779-5885 or (866) 890-9587

Madonna Needle Works ⒺⓃⒸ
15790 Monterey Road, Suite 300, 95037
(408) 776-6857

Quilts and Things Ⓠ
16985 Monterey Street, Suite 316, 95037
(408) 776-8438

Morro Bay

Morro Fleece Works ⓎⓈ
1920 Main Street, 93442
(805) 772-9665
M-F 10-4 and by appt.
www.morrofleeceworks.com

Lina G all the trimmings ⓆⒺⓎⓌⓈ
468 Morro Bay Blvd., 93442
(805) 772-7759

The Cotton Ball ⓆⒺⓎⓂ
2830 Main Street, 93442
(805) 772-2646

Mountain View

Custom Handweavers ⓎⓌⓈ
2263 Old Middlefield Way, 94043
(650) 967-0831

Mt. Shasta

Weston's Quilting & Fiber Arts ⓆⒺⓎ
➡ SEE AD BELOW
414 Chestnut Street, 96067
(530) 926-4021
M 11-3, Tu-Sa 10-5
www.westonsquiltingandfiberarts.com

Murphys

Maisieblue Ⓨ
66 Scott Street, 95247
(209) 728-8261

Murrieta

Primitive Gatherings Quilt Shop Ⓠ
26855 Jefferson Avenue, Unit D, 92562
(951) 304-9787

Napa

Yarns on First Ⓨ
1305 1st Street, 94559
(707) 257-1363

Newbury Park

A ThreadGarden/BeadTime ⒺⓃⒸ
3533 Old Conejo Road #112, 91320
(805) 482-5256

The Quilters' Studio Q E M
1090 Lawrence Drive, Suite 101, 91320
(805) 480-3550

Newport Beach

Sheared Sheep Y
1665 Westcliff Drive, Suite A, 92660
(949) 722-7977

Norco

Sewn Together Q
1700 Hamner Avenue, Suite 112, 92860
(951) 479-5121

Northridge

Candy's Quiltworks Q
8549 Reseda Blvd., 91324
(818) 349-7397

Kingdom Sewing and Vacuum of Northridge M
8923 Reseda Blvd., 91324
(818) 993-8933

Authorized Retailer

Oakdale

A Quilter's Place Q
7450 River Road, Suite 4, 95361
(209) 844-5070

Lilly Pad Sewing Q M
1214 W. F Street, A-4, 95361
(209) 848-0190

Oakhurst

Bear Paw Quilts & More Q E
40761 Highway 41, Suite 7, 93644
(559) 683-7397

Oakland

A Verb for Keeping Warm Q E Y W S
6328 San Pablo Avenue, 94608
(510) 595-8372

Piedmont Fabric Q
4009 Piedmont Avenue, 94611
(510) 655-1213 or (510) 653-8015

Piedmont Yarn and Apparel Y S
4171 Piedmont Avenue, Suite 102, 94611
(510) 595-9595

Sew Images Q E C M
4172 Piedmont Avenue, 94611
(510) 601-8739

Ojai

Cattywampus Crafts Q E Y
209 W. Ojai Avenue, 93023
(213) 280-8981

Orange

Fabric Land of Orange Q
936 E. Lincoln Avenue, 92865
(714) 974-1214

Orange Quilt Bee Q E
628 E. Katella Avenue, 92867
(714) 639-3245

Orcutt

Old Town Quilt Shop Q
165 W. Clark Avenue, Suite A, 93455
(805) 938-5870

Oroville

Pieces of Love Quilt Shop Q E
2216 Fifth Avenue, 95965
(530) 990-0699

Pacific Grove

Back Porch Fabrics Q
157 Grand Avenue, 93950
(831) 375-4453

Monarch Knitting Y
529 Central Avenue, Suite 4, 93950
(831) 647-9276

Pacifica

The Royal Bee Yarn Company LLC Y C
90 Eureka Square, 94044
(650) 898-8329

Palm Desert

Harriet's Yarns & Needlepoint Ⓨ Ⓝ
77-780 Country Club Drive, Suite F, 92211
(760) 772-3333

Monica's Quilt & Beads Creations Ⓠ
77780 Country Club Drive, Suite C-D, 92211
(760) 772-2400

The Quilter's Faire Ⓠ
34500 Gateway Drive, Suite 110, 92211
(760) 328-8737

Palo Cedro

Blue Iris Quilt Shop Ⓠ Ⓔ Ⓜ
9348 Deschutes Road, 96073
(530) 547-2228

Paradise

Debbie's Quilt Shop Ⓠ
6455 Skyway, 95969
(530) 877-8458

Pasadena

Skein Fine Yarn Store Ⓨ
1101 E. Walnut Street, 91106
(626) 577-2035

Wollhaus Ⓨ
696 E. Colorado Blvd, Suite 2, 91101
(626) 799-0355

Paso Robles

Fabricworm / Birch Fabrics Ⓠ
1244 Pine Street, Suite D, 93446
(805) 239-8888

The Quiltery Ⓠ
1413 Riverside Avenue, 93446
(805) 227-4561

Patterson

Village Yarn & Etc. Ⓨ Ⓢ
32 S. 3rd Street, 95363
(209) 892-3786

Petaluma

Quilted Angel Ⓠ
200 G Street, 94952
(707) 763-0945

StitchCraft Ⓠ
170 Kentucky Street, 94952
(707) 773-4739

Pismo Beach

The Sewing Cafe Ⓠ Ⓜ
541 Five Cities Drive, 93449
(805) 295-6585

Placerville

Kelsey's Needle Krafts Ⓔ Ⓝ Ⓒ
447A Main Street, 95667
(530) 622-6205
M-Sa 10-5, Su 12-4
http://www.kelseys-needlekrafts.com

High Sierra Quilters Ⓠ
1444 Broadway, 95667
(530) 622-9990

Lofty Lou's Yarn Shop, LLC Ⓨ Ⓦ Ⓢ
263 Main Street, 95667
(530) 642-2270

Pleasanton

Knit This, Purl That! Ⓨ
205A Main Street, 94566
(925) 249-9276

Point Reyes Station

Black Mountain Artisans Ⓨ Ⓢ
11245 Main Street, 94956
(415) 663-9130

Porterville

Calico Mermaid Ⓠ
122 N. Main Street, 93257
(559) 793-2510

Portola

Blue Petunia Quilts Ⓠ Ⓔ
74631 Highway 70, 96122
(530) 832-4026
Everyday 10-6
www.bluepetuniaquilts.com

Poway

Paradise Sewing Center Ⓠ Ⓔ Ⓜ
13242 Poway Road, 92064
(858) 679-9808 or (760) 745-4140

Quincy

The WoolRoom Ⓨ
390 Jackson Street, 95971
(530) 283-0648

Ramona

Ramona Country Yarn Store Ⓨ
780 Main Street, Suite B, 92065
(760) 789-7305

Rancho Cordova

Rita's Fabric Friendship & Fun aka Rita Traxler Designs Ⓠ
11345 Trade Center Drive, Suite 150, 95742
(916) 289-7841

Rancho Cucamonga

Richard's Fabrics Ⓠ
8663 Baseline Road, 91730
(909) 987-6061
Tu-Sa 10-6
https://www.facebook.com/pages/Richards-Fabrics/126553287400247

Rancho Santa Margarita

Moore's Sewing Center* Ⓜ
22532 Avenida Empresa, 92688
(949) 829-9459

Red Bluff

Stitch by Stitch ⓆⒺⓎ
810 Main Street, 96080
(530) 200-3110

Redding

Ewe-Baa Street Yarn Ⓨ
1725 Yuba Street, 96001
(530) 246-9276

Hokema's Sewing and Vacuum Center ⓆⒺⓂ
2736 Bechelli Lane, 96002
(530) 223-1970

Sew Simple ⓆⒺ
2223 Larkspur Lane, 96002
(530) 222-1845

The Sewing Room ⓆⒺ
2665 Park Marina Drive, 96001
(530) 246-2056

Redlands

Hands On Knitting Center ⓎⓌⓈ
912 New York Street, Suite A, 92374
(909) 793-8712
MTuThFSa 10-6, W 10-9
www.handsonknittingcenter.com

KnitWorks Yarn Company Ⓨ
461 Tennessee Street, Suites A & B, 92373
(909) 748-5656

Redondo Beach

L'Atelier Riviera Village ⓎⓌ
1722 S. Catalina Avenue, 90277
(310) 540-4440

Reedley

Mennonite Quilt Center Ⓠ
1012 G Street, 93654
(559) 638-3560

Richmond

Bay Quilts ⓆⒺ
5327 Jacuzzi Street 3-C, 94804
(510) 558-0218

Ridgecrest

Quilt 'N Home ⓆⓂ
425 E. Ridgecrest Blvd., 93555
(760) 371-9060

Riverside

Designer Hand Knits ⓎⓌ
6730 Brockton Avenue, 92506
(951) 275-9711

Easy Quilting Corner Ⓠ
1405 Spruce Street, Suite D, 92507
(951) 224-9998

Gaye Marie's Sewing Lab ⓆⓂ
7107 Arlington Avenue, Suite J, 92503
(951) 687-7397

The Quilter's Cocoon Ⓠ Ⓜ
9901 Indiana Avenue, #104, 92503
(951) 351-0346

Roseville

Got Your Goat Yarn Studio Ⓨ
1850 Douglas Blvd., Suite 910, 95661
(916) 899-5416

Meissner Sewing & Vacuum Center Ⓠ Ⓜ
9250 Fairway Drive, Suite 110, 95678
(916) 791-2121

Sacramento

Fabric Garden Ⓠ Ⓔ
➡ SEE AD BELOW
2654 Marconi Avenue, Suite 155, 95821
(916) 483-2955
M-F 10-6, Sa 10-4
www.fabricgardenquiltshop.com

Meissner Sewing & Vacuum Centers Ⓠ Ⓜ
2417 Cormorant Way, 95815
(916) 920-2121

Quilters' Corner, Inc. Ⓠ Ⓔ
9792 B Business Park Drive, 95827
(916) 366-6136

Rumpelstiltskin Yarn Store Ⓨ Ⓦ Ⓢ
1021 R Street, 95811
(916) 442-9225

San Anselmo

Atelier Marin Ⓨ Ⓦ Ⓢ
217 San Anselmo Avenue, 94960
(415) 256-9618

San Clemente

Strands Knitting Studio Ⓨ
111 Avenida Granada, 92672
(949) 496-4021

San Diego

Apricot Yarn & Supply Ⓨ
2690 Historic Decatur Road, Suite 101, 92106
(619) 223-3603
Tu-Sa 10-5, Su 11-5
www.apricotyarn.com

Aranitas Yarn by Sophia Ⓨ
2925 Lincoln Avenue, 92104
(619) 674-8480

Needlecraft Cottage Ⓨ Ⓝ Ⓒ
870 Grand Avenue, 92109
(858) 272-8185

Rosie's Calico Cupboard Ⓠ Ⓜ
7151 El Cajon Blvd., Suite F, 92115
(619) 697-5758

Sew Hut Ⓠ Ⓜ
4226 Balboa Avenue, 92117
(858) 273-1377

South Park Dry Goods Co. Ⓠ Ⓔ Ⓨ
3010 Juniper Street, 92104
(619) 550-5765

The Black Sheep Ⓨ Ⓦ Ⓢ
11675 Sorrento Valley Road, #H, 92121
(858) 481-6708

San Francisco

Apparel City Sewing Machine Company Ⓠ Ⓔ Ⓜ
1330 Howard Street, 94103
(800) 613-6660

Atelier Yarns Ⓨ Ⓦ
1945 Divisadero Street, 94115
(415) 771-1550

Britex Fabrics Ⓠ Ⓔ Ⓝ Ⓒ
117 Post Street, 94108
(415) 392-2910

Carolina Homespun* Ⓨ Ⓦ Ⓢ
455 Lisbon Street, 94112
(415) 584-7786 or (800) 450-7786

Cliff's Variety Ⓠ Ⓔ Ⓨ Ⓝ
479 Castro Street, 94114
(415) 431-5365

Discount Fabrics Ⓠ Ⓔ
2170 Cesar Chavez Street, 94124
(415) 685-4064

Fabric Outlet Ⓠ Ⓔ Ⓨ Ⓒ
2109 Mission Street, 94110
(415) 552-4525

Golden Gate Needlepoint Ⓝ
3310 Sacramento Street, 94118
(415) 345-8779

ImagiKnit Ⓨ Ⓦ Ⓢ
3897 18th Street, 94114
(415) 621-6642

Mendel's Far Out Fabrics Ⓠ Ⓔ Ⓨ
1556 Haight Street, 94117
(415) 621-1287

Needlepoint Inc. Ⓝ
326 Jackson Street, 94111
(415) 392-1622 or (800) 345-1622

The Hobby Company of San Francisco Ⓨ Ⓝ Ⓒ
5150 Geary Blvd., 94118
(415) 386-2802

San Jose

California Sewing & Vacuum Ⓠ Ⓜ
3403 Stevens Creek Blvd., 95117
(408) 246-0944

Green Planet Yarn Ⓨ
1702 Meridian Avenue, Suite H, 95125
(408) 620-1042

Nichi Bei Bussan Ⓠ
140 E. Jackson Street, 95112
(408) 294-8048

Ray's Sewing Machine Center* Ⓜ
545 Meridian Avenue, Suite F, 95126
(408) 295-6901
Handi Quilter® Authorized Retailer
Designed by a Quilter, for Quilters.®

San Juan Bautista

Family Threads Quilt Shop Ⓠ
107D The Alameda, 95045
(831) 623-0200

San Luis Obispo

Picking Daisies Ⓠ Ⓔ
570 Higuera Street, #120, 93401
(805) 783-2434

Yarns At The Adobe Ⓨ
964 Chorro Street, 93401
(805) 549-9276

San Marcos

Grand Country Quilters Ⓠ
801 Grand Avenue, Suite 1, 92078
(760) 471-1114

Quilt in a Day Ⓠ
1955A Diamond Street, 92078
(760) 591-0929 or (800) 777-4852

SewingMachinesPlus.com Ⓠ Ⓔ Ⓜ
713 Center Drive, 92069
(760) 739-8222 or (800) 401-8151

Yarning for You Ⓨ Ⓦ
1001 W. San Marcos Blvd., Suite 108C, 92078
(760) 744-5648

San Marino

A Stitch In Time Ⓨ Ⓝ
2465 Huntington Drive, 91108
(626) 793-5217

San Mateo

Always Quilting Ⓠ Ⓔ Ⓜ
4230 Olympic Avenue, 94403
(650) 458-8580
M-Sa 10-4, Su 1-4
www.alwaysquiltingonline.com
Handi Quilter® Authorized Retailer
Designed by a Quilter, for Quilters.®

ScruffyQuilts Q
11 37th Avenue, 94403
(650) 274-0292
TuWThFSaSu 10-5
www.scruffyquilts.com

City Needlework N
61 E. 4th Avenue, 94401
(650) 348-2151

Luv 2 Stitch N
715 Bermuda Drive, 94403
(650) 571-9999

San Rafael

Come To The Point! E Y N W C
10 California Avenue, 94901
(415) 485-4942

Dharma Trading Co. Y W S
1604 4th Street, 94901
(415) 456-1211

Santa Ana

Ursula's Yarn Boutique Y
2441 N. Tustin Avenue, Suite D, 92705
(714) 834-1908

Santa Barbara

Cardigans Y
3030 State Street, 93105
(805) 569-0531

Santa Clarita

Queen Anne Stitches N C
20655 Soledad Canyon Road, Suite 30, 91351
(661) 286-1248

Santa Cruz

Hart's Fabric Store Q
1620 Seabright Avenue, 95062
(831) 423-5434

Judy's Sewing Center Q M
806 Ocean Street, 95060
(831) 464-8181

The Swift Stitch Y
402 Ingalls Street, #12, 95060
(831) 427-9276

Yarn Shop Santa Cruz Y
765 Cedar Street, Suite 103, 95060
(831) 515-7966

Santa Monica

Sewing Arts Center Q E M
3330 Pico Blvd., 90405
(310) 450-4300
M-Th 10-6:30, F-Su 10-5
www.sewingarts.com

Compatto Yarn Salon Y W
2112 Wilshire Blvd., 90403
(310) 453-2130

Wildfiber Studio E Y W S
1453 14th Street, Suite E, 90404
(310) 458-2748

Santa Monica (Los Angeles)

Aristeia Needlepoint N
➡ SEE AD AT LEFT
200 26th Street, 90402
(310) 260-6330
MTu 10-6, WTh 10-5, FSa 10-4
www.aristeianeedlepoint.com

Santa Rosa

Cast Away E Y W
100 4th Street, 95401
(707) 546-9276

Meissner Sewing & Vacuum Centers Q M
1455 Santa Rosa Avenue, 95404
(707) 575-5259

Village Sewing Center Q M
506 Lewis Road, 95404
(707) 544-7529

Sebastopol

Yarnitudes Y W S
3598 Gravenstein Highway S, 95472
(707) 827-3618
MTuThFSa 10-5:30, W 10-7:30, Su 11:30-4:30
www.yarnitudes.com

Simi Valley

Quilty Pleasures Q E N
1742 E. Los Angeles Avenue, Suite A, 93065
(805) 581-1577

Solana Beach

Starry Night Hollow Q
722 Genevieve Street, Suite Q, 92075
(858) 345-1845 or (760) 944-3700

Solvang

Thumbelina Needlework E N C
1683-A Copenhagen Drive, 93463
(800) 789-4136 or (805) 688-4136

Sonoma

Broadway Quilts Q E
20525 Broadway, 95476
(707) 938-7312

Sonora

Quail's Nest Quilt Co., LLC Q M
14675 Mono Way, 95370
(209) 536-4009

South Lake Tahoe

Knits & Knots Y W S
989 Tallac Avenue, 96150
(530) 494-9622

South San Francisco

Cottage Yarns Y
607 W. Orange Avenue, 94080
(650) 873-7371

Springville

Totally Tina's Fabrics Q
36527 Highway 190, Suite 101, 93265
(559) 361-7866

Stanton

Fabric Outlet & Crafts Q
10450 Beach Blvd., 90680
(714) 995-2723

Stockton

Quilters' Hollow Q E M
8855 Thornton Road, Suite B, 95209
(209) 477-5253

Studio City

La Knitterie Parisienne Y
12642 Ventura Blvd., 91604
(818) 766-1515

Lani's Needlepoint N
12426 Ventura Blvd., 91604
(818) 769-2431

Sunnyvale

The Granary Quilt Shop, Inc. Q
1326 S. Mary Avenue, 94087
(408) 735-9830
MTuWF 10-6, Th 10-8, Sa 10-5
www.thegranaryquilts.com

Eddie's Quilting Bee & House of Sewing Q M
480 S. Mathilda Avenue, 94086
(408) 830-9505

Susanville

Country Pines Quilt Shop Q
704-395 Richmond Road E, 96130
(530) 260-9600 or (530) 257-4071

Tarzana

NeedleHearts N
➡ SEE AD BELOW
18900 1/2 Ventura Blvd., 91356
(818) 344-6277
M-Th 10-4, (MTh evening 7-9), F 10-3, Sa 11-3
www.needlehearts.com

Zoe's Knit Studio Y
18596 Ventura Blvd., 91356
(818) 881-9637

Tehachapi

5 Heart Quilts & Fabric Q
104 W. Tehachapi Blvd., 93561
(661) 822-8709

Debbie's Fabrics ETC. Q
112 E. Tehachapi Blvd., 93561
(661) 823-7114

Temecula

Moore's Sewing Center Q M
26490 Ynez Road, Suites F & G, 92591
(951) 297-3796

Needle in a Fabric Stash Q
43049 Margarita Road, #A102, 92592
(951) 587-8274

Temecula Quilt Company Q
33353 Temecula Parkway, #103, 92592
(951) 302-1469

Temecula Valley Sewing Center Q M
28780 Old Town Front Street #A2, 92590
(951) 694-9576

Thousand Oaks

Cotton & Chocolate Quilt Company Q E
1724 E. Avenida De Los Arboles, Unit E, 91362
(805) 241-0061

Eva's Needlework Y N
1321 E. Thousand Oaks Blvd., #120, 91362
(805) 379-0722

Truckee

Atelier E Y W
10128 Donner Pass Road, 96161
(530) 386-2700

Turlock

Macedo's Mini Acre Y S
11175 Golf Link Road, 95380
(209) 648-2384

Tustin

Mel's Sewing & Fabric Center Q E M
600 E. 1st Street, 92780
(714) 669-0583

Twain Harte

Twain Harte Pharmacy Q E Y N C
18711 Tiffeni Drive, Suite 45, 95383
(209) 586-3225

Ukiah

Heidi's Yarn Haven E Y
180 S. School Street, 95482
(707) 462-0544

Village Sewing Center Q M
1252 Airport Park Blvd., Suite A-2, 95482
(707) 467-9383

Upland

Needles & Niceties E Y C
1655 N. Mountain Avenue, Suite 116, 91784
(909) 985-6264

Upland Vacuum & Sewing Q M
113 N. 2nd Avenue, 91786
(909) 949-4884

Vacaville

A Quilted Heart Q E
878 Alamo Drive, 95688
(707) 447-9000

Meridian Jacobs Y W S
7811 N. Meridian Road, 95688
(707) 688-3493

Valley Center

Inspirations Quilt Shop Q
27350 Valley Center Road, Suite B, 92082
(760) 751-9400

Valley Village

The Altered Stitch Y W S
12443 Magnolia Blvd., 91607
(818) 980-1234

Van Nuys

A-Major-Knitwork Y
6746 Balboa Blvd., 91406
(818) 787-2659

Ventura

Fabric Town USA Q E Y C
2686 E. Main Street, 93003
(805) 643-3434

superbuzzy Q E Y C
1794 E. Main Street, 93001
(805) 643-4143

Victorville

Moore's Sewing Center Q M
16210 Bear Valley Road, 92395
(760) 240-4477

Visalia

Thimble Towne Q
➡ SEE AD PAGE 43
400 W. Caldwell Avenue, Suite F, 93277
(559) 627-5778
Tu-F 9:30-5:30, Sa 9:30-4
www.thimbletowne.com

Vista

Fat Quarters Quilt Shop Q E
728 Civic Center Drive, 92084
(760) 758-8308

Walnut Creek

Monaluna Q E
➡ SEE AD PAGE 282
2061 Mt. Diablo Blvd., 94596
(925) 448-8055
Th-Sa 11-5:30
www.monaluna.com

Fashionknit Y
1867 Ygnacio Valley Road, 94568
(925) 933-3994

The Sewing Machine Shop Q E C M
1661 Botelho Drive, 94596
(925) 937-7575

Weaverville

Sweet Sheep Y W
515 Main Street, 96093
(530) 623-8650

Willows

Quilt Corral Q E M
245 W. Wood Street, 95988
(530) 934-8116
M-F 10-5, Sa 10-2
www.thequiltcorral.net

Winters

Cloth Carousel - Fabric Q E Y N C
9 Main Street, 95694
(530) 795-2580

Cloth Carousel - Yarn E Y S C
14 Main Street, 95694
(530) 794-6114

Woodland Hills

Quilt Emporium Q
4918 Topanga Canyon Blvd., 91364
(818) 704-8238

Yorba Linda

Velona Needlecraft
Q E Y N W S C
22435 La Palma Avenue, #A, 92887
(714) 692-2286
Tu 10-8, WThF 10-6, Sa 10-5
www.velona.net

Yuba City

Sew So Shop Q M
990-C Klamath Lane, Suite 18, 95993
(530) 742-7626

Yucca Valley

Kim's Fabric Outlet Q M
29 Palms Highway, 92284
(760) 369-3609

Quilting Between Friends Q
7379 Hopi Trail, 92284
(760) 365-4519

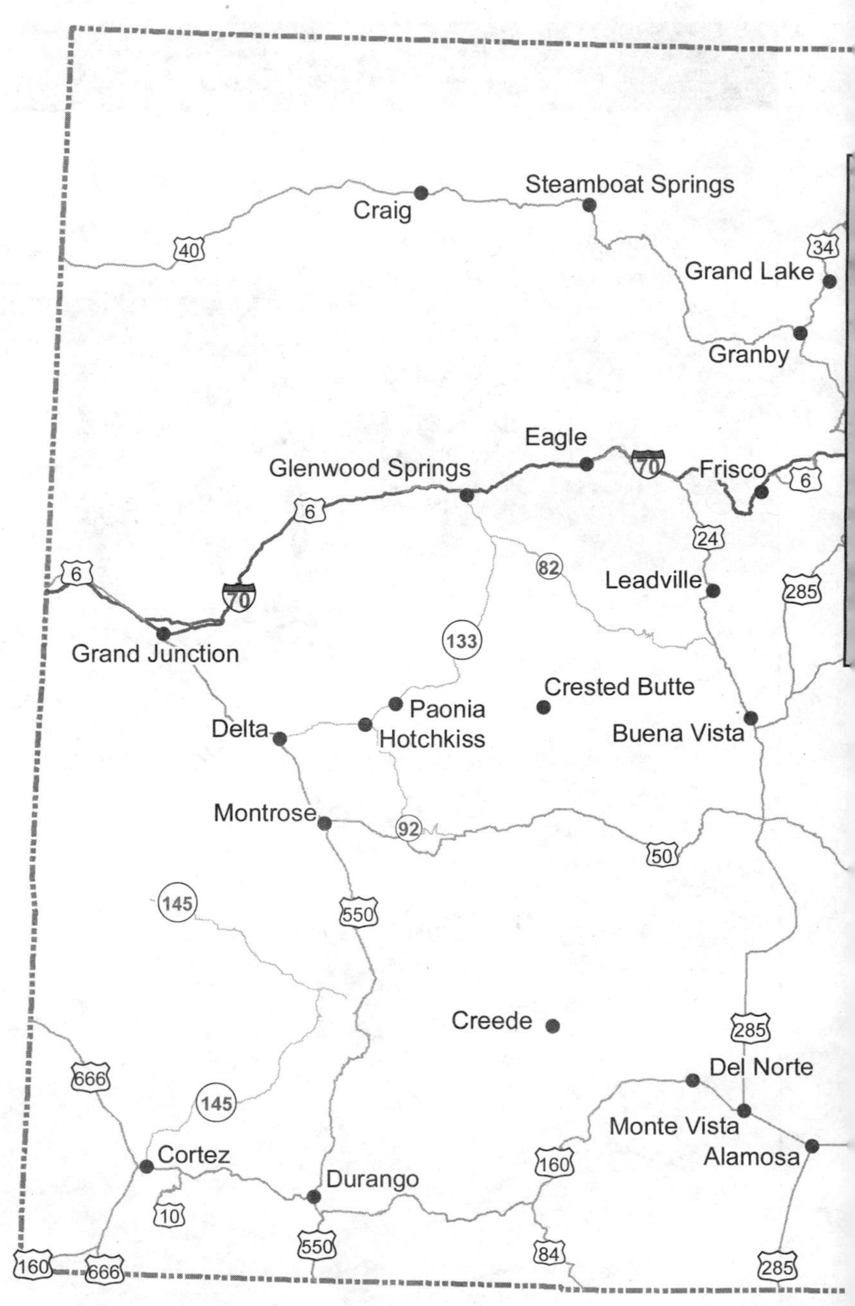
Craig
Steamboat Springs
40
34
Grand Lake
Granby
Eagle
Glenwood Springs
70
Frisco
6
6
24
6
82
Leadville
70
285
133
Grand Junction
Crested Butte
Paonia
Delta
Hotchkiss
Buena Vista
Montrose
92
50
145
550
Creede
285
Del Norte
666
145
Monte Vista
Alamosa
Cortez
160
Durango
10
550
84
285
160
666

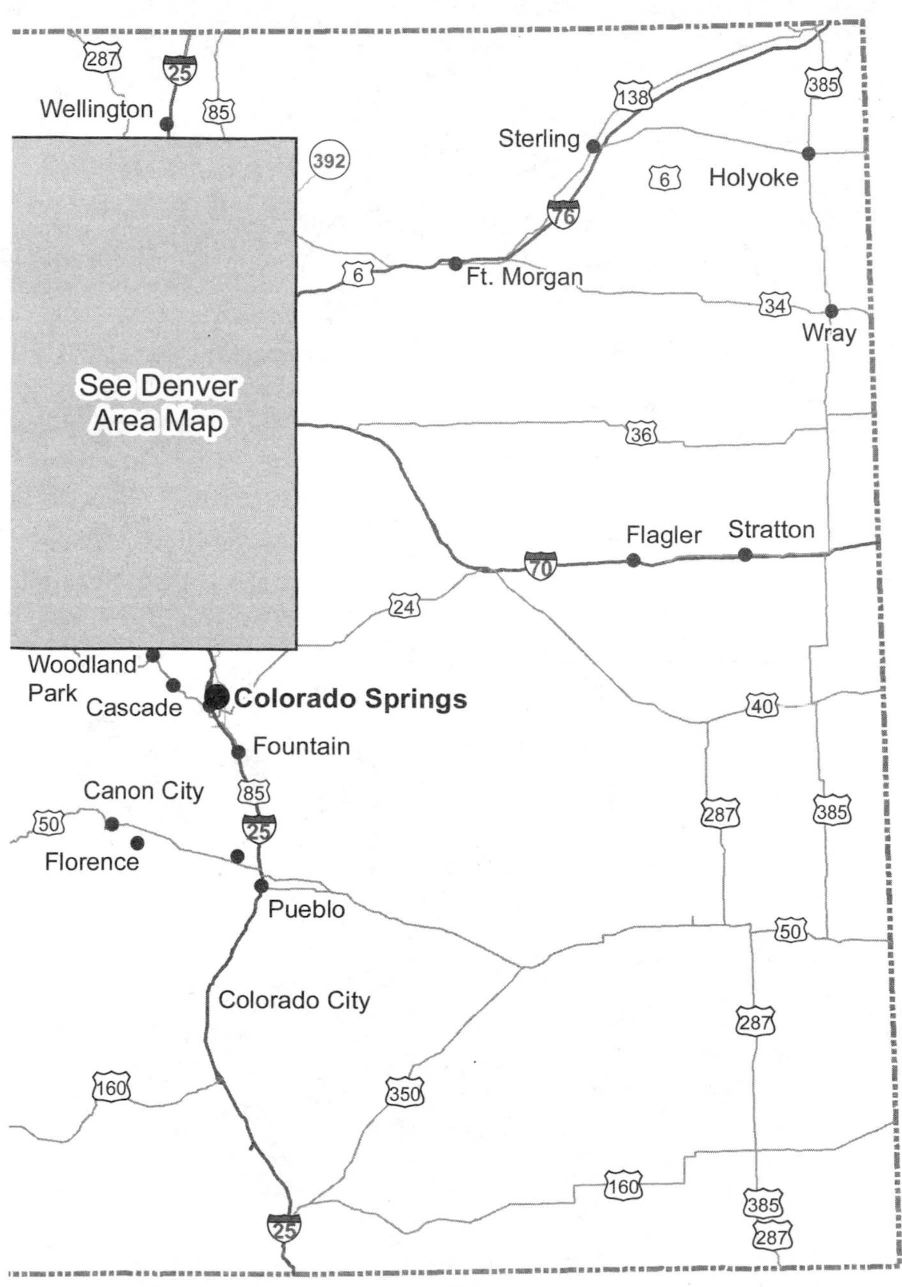

287
25
85
Wellington
138
385
Sterling
392
6
Holyoke
76
6
Ft. Morgan
34
Wray
See Denver
Area Map
36
Flagler
Stratton
70
24
Woodland
Park
Cascade
Colorado Springs
40
Fountain
Canon City
85
287
385
50
25
Florence
Pueblo
50
Colorado City
287
160
350
160
385
287
25

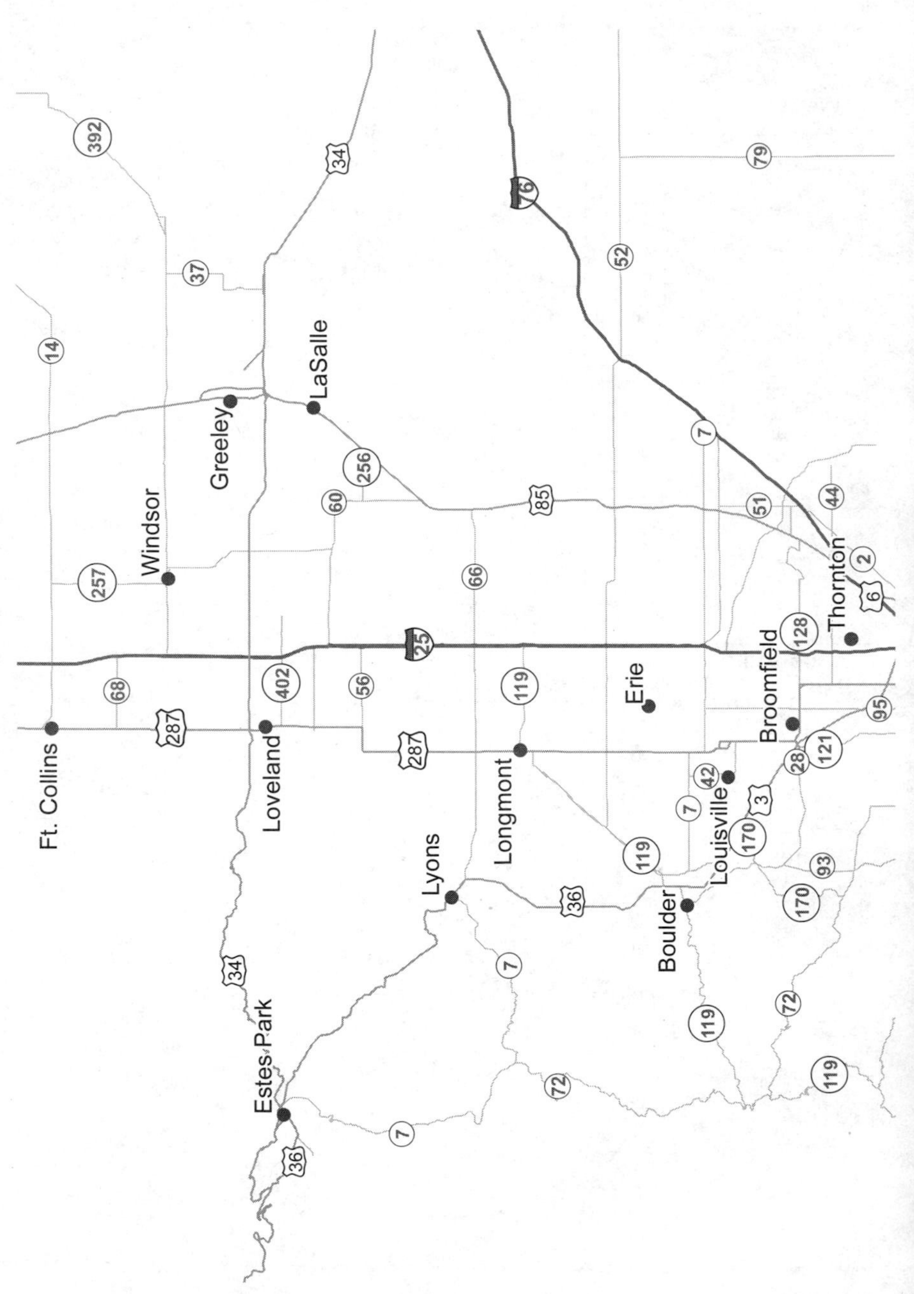

Ft. Collins
Windsor
Greeley
LaSalle
Loveland
Estes Park
Lyons
Longmont
Erie
Boulder
Louisville
Broomfield
Thornton

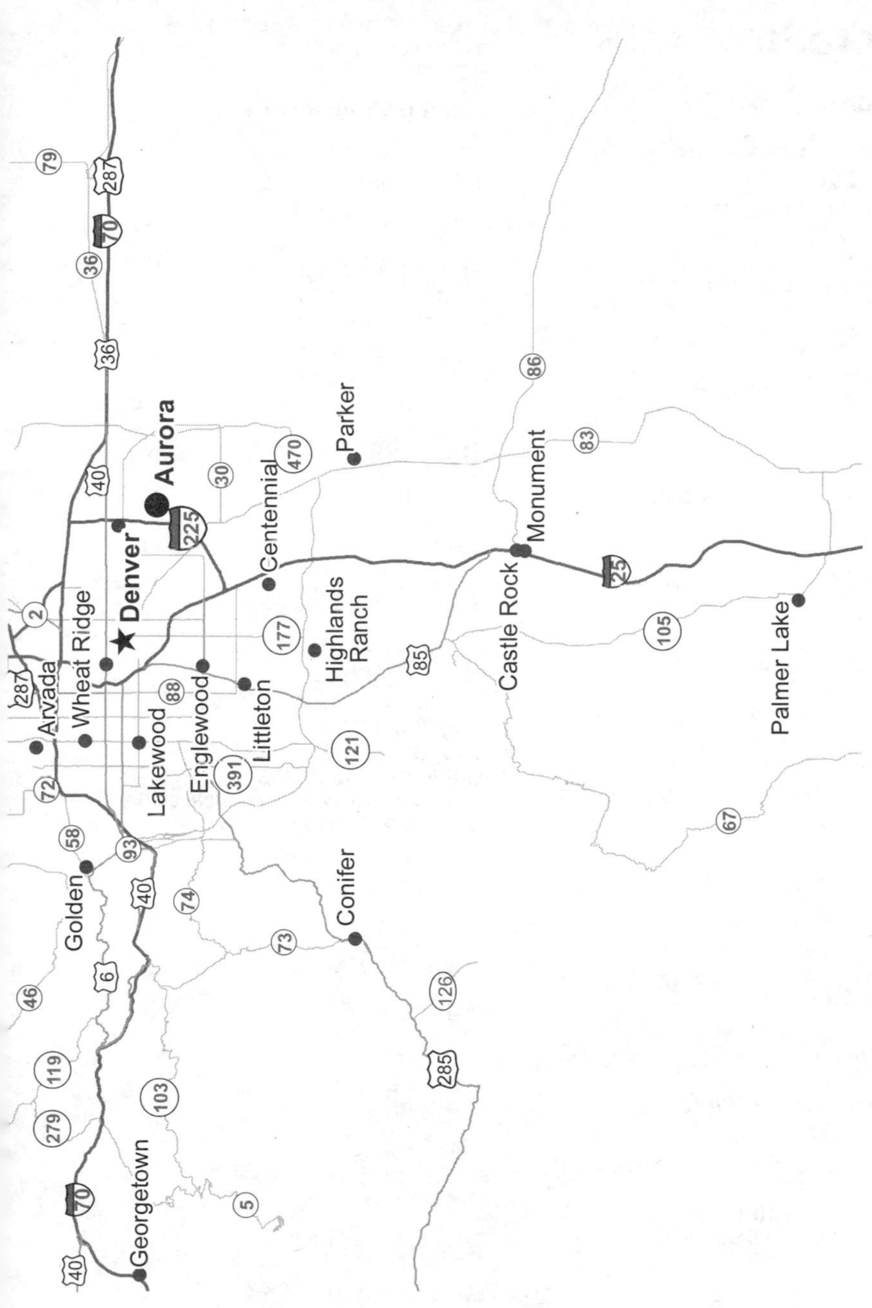
Aurora
Denver
Parker
Centennial
Monument
Castle Rock
Highlands Ranch
Wheat Ridge
Arvada
Lakewood
Englewood
Littleton
Palmer Lake
Golden
Conifer
Georgetown

Colorado

Alamosa

Alamosa Quilt Company, LLC Q E M
710 Del Sol Drive, 81101
(719) 937-2555
M-F 10-5, Sa 10-3
www.alamosaquiltcompany.com

Arvada

Ancient Treasures Alpaca Ranch Yarn Shop Y S
7870 Indiana Street, 80007
(303) 882-9778

Rocky Mountain Sewing & Vacuum* M
7330 W. 88th Avenue, Unit J, 80021
(303) 404-0370

Handi Quilter® Authorized Retailer
Designed by a Quilter, for Quilters.®

Aurora

Colorado Fabrics Q
4042 S. Parker Road, 80014
(303) 730-2777

Rocky Mountain Sewing & Vacuum* M
15400 E. Smoky Hill Road, 80015
(720) 870-2711

Thread Loft Q
15464 E. Hampden Avenue, 80013
(720) 219-8417

Boulder

Shuttles, Spindles & Skeins Y W S
635 S. Broadway, Unit E, 80305
(303) 494-1071
M 12-6, Tu-Sa 10-6
www.shuttlesspindlesandskeins.com

Blakeman Vacuum & Sewing Q M
3175 28th Street, Suite #3, 80301
(303) 449-1281

Handi Quilter® Authorized Retailer
Designed by a Quilter, for Quilters.®

Elfriede's Fine Fabrics Q
2425 Canyon Blvd., Suite A, 80302
(303) 447-0132

Fabricate Q E Y W M
2017 17th Street, 80302
(303) 997-8245

Gypsy Wools E Y W S C
7464 Arapahoe Road, call first, 80303
(303) 442-1884

Broomfield

The Quilt Store Q
12710 Lowell Blvd., 80020
(303) 465-0750

Buena Vista

Bev's Stitchery Q
202 Tabor Street
1/2 Block N of Main Stoplight on Hwy. 24, 81211
(719) 395-8780
M-F 9:30-5, Sa 9:30-3
https://www.facebook.com/pages/Bevs-Stitchery/290306077760616

Serendipity Yarn & Gifts E Y W S
321 W. Main Street, 81211
(719) 395-3110

Canon City

First Stitches Q M
212 S. 4th Street, 81212
(719) 285-8088

Cascade

Quilt Cabin Q
8815 W. US Highway 24, 80809
(719) 684-7819

Castle Rock

Everything Alpaca Y W S
207 5th St., 80104
(303) 660-6684

Sew-Ciety, Inc. Q M
1025 S. Perry Street, Unit 101B, 80104
(720) 733-8102

Centennial

Above & Beyond Sewing and Vacuum Q M
15416 E. Orchard Road, 80016
(303) 693-6286

Colorful Yarns Y
2001 E. Easter Avenue, Suite 101, 80122
(303) 798-2299

Holly's Quilt Cabin Q
8210 S. Holly Street, 80122
(720) 529-9659 or (888) 768-5922

Piney Creek Yarn Y W S
15422 E. Orchard Road, 80016
(720) 596-4462

Thread Play Q E N C M
8223 S.Quebec Street, 80122
(303) BER-NINA or (303) 237-6462

Colorado City

Kelly J's Sewing Center Q
6850 Highway 165, 81019
(719) 676-3425

Colorado Springs

High Country Quilts Q E M
4727 N. Academy Blvd., 80918
(719) 598-1312
M-Sa 9:30-6
www.hcquilts.com

Entwine Studio E Y W S C
6755 Shoup Road, 80909
(719) 433-3207

EWE and Me ... a yarn boutique Y
1025 Garden of the Gods, Unit F, 80907
(719) 203-5240

Ladybug Hill Quilts Q M
929 E. Fillmore Street, 80907
(866) 593-5949 or (719) 593-5949

Mill Outlet Fabric Shop Q
2906 N. Prospect Street, 80907
(719) 632-6296

Nanas Quilt Cottage Q E M
35 S. 26th Street, 80904
(719) 634-9500

Rocky Mountain Sewing & Vacuum* M
5611 N. Academy Blvd, 80918
(719) 597-8888

Ruth's Stitchery Q E C M
4440 Austin Bluffs Parkway, 80918
(719) 591-1717

The Yarn Outlet LLC Y W
416 S. 8th Street, 80905
(719) 227-3665

Woolly Works Knit Shop Y
9 E. Bijou Street, 80903
(719) 661-6062 or (719) 822-4979

Conifer

Knit Knook Y
10903 U.S. Highway 285, 80433
(303) 838-2118

Cortez

Cortez Quilt Company, LLC Q M
40 W. Main Street, 81321
(970) 565-7541

Southwest Farm to Yarn Collective Y W S
360 W. First Street, Suite B, 81321
(970) 560-6777

Craig

Quilters Quest* Q
335 E. Victory Way, 81625
(970) 826-0111

The Embroidery Shoppe, LLC Q E
519 Yampa Avenue, 81625
(970) 824-6770

Creede

The Yarne Shoppe / Bristol Yarnworks Studio* Ⓨ Ⓦ Ⓢ
39542 Highway 149, 81130
(719) 658-2455

Crested Butte

The Yarn Studio* Ⓨ
126 Elk Avenue, #1W, 81224
(970) 201-5760

Del Norte

Kathy's Fabric Trunk Ⓠ Ⓔ Ⓨ Ⓒ
610 Grand Avenue, 81132
(719) 657-9314

Delta

Bold Line Quilts & Crafts Ⓠ Ⓔ Ⓨ Ⓝ Ⓒ Ⓜ
3656 2195th Road, 81416
(970) 209-4141

Clubb's Ⓠ Ⓔ Ⓨ Ⓝ Ⓦ Ⓢ Ⓒ
417 Main Street, 81416
(970) 874-3596 or (970) 874-6391

Denver

Treelotta Ⓠ
29 S. Fox Street, 80223
(720) 339-6260
check website for hours
www.treelotta.com

A Stitching Shop Ⓔ Ⓝ Ⓒ
4444 Morrison Road, 80219
(303) 727-8500

Creative Creations Studio* Ⓠ
9967 Clark Drive, 80260
(303) 489-6004

Fancy Tiger Crafts Ⓠ Ⓔ Ⓨ Ⓦ Ⓢ Ⓒ Ⓜ
59 Broadway, 80203
(303) 733-3855

LambShoppe* Ⓨ
3512 E. 12th Avenue, 80206
(303) 322-2223

Yarn Shoppe Studio Ⓨ
1615 California Street, #403, 80202
(720) 473-2598

Durango

Durango Quilt Company* Ⓠ Ⓔ Ⓜ
21516 Highway 160 W, 81303
(970) 247-2582

Stitch* Ⓠ Ⓜ
153 E. 15th Street, 81301
(970) 247-1085

Yarn Durango Ⓔ Ⓨ Ⓝ Ⓦ Ⓢ Ⓒ
755 E. 2nd Avenue, 81301
(970) 259-9827

Eagle

Alpaca, LLC* Ⓨ Ⓢ
106 Broadway, 81631
(970) 328-1211

Englewood

Wooden Spools . . .Quilting, Knitting and More Ⓠ Ⓨ Ⓦ
2805 S. Broadway, 80113
(303) 761-9231
MWThF 10-6, Tu 10-9, Sa 10-5, Su 12-4
www.woodenspools.com

Blazing Star Ranch Ⓨ Ⓦ Ⓢ
3424 S. Broadway, 80113
(303) 514-8780

Diversions Needlepoint* Ⓝ
410 E. Hampton Street, 80110
(303) 761-7766

Erie

A Quilter's Corner Ⓠ Ⓜ
71 Erie Parkway, #104, 80516
(720) 328-8181

Estes Park

Cottage Bliss Gifts and Fabric, Inc.* Ⓠ Ⓔ
870A Moraine Avenue, 80517
(970) 577-1557

The Stitchin' Den Ⓠ Ⓨ Ⓝ Ⓢ Ⓒ
165 Virginia Drive, 80517
(970) 577-8210

Flagler

Witt's Family Store* Q
408 Main Avenue, 80815
(719) 765-4573

Florence

The Loralie Antique Mall Q
109 W. Main Street, 81226
(719) 784-3797

Fountain

Na-La's Quilt Shoppe Q
117 S. Main Street, 80817
(719) 382-6252

Frisco

Knititation Yarn & Fiber Arts* Y W S
107 S. 6th Avenue, 80443
(719) 839-5817

Ft. Collins

Jukebox Quilts* Q M
406 N. College Avenue, 80524
(970) 224-9975

Lambspun of Colorado E Y W S
1101 E. Lincoln Avenue, 80524
(970) 484-1998

My Sister Knits Y
1408 W. Mountain Avenue, 80521
(970) 407-1461

The Fig Leaf* Q E M
2834 S. College Avenue, 80525
(970) 495-1766

The Loopy Ewe Q E Y W S
4856 Innovation Drive, Suite A, 80525
(888) 527-9181 or (970) 568-5290

The Presser Foot* Q E
1833 E. Harmony, Unit 1, 80525
(970) 484-1094

The Sewing Circle Q E M
4112 S. College Avenue, 80524
(970) 672-2147

Your Daily Fiber Y W S
4019 S. Mason Street, Suite 3, 80524
(970) 484-2414

Ft. Morgan

Inspirations Quilt Shop Q E M
423 Main Street, Suite 300, 80701
(970) 542-0810

Georgetown

The Quilted Purl* Q Y
707 Taos Street, 80444
(303) 569-1115

Glenwood Springs

Art on 8th / Mountain Valley Weavers W
209 8th Street, 81601
(970) 928-0774

Glenwood Sewing Center* Q E C M
822 Grand Avenue, 81601
(970) 945-5900 or (800) 371-5967

Golden

Golden Quilt Company Q
1108 Washington Avenue, 80401
(303) 277-0717
M-Sa 10-5:30, Su 12-4
www.goldenquiltcompany.com

Granby

Lonesome Stone Yarn and Dyeworks* Y W S
946 County Road 60, 80446
(970) 887-9591

The Fabric Nook Q E Y
387 E. Agate, 80446
(970) 887-2005

Grand Junction

Fireside Country Store Y W S
23 Road, 81505
(970) 858-9288 or (970) 263-9999

Glenwood Sew Q M
561 25 Road, 81505
(970) 233-8771

Hi Fashion Sewing Machines & Quilt Shop Q M
2584 Patterson Road, Unit B, 81505
(970) 242-1890

Handi Quilter® Authorized Retailer
Designed by a Quilter, for Quilters®

Owls Nest Quilters Q E M
527 Bogart Lane, 81505
(970) 241-5700

The Craft Studio and Yarn Shop Y W S C
634 Main Street, 81501
(970) 314-9013

Grand Lake

Cabin Quilts & Stitches Q Y
908 Grand Avenue, 80447
(970) 627-3810

Greeley

Country Crafts E C
2200 Reservoir Road, 80631
(970) 353-1774
M-F 10-5, Sa 10-4
www.countrycraftsandsupplies.com

Sew Downtown Q M
3820 W. 10th Street, Suite B3, 80634
(970) 352-9230
Tu-F 9-5, Sa 10-4
www.sewdowntown.com

Highlands Ranch

A Quilter's Choice - APQS West Q
8698 Aberdeen Circle, 80130
(435) 414-2026

Holyoke

Creative Traditions LLC Q E Y C
115 S. Interocean Avenue, 80734
(970) 854-3699

Hotchkiss

Delicious Orchards Y
39126 Highway 133, 81419
(970) 527-1110

Lakewood

Showers Of Flowers Yarn Shop* Y
6900 W. Colfax Avenue, 80214
(303) 233-2525

LaSalle

The Fleece Factory of the Rockies* Y S
24138 County Road 38, 80645
(970) 284-7711

Leadville

Fire On The Mountain* Y S
715 Harrison Avenue, 80461
(719) 486-2071

Mountain Top Quilts Q E N C
129 E. 7th Street, 80461
(719) 486-3454

Littleton

The Creative Needle Q E N C M
6905 S. Broadway, Suite 113, 80122
(303) 794-7312
MTuThFSa 9:30-5, W 9:30-8, Most Su 12-4
http://www.thecreativeneedle.com

Craft Scraps* Q Y C
5856 S. Lowell Blvd., #27, 80123
(303) 798-2192

Fabric Expressions* Q
3625 W. Bowles Avenue, Suite 13, 80123
(303) 798-2556

Rocky Mountain Sewing & Vacuum* M
8601 W. Cross Drive, Unit P1, 80123
(303) 979-2334

Handi Quilter® Authorized Retailer
Designed by a Quilter, for Quilters®

Longmont

Longmont Yarn Shoppe Y W S
454 Main Street, 80501
(303) 678-8242

Maggie's Sewing and Fabric Q M
1450 Main Street, 80501
(303) 651-7752

The Presser Foot Q E M
2430 Main Street, 80501
(303) 485-6681

Louisville

FingerPlay Studio Y
901 Front Street, #110, 80027
(303) 604-4374

Loveland

Quilter's Dream Q
517 Denver Avenue, 80537
(970) 461-8373

Stitches Quilting and Sewing Q
1479 W. Eisenhower, 80528
(970) 541-1520

Lyons

Lyons Quilting Q
42 E. Main Street, 80540
(303) 823-6067

Monte Vista

Shades, Quilts & Etc. Q E Y C
129 Adams Street, 81144
(719) 852-2179
M-F 10-5, Sa 10-3
www.shadesquiltsandetc.com

Montrose

Ladybugz Quilt & Yarn Q E Y W
➡ SEE AD BELOW
330 S. 8th Street, 81401
(970) 249-1600
M-F 9:30-5, Sa 9:30-4, Su 12-4
www.ladybugzquilt.com

CJ's* E Y
428 E. Main Street, 81401
(970) 249-5588

Fabrics & More* Q Y
341 N. 1st Street, 81401
(970) 240-6089

Monument

Frankie's Fabric Shoppe* Q E
252 Front Street, 80132
(719) 418-3614

Palmer Lake

Sew Motion* Q E Y C
862 Highway 105, 80133
(719) 481-1565

Paonia

Desert Weyr, LLC Ⓨ Ⓦ Ⓢ
16870 Garvin Mesa Road, 81428
(970) 527-3573

Parker

High Prairie Quilts* Ⓠ Ⓔ
18870 E. Plaza Drive, Suite 102, 80134
(303) 627-0878

Pueblo

Creative Sewing Design* Ⓠ
2729 N. Elizabeth Street, 81003
(719) 562-0385

First Stitches* Ⓠ Ⓜ
805 Eagleridge Blvd., Suite 120, 81008
(719) 225-8142

Southern Colorado Sewing Center Ⓠ Ⓔ Ⓝ Ⓒ Ⓜ
1000 W 6th Street
Suite K, 81003
(719) 542-0154

Stitcher's Garden Ⓠ Ⓔ Ⓨ
308 S. Union Avenue, 81003
(719) 545-3320

Steamboat Springs

Sew Steamboat* Ⓠ Ⓨ
929 Lincoln Avenue, 80477
(970) 879-3222

Sterling

FiberSpace* Ⓨ Ⓦ
113 N. 2nd Street, 80751
(970) 521-9041

Quilts-N-Creations Ⓠ Ⓔ Ⓒ Ⓜ
125 N. 2nd Street, 80751
(970) 522-0146

Stratton

Benay's Country Quiltin'* Ⓠ
32131 County Road HH, 80836
(970) 362-4650 or (719) 348-5650

Thornton

Above & Beyond Sewing and Vacuum Ⓠ Ⓜ
3987 E. 120th Avenue, 80241
(303) 317-2004

Wellington

Double K Diamond Llamas and Fiber* Ⓨ Ⓦ Ⓢ
16423 N. County Road 9, 80549
(970) 568-3747

Wheat Ridge

The Craft Box Ⓠ Ⓔ Ⓨ Ⓝ Ⓒ
6191 W. 44th Avenue, 80033
(303) 279-1069

Windsor

Quilter's Stash* Ⓠ Ⓜ
1180 W. Ash Street, Suite 100, 80550
(970) 686-5657

Woodland Park

Nikki's Knots Ⓨ Ⓦ
761 Gold Hill Place, 80863
(719) 686-6424

Nuts 'n Bolts Needleworks* Ⓠ Ⓔ Ⓒ
200 S. Chestnut Street, 80863
(719) 687-2272

Wray

Rainbow Fabrics and Crafts* Ⓠ Ⓔ Ⓨ Ⓝ Ⓒ
409 Main Street, 80758
(970) 332-4343

you keep me in Stitches Ⓠ
926 Paul Street, 80758
(970) 630-2856

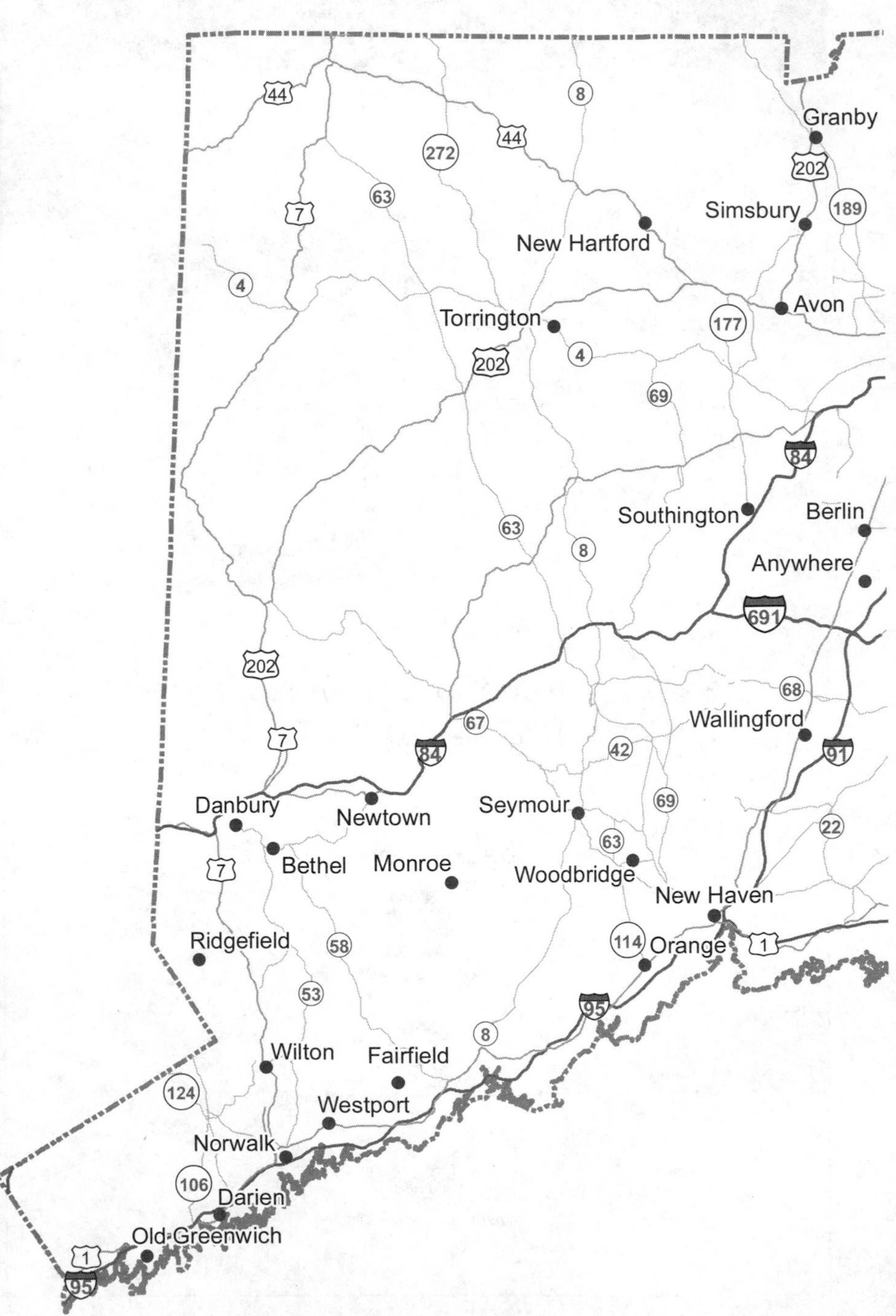

Granby
Simsbury
New Hartford
Avon
Torrington
Southington
Berlin
Anywhere
Wallingford
Danbury
Newtown
Seymour
Bethel
Monroe
Woodbridge
New Haven
Ridgefield
Orange
Wilton
Fairfield
Westport
Norwalk
Darien
Old Greenwich
44
8
272
202
189
63
7
4
177
69
84
8
691
68
67
42
91
22
58
114
1
53
95
124
106

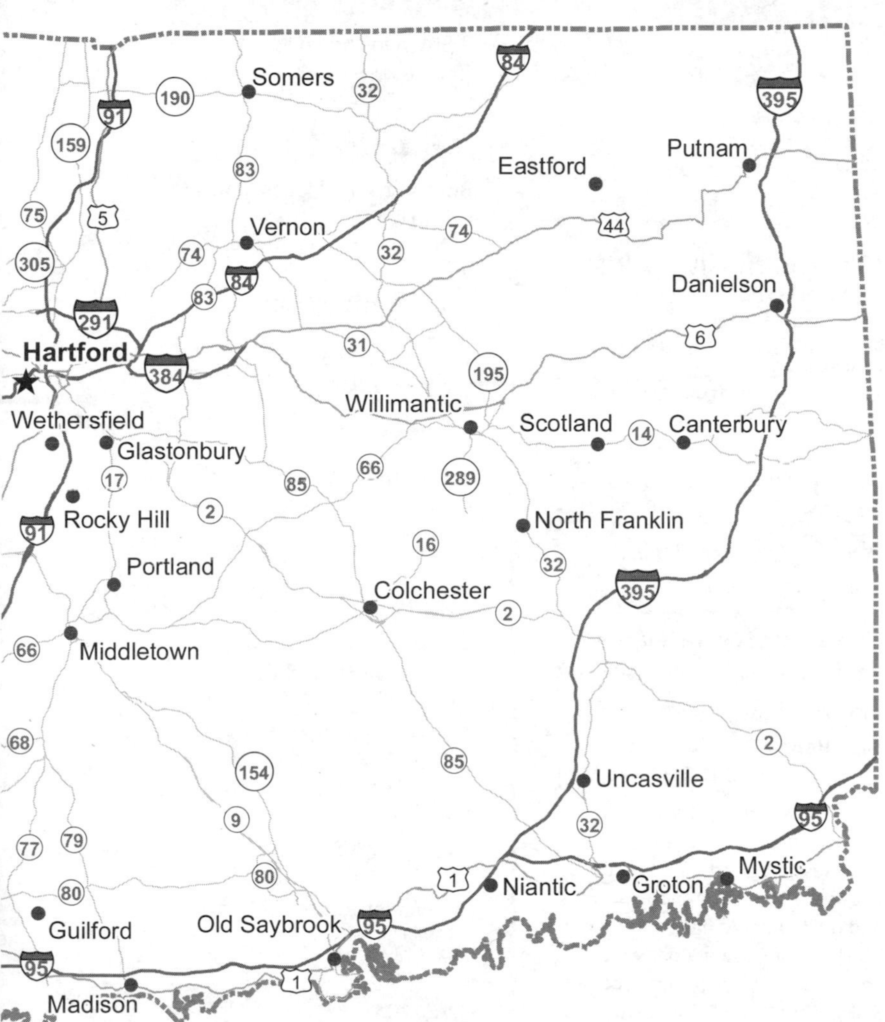
Somers
Vernon
Hartford
Wethersfield
Glastonbury
Rocky Hill
Portland
Middletown
Guilford
Madison
Old Saybrook
Niantic
Groton
Mystic
Uncasville
Colchester
North Franklin
Willimantic
Scotland
Canterbury
Danielson
Putnam
Eastford
91
190
32
84
395
159
83
75
5
305
74
44
291
384
31
195
6
14
17
85
66
289
2
16
68
154
9
77
79
80
1
95

Connecticut

Avon

Knit & Pearls Ⓨ Ⓦ
395 W. Avon Road, 06001
(860) 404-0694

Berlin

Lisa's Clover Hill Quilts Ⓠ Ⓔ
➡ SEE AD BELOW
Webster Mill Plaza
27 Webster Square Road, 06037
(860) 828-9325
TuWFSa 10-5, Th 10-8, Su 12-5
www.lisascloverhillquilts.com

Bethel

A Stitch in Time Ⓨ Ⓝ
10 Stony Hill Road, 06801
(203) 748-1002

Canterbury

Burgis Brook Alpacas / In The Crimp Ⓨ Ⓦ Ⓢ
44 N. Canterbury Road (Route 169), 06331
(203) 605-0588

Little River Farm Store and Fiber Studio Ⓨ Ⓦ Ⓢ
99 Miller Road, 06331
(860) 456-1997

Colchester

Colchester Mill Fabrics and Quilting Ⓠ Ⓔ Ⓨ Ⓝ Ⓒ
120 Lebanon Avenue, 06415
(860) 537-2004

Danbury

Pieceful Acre Needlearts Ⓨ Ⓢ
66 Sugar Hollow Road, 06810
(203) 731-9601 or (203) 731-9601

Stitch in Time Sewing Center / Jack's Fabrics Ⓠ Ⓜ
19 Sugar Hollow Road, 06810
(203) 748-7283

Danielson

The Velvet Tomato at Heart & Home Ⓠ
65 Main Street, 06239
(860) 774-2623

Darien

House of Needlepoint Ⓝ
839 Post Road, 06820
(203) 655-9112

Stitch in Time Sewing Center / Jack's Fabrics Ⓠ Ⓜ
425 Post Road, 06820
(203) 655-9020

Eastford

Still River Fiber Mill, LLC Y W S
210 Eastford Road, 06242
(860) 974-9918

Fairfield

Poster's Arts and Crafts Q E Y N S C M
2353 Black Rock Turnpike, 06825
(203) 372-0717

Glastonbury

Close to Home Q E M
277 Hebron Avenue, 06033
(860) 633-0721

Village Wool Y
2279 Main Street, 06033
(860) 633-0898

Granby

Marji's Yarncrafts Y
381 Salmon Brook Street, 06035
(860) 653-9700

Groton

Driftwood Yarns Y S
1 Fort Hill Road, 06340
(860) 415-8118

That's Sew Debbie! Q M
301 Route 12, 06340
(860) 333-1394

Guilford

Cate's Sew Modern Q E M
50 York Street, 06437
(203) 421-6853

Madison

Madison Wool Y W S
56A Wall Street, 06443
(203) 245-5921

Middletown

Pamela Roose, Specialty Hand Knits & Yarn Y
88 Court Street, 06457
(860) 788-2715

Monroe

The BOLT Quilt Shop Q M
150 Main Street, Route 25, 06468
(203) 445-2658

Mystic

CT Quilt Works Q E M
5A Roosevelt Avenue, 06355
(860) 245-0111

Mystic River Yarns Y
14 Holmes Street, 06355
(860) 536-4305

The Needlepoint Nook of Mystic N
2 Pearl Street, 06355
(860) 536-7380

New Hartford

Quilted Ewe Q Y S M
37 Greenwoods Road, 06057
(860) 379-3260

New Haven

Knit New Haven Y S
26 Whitney Avenue, 06510
(203) 777-5648

Newtown

The Quilt Shop by Lois Q M
12 Queen Street, 06470
(203) 270-0341
TuW 10-5, Th 10-6:30, FSa 10-4
www.thequiltshopbylois.com

Niantic

Twist Yarn Shoppe Y
180 Flanders Road, Unit #2, 06357
(860) 451-8213

North Franklin

Stitch Chicks Quilt Shop, LLC Ⓠ
43 Manning Road, 06254
(860) 642-8099

Norwalk

Christie's Quilting Boutique Ⓠ Ⓜ
176 Main Street, 06851
(203) 807-8458
See website for hours
www.christiesquiltingboutique.com

Old Greenwich

The Village Ewe Ⓝ
244 Sound Beach Avenue, 06870
(203) 637-3953

Old Saybrook

The Knit Ⓨ
900 Boston Post Road, 06475
(860) 388-0423
Tu 12-8, W-Sa 10-6, Su 10-4
www.theknitknits.com

My Friends and Me Ⓠ Ⓔ Ⓜ
1712 Boston Post Road, 06475
(860) 853-8601

Orange

Close to Home Ⓠ Ⓔ Ⓜ
196 Boston Post Road, 06477
(203) 878-1654

Portland

Patches and Patchwork Ⓠ Ⓔ Ⓜ
216 Main Street, 06480
(860) 342-4567

Putnam

Woolworks, Ltd. Ⓨ Ⓢ
154 Main Street, 06260
(860) 963-1228

Ridgefield

nancy O Ⓨ
23 Catoonah Street, 06877
(203) 431-2266

Rocky Hill

Affordable Fabrics Ⓠ
2119 Silas Deane Highway (Route 99), 06067
(860) 563-7647

Scotland

Pins to Needles Ⓠ
6 Huntington Road, 06264
(860) 450-4440

Seymour

The Yankee Quilter Ⓠ Ⓜ
5 Klarides Village Drive, 06483
(203) 888-9196

Simsbury

Sew Inspired Quilt Shop & Studio Ⓠ Ⓜ
➡ SEE AD AT RIGHT
8 Wilcox Street, 06070
(860) 651-8885
MWFSa 10-6, TuTh 10-8, Su 12-4
www.sewinspiredquilts.com

Handi Quilter® Authorized Retailer
Designed by a Quilter, for Quilters.®

Somers

Knitting Criations Ⓨ Ⓢ
60 Springfield Road, 06071
(860) 749-4005
TuWTh 10-6, F 10-5, Sa 10-4
www.knittingcriations.com

Southington

New England Yarn and Spindle LLC Ⓨ Ⓢ
995 Queen St. Unit 3, 06489
(860) 426-1006
MTuWF 11-6, Th 11-8, Sa 11-4, Su 12-4; check website for summer hours
http://www.newenglandyarn.com

Close to Home Ⓠ Ⓔ Ⓜ
995 Queen Street, 06489
(860) 793-6639

Torrington

In Sheep's Clothing Ⓨ Ⓦ Ⓢ
10 Water Street, 06790
(860) 482-3979

Uncasville

Affordable Fabrics Ⓠ
480 Route 32, 06382
(860) 848-0690

Vernon

Knit Two-Gether Ⓨ
435-K Hartford Turnpike, 06066
(860) 870-3883
M pls. call ahead, WF 10-5, TuTh 10-8, Sa 10-4, Su 11-4
www.knittwo-gether.com

Quilting By The Yard, LLC Ⓠ
435 Hartford Turnpike, Suite O, 06066
(860) 896-1056

Wallingford

Yankee Cloth Ⓠ Ⓔ
411 Center Street, 06492
(203) 265-1932
Call for shop hours
www.yankeecloth.com

Country Yarns Ⓨ Ⓢ
9 S. Colony Street, 06492
(203) 269-6662

Westport

Westport Yarns Ⓨ Ⓦ
582 Post Road E, 06880
(203) 454-4300

Wethersfield

Thistle Needleworks Ⓔ Ⓝ Ⓒ
506 Silas Deane Highway, 06109
(860) 257-2718 or (800) 635-9757

Willimantic

Quilter's Dream Ⓠ Ⓨ Ⓝ Ⓦ Ⓢ Ⓜ
1158 Main Street, 06226
MTuWFSa 10-6, Th 10-8, Su 12-5
http://www.quiltersdream.com

Wilton

The Enriched Stitch Ⓝ
196 Danbury Road, 06897
(203) 210-5107

Woodbridge

The Yarn Barn Ⓨ Ⓝ
1666 Litchfield Turnpike, 06525
(203) 389-5117

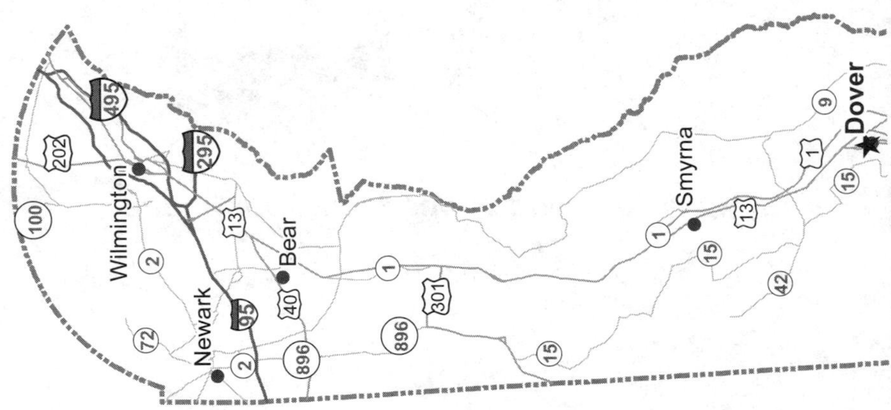
Wilmington
Newark
Bear
Smyrna
Dover
495
295
95
202
13
40
301
1
100
2
72
896
15
42
9

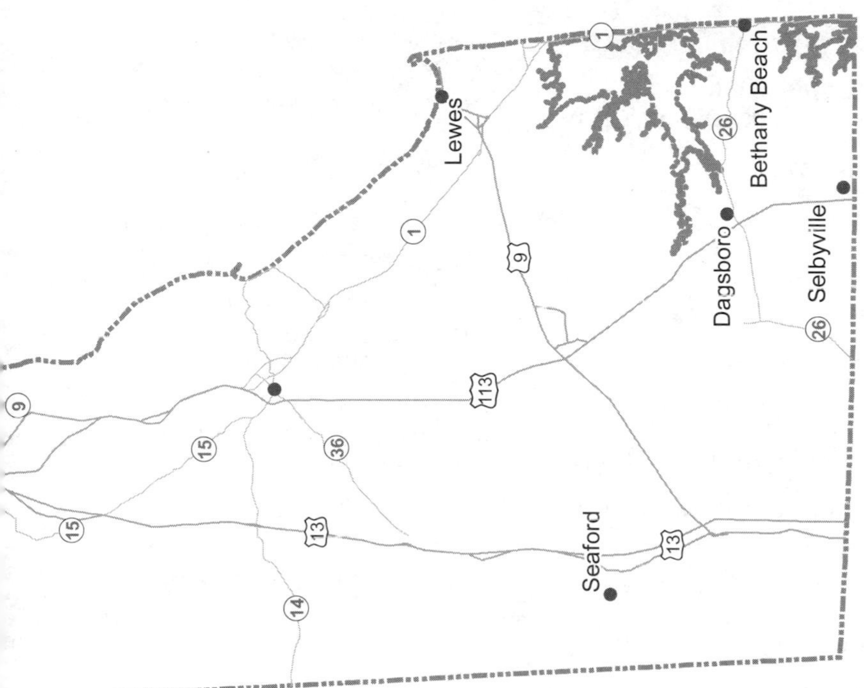
Lewes
Bethany Beach
Dagsboro
Selbyville
Seaford
1
9
113
36
15
13
14
26

Delaware

Bear

Milady Creates Ⓠ
152 Cornwell Drive, 19701
(302) 365-6687

Bethany Beach

Sea Needles ⒺⓎⓃⒸ
780 Garfield Parkway, Route 26 W, 19930
(302) 539-0574
M-Sa 10-5
www.seaneedles.com

Dagsboro

Serendipity Quilt Shop ⓆⒺⒸ
31821 Cannon Street, 19939
(302) 732-6304

Dover

Delaware Sewing Centers, Inc. ⓆⒺⓂ
1716 S. Governor's Avenue, 19904
(302) 674-9030 or (800) 231-9030

Shady Lane Selections ⓆⒸ
1121-B Victory Chapel Road, 19904
(302) 674-3623

Lewes

Mare's Bears Quilt Shop Ⓠ
528 E. Savannah Road, 19958
(302) 644-0556

Newark

Blue Hen Quilt Shop ⓆⓂ
73 Marrows Road, 19713
(302) 533-5215

Seaford

Butler's Sewing Center ⓆⓂ
1023 W. Stein Highway, 19973
(302) 629-9155

Selbyville

Oceanna Fabrics & Catherine's Quilting Ⓠ
64 W. Church Street, 19975
(302) 524-8378

Smyrna

The Yarn Maven Ⓨ
62 W. Commerce Street, 19977
(302) 508-5256

Wilmington

Hayes Sewing Machines ⓆⓂ
4425 Concord Pike
Concord Square Shopping Center, 19803
(302) 764-9033
MF 10-9, TuWTh 10-6, Sa 10-5
www.trevhayes.com

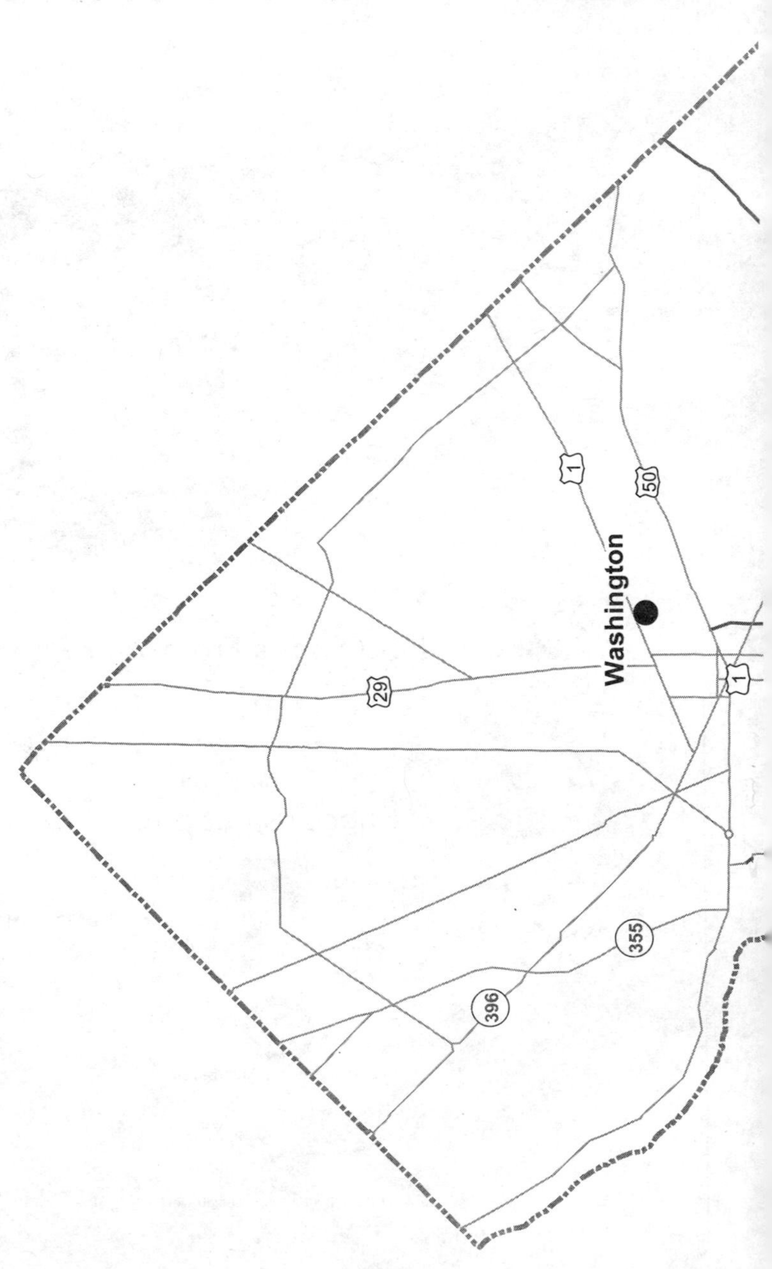
1
50
Washington
29
1
355
396

4
637
210
295
295
695
1
50

District of Columbia

Washington

Looped Yarn Works Ⓨ
1732 Connecticut Avenue, NW #200, 20009
(202) 714-5667

The Point of It All Ⓝ
5232 44th Street NW, 20015
(202) 966-9898

NeedleTravel

Download our App!

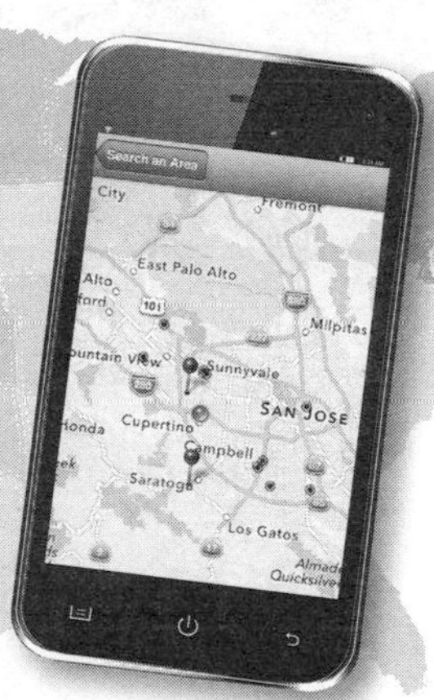

Find Shops From Your Phone

It's Free!

Check us out on:

www.facebook.com/Needletravel

http://www.pinterest.com/needletravel

https://twitter.com/Needletravel

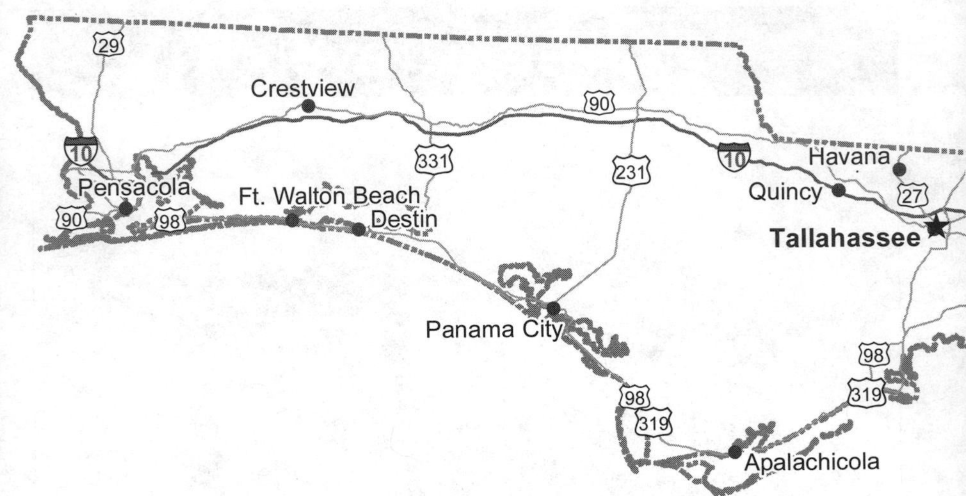
29
Crestview
90
10
331
231
10
Havana
Quincy
27
Pensacola
Ft. Walton Beach
Destin
90
98
Tallahassee
Panama City
98
98
319
319
Apalachicola

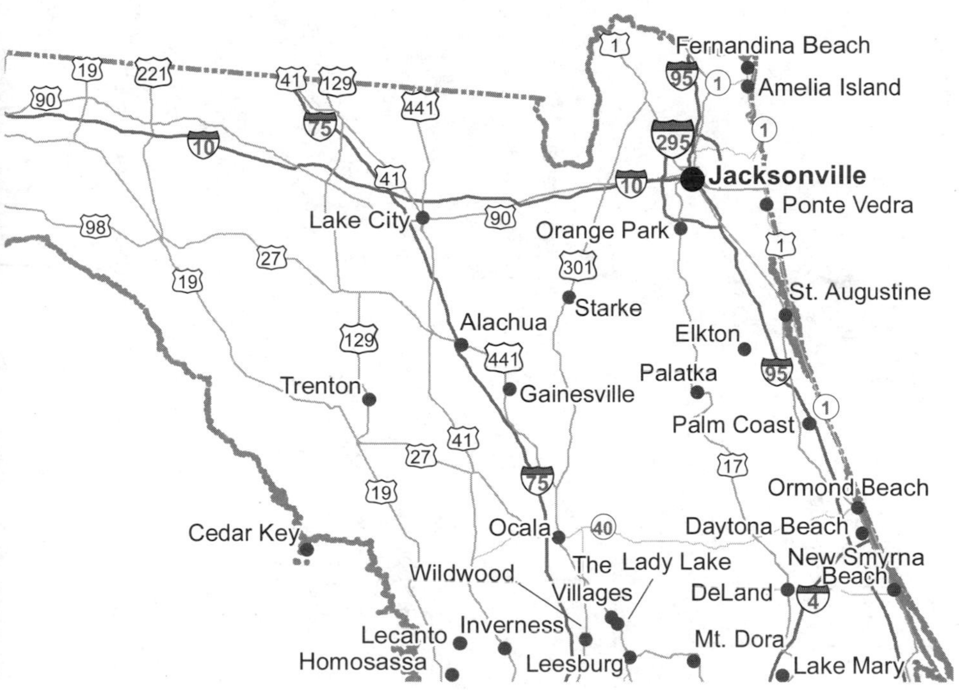
Fernandina Beach
Amelia Island
Jacksonville
Ponte Vedra
Orange Park
St. Augustine
Starke
Alachua
Lake City
Elkton
Palatka
Gainesville
Trenton
Palm Coast
Ormond Beach
Daytona Beach
New Smyrna Beach
Cedar Key
Ocala
The Villages
Lady Lake
Wildwood
DeLand
Inverness
Lecanto
Homosassa
Leesburg
Mt. Dora
Lake Mary
19
221
41
129
90
75
10
441
1
95
295
98
27
301
17
40
4

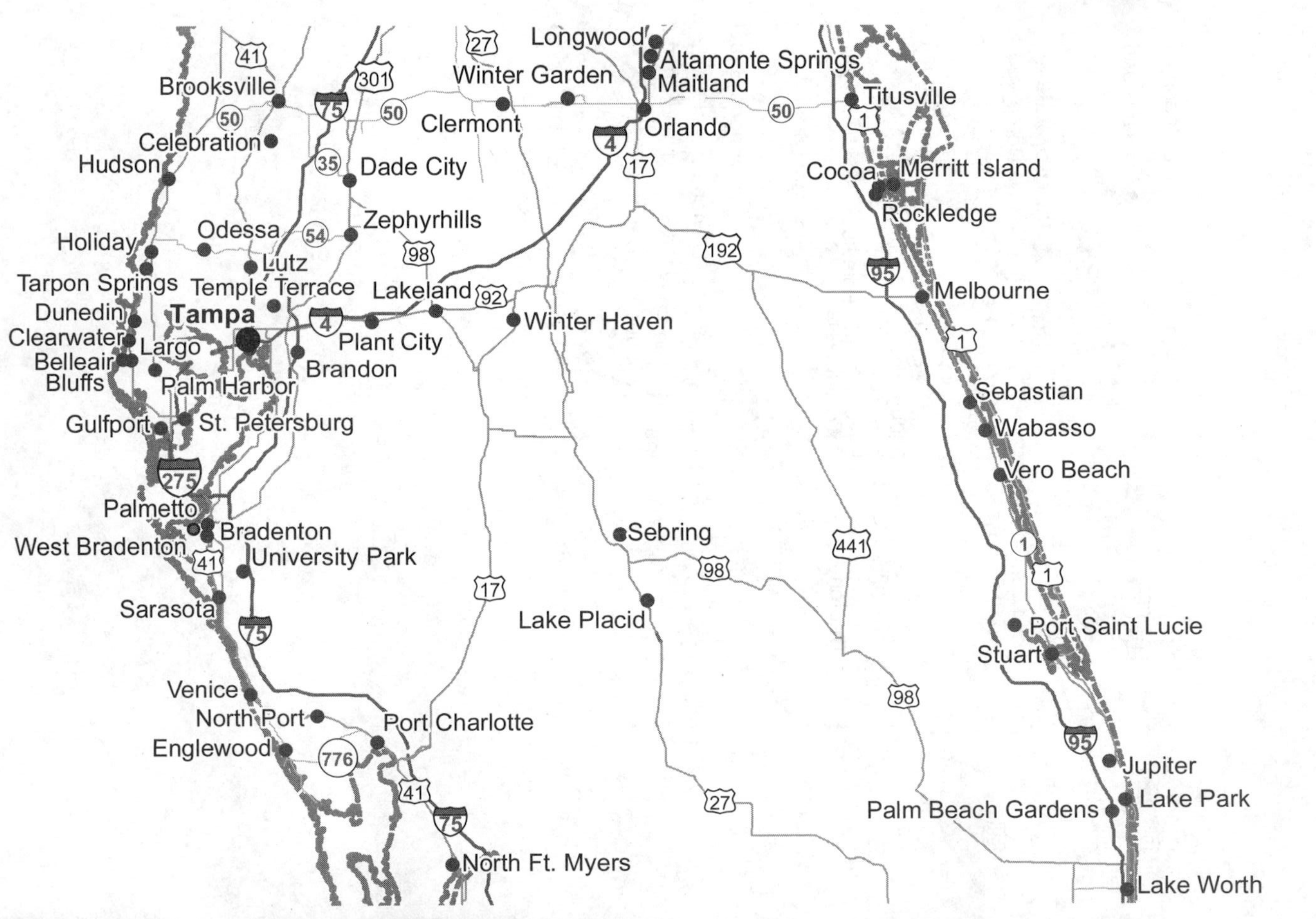
Longwood
Altamonte Springs
Maitland
Orlando
Winter Garden
Clermont
Brooksville
Celebration
Hudson
Dade City
Zephyrhills
Holiday
Odessa
Lutz
Tarpon Springs
Temple Terrace
Lakeland
Dunedin
Tampa
Clearwater
Largo
Belleair Bluffs
Plant City
Brandon
Palm Harbor
Gulfport
St. Petersburg
Winter Haven
Palmetto
Bradenton
West Bradenton
University Park
Sarasota
Sebring
Lake Placid
Venice
North Port
Port Charlotte
Englewood
North Ft. Myers
Titusville
Cocoa
Merritt Island
Rockledge
Melbourne
Sebastian
Wabasso
Vero Beach
Port Saint Lucie
Stuart
Jupiter
Lake Park
Palm Beach Gardens
Lake Worth
41
301
27
75
50
35
54
98
4
17
92
192
95
1
275
441
776
27

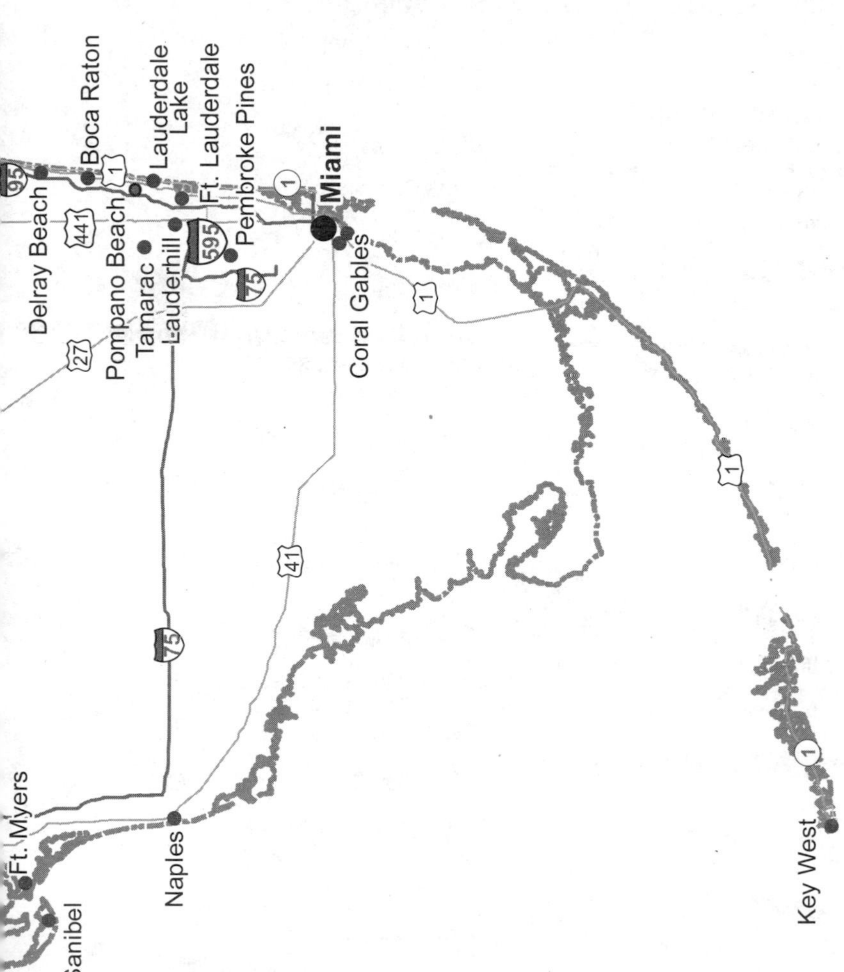

Delray Beach
Boca Raton
Pompano Beach
Tamarac
Lauderhill
Lauderdale Lake
Ft. Lauderdale
Pembroke Pines
Miami
Coral Gables
Ft. Myers
Naples
Sanibel
Key West
95
441
1
27
595
75
41

Florida

Alachua

Julie's Pins and Needles Ⓠ
14911 Main Street, 32615
(904) 214-6633
Tu-F 10-5, Sa 10-3
www.juliespinsandneedlesshop.com

Altamonte Springs

Needle Orts ⓃⒸ
580 Cape Cod Lane, Suite 3, 32714
(407) 869-0078 or (877) 869-0078
W-Sa 10-5
www.needleorts.com

Amelia Island

Bristly Thistle Ⓝ
811 Beech Street, 32034
(904) 729-4020

Apalachicola

Downtown Books and Purl Ⓨ
67 Commerce Street, 32320
(850) 653-1290

Belleair Bluffs

The Flying Needles Ⓝ
432 N. Indian Rocks Road, 33770
(727) 581-8691

Boca Raton

Marion's Nimble Needle Ⓝ
23269 Route 441, Suite 113, 33428
(561) 477-1219

Sew Much Fun ⒺⓂ
7491 N. Federal Highway, Unit C11, 33487
(561) 999-9992

StitchCraft ⓆⒺⒸⓂ
399 S. Federal Highway, 33432
(561) 447-4147

Bradenton

Bits & Pieces Ⓠ
1303 13th Avenue W, 34205
(941) 932-5869

Brandon

Gigi's Fabric Shop ⓆⓂ
706 W. Lumsden Road, 33511
(813) 661-9000

Brooksville

Nana's Quilt Shop ⓆⒺⓂ
18851 Cortez Blvd., 34601
(352) 796-0011

Cedar Key

The Salty Needle Quilt Shop Ⓠ
434 2nd Street, 32625
(352) 543-9779
M-Sa 10-5
www.thesaltyneedlequiltshop.com

Celebration

Little Thimble LLC ⓆⒺⓎⒸⓂ
660 Celebration Avenue, Suite 130, 34747
(321) 939-4091

Clearwater

Country Quilts and Bears Ⓠ
1983 Drew Street, 33765
(727) 461-4171

Clermont

Quilters Anonymous, Inc. Ⓠ
9225 Pine Island Road, 34711
(352) 241-6768
M-F 9-3, please call ahead
www.quiltersanon.com

Clermont Sewing & Quilting ⓆⓂ
741 W. Montrose Street, 34711
(352) 243-4568

Cocoa

Knit & Stitch Boutique ⓎⓌⓈ
15 Stone Street, 32922
(321) 632-4579

Coral Gables

The Knitting Garden ⓎⓌ
1923 Ponce De Leon Blvd., 33134
(305) 774-1060

Crestview

Margie's Sew Much Fun Ⓠ Ⓜ
➡ SEE AD BELOW
2014 Lacey Lane, 32536
(850) 682-6920 or (866) 739-6274
M-Sa 9-6
www.margiessewmuchfun.com

A Quilter's Place Ⓠ Ⓜ
4780 Live Oak Church Road, 32536
(850) 398-5566

Granny's Attic Ⓠ Ⓔ Ⓨ Ⓝ Ⓒ
440 N. Main Street, 32536
(850) 682-3041

Dade City

Quilts on Plum Lane Ⓠ Ⓔ
14215 7th Street, 33523
(352) 518-0003
MTuWFSa 10-5, Th 10-7
www.quiltsonplumlane.net

Daytona Beach

The Sewing Garret Ⓠ Ⓜ
949 Beville Road, Building B, 32119
(386) 767-3545

DeLand

Fabrications Ⓠ Ⓔ Ⓨ
145 W. Wisconsin Avenue, 32720
(386) 624-7340

Quilt Shop of DeLand, Inc. Ⓠ Ⓜ
115 W. Rich Avenue, 32720
(386) 734-8782 or (866) 734-8782

Delray Beach

Stitches By The Sea, Inc. Ⓝ
710 E. Atlantic Avenue, 33483
(561) 865-5775
M-Sa 10-4
www.stitchesbythesea.us

Destin

Coastal Stitches, Inc. Ⓠ Ⓔ Ⓝ Ⓜ
803 Harbor Blvd., 32541
(850) 376-9405

Destin Yarn Shop Ⓨ
12273 US Highway 98 W, Unit 109, 32550
(850) 650-0006

TJ's Fabrics Ⓠ
36074 Emerald Coast Parkway, 32541
(850) 598-9446

Dunedin

Rainbows End Quilt Shoppe Ⓠ Ⓜ
941 Broadway Street, 34698
(727) 733-8572

Elkton

Adela's Yarn Ⓨ
5445 Saint Ambrose Church Road, 32033
(904) 692-2101

Englewood

A Bit O'Yarn Ⓨ Ⓦ
232 N. Indiana Avenue, 34223
(941) 460-1958
MTh 10-8, TuWF 10-5, Sa 10-2
www.abitoyarn.com

Fernandina Beach

Lollipops Quilt Shop Ⓠ Ⓔ Ⓜ
1881 S. 14th Street, Suite 1, 32034
(904) 310-6616

Ft. Lauderdale

Cross Stitch Cupboard Ⓔ Ⓝ Ⓒ
1600 NE 26th Street, Suite B, 33305
(954) 563-8900
Tu 10-8, W-Sa 10-5
www.crossstitchcupboard.com

Once Upon A Quilt...where dreams come true, Inc. Ⓠ Ⓜ
3404 Griffin Road, 33312
(954) 987-8827

Yarns and Arts Ⓨ
3330 NE 32nd Street, 33308
(954) 990-5772 or (954) 326-1422

Ft. Myers

Flash Sew and Quilt Ⓠ Ⓔ
6810 Shoppes at Plantation Drive, #10, 33912
(239) 288-4059

Hooked On Ewe Yarn Shop Ⓨ Ⓝ
16876 McGregor Blvd., Suite 103A, 33908
(239) 247-1080

Kay's Quilt Shop Ⓠ
3220 Forum Blvd., Unit 101, 33905
(239) 337-5297

Tops Vacuum and Sewing* Ⓜ
5100 S. Cleveland Avenue, Suite 202, 33907
(239) 939-4445

Handi Quilter® Authorized Retailer
Designed by a Quilter, for Quilters.®

Ft. Walton Beach

Stitcher's Quest Ⓠ Ⓜ
745 N. Beal Parkway, Suite 5, 32547
(850) 864-4555

The Sewing Center Around the Block Ⓠ Ⓔ Ⓜ
913F N. Beal Parkway NW, 32547
(850) 243-8261

Gainesville

Yarnworks Ⓨ Ⓝ Ⓢ
4113 NW 13th Street, 32609
(352) 337-9965

Gulfport

FAB Fiber LLC Ⓔ Ⓨ Ⓦ Ⓢ
5708 Gulfport Blvd., 33707
(727) 827-2235

Fabric Smart Ⓠ
5401 Gulfport Blvd. S, 33707
(727) 914-8850

Havana

Cindy's Needlework Cottage Ⓠ Ⓔ Ⓝ Ⓦ Ⓒ
1210 Collins Road I, 32333
(850) 539-7201

Holiday

A & A White Sewing Center Ⓠ Ⓔ Ⓜ
3307 US Highway 19 N, 34691
(727) 232-6718 or (727) 232-6718

Homosassa

Alpaca Magic Ⓨ Ⓦ Ⓢ
4920 Grover Cleveland, 34446
(352) 628-0156

Hudson

Quilt Til You Wilt & Embroidery Studio Ⓠ Ⓔ Ⓜ
9609 Fulton Avenue, 34667
(727) 862-6141

Inverness

Citrus Sew & Vac Ⓠ Ⓔ Ⓜ
39 N. Florida Avenue (41 N), 34453
(352) 726-9743

Jacksonville

A Stitch In Time ⒺⓎⓃⒸ
➡ SEE AD BELOW
5724 St. Augustine Road, 32207
(904) 731-4082 or (888) 255-7957
Tu-F 10:30-6, Sa 10:30-4
www.astitchintime.com

Ladybug Quilt Shop Ⓠ
➡ SEE AD BELOW
1400 Cassat Avenue, Suite 4, 32205
(904) 527-8994
MTuThF 10-5, Sa 10-4
www.ladybugquiltshop.com

Paula's Fine Fabrics ⓆⒺⓂ
8358 Point Meadows Drive, Suite 4, 32256
(904) 519-7705
M-Sa 10-5
www.paulasfinefabrics.com

Cinnamon's Quilt Shoppe ⓆⒺ
4220 Hood Road, 32257
(904) 374-0532

Jupiter

Knit or Knot Yarns Ⓨ
➡ SEE AD BELOW
1432 Cypress Drive, #1, 33469
(561) 746-1005
Winter: MWThFSa 10-4, Tu 10-7;
Summer: M-F 10-4, Sa 10-2
www.knitorknotyarns.com

The Inspired Sewist ⓆⒺⓂ
661 Maplewood Drive, Suite 14, 33458
(561) 747-0525

Key West

Seam Shoppe ⓆⒺⓎⒸ
1113 Truman Avenue, 33040
(305) 296-9830

Lady Lake

The Yarn Lady ⓎⓌ
304 Oak Street, 32159
(352) 775-9974
Winter: (Oct.-Apr.) Tu-Sa 10-4,
Summer: (May-Sept.) W-Sa 10-4
www.theyarnlady.com

A Quilting Palette, LLC Q E
732 S. US Highway 441, Plaza 1, 32159
(352) 751-0405

The Sewing Studio at Lady Lake Q M
918 Bichara Blvd., 32159
(352) 753-0219

Lake City

Fabric Art Shop Q E Y M
➡ SEE AD BELOW
4136 W. US Highway 90, 32055
(386) 755-0179
M-Sa 10-6, Su 1-5
www.fabricartshop.com

Lake Mary

Bernina Sewing Centre Q M
3593 Lake Emma Road, 32746
(407) 805-9300

Lake Park

Needlepoint Alley N
905 US Highway 1, Unit K, 33403
(561) 691-3223

Lake Placid

Granny Sue Quilts Q
115 Lakeshore Drive, 33852
(863) 633-8317

Lake Worth

Just Imaginknit Y
6663 Lake Worth Road, Suite B, 33467
(561) 433-3444

Quilt a Bit Q
2914 S. Jog Road, 33467
(561) 304-7211

Lakeland

Carolyn's Frame Up and Cross Stitch Cranny E N C
2254 E. Edgewood Drive, 33803
(863) 940-4577 or (863) 450-9399

Fabric Warehouse Q E M
3030 N. Florida Avenue, 33805
(863) 680-1325

Largo

Criativity Y W S
720 9th Avenue SW, 33770
(727) 584-4191

Keep Me In Stitches, Inc. Q M
10459 Ulmerton Road, 33771
(727) 648-2490

The Crafty Framer C
2480 E. Bay Drive, #A6, 33771
(727) 518-1400

Tops Vacuum and Sewing* M
13002 Seminole Blvd #6, 33778
(727) 585-6676

Handi Quilter® Authorized Retailer
Designed by a Quilter, for Quilters.®

Lauderdale Lake

A To Z Fabric Q
3999 NW 19th Street, 33311
(954) 677-2499

Lauderhill

Sheep Thrills Y W S
4701 N. University Drive, 33351
(954) 742-1908
MThFSa 11-6, Tu 11-8, Su 12-5
www.sheepthrillsknitting.com

Lecanto

Funny Farm Alpaca Yarn Y W S
718 W. Rusk Lane, 34461
(352) 228-3251

Leesburg

Serendipity Farm's Studio Y W S
9501 Silver Lake Drive, 34788
(757) 651-2632

Longwood

Knit! Ⓨ Ⓦ Ⓢ
900 Fox Valley Drive, Suite 106, 32779
(407) 767-5648

The Knitting Patch Ⓨ
1425 W. State Road 434, Suite 101, 32750
(407) 331-5648

Lutz

Scrap and Sew Ⓠ Ⓔ Ⓜ
16541 Pointe Village Drive, Suite 108, 33558
(813) 749-0888

Sweet Darling Quilts Ⓠ
26240 Wesley Chapel Blvd., 33559
(813) 994-2994

Maitland

The Sewing Studio Fabric Superstore Ⓠ Ⓔ Ⓜ
9605 S US Highway 17-92, 32751
(407) 831-6488 or (800) 831-1492
M-F 9-8:30, Sa 9-5:30, Su 12-5
(Bargain Annex: M-F 9-6, Sa 9-5:30, Su 12-5)
www.sewing.net

Melbourne

Boutique 4 Quilters Ⓠ Ⓜ
2945 W. New Haven Avenue, 32904
(321) 768-2060

Quilts and Lace Ⓠ Ⓜ
7720 N. Wickham Road, Suites 111, 112 & 113, 32940
(321) 622-8602

Merritt Island

Jane's Sew Central Ⓠ Ⓔ Ⓜ
353 E. Merritt Island Causeway, 32952
(321) 338-2959
M-F 10-5, Sa 10-4
www.sewcentral.net

Miami

Absolutely Needlepoint Ⓝ
13969 S. Dixie Highway, 33176
(305) 858-1212

Elegant Stitches Ⓨ
13861 S. Dixie Highway, 33176
(305) 232-4005

New York Fabrics Inc. Ⓠ
11320 Quail Roost Drive, 33157
(305) 256-9372

New York Fabrics Inc. Ⓠ Ⓨ
13812 SW 152nd Street, 33177
(305) 251-4885 or (786) 509-7095

Ultra Fabrics Ⓠ
8584 SW 40th Street, 33155
(305) 553-1077

Mt. Dora

SEW-MINI Things Ⓠ Ⓔ Ⓜ
3820 N. Highway 19A, 32757
(352) 483-0082 or (888) 238-6903

Naples

Castle Creek Fiber Studio Ⓨ Ⓦ
➡ SEE AD NEXT PAGE
4270 Tamiami Trail East, Suite 10, 34112
(239) 793-8141
M-F 10-5, Sa 10-4
www.castlecreekstudio.com

Flash Sew and Quilt Ⓠ Ⓔ
1575 Pine Ridge Road, Suite 13, 34109
(239) 304-8387

Needlepoint In Paradise Ⓝ
975 Imperial Golf Course Blvd., #118, 34110
(239) 591-0654

Tops Vacuum and Sewing* Ⓜ
5367 North Airport Pulling Road, 34109
(239) 591-4422

Handi Quilter® Authorized Retailer
Designed by a Quilter, for Quilters.®

New Smyrna Beach

Seaside Sewing & Quilts Ⓠ
403 Mary Avenue, 32168
(386) 402-8995

North Ft. Myers

Quilt Lovers' Hangout Ⓠ
3323 N. Key Drive, #1, 33903
(239) 995-0045

Sewing Boutique Ⓠ Ⓔ Ⓨ Ⓒ Ⓜ
13500 N. Cleveland Avenue, 33903
(239) 656-4489

Susie Q's Quilts and Sewing Center Ⓠ Ⓔ
1890 N. Tamiami Trail, 33903
(239) 656-2722

North Port

Traveling Fiber Artist Ⓔ Ⓨ Ⓦ Ⓢ
2765 Arugula, 34289
(817) 707-1012

Ocala

A-White Sew and Vac Ⓠ Ⓠ Ⓜ
3101 SW 34th Avenue, #703, 34474
(352) 854-0022

Brick City Cross Stitch Ⓒ
4901 E. Silver Springs Blvd., Suite 606, 34470
(352) 629-2991

Tomorrow's Treasures Quilt Shop Ⓠ Ⓜ
6122 SW Highway 200, 34476
(352) 690-1915
Handi Quilter® Authorized Retailer
Designed by a Quilter, for Quilters.®

Odessa

Fiber Art Gallery, LLC Ⓠ Ⓨ Ⓦ Ⓢ
8727 Gunn Highway, 33556
(813) 792-5999

Orange Park

Calico Station Ⓠ Ⓔ Ⓜ
1857 Wells Road, 32073
(904) 269-6911
M-Sa 9:30-5
www.calicostation.com

Country Crossroads Quilt Shop Ⓠ
799 Blanding Blvd., Suite 3, 32065
(904) 276-1011

Orlando

Quilts & More Ⓠ
11601 S. Orange Blossom Trail, 32837
(321) 800-6620

The Black Sheep Ⓔ Ⓨ Ⓝ
1201 W. Fairbanks Avenue, 32804
(407) 894-0444

Ormond Beach

She Sells Yarn & More Ⓨ
600 S. Yonge Street (US 1), Suite 16A, 32174
(386) 238-9109
TuTh 10-8, WFSa 10-5
www.shesellsyarn.com

Byrd's Nest Quilt Shop ⓆⒺⓂ
156 E. Granada Blvd., 32176
(386) 615-8789

Palatka

Miss D's Quilt Shop ⓆⓂ
305 St. Johns Avenue, 32177
(386) 385-5678
M-F 10-5:30, Sa 9-4
www.missdsquilts.com

Palm Beach Gardens

Laura's Sewing & Quilt Shop ⓆⒺⓂ
3966 Northlake Blvd., 33403
(561) 799-5228

Palm Coast

Cut Up and Sew ⓆⒺⓂ
160 Cypress Point Parkway, Unit D116, 32164
(386) 447-1103

Palm Harbor

MK Quilts ⓆⓂ
38565 US Highway 19 N., 34684
(727) 741-8070

Tops Vacuum and Sewing* Ⓜ
3327 Tampa Road #215, 34684
(727) 787-7043

Palmetto

Quilters Haven & More ⓆⓂ
925 10th Street E (US Hwy 301), 34221
(941) 729-0511 or (800) 775-4445
Winter: (Nov-Apr): M-Sa 9:30-4;
Summer: (May-Oct): Tu-Sa 9:30-4
www.quiltershavenandmore.com

Panama City

Quilting By The Bay ⓆⒺ
2303 Winona Drive, 32405
(850) 215-7282

Pembroke Pines

Raging Wool Yarn Shop ⓎⓌⓈ
1850 NW 122nd Terrace, 33026
(954) 385-0861

Pensacola

Martelli Solutions For Sewing, Quilting and Embroidery ⓆⓂ
➡ **SEE AD PAGE 321**
5450 N. W Street, 32505
(850) 432-4434

A & E Fabric & Crafts ⓆⓎⓂ
923 N. New Warrington Road, 32506
(850) 455-0112
M-Sa 9-5
www.aefabric.com

Derrel's of Pensacola ⓆⓂ
6705 N. Davis Highway, 32504
(850) 438-5444

Dixie Knits Ⓨ
116 W. Government Street, 32503
(850) 361-1088

Plant City

Inspire! Quilting & Sewing ⓆⓂ
101 N. Collins Street, 33563
(813) 704-4867

Pompano Beach

Ace Sewing & Vacuum Center Ⓜ
509 E. Sample Road, 33064
(800) 992-4739

Ponte Vedra

PV Arts & Crafts Ⓨ
288-1 Solana Road, 32082
(904) 473-5171

Port Charlotte

Charlotte Sewing Studio ⓆⒺⓂ
1109 Tamiami Trail, 33953
(941) 235-3555

Expert Sewing Center ⓆⓂ
3846 Tamiami Trail, Unit D, 33952
(941) 766-7118

Golden Needle ⓃⒸ
1225 Tamiami Trail, Unit A3, 33953
(941) 743-4410

The Knit N Stitch Shop ⒺⓎⓃⓌⒸ
18505 Paulson Drive, 33954
(941) 408-7416

Port Saint Lucie

Laura's Sewing & Quilt Shop ⓆⒺⓂ
1707 NW St. Lucie West Blvd., Suite #102, 34986
(772) 344-5229

Pam's Fabric Nook ⓆⒺⓂ
8615 S. US Highway 1, 34952
(772) 800-3019 or (772) 800-3019

Quincy

Lady Bird Quilts Ⓠ
2029 Bristol Highway, 32351
(850) 329-8276

Rockledge

Quilting Folks Sewing Gallery ⓆⓂ
6420 3rd Street, Suite 101, 32955
(321) 253-3882

The Quilt Place Ⓠ
575 Barton Blvd., 32955
(321) 632-3344

Sanibel

Three Crafty Ladies ⓆⓎⒸ
1628 Periwinkle Way, 33957
(239) 472-2893

Sarasota

Needlepoint Studio of Sarasota ⒺⓃ
7390 S. Tamiami Trail, 34231
(941) 924-3696
Tu-F 10-5, Sa 10-4
www.needlepointstudio.com

A Good Yarn ⓎⓌⓈ
7222 S. Tamiami Trail, 34231
(941) 487-7914

A Quilter's Stash Ⓠ
6388 N. Lockwood Ridge Road, 34234
(941) 351-5559

Alma Sue's Quilt Shop Ⓠ
3737 Bahia Vista Street, Suite 11, 34232
(941) 330-0993

Picasso's Moon Yarn Shop ⓎⓈ
200 S. Washington Blvd., Suite 11, 34236
(941) 932-0103

Sew Worth It! ⓆⒸⓂ
5507 Palmer Crossing Circle, 34233
(941) 924-5600

The Modern Sewist ⓆⓂ
2264 Gulf Gate Drive, 34231
(941) 706-3846

Tops Vacuum & Sewing, Inc. Ⓜ
2120 Bee Ridge Road, 34239
(941) 926-2699

Sebastian

Marilou's Quilting and Sewing Center ⓆⓂ
8802 N. US Highway 1, 32958
(772) 589-0011

Sebring

Crafty Quilters Inc. Q M
13221 US Highway 98, 33876
(863) 658-2148

The Fabric & Sewing Shop Q E M
1422 Prosper Avenue, 33870
(863) 382-1422

St. Augustine

Bee's Quilt Shop & Studio Q M
1690 US 1 S, Suite I, 32084
(904) 826-4007

St. Petersburg

Jay's Fabric Center Q
801 Pasedena Avenue S, 33707
(727) 381-6600

Silk Road Needle Arts E N C
2887 22nd Avenue N, Suites C & D, 33713
(727) 327-5127 or (800) 377-0079

Stash - A Place For Yarn Y
2820 1st Avenue N, 33713
(727) 822-9276

Whim So Doodle Q
237 2nd Avenue S, 33701
(727) 827-4911

Starke

Elza M Studios Y W S
14272 SW 75th Avenue, 32091
(904) 964-6673 or (443) 786-0021

Stuart

Needlepoint Land N
3836 SE Dixie Highway, 34997
(772) 223-9700

Tallahassee

BERNINA Connection Q M
1400 Village Square Blvd., Suite 4, 32312
(850) 386-7397

Crafty Threads Q
3982 Elysian Court, 32311
(813) 855-3066 or (888) 74Q-UILT

Fay's Needlecraft Boutique Y
2702 Apalachee Parkway, 32301
(850) 878-7993

Yarn Therapy Inc. Y W S
215 Lake Ella Drive, 32303
(850) 577-0555

Tamarac

Cynthia's Fine Fabric & Notions Q E M
8126 N. University Drive, 33321
(954) 724-2900
M-F 10-6, Sa 10-5
www.cynthiasfinefabrics.com

Tampa

Happy Apple Quilts / Florida Quilting Center Q M
13013 W. Linebaugh Avenue, 33626
(813) 925-9037

Keep Me In Stitches Q M
4504 W. Kennedy Blvd., 33609
(813) 282-1526

Roxy's Yarns Y W S
3347 S. Westshore Blvd., 33629
(813) 839-7699

Tops Vacuum & Sewing, Inc. M
14922 Dale Mabry Highway, #6, 33618
(813) 963-6732

Tarpon Springs

Custom Couture of Tarpon Springs Y
208 E. Tarpon Avenue, 34689
(727) 238-7194

Temple Terrace

Bernina Sewing Center Q M
5405 E. Fowler Avenue, 33617
(813) 969-2458

The Villages

The Sewing Studio at Lady Lake Q M
918 Bichara Blvd., 32159
(352) 753-0219

Titusville

Kathy's Quilt Studio Q E
3550 S. Washington Avenue, Suite 7, 32780
(321) 529-0117

Trenton

Suwannee Valley Quilt Shop Q M
517 N. Main Street, 32693
(352) 463-3842

University Park

Cotton Patch Quilt Shop Q E M
8480 Cooper Creek Blvd., Suite 101, 34201
(941) 359-3300

Venice

Needlefish Yarns Y
258 W. Miami Avenue, 34285
(941) 486-1584
MTuWF 10-5, Th 10-7, Sa 10-4
www.needlefishyarns.com

Crazy Quilter's Fabric and Notions Q
711 Shamrock Blvd., 34293
(941) 451-8959

Deborah's Quilt Basket Q
337 W. Venice Avenue, 34285
(941) 488-6866

Vero Beach

Crafts & Stuff Y
658 21st Street, 32960
(772) 562-0540

Knitty Gritty Yarn Shop Y W
1436 Old Dixie Highway, Suite F, 32960
(772) 778-9199

Needle Nicely N
1531 US Highway 1, 32960
(772) 567-6688

The Dragonfly Quilt Shop Q
1436 Old Dixie Highway, Suite E, 32960
(772) 567-9600

Wabasso

Marilou's Quilting and Sewing Center Q M
8802 N. US Highway 1, 32958
(772) 589-0011

West Bradenten

Tops Vacuum and Sewing* M
5206 Manatee Avenue, 34209
(941) 792-8048

Wildwood

Sharky's Vac N Sew Q
700 N. Main Street, 34785
(352) 330-2483

Winter Garden

Nancy's Quilt Shop Q M
121 W. Plant Street, 34787
(407) 614-8755

Winter Haven

Four Purls Y W S
334 3rd Street NW, 33881
(863) 662-8288

Heart of Florida Sewing Machine Q M
365 5th Street SW, 33880
(863) 875-5675

Heart to Heart Fabrics & More Q M
6310 Cypress Gardens Blvd., 33884
(863) 298-8185

Heartfelt Quilting & Sewing Q M
355 5th Street SW, 33880
(863) 299-3080

Zephyrhills

Cuttin Up Fabrics Q
38434 Fifth Avenue, 33542
(813) 782-0999

Quilter's Quarters Q M
4833 Allen Road, 33541
(813) 779-2615

NeedleTravel

Download our App!

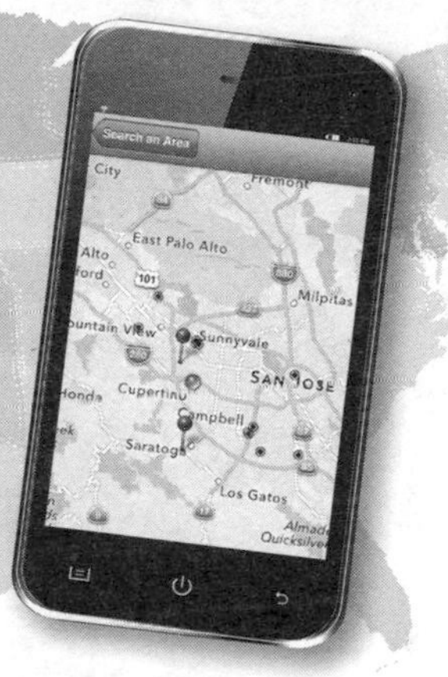

Find Shops From Your Phone

It's Free!

Check us out on:

www.facebook.com/Needletravel

http://www.pinterest.com/needletravel

https://twitter.com/Needletravel

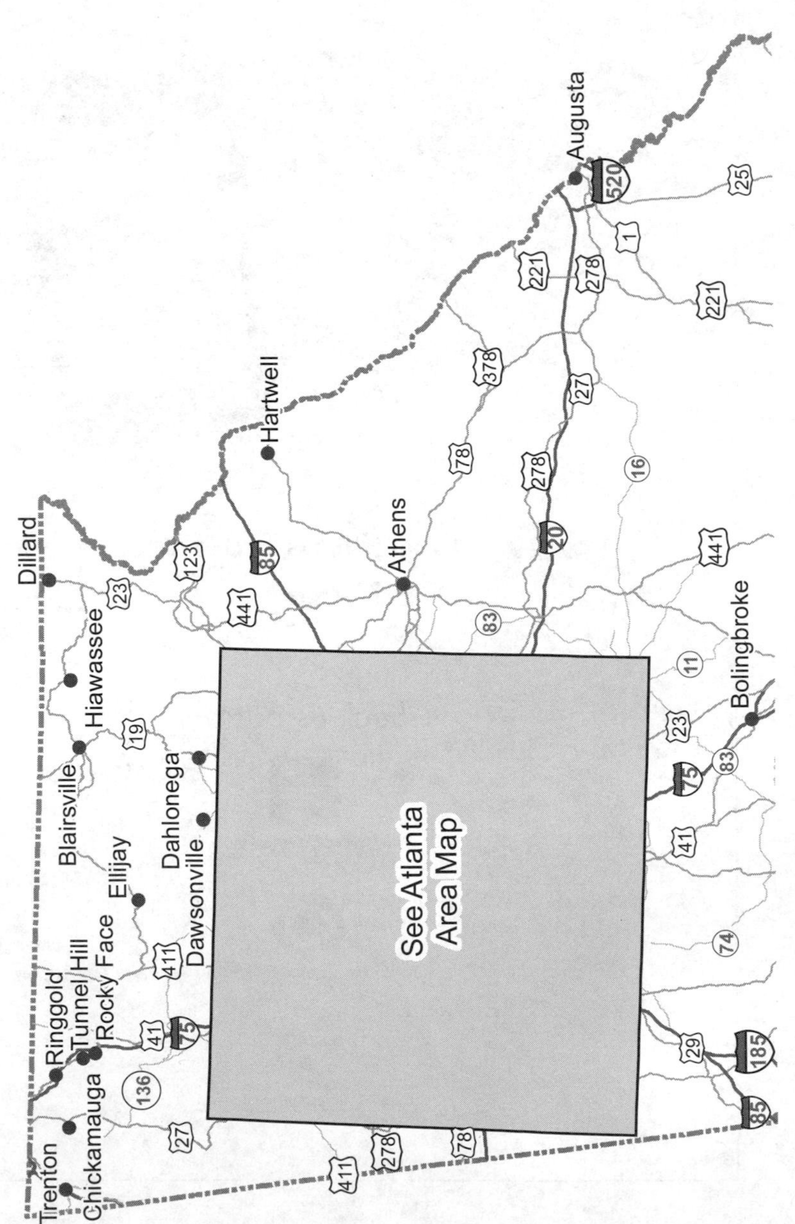
Dillard
Hiawassee
Blairsville
Ellijay
Dahlonega
Dawsonville
Ringgold
Tunnel Hill
Rocky Face
Chickamauga
Trenton
Hartwell
Athens
Augusta
Bolingbroke
See Atlanta
Area Map

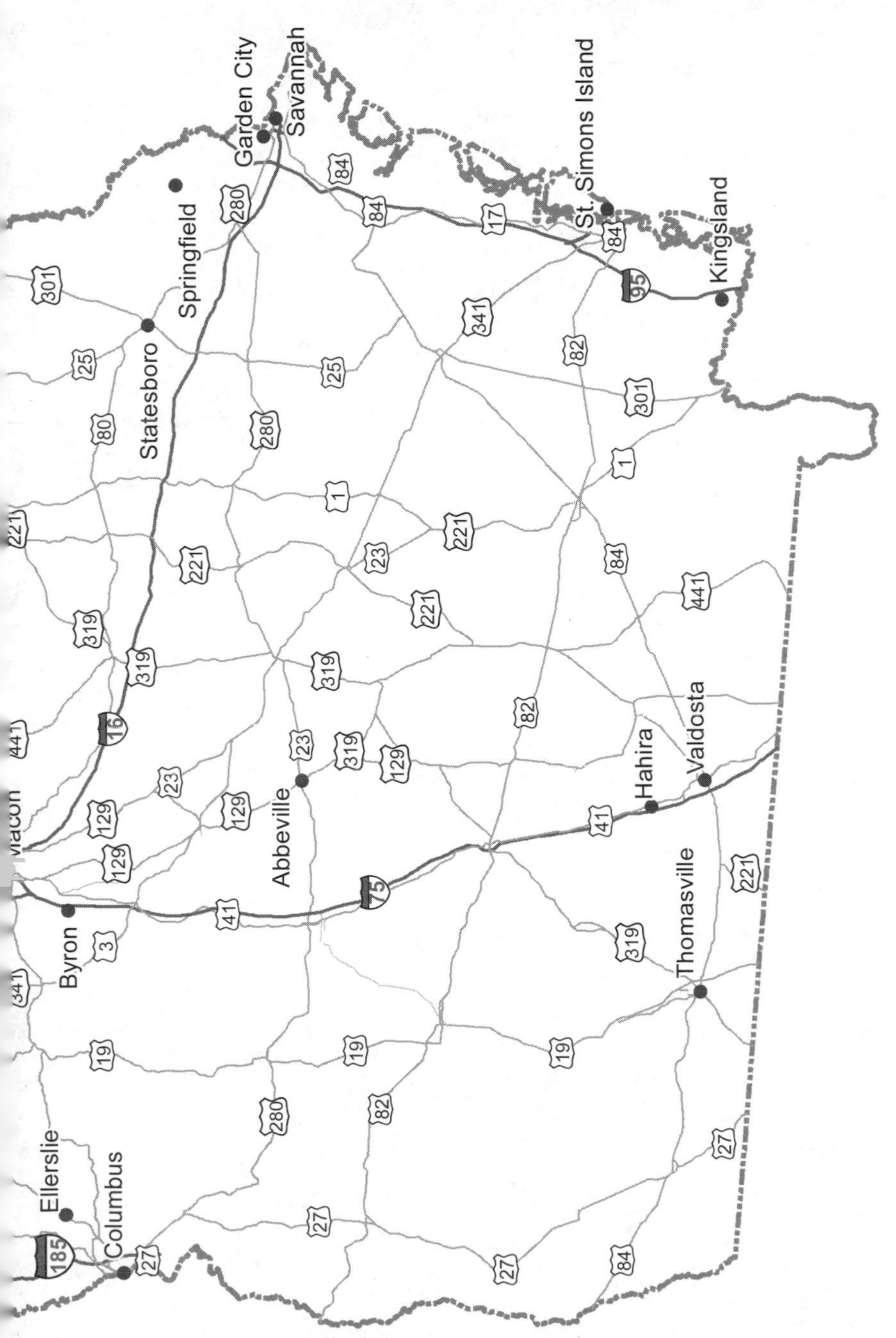
Savannah
Garden City
St. Simons Island
Kingsland
Springfield
Statesboro
Abbeville
Hahira
Valdosta
Thomasville
Byron
Ellerslie
Columbus
Macon

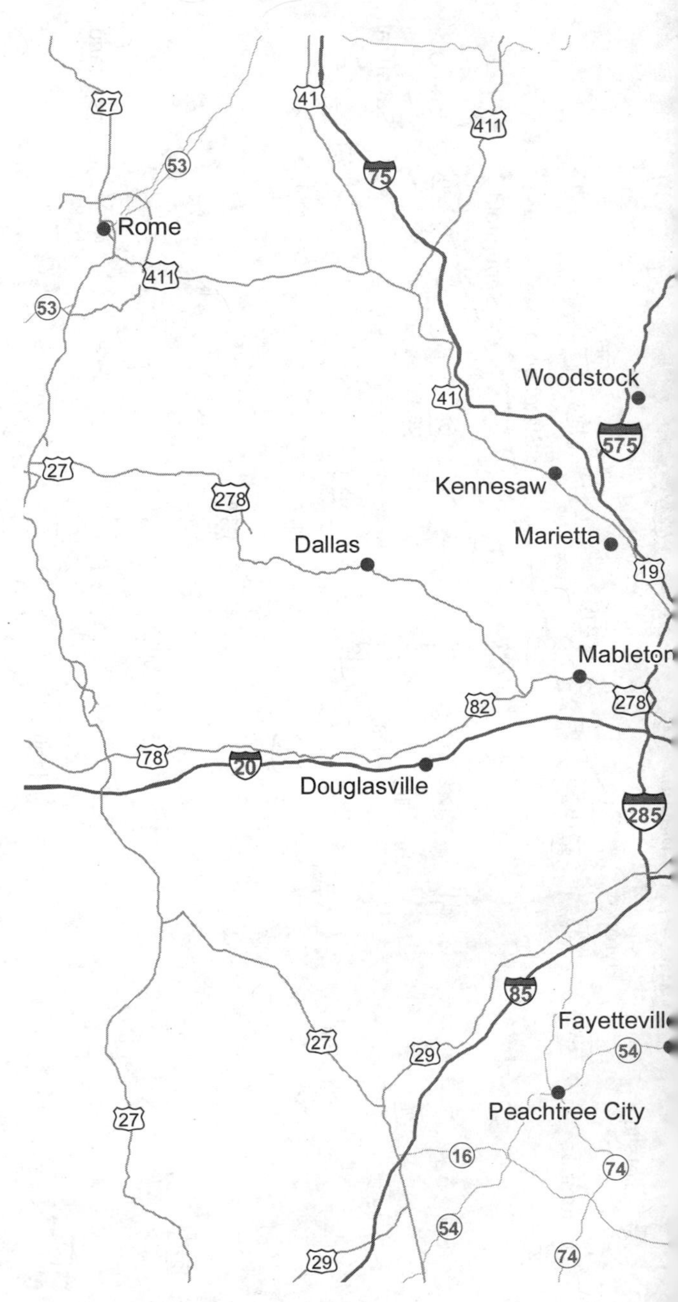

27
41
411
53
75
Rome
411
53
Woodstock
41
575
27
Kennesaw
278
Dallas
Marietta
19
Mableton
82
278
78
20
Douglasville
285
85
Fayettevill
27
29
54
27
Peachtree City
16
74
54
29
74

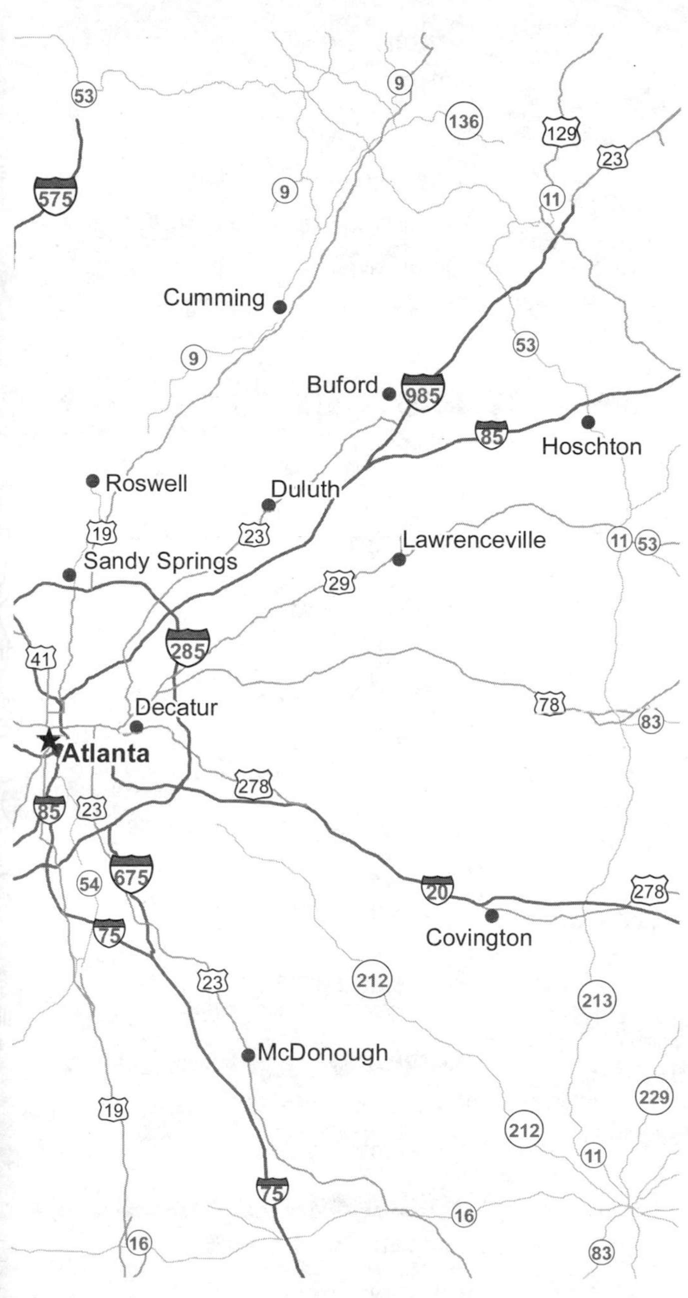
Cumming
Buford
Hoschton
Roswell
Duluth
Lawrenceville
Sandy Springs
Decatur
Atlanta
Covington
McDonough
53
575
9
136
129
23
11
985
85
19
29
285
41
78
83
278
675
54
75
20
212
213
229
16

Georgia

Abbeville

That's Sew Nice [Q]
203 Church Street N, 31001
(229) 425-1492

Athens

Revival Yarns [Y]
297 Prince Avenue, Suite 17, 30601
(706) 850-1354

Atlanta

In Stitches [N]
3137 E. Shadowlawn Avenue NE, 30305
(404) 816-4612

Labors of Love Needlepoint Shop [N]
500 Amsterdam Avenue NE, Suite L4, 30306
(470) 343-2105

Needle Nook [Y] [N]
2165 Briarcliff Road, 30329
(404) 325-0068

Yarning for Ewe [Y]
3220 Cobb Parkway, Suite 102, 30339
(678) 909-4963

Augusta

Augusta Sewing Center [Q] [E] [M]
3230 Washington Road, 30907
(706) 860-5434

Jeff's Sewing & Vacuum Center [Q] [M]
3833 Washington Road, 30907
(706) 863-0090

Blairsville

Fabrics Galore and Quilting Store [Q] [M]
19 Cobalt Street, Suite G, 30512
(706) 745-6918
M-Sa 10-5
www.fabricsgaloreandquiltingstore.com

Knitter's Knitch [Y]
64 Bracketts Way, Suite 6, 30512
(706) 835-1078

Bolingbroke

Yarn Love [Y]
8175 Rivoli Road, 31004
(478) 342-2251

Buford

Georgia Sewing & Quilting [Q] [E] [M]
81 Maddox Road, 30518
(770) 831-7990

Byron

Birdhouse Quilts [Q]
103 Peach Wood Drive, 31008
(478) 654-6880

Chickamauga

Memories & More [Q] [E] [C]
121 Gordon Street, 30707
(706) 375-5300

Columbus

Sew Much Fun [Q] [M]
7801 Veteran's Parkway, 31909
(706) 317-0024

Covington

Patrick's [Q]
10285 Covington Bypass Road, 30014
(770) 786-3220
M-F 9-5:30, Sa 9-3:30
http://www.patrickfeed.com

Cumming

Thread Bear Fabrics [Q] [E]
515 Sawnee Corners Blvd., Suite 500, 30040
(770) 781-0001

Dahlonega

Magical Threads, Inc. [Q] [Y] [N]
315 Church Street, 30533
(706) 867-8918

The Common Thread Ⓠ Ⓔ Ⓒ Ⓜ
598 Grove Street N, 30533
(706) 864-0740

Dallas

Eat.Sleep.Knit Ⓨ
1060 Cedarcrest Road, 30132
(770) 432-9277

Dawsonville

Miller's Cloth Shop Ⓠ
1396 New Hope Road, 30534
(706) 265-2387

Decatur

Intown Quilters Fabric & Yarn Ⓠ Ⓔ Ⓨ Ⓒ
Please call for new location, 30033
(404) 634-6924

Dillard

Rosemary's Fabrics Ⓠ
1190 Franklin Street, 30537
(706) 746-4471

Douglasville

Cornerstone Sew and Vac Ⓠ
6853 Douglas Blvd., 30135
(770) 949-5775

Duluth

Atlanta Sewing Center Ⓠ Ⓜ
2148 Duluth Highway NE, #111, 30097
(770) 622-1880

Ellerslie

Sunday Best Quiltworks Ⓠ
4517 Harris Road, 31807
(706) 569-7744

Ellijay

Strings & Stitches Yarn Shoppe Ⓨ Ⓢ
449 Industrial Blvd., Suite 165, 30540
(706) 698-5648

Fayetteville

Quilt N Fabric / Seams Sew Right Inc. Ⓠ Ⓜ
935 W. Lanier Avenue, Suite 1016, 30214
(678) 817-7878

Garden City

Sew Much More Ⓠ Ⓜ
4831 Augusta Road, Suite A, 31408
(912) 966-5626

Hahira

Sew Blessed Ⓠ Ⓜ
213 W. Main Street, 31632
(229) 794-0076

Sew Blessed Quilting Ⓠ Ⓜ
201 S. Church Street, 31632
(229) 794-1100

Hartwell

Annies Pretty Pieces Ⓠ
138 N. Forest Avenue, Suite E, 30643
(706) 377-3313

Hiawassee

Noblet's 5 and 10 Cent Store Ⓔ Ⓨ
159 Main Street, 30546
(706) 896-3846

Hoschton

City Square Quilts Ⓠ Ⓔ Ⓜ
84A Jopena Blvd., 30548
(706) 921-4958

Yarn Junkees Ⓨ Ⓦ Ⓢ
25 City Square, 30548
(706) 921-4116

Kennesaw

Cottontail Quilts Ⓠ
2259 Lewis Street NW, 30144
(678) 355-6776
M-Sa 9:30-5
www.cottontailquiltshop.com

Ashby Sewing Center Q E M
2255 Old 41 Highway NW, Suite 140, 30144
(770) 427-9947

Kingsland

Beyond Fabric Q
1630-B Boone Street, 31548
(912) 673-8662

Lawrenceville

Yarn Garden Knit Shop Y
159 W. Pike Street, 30046
(678) 225-0920

Mableton

Stitch'n Quilt Q
5590 Mableton Parkway SW, Suite 146, 30126
(770) 944-3356

Macon

Couture Sewing Center Q E M
3755 Bloomfield Road, Suite 5A, 31206
(478) 474-7224

Magical Stitches Q E M
4126 Hartley Bridge Road, 31216
(478) 788-0555

Marietta

Atlanta Sewing Center Q M
50 Barrett Parkway, Suite 4005, 30066
(770) 428-5522

Red Hen Stitch Shop Q E
22 Trammell Street, Suite B, 30064
(770) 794-8549

Tiny Stitches Q E C M
2518 E. Piedmont Road, 30062
(770) 565-1113

McDonough

A Scarlet Thread Q M
1601 McDonough Place, 30253
(678) 583-2296

Peachtree City

Sugarfoot Yarns Y
100 N. Peachtree Parkway, Suite 17, 30269
(770) 487-9001

Ringgold

It's Sew Time Q
7847 Nashville Street, 30736
(706) 937-3777

Rocky Face

Sew'N So Quilt Shop Q E
600 LaFayette Road, 30740
(706) 217-8111

Rome

The Stitchery Q E M
9 Central Plaza, 30161
(706) 622-2345

Roswell

Cast-On Cottage and Needlepoint Garden Y N
Coleman Village
860 Marietta Highway, 30075
(770) 998-3483
M-Th 10-6, FSa 10-4
www.castoncottage.com

Sandy Springs

The Nimble Needle N
214 Johnson Ferry Road NE, 30328
(404) 843-8687

Savannah

Fabrika Fine Fabrics Q
2 E. Liberty Street, 31401
(912) 236-1122

Measure: A Fabric Parlor Q E C
311 Whitaker Street, 31401
(912) 209-0942

The Frayed Knot Y W S
6 W. State Street, 31401
(912) 233-1240

Unwind Yarn & Gifts Y
7710 Waters Avenue, 31406
(912) 303-3970

Springfield

Quarterdeck Quilts Q
490 Stillwell Road, 31329
(912) 754-1865

St. Simons Island

The Stitchery of St. Simons E Y N C
➡ SEE AD BELOW
3411 Frederica Road, 31522
(912) 638-3401
M-Sa 10-5
www.shopthestitchery.com

Statesboro

Deb-Bees Creations Q E M
17943 Highway 80 W, 30458
(912) 764-5423

Thomasville

Fuzzy Goat Y
223 W. Jackson Street, 31792
(229) 236-4628

Trenton

The Quilter's Garden Quilt Shop Q
12695 N. Main Street, 30752
(423) 504-2422

Tunnel Hill

Janet's Place Quilt Shop Q
3590 Chattanooga Road, 30755
(706) 516-4038 or (706) 847-1225

Valdosta

Pinwheels Quilting Q E M
361 Northside Drive, 31602
(229) 232-4531
Tu-F 10:30-5, Sa 10:30-4
www.pinwheelsquilting.com

Woodstock

Sew Main Street Q E
8826 Main Street, 30188
(678) 401-6126

The Whole Nine Yarns Y S
8826 Main Street, 30188
(678) 494-5242

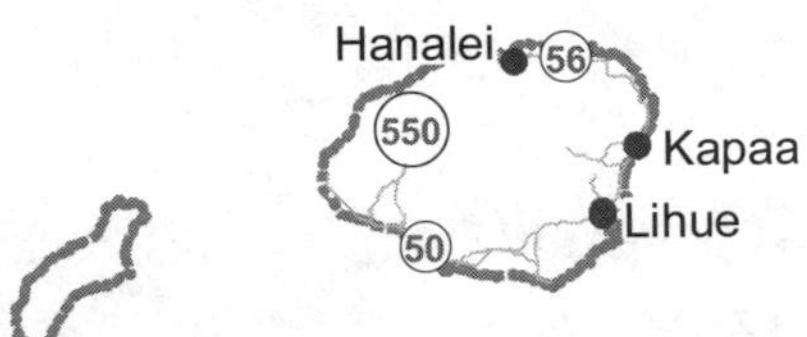
Hanalei
56
550
Kapaa
Lihue
50

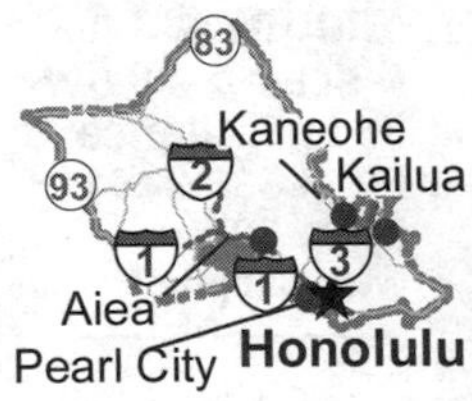
83
Kaneohe
Kailua
93
2
1
3
1
Aiea
Pearl City
Honolulu

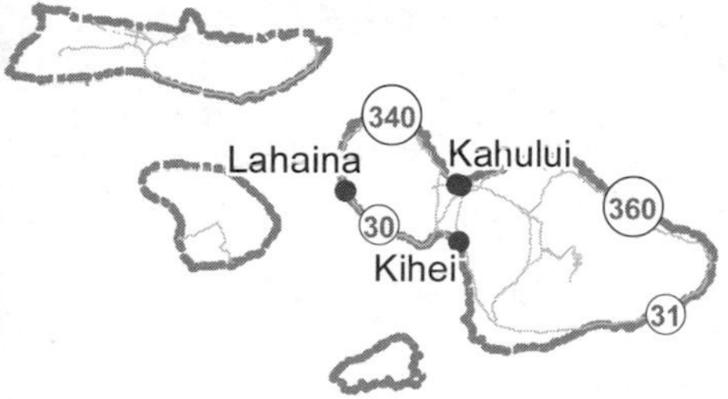
340
Lahaina
Kahului
360
30
Kihei
31

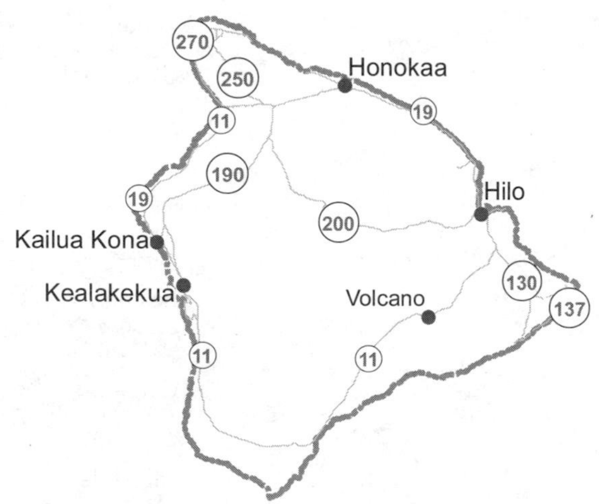
270
250
Honokaa
19
11
190
19
Hilo
200
Kailua Kona
Kealakekua
130
Volcano
137
11
11

Hawaii

Aiea

Hawaii Fabric Mart Q
98-023 Hekaha Street, Building 1, 96701
(808) 488-8882

Hanalei

Hanalei Strings Y
5-5190 Kuhio Highway, 96714
(808) 826-9633

Hilo

Ben Franklin Crafts* Y
333 Kilauea Avenue, 96720
(808) 935-0005

Discount Fabric Warehouse Q E M
933 Kanoelehua Avenue, #7, 96720
(808) 935-1234

Dragon Mama Q
266 Kamehameha Avenue, 96720
(808) 934-9081

Kilauea Kreations II Q M
680 Manono Street, 96720
(808) 961-1100

Strings Fabric and Needlework Shoppe Q Y N
285 Kinoole Street, #202, 96720
(808) 937-2160

Honokaa

Topstitch Q
45-3599 Mamane Street, 96272
(808) 885-4482

Honolulu

Aloha Fabrics Hula & Crafts Q
650 Iwilei Road, Unit 185, 96817
(808) 847-2998

Ben Franklin Crafts* Y
2810 Paa Street, 96819
(808) 833-3800

Fiddlesticks Too E N C
1320 Hart Street, Suite 101, 96817
(808) 533-4565 or (800) 897-8482

Flora-Dec Sales, Inc. Y
373 N. Nimitz Highway, 96817
(808) 537-6194

Hawaii Fabric Mart Q
1631 Kalakaua Avenue, 96826
(808) 947-4466

Hidden Yardage Q
50 S. Beretania Street, C113, 96813
(808) 523-3330

Isle Knit Y
1188 Bishop Street, Suite 1403, 96813
(808) 533-0853

June Fabrics Q
938 Austin Lane, 96817
(808) 845-5400

Kaimuki Dry Goods Q
1144 10th Avenue, 96816
(808) 734-2141

Kuni Island Fabrics Q
2563 S. King Street, 96826
(808) 955-1280

Needlepoint, Etc. N
1134 S. King Street, 96814
(808) 591-0377

The Calico Cat Q E
1223 Koko Head Avenue, Suite 2, 96816
(808) 732-3998

US Sewing & Vacuum Q M
670 Auahi Street, A7, 96813
(808) 536-6044

Wholesale Hawaiian Fabric.com Q
3207 Martha Street, 96815
(808) 381-3909

YarnStory Y W S
1411 S. King Street, Suite 201, 96814
(808) 724-7224

Kahului

Sew Special Q E C M
➡ **SEE AD BELOW**
275 Ka'ahumanu Avenue, #1048, 96732
(808) 877-6128
M-Sa 9:30-9, Su 10-5
www.sewspecialmaui.net

Discount Fabric Warehouse Q E
230 Hana Highway, 96732
(808) 871-6900

Hawaii Fabric Mart Q
285 Dairy Road, 96732
(808) 871-5770

Kailua

Ben Franklin Crafts* Y
1020 Keolu Drive, 96734
(808) 261-4621

Yarn & Needlecrafts and Strictly Christmas E Y N C
46 Hoolai Street, 96734
(808) 262-9555

Kailua Kona

Discount Fabric Warehouse Q E M
74-5605 Luhia Street, 96740
(808) 326-7474

Fabric & Quilting Delights Q E
73-1479 Hookele Street, 96740
(808) 329-8177

Island Yarn & Art Supplies Y W S
73-5568 Olowalu Street, 96740
(808) 326-2820

Kapa Fabrics Q
76-964 Hualalai Road, 96740
(808) 329-1880

Quilt Passions Q E Y N C
75-5706 Kuakini Highway, Suite 111, 96740
(808) 329-7475

Kaneohe

Aloha Yarn Y
46-018 Kamehameha Highway, Suite 209, 96744
(808) 234-5865

Hawaii Fabric Mart Q
45-681 Kamehameha Highway, 96744
(808) 234-6604

Kapaa

Vicky's Fabric Shop Q
4-1326 Kuhio Highway, 96746
(808) 822-1746

Kealakekua

Kimura's Fabrics Q E Y
79-7408 Mamalahoa Highway, 96750
(808) 322-3771

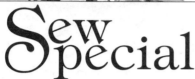

Kihei

The Maui Quilt Shop Q E Y N C
1280 S. Kihei Road, 96753
(808) 874-8050

Lahaina

Quilts 'n Fabric Land* Q E Y C
658 Front Street, Suite 134B, 96761
(808) 662-0951

Lihue

Discount Fabric Warehouse Q E M
3-3215 Kuhio Highway, 96766
(808) 246-2739

Kapaia Stitchery Q N C
3-3551 Kuhio Highway, 96766
(808) 245-2281

Twisted Turtles Yarn Shop Y S C
3501 Rice Street, Suite 1008, 96766
(808) 631-0911

Pearl City

Ben Franklin Crafts* Y
850 Kamehameha Highway, 96782
(808) 455-1909

US Sewing & Vacuum Q M
719 Kam Highway, 96701
(808) 455-6777

Volcano

Kilauea Kreations Q M
19-3972 Old Volcano Road, 96785
(808) 967-8090

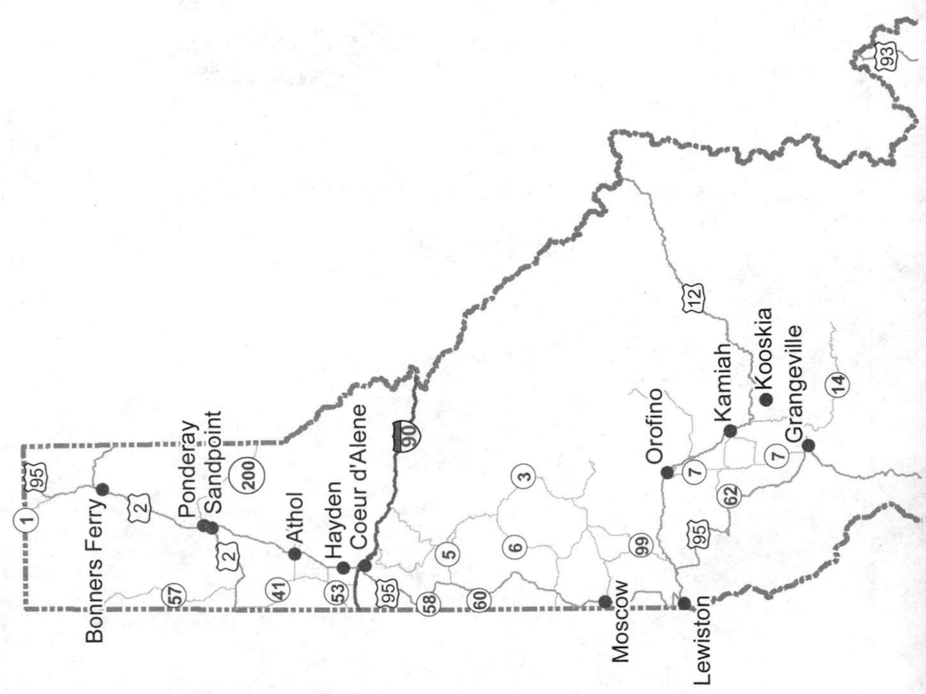

Bonners Ferry
Ponderay
Sandpoint
Athol
Hayden
Coeur d'Alene
Moscow
Lewiston
Orofino
Kamiah
Kooskia
Grangeville
1
95
2
57
200
41
53
90
58
60
3
6
5
99
7
62
12
14
93

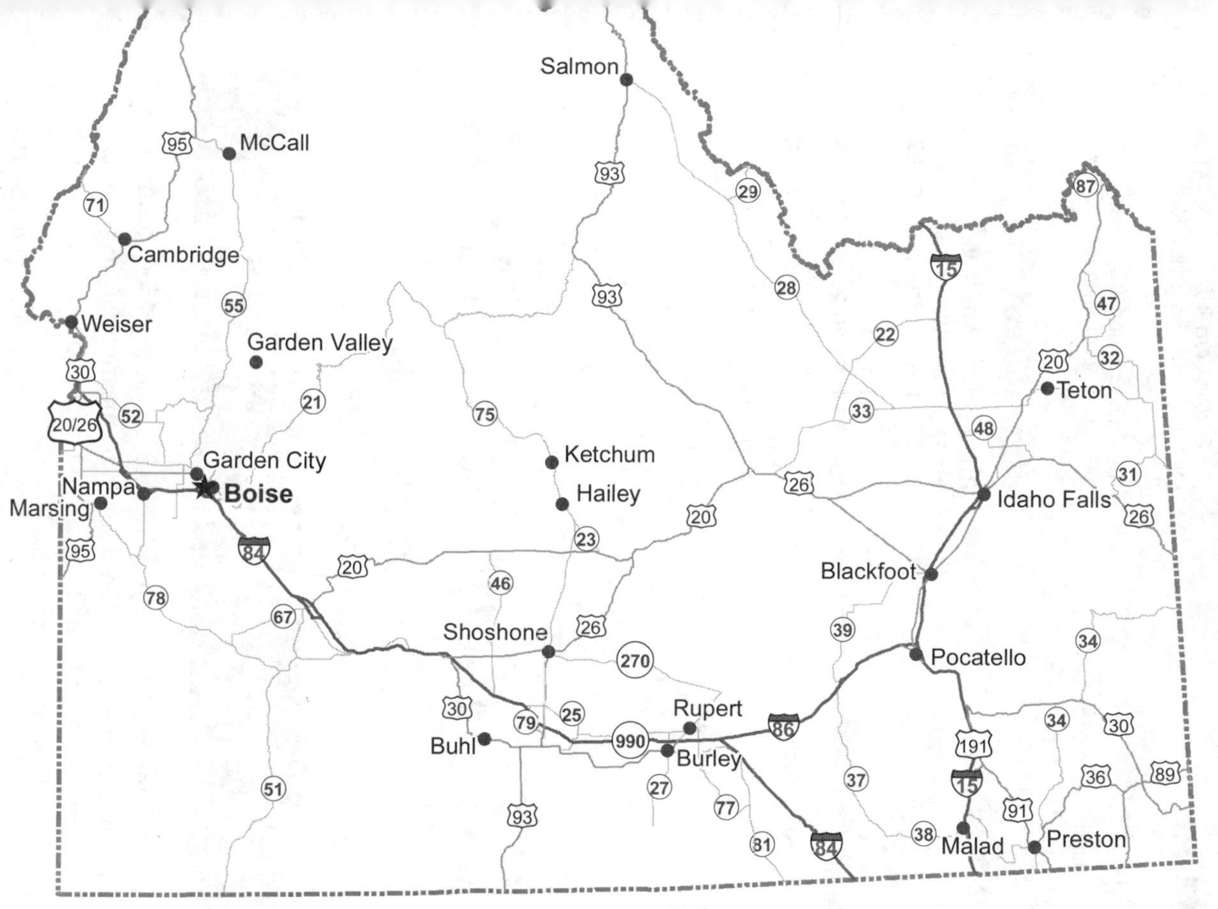

Salmon
McCall
Cambridge
Weiser
Garden Valley
Garden City
Boise
Nampa
Marsing
Ketchum
Hailey
Shoshone
Buhl
Rupert
Burley
Blackfoot
Pocatello
Idaho Falls
Teton
Malad
Preston
95
71
55
30
20/26
52
21
75
93
29
28
87
15
47
22
20
32
33
48
31
26
23
84
46
78
67
39
34
270
25
79
990
86
191
36
89
51
27
77
37
91
38
81

Idaho

Athol

Auntie Linda's Quilt Shop* Q
8948 E. Scout Trail, 83801
(208) 683-8948

Blackfoot

B&R Craft and Hobbies Q
484 W. Bridge Street, 83221
(208) 785-3780

Boise

CLOTH textile studio* Q E
2911 W. State Street, 83702
(208) 789-2096

Jones Sew and Vac Q M
7615 W. Fairview Avenue, 83704
(208) 323-6087

The Cotton Club Q E
605 S. Americana Blvd., Suite 2, 83702
(208) 345-5567

The Quilt Crossing Q E M
10959 W. Fairview Avenue, 83713
(208) 376-0087

Bonners Ferry

Alley Fabric Nook Q C
➡ SEE AD BELOW
6485 Harrison Street, Suite 102, 83805
(208) 267-6665
Tu-F 10-4, Sa 10-2
www.alleyfabricnook.net

A Little Comfort Quilting Q
7189 Main St., #641, 83805
(208) 267-9200

Callie's Niche Q
6429 Bonner Street, 83805
(208) 267-1583

Buhl

Bobbins Quilt and Sew Q E N C M
1007 Main Street, 83316
(208) 543-0956

Burley

Hem-Stitching Etc. Q M
1239 E. 16th Street, 83318
(208) 878-0236

Mill End Fabrics Q
1358 Overland Avenue, 83318
(208) 878-5713

Sandy's Bernina Sales & Sewing* Q M
1234 Oakley Avenue, 83318
(208) 678-1573

Cambridge

Dinah's Fabrics & Totes Q
65 N. Superior Street, 83610
(208) 257-3377

Coeur d'Alene

Knit-n-Crochet Y
600 W. Kathleen Avenue, Suite 30, 83815
(208) 676-9276 or (208) 676-YARN
MTuThF 9-5, W 9-8, Sa 9-3
www.knit-n-crochet.com

Bear Paw Quilting and Bernina Q E M
600 W. Kathleen Avenue, Suite 10, 83815
(208) 664-1554

KnitKnit Y
311 E. Coeur d'Alene Avenue, Suite E, 83814
(208) 667-1167

Garden City

Quilt Expressions Q M
5689 Chinden Blvd., 83714
(208) 338-8933 or (800) 544-5839

The Twisted Ewe Y S
3640 W. Chinden Blvd., 83714
(208) 287-3693

Garden Valley

Stitch n' Snip Q E Y
342 S. Middlefork Road, 83622
(208) 462-4602

Grangeville

Home Grown Quilts Q E Y C M
207 W. Main Street, 83530
(208) 983-0254

Quilt Treasures Q E M
120 W. Main Street, 83530
(208) 983-0092 or (208) 983-0092

Hailey

Sun Valley Fabric Granary Q E C
122 S. Main Street, 83333
(208) 788-1331

Hayden

Alpaca Direct Y S
1016 W. Hayden Avenue, 83835
(208) 209-7079

Idaho Falls

Daydreams Quilt N Sew Q
802 Pancheri Drive, 83402
(208) 227-8394

Gary's Sewing Center* M
1576 W. Broadway Street, 83402
(208) 522-1422

The Yarn Connection Y
140 S. Freeman Avenue, 83401
(208) 524-8256

Kamiah

Quilt House Bed and Breakfast and Quilt Shop Q
247 Flying Elk Drive, 83536
(208) 935-7668

Ketchum

Sun Valley Needle Arts Y N
190 1st Avenue N, 83340
(208) 928-7620

Kooskia

B Creative Q E Y N W S C
210 Big Cedar Road, 83539
(208) 926-4323

Lewiston

Becky's Fabrics & Bernina Q M
1702 21st Street, Mall 21, Suite 112, 83501
(208) 743-4448

Handi Quilter® Authorized Retailer
Designed by a Quilter, for Quilters.®

Emerald Garden Q
2125 14th Avenue, 83501
(208) 743-1849

Home Grown Quilts Q M
302 Thain Road, Suite D, 83501
(208) 743-0503

Malad

Allen Drug & Variety Q E Y N C
4 N. Main Street, 83252
(208) 766-2241

Marsing

Sleepy Hollow Quilt Shop Q E C
107 Main Street, 83639
(208) 899-5623

McCall

Keep Me In Stitches Y
➡ SEE AD BELOW
136 E. Lake Street, 83638
(208) 634-2906
M-Sa 10:30-5, Sometimes Su 12-4
www.kmismccall.com

Keep Me
In Stitches
yarns
books
patterns
handspuns
wool rovings
Dyeing to Please handpaints
136 E. Lake St., McCall, ID 83638
p: (208) 634-2906 f: (208) 634-2906
www.KMISMcCall.com
yarns@frontiernet.net
Open: Mon. - Sat.: 10 - 5:30

Granny's Attic Quilts Q E
104 N. 3rd Street, 83638
(208) 634-5313

Huckleberry Patches* Q
136 E. Lake Street, 83638
(208) 634-4933

Moscow

Stitches & Petals Q
1016 W. Pullman Road, 83843
(208) 882-5672

The Yarn Underground, LLC Y S
409 S. Washington Street, 83843
(208) 882-7700

Nampa

Bluebird Quilt Studio Q
311 14th Avenue S, 83651
(208) 467-4148

Handi Quilter® Authorized Retailer
Designed by a Quilter, for Quilters.®

Hartwell's Lazy PJ Ranch Y W S
6 S. Middleton Road, 83651
(208) 466-1240

Puffy Mondaes E Y W S C
200 12th Avenue S, 83651
(208) 407-3359

Quilting Bliss, LLC Q
310 3rd Street S, 83651
(208) 402-5962

Orofino

Material Girls Quilting, Etc.* Q Y
10492 Highway 12, 83544
(208) 476-4646

Wild Hare Q E Y N C
222 Johnson Avenue, 83544
(208) 476-3358

Handi Quilter® Authorized Retailer
Designed by a Quilter, for Quilters.®

Wild Hare Q E Y N C
222 Johnson Avenue, 83544
(208) 476-3358

Pocatello

Jones Sew and Vac Ⓠ Ⓔ Ⓜ
735 Yellowstone Avenue, 83201
(208) 233-0670

Sages Creek Quilt Company* Ⓠ
1625 N. 2nd Avenue, 83201
(208) 232-0709

Ponderay

Selkirk Quilts Ⓠ
205 Vermeer Drive, Suite A, 83852
(208) 265-0128

Preston

Fabric Farm & Quilts* Ⓠ
1173 S 1600 E, 83263
(208) 852-1419

Suppose Quilt Boutique* Ⓠ Ⓔ Ⓒ
21 N. State Street, 83263
(208) 852-1449

Rupert

The Gathering Place* Ⓠ Ⓔ Ⓒ
524 6th Street, 83350
(208) 436-0455

Salmon

Copper Mountain Quilting* Ⓠ
605 Lena Street, Unit A, 83467
(208) 742-1758

Sandpoint

Blue Flag Handweaving Studio Ⓨ Ⓦ Ⓢ
1223B Michigan Street, 83864
(208) 263-4600

Something Olde Something New* Ⓨ Ⓦ Ⓢ
504 Oak Street, 83864
(208) 263-9447

Shoshone

Karen's Place* Ⓠ
115 S. Rail Street W, 83352
(208) 358-5279

Salli's Back Porch Fabrics Ⓠ
465 N. 150 W, 83352
(208) 316-1003 or (208) 316-1003

Teton

Shogun Crafts* Ⓠ
3 W. Main Street, 83451
(208) 458-4912

Weiser

Judy Ann's Quilting, Etc. Ⓠ
35 E. Commercial Street, 83672
(208) 405-5121

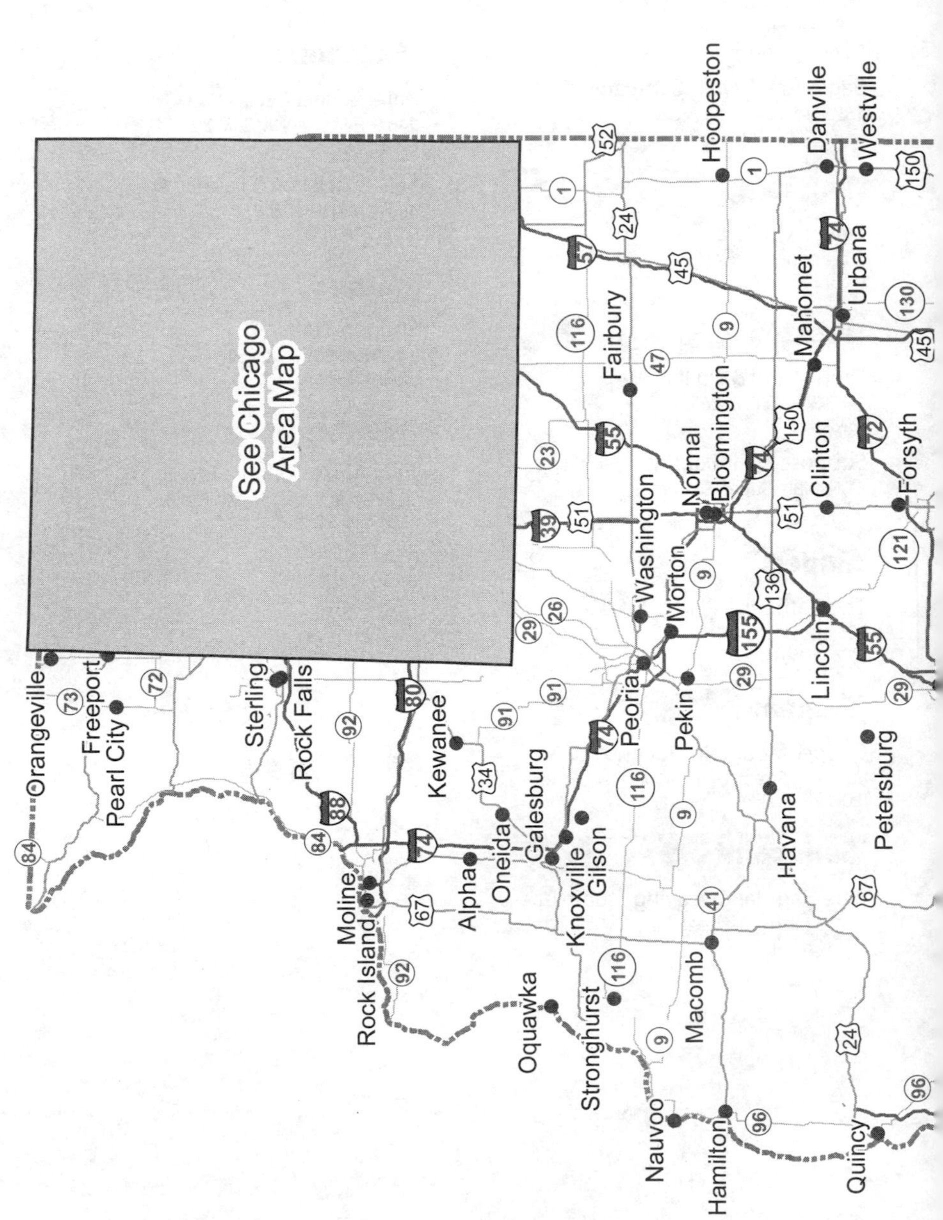

See Chicago Area Map
Orangeville
Freeport
Pearl City
Sterling
Rock Falls
Kewanee
Moline
Rock Island
Alpha
Oneida
Galesburg
Knoxville
Gilson
Peoria
Pekin
Washington
Morton
Normal
Bloomington
Fairbury
Hoopeston
Danville
Westville
Urbana
Mahomet
Clinton
Forsyth
Lincoln
Havana
Petersburg
Oquawka
Stronghurst
Macomb
Nauvoo
Hamilton
Quincy
84
73
72
92
88
80
74
67
34
91
29
26
39
51
23
55
116
47
9
24
57
45
1
52
150
130
72
136
155
121
41
96

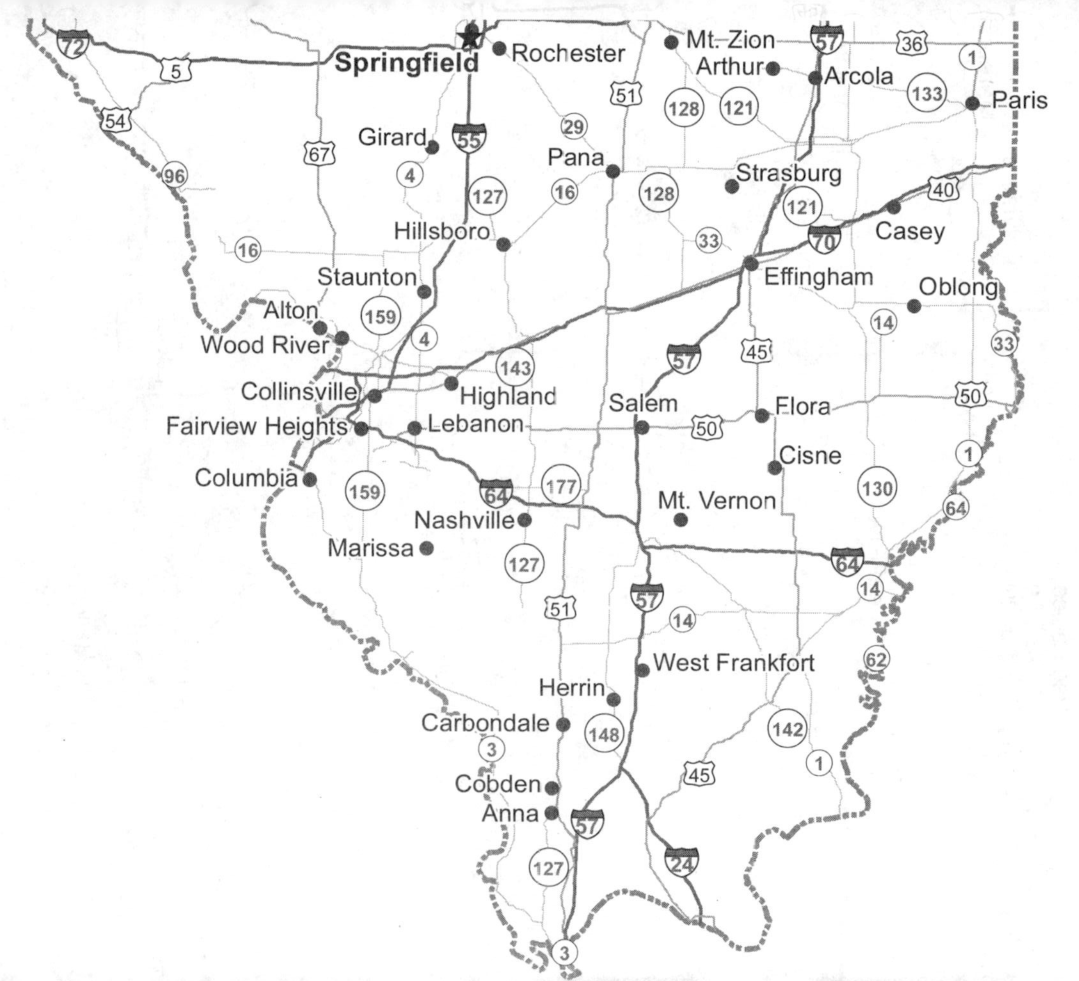

Springfield
Rochester
Mt. Zion
Arthur
Arcola
Paris
Girard
Pana
Strasburg
Casey
Hillsboro
Effingham
Oblong
Staunton
Alton
Wood River
Collinsville
Highland
Salem
Flora
Fairview Heights
Lebanon
Cisne
Columbia
Mt. Vernon
Nashville
Marissa
West Frankfort
Herrin
Carbondale
Cobden
Anna

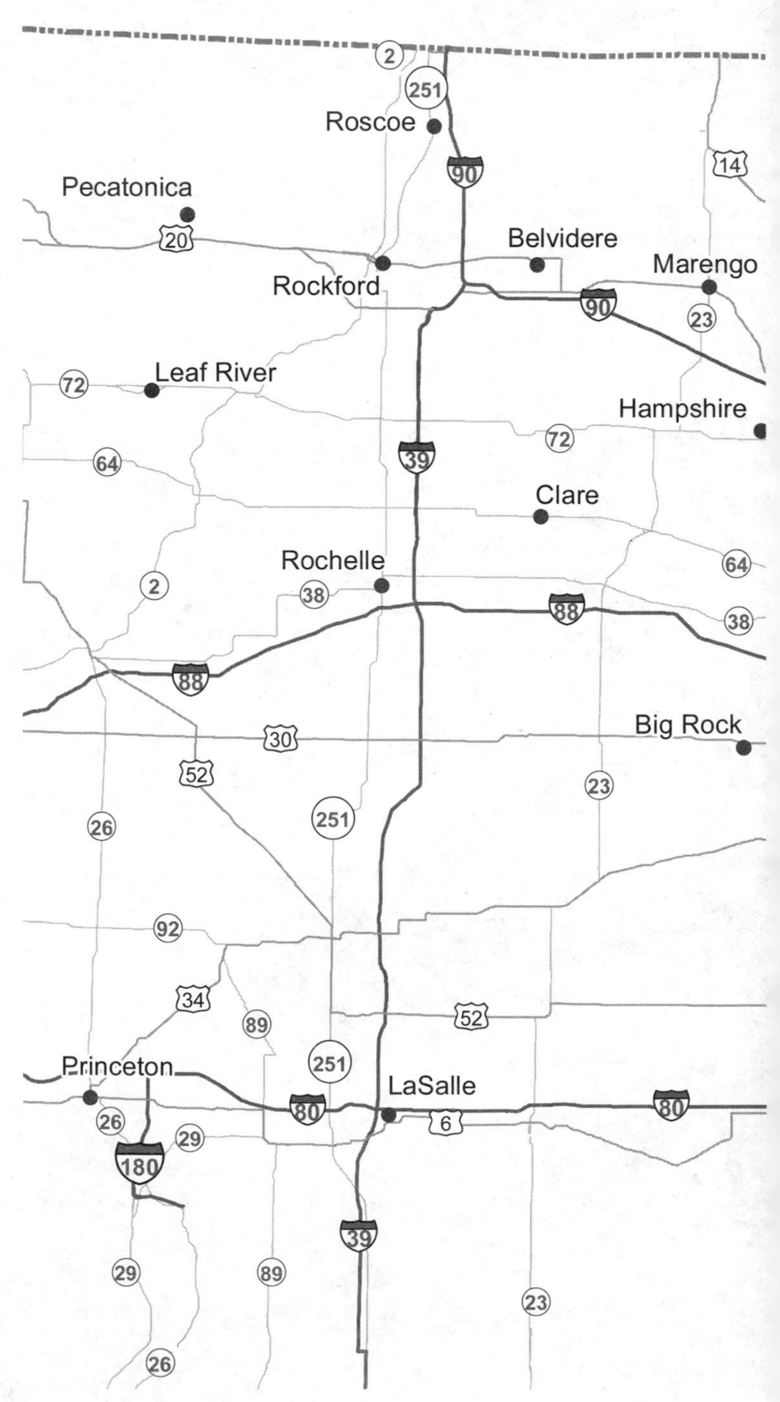
2
251
Roscoe
90
14
Pecatonica
20
Belvidere
Rockford
Marengo
90
23
72
Leaf River
Hampshire
72
39
64
Clare
Rochelle
64
2
38
88
38
88
30
Big Rock
52
23
26
251
92
34
89
52
251
Princeton
LaSalle
80
80
26
6
29
180
39
29
89
23
26

Richmond
Winthrop Harbor
Lake Villa
Woodstock
Libertyville
Crystal Lake
Lake Forest
Fox River Grove
Highland Park
Northbrook
Arlington Heights
Carpentersville
Winnetka
Mt. Prospect
Northfield
Elgin
Evanston
South Elgin
St. Charles
Oak Park
Forest Park
Geneva
Winfield
Glen Ellyn
Berwyn
Wheaton
La Grange
Chicago
Downers Grove
Westmont
Naperville
Woodridge
Yorkville
Lemont
Oswego
Plainfield
Lockport
Crest Hill
Mokena
Frankfort
Morris
Braidwood
Grant Park
Bourbonnais
94
12
47
31
14
83
62
90
72
294
47
20
290
83
41
25
90
355
290
88
55
30
41
31
90
30
20
294
57
94
34
55
171
7
83
45
80
6
52
57
52
45
47
55
1

Illinois

Alpha

Alpha Fiberworks Y
112 W. D Street, 61413
(309) 351-2284

Alton

Dora's Spinning Wheel Q E C
96 Northport Drive, 62002
(618) 466-1900

Anna

The Here and Now Shop Q E Y C
319 S. Main Street, 62906
(618) 833-0845

Arcola

Miller's Dry Goods Q
570 E. County Road 300 N, 61910
(217) 268-5117

Arlington Heights

Linda Z's Sewing Center Q E M
1216 E. Central Road, 60005
(847) 394-4590

Quilter's Destination Q M
945 E. Rand Road, 60004
(847) 506-6410

Arthur

Stitch & Sew Fabrics Q M
220 S. Vine Street, 61911
(217) 543-2287 or (888) 502-2287

Belvidere

Sunshine Stitches Q
1490 N. State Street, 61008
(815) 323-5022

Berwyn

TLD Design Center & JAD Gallery Y W S
2619 Ridgeland Avenue, 60402
(630) 963-9573

Big Rock

Esther's Place Q E Y W S
201 W. Galena Street (US 30), 60511
(630) 556-9665

Bloomington

The Yarn Garden Y W S
318 N. Main Street, 61701
(309) 808-0370
Tu 10-8, W-Sa 10-5
www.theyarngardenbloomington.com

Boline's Quilt Fabric Warehouse Q
414 Olympia Drive, 61704
(888) 214-3819

Le Mouton Rouge Knittery Y
1206 Towanda Avenue, Suite 1, 61701
(309) 319-7692

Peace & Applique Quilt Shop Too Q M
806 Four Seasons Road, 61701
(309) 662-7380

Sheila's Spinning Bunny Y W S
318 N. Main Street (inside The Yarn Garden), 61701
(309) 808-0370 or (309) 452-3837

Treadle Q E Y C
2101 Eastland Drive, 61704
(309) 662-1733

Bourbonnais

B & J Sewing Center Q M
616 S. Main Street, 60914
(815) 937-9955

Braidwood

Countryside Village Gifts Q
1540 N. Division Street, 60408
(815) 458-2191

Carbondale

Calico Country Sew & Vac Q E M
2525 Fairview Drive, 62902
(618) 529-5665

Carpentersville

Sewing Concepts Q E M
194 S. Western Avenue, 60110
(847) 836-7800
M-F 10-6, Sa 10-4
www.sewingconcepts.com

Casey

The Yarn Studio Y W
➡ SEE AD BELOW
2 E. Main Street, 62420
(217) 932-5851
Hours vary seasonally, please call ahead
www.the-yarn-studio.com

Chicago

Crafts by Claudia Q Y
4300 S. Archer Avenue, 60632
(773) 247-4387

Firefly Fiber Arts Studio Y W S
2052 W. North Avenue, 60647
(773) 697-4046

Fishman's Fabric Q
1101 S. Desplaines Street, 60607
(312) 922-7250

Knit 1 Y
3856 N. Lincoln Avenue, 60613
(773) 244-1646

Nina Chicago Y
1655 W. Division Street, 60622
(773) 486-8996

Oak Fabrics Q
3738 N. Lincoln Avenue, 60613
(773) 245-6633

Second City Quilt Company Q
2153 W. Irving Park Road, 60618
(773) 530-1532

Sister-Arts Studio, Inc. Y W S
721 W. Wrightwood Avenue, 60614
(773) 929-7274

The Quilter's Trunk, LLC Q M
10352 S. Western Avenue, 60643
(773) 980-1100

Yarnify! Y S
47 W. Polk Street, Suite G2B, 60605
(312) 583-9276

Cisne

Your Quilting Stash Q
1722 County Road 725 E, 62823
(618) 835-2681

Clare

Basketcases Unlimited Q E
26271 Malta Road, 60111
(815) 393-3414

Clinton

Quilters Delight Q E
301 W. Washington Street, 61727
(217) 937-0159

Cobden

Southpass Beads and Fibers Ⓔ Ⓨ Ⓦ Ⓒ
203 E. Ash Street, 62920
(618) 893-6170
W-F 12-6, Sa 10-5 and by appt.
www.southpassbeads.etsy.com

Collinsville

O'Sewpersonal Ⓠ Ⓜ
1966 Vandalia Street, 62234
(618) 345-3661

Handi Quilter® Authorized Retailer
Designed by a Quilter, for Quilters.®

Columbia

Warm N Cozy Quilting Ⓠ Ⓒ
816 S. Main Street, Suite 2, 62236
(618) 719-2565

Crest Hill

A Quilter's Paradise - Roberts Sewing Center Ⓠ Ⓔ Ⓜ
2011 Weber Road, 60403
(815) 729-1600 or (800) 273-9111

Crystal Lake

Material Girl Inc. Ⓠ
21 N. Williams Street, 60014
(815) 459-2084
M-Sa 10-5, Su 12-3
www.materialgirlfabricshop.com

Welcome Stitchery Ⓝ Ⓒ
48 Brink Street, 60014
(815) 455-5470
MTuWF 9:30-4, Th 9:30-8, Sa 9:30-3
www.welcomestitchery.com

Sunflower Samplings Ⓨ
89 N. Williams Street, 60014
(815) 455-2919

Danville

Threads of Time Creative Sewing & Retreat Center Ⓠ Ⓔ Ⓜ
207 S. Buchanan Street, 61832
(217) 431-9202

Downers Grove

Knitche, Inc. Ⓨ Ⓦ Ⓢ
5221 Main Street, 60515
(630) 852-5648

Effingham

The Wooden Spool Ⓠ Ⓔ
804 S. Henrietta Street, 62401
(217) 347-9669

Elgin

Elgin Knit Works Ⓨ
8 Douglas Avenue, 60120
(847) 627-4700

Evanston

CloseKnit, Inc. Ⓨ
1630 Orrington Avenue, 60201
(847) 328-6760

Evanston Stitchworks* Ⓠ Ⓨ
906 Sherman Avenue, 60202
(773) 320-5802

The Needle's Excellency Ⓝ
1630 Central Street, 60201
(847) 864-8228 or (847) 864-8036

Vogue Fabrics Ⓠ Ⓜ
718 Main Street, 60202
(847) 864-9600

Fairbury

Lost Arts Ⓠ Ⓔ Ⓨ Ⓝ Ⓒ
132 E. Locust Street, 61739
(815) 692-8536

Fairview Heights

Jackman's Fabrics Ⓠ Ⓜ
1000 Lincoln Highway, 62208
(618) 632-2700

The Bead Place Ⓨ
5500 N. Illinois Street, 62208
(618) 222-0772

Flora

Bear Paw Quilt Co. Ⓠ
117 W. North Avenue, 62839
(618) 662-3391

My Mother's Legacy Q M
704 N. State Street, 62839
(618) 662-2360

Forest Park

Knit Nirvana: A Yarn Boutique Y S
7453 Madison Street, 60130
(708) 771-5232

Forsyth

The Fabric Cobbler Q M
324 E. Ruehl Street, 62535
(217) 853-4629

Fox River Grove

Pieceful Gathering Quilt Shop Q
106 NW Highway (Rt. 14), 60021
(847) 516-7911

Frankfort

Yarns to Dye For Y
59 W. Bankview Drive, 60423
(815) 469-4906

Freeport

Wall of Yarn Y W
14 W. Stephenson Street, 61032
(815) 616-8402

Galesburg

Galesburg Sewing Center* M
243 E. Main Street, 61401
(309) 343-5019

Knit 102 Y
31 N. Kellogg Street, 61401
(309) 343-0965

Quilting Bee Q E C
1580 E. Knox Street, Suite 1, 61401
(309) 343-2063

Geneva

Aunt Sassy's Quilts Q
11 N. 1st Street, Suite 1, 60134
(815) 787-8458

Creative Sewing Center Q M
11 N. 1st Street, Suite 2, 60134
(630) 208-6789

Gilson

Wooden Eagle Barn Q
1291 US Highway 150 E, 61436
(309) 289-6880

Girard

Quilting In Aisle 3 Q
162 1/2 W. Center Street, 62640
(217) 503-0084

Glen Ellyn

A Different Box of Crayons Q
439 Pennsylvania Avenue, 60137
(630) 793-9321

String Theory Yarn Company Y
477 N. Main Street, 60137
(630) 469-6085

Tomorrow's Heirlooms, Inc. E N C
20 N. Park Blvd., 60137
(630) 790-1660

Grant Park

Rocking Chair Quilts Q
301 S. Meadow Street, 60940
(815) 465-2428

Hamilton

Sew Inspired Quilts of Nauvoo* Q E C
1024 Broadway Street, 62341
(217) 847-9909

Hampshire

Stitching On State Q E M
290 S. State Street, 60140
(847) 683-4739

Havana

Ma's Got'a Notion Q E
305 W. Main Street, 62644
(309) 543-6613

Herrin

The Yarn Shoppe Y
105 N. 16th Street, 62948
(618) 988-9276

Highland

Rosemary's Fabric & Quilts Q
812 Ninth Street, 62249
(618) 654-5045

The Machine Shop Q E M
518 Broadway, 62249
(618) 654-2233

Authorized Retailer

Highland Park

Mia Bella Yarn & Accessories Y S
1815 St. Johns Avenue, 60035
(847) 748-8419

Hillsboro

Stitcher's Station E Y N C
1133 Vandalia Road, 62049
(217) 532-5984

Hoopeston

The Sewing Boutique Q E M
222 E. Main Street, 60942
(217) 283-7125

Kewanee

The Quilt Box Q E C M
109 E. 3rd Street, 61443
(309) 854-9000

Knoxville

Bent Needle Quilting and Embroidery Q E C
506 Henderson Road, 61448
(309) 335-6901

Sit-N-Knit Yarn Shop Y
236 E. Main Street, 61448
(309) 289-2379 or (309) 368-8841

La Grange

Idea Studio Needle Arts E Y N C
515 S. La Grange Road, 60525
(708) 352-1789

Lake Forest

The Forest Needle E N
1341 N. Western Avenue, 60045
(847) 235-2407
Tu-F 10-5, Sa 10-3
www.forestneedle.com

Lake Villa

Sewing Source Q E M
122 E. Grand Avenue, 60046
(847) 356-5100

LaSalle

Quilting In The Valley Q E M
1157 1st Street, 61301
(815) 410-5068
M-F 9-6, Sa 9-5, Su 12-5
www.quiltinginthevalley.com

Leaf River

Leaf River Quilt Co. Q
6679 W. IL Route 72
(4 miles west of Leaf River), 61047
(815) 738-2855

Lebanon

Calico Moon ⓆⒺ
216 W. St. Louis Street, 62254
(618) 537-6240

Lemont

Inspired Needle Ltd. ⒺⓃⒸ
315 E. Illinois Street, 60439
(630) 243-9620
Tu 10-8, W-Sa 10-4
www.inspiredneedle.com

Libertyville

2 Needle Chicks ⒺⓎⓃⓈⒸ
406 Peterson Road, 60048
(847) 549-3611
TuTh 10-7, WFSa 10-5, Su 12-5
www.2needlechicks.com

Lincoln

Make It Sew Ⓠ
429 Pulaski Street, 62656
(217) 314-0915

Serendipity Stitches ⓎⓌ
129 S. Kickapoo Street, 62656
(217) 732-8811

Lockport

Thimbles ⓆⒺⓂ
940 S. State Street, 60441
(815) 836-8735
MTuWFSa 9:30-4, Th 9:30-7, Su 12-4
www.thimblesquilts.com

Betsy's Yarn and Tea Shop Ⓨ
201 W. 10th Street, 60441
(815) 836-0470

Macomb

The Bird's Nest Knit & More LLC ⒺⓎⓈⒸ
129 S. Randolph Street, 61455
(309) 313-2826
Tu-F 9:30-5, Sa 9:30-3
www.birdsnestmacomb.com

Piece to Peace Treasures Ⓠ
1508 W. Jackson Street, 61455
(309) 836-5999

Mahomet

A Quilting Bee Ⓠ
➡ SEE AD BELOW
406 E. Main Street, 61853
(217) 714-1809
Tu-Sa 10-6
www.aquiltingbee.com

Marengo

The Fold ⓎⓌⓈ
3316 Millstream Road, 60152
(815) 568-5730

Marissa

Bernina At Fancyworks ⓆⓂ
106 N. Main, 62257
(618) 295-2909

Mokena

Top Shelf Quilts Q E
19081 Old LaGrange Road, Suite 100, 60448
(815) 806-1694

Moline

Quilts by the Oz Q
5341 Avenue of the Cities, 61265
(309) 762-9673

Morris

The Fabric Center Q M
301 Liberty Street, 60450
(815) 942-5715

Morton

The Quilt Corner Q E M
2037 S. Main Street, 61550
(309) 263-7114

Mt. Prospect

Mosaic Yarn Studio Y W
109 W. Prospect Avenue, 60056
(847) 390-1013

Mt. Vernon

Quilts Plus Q E
15829 N. Angling Lane, 62864
(618) 237-1818

Mt. Zion

Stewart's Sewing Machines Q M
415 N. State Highway 121, 62549
(217) 864-6142

Naperville

Stitchers Garden N
1163 E. Ogden Avenue, Suite 713, 60563
(630) 946-6216

Nashville

Lee's Variety Quilting and Fabric Q E Y
212 E. St. Louis Street, 62263
(618) 327-8898

Nauvoo

Art Needlework Shop Q E Y N C
1265 Mulholland Street, 62354
(217) 453-6769

Normal

Sewing Studio Q M
1503 E. College Avenue, Suite C, 61761
(309) 452-7313

Northbrook

Quilter's Heaven Q M
1747 Dundee Road, 60062
(847) 272-7245
M-F 10-5, Sa 9-4, Th evening by appt.,
www.quiltersheaveninc.com

Emily's Stitchery N
1512 Shermer Road, Unit C, 60062
(847) 291-6550

Three Bags Full Knitting Studio Y
1927 Cherry Lane, 60062
(847) 291-9933

Northfield

The Canvasback N
1747 Orchard Lane, 60093
(847) 446-4244

Oak Park

Dye Hard Yarns Y S
1107 Westgate Street, 60301
(708) 613-4456

Oblong

The Village Stitchery Quilt Shop & Retreat Center Q E C
108 E. Main Street, 62449
(618) 592-4134

Oneida

Feed Mill Fabric and Quilting Q E Y W S C M
246 W. Highway Street (US Rte. 34), 61467
(309) 635-8283
Tu-F 10-6, Sa 10-4
www.feedmillfabric.com

Oquawka

River Bank Fabric and More Q
307 Schuyler Street, 61469
(309) 559-1070

Orangeville

Uniquely Yours Quilt Shop Q
12530 N. IL Route 26, 61060
(815) 789-4344

Oswego

Prairie Stitches Quilt Shoppe Q
72 S. Main Street, 60543
(630) 554-9701

Pana

The Fabric Patch Q M
208 N 2600 East Road, 62557
(217) 561-1157 or (217) 562-4725

Paris

Lori's Pins 'n Needles Q E C M
1122 N. Main Street, 61944
(217) 465-5541

Pearl City

Yellow Creek Quilt Designs Q E
160 S. Main Street, 61062
(815) 443-2211

Pecatonica

Lucky Quilt Company Q E M
421-425 Main Street, 61063
(815) 239-1026

Pekin

Nonnie's Attic Fabric Shop Q
804 Derby Street, 61554
(309) 346-2125

Peoria

Prairie Points Q E M
8851 N. Knoxville Avenue, 61615
(309) 692-4340

The Fiber Universe Y W S
305 SW Water Street, 61602
(309) 673-5659

Petersburg

Sewing Seeds Q Y
111 E. Douglas Street, 62675
(217) 501-4768

Plainfield

Elemental Yarns Y
24123 W. Lockport Street, 60544
(815) 729-7410

Harvest House Quilting Q
24231 Apple Tree Lane, 60585
(815) 609-5831

Princeton

Quilter's Garden Q
527 S. Main Street, 61356
(815) 879-3739

Quincy

A to Z Quilting Q E
826 State Street, 62301
(217) 223-9280

Knit Your Dreams Y
635 N. 66th Street, 62305
(217) 222-3335

Sew What Shoppe Q M
420 N. 24th Street, 62301
(217) 222-7458

Richmond

Wool Warp and Wheel Y W S
5605 Mill Street, 60071
(815) 678-4063

Rochelle

Lottie's Keep Ⓔ Ⓨ Ⓝ Ⓢ Ⓒ
1065 N. Caron Road, 61068
(815) 561-6399

Needles Quilting and Yarns Ⓠ Ⓔ Ⓨ
430 N. Lincoln Highway, 61068
(815) 384-2107

Rochester

Peace & Applique Quilt Shop Ⓠ Ⓜ
145 E. Main Street, 62563
(217) 498-6771

Rock Falls

Country at Heart Quilt Shop Ⓠ Ⓔ Ⓜ
9843 Hoover Road, 61071
(815) 625-7484

Rock Island

Quilt Addicts Anonymous Ⓠ
1232 30th Street, 61201
(224) 280-8177

Rockford

It's For Quilting, Etc., LLC Ⓠ Ⓔ Ⓜ
2252 New Milford School Road, 61109
(815) 874-0152

Knit One Purl Two Ⓨ
6409 E. Riverside Blvd., 61114
(815) 904-6030

Quilter's General Store Ⓠ
6903 Harrison Avenue, 61108
(815) 397-5160

Quilters Haven Ⓠ Ⓜ
4616 E. State Street, 61108
(815) 227-1659

Roscoe

Sunday Knits Ⓨ
240 Lovesee Road, 61073
(815) 623-7487

Salem

The Cloth Cottage Ⓠ Ⓔ Ⓨ Ⓝ Ⓒ
423 S. Broadway, 62881
(618) 548-0028

South Elgin

Twisted Stitch Ⓠ Ⓜ
218 Randall Road, 60177
(224) 238-3424

Springfield

Nancy's Knitworks Ⓨ
1305 W. Wabash, Suite D, 62704
(217) 546-0600

Sew Unique Ⓠ Ⓜ
1050 N. Grand Avenue W, 62702
(217) 523-4293

St. Charles

Fine Line Creative Arts Center Ⓨ Ⓦ Ⓢ
37W570 Bolcum Road, 60175
(630) 584-9443

Wool & Company Ⓨ
107A W. Main Street, 60174
(630) 444-0480

Staunton

Itch'n to be Stitch'n Ⓠ Ⓔ Ⓝ Ⓜ
111 W. Main Street, 62088
(618) 635-2429

Sterling

Quilt Supplies for U Ⓠ
2503 Locust Street, 61081
(815) 622-9413

Strasburg

Oliviers Country Creations* Ⓠ Ⓔ Ⓨ Ⓒ
506 S. Walnut Street, 62465
(217) 690-0021 or (217) 644-2677

Stronghurst

Quilts & More Ⓠ
200 E. Nichols Street, 61480
(309) 924-2334

Urbana

Klose Knit* Ⓨ Ⓢ
311 W. Springfield Avenue, 61801
(217) 344-2123

Sew Sassy Ⓠ Ⓔ Ⓜ
156A Lincoln Square Mall, 61801
(217) 328-1591

Washington

Peddler's Way Quilt Company Ⓠ Ⓔ Ⓜ
127 Peddlers Way, 61571
(309) 444-7667

West Frankfort

Calico Country Sew & Vac Ⓠ Ⓔ Ⓜ
310 S. Logan, 62896
(618) 932-2992

Sew Special Quilts Ⓠ Ⓔ
1810 E. Main Street, 62896
(618) 439-1672

Westmont

TLD Design Center & Gallery Ⓨ Ⓦ Ⓢ
26 E. Quincy Street, 60559
(630) 963-9573

Westville (north of)

Cooke's Craft Cottage Ⓔ Ⓨ Ⓝ Ⓒ
5 Lyons Road, 61883
(217) 267-2088

Wheaton

Blue Willow Mercantile Ⓠ Ⓜ
1213 Butterfield Road, 60189
(630) 868-3833

Handi Quilter® Authorized Retailer
Designed by a Quilter, for Quilters.®

Winfield

The Quilt Merchant Ⓠ
27 W. 209 Geneva Road, 60190
(630) 480-3000

Winnetka

The Classic Stitch Ⓝ
549 Chestnut Street, 60093
(847) 881-2930

Winthrop Harbor

The Black Cat Stitchery Ⓝ Ⓒ
628 Sheridan Road, 60096
(224) 789-7224

Wood River

Patchwork Plus Ⓠ Ⓔ
62 E. Ferguson Avenue, 62095
(618) 251-9788 or (877) 529-9562

Woodridge

Quilters Quest Ⓠ Ⓔ Ⓜ
7440 Woodward Avenue, Suite M, 60517
(630) 969-2205 or (800) 988-2205

Woodstock

Sewing Concepts Ⓠ Ⓔ Ⓜ
110 S. Johnson Street, 60098
(815) 338-7754
MTuWF 10-5:30, Th 10-8, Sa 9-4
www.sewingconcepts.com

That Quilt Shop Inc. Ⓠ
1818 S. Rose Farm Road, 60098
(815) 338-9353

Woodstock Quilts* Ⓠ
216 S. Seminary Avenue, 60098
(815) 338-1212

Yorkville

Sewing ETC. Ⓠ Ⓔ
2661 N. Bridge Street, 60560
(630) 882-9328

Handi Quilter® Authorized Retailer
Designed by a Quilter, for Quilters.®

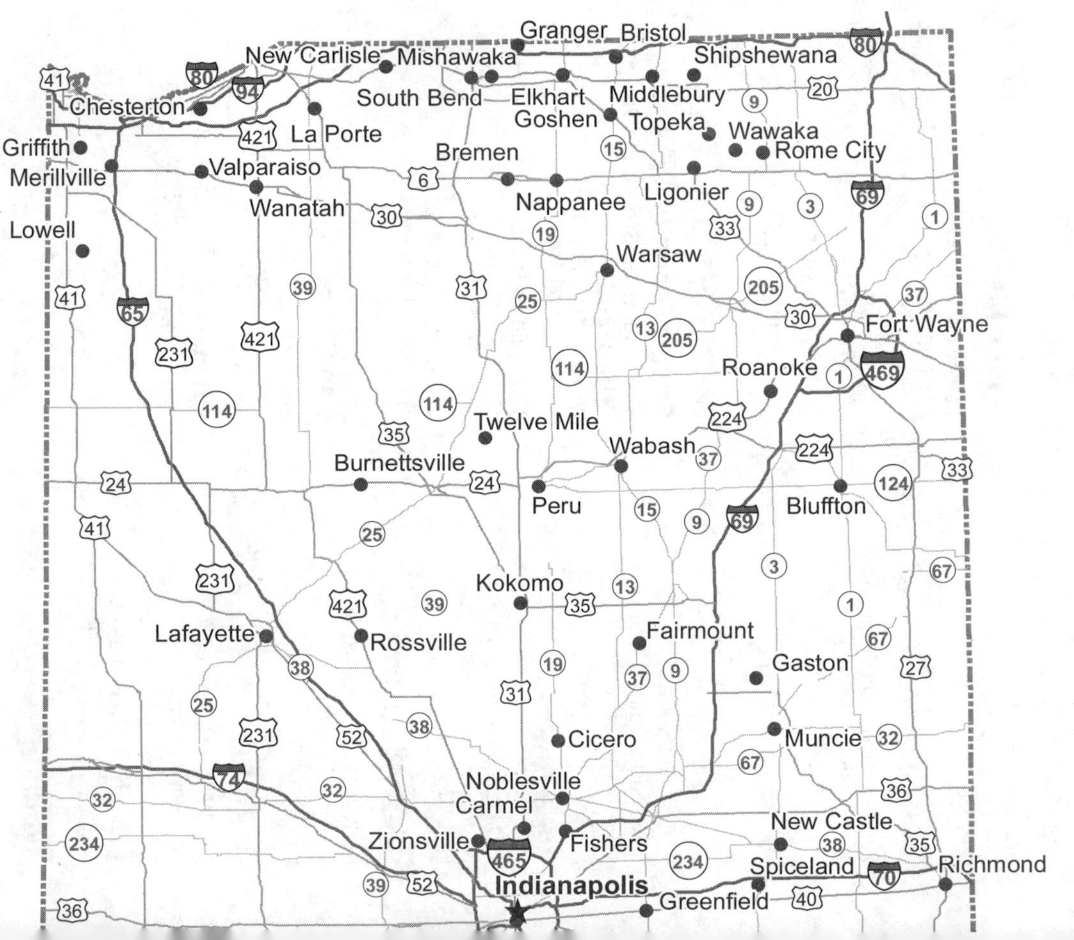

Granger
Bristol
New Carlisle
Mishawaka
Shipshewana
Chesterton
South Bend
Elkhart
Middlebury
Goshen
Topeka
Wawaka
Rome City
La Porte
Griffith
Bremen
Valparaiso
Merillville
Nappanee
Ligonier
Wanatah
Lowell
Warsaw
Fort Wayne
Roanoke
Twelve Mile
Wabash
Burnettsville
Peru
Bluffton
Kokomo
Fairmount
Lafayette
Rossville
Gaston
Cicero
Muncie
Noblesville
Carmel
New Castle
Zionsville
Fishers
Spiceland
Richmond
Indianapolis
Greenfield

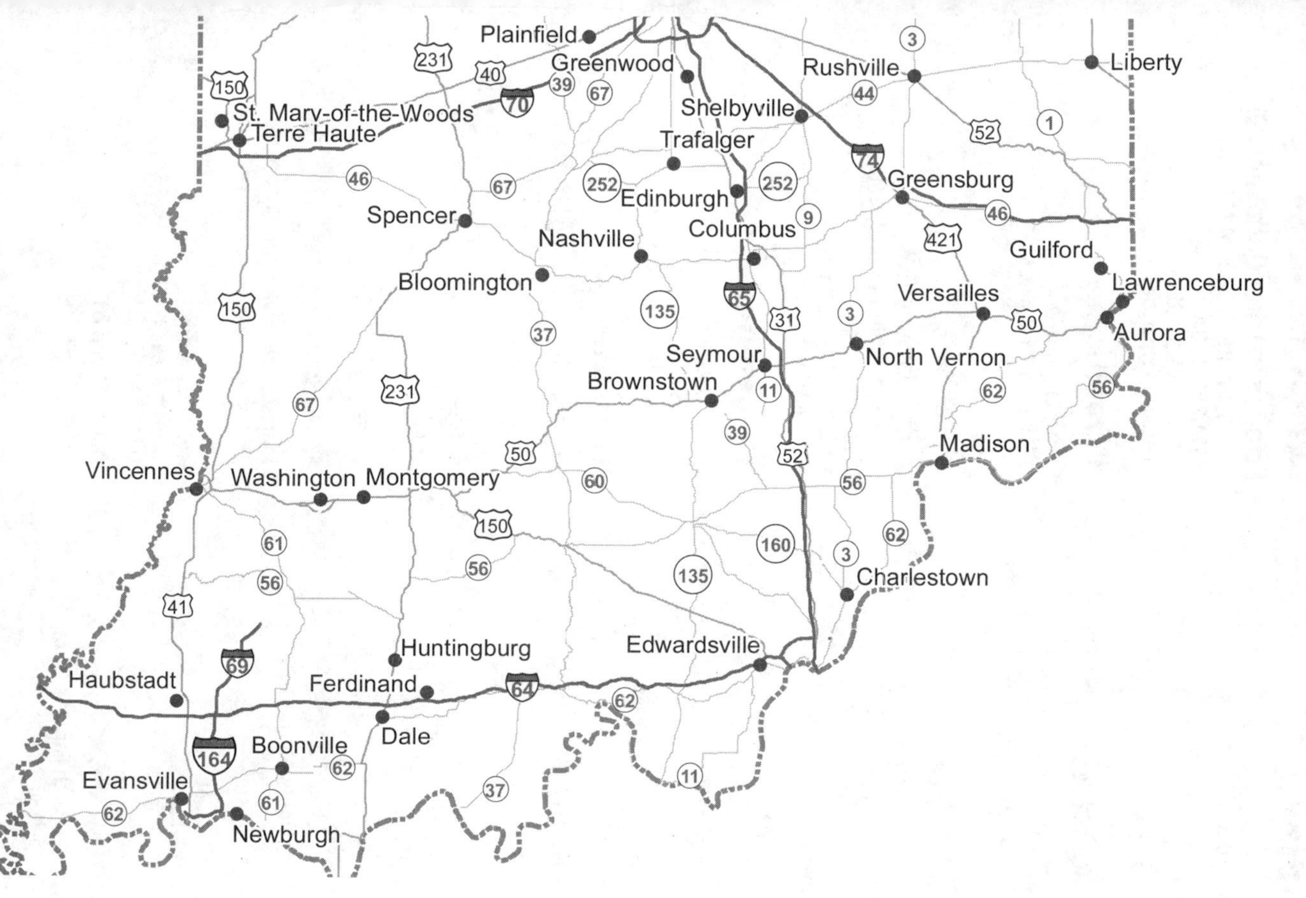
Plainfield
Greenwood
Liberty
Rushville
St. Mary-of-the-Woods
Terre Haute
Shelbyville
Trafalger
Greensburg
Edinburgh
Spencer
Columbus
Nashville
Guilford
Bloomington
Lawrenceburg
Versailles
Aurora
Seymour
North Vernon
Brownstown
Madison
Vincennes
Washington
Montgomery
Charlestown
Huntingburg
Edwardsville
Haubstadt
Ferdinand
Dale
Boonville
Evansville
Newburgh
3
231
40
39
67
44
150
70
52
1
74
46
67
252
252
46
9
421
135
65
31
3
150
37
50
56
62
231
67
11
39
52
50
56
60
150
160
62
3
61
135
56
56
41
69
64
62
164
62
37
11
61
62

Indiana

Aurora

Distinctive Knits Yarn Shop Y
322 2nd Street, 47001
(812) 926-2970

Bloomington

The Tailored Fit Q M
611 W. 11th Street, 47404
(812) 323-2665
M-F 10:30-6, Sa 12-5
www.thetailoredfit.com

Fancy Works E N C
3635 W. State Road 46, 47404
(812) 935-6353 or (877) 470-5031

Klaiber's Sewing Center Q M
617 W. 17th Street, 47404
(812) 336-0487

Bluffton

Quilts N Gifts LLC Q M
2190 Commerce Drive, Suite 2, 46714
(260) 565-4438

Boonville

City Stitch Yarn Shop Y S
115 E. Locust Street, 47601
(812) 629-6526

The Village Mercantile Q E
123 S. 2nd Street, 47601
(812) 897-5687

Bremen

Country Quilt Creations Q E
1611 N. 3rd Street, 46506
(574) 546-5747

The Loft Art Studio Y S
4122 SR 331 S, 46506
(574) 248-0453

Bristol

Lavender Patch Fabric & Quilts Q
112 E. Vistula Street, 46507
(574) 848-0011

Brownstown

Scrappy Patches Quilt Shop Q
408 W. Spring Street, 47220
(812) 358-1734
M-F 9-5, Sa 9-12
www.scrappypatchesquiltshop.com

Burnettsville

Betty's Quilting Q
326B S. Main Street, 47926
(765) 337-1332

Carmel

Quilt Quarters Q M
9840 N. Michigan Road, 46032
(317) 757-8340
MWFSa 10-5, TuTh 10-7
www.quiltquarters.com

Charlestown

Quilters Corner Cottage Q
263 Madison Street, 47111
(502) 939-9743

Chesterton

Sweet Stitches Quilt Shop LLC Q E M
1585 S. Calumet Road, 46304
(219) 250-5942

Cicero

Tabby Tree Weaver Y W S
269 W. Jackson Street, 46034
(317) 984-5475

Columbus

Homestead Weaving Studio Y W S
6285 Hamilton Creek Road, 47201
(812) 988-8622

Sew Crazy Q E M
3623 25th Street, 47203
(812) 418-8200

Shabby Sheep & Ewe Y
1113 16th Street, 47201
(812) 372-9276

Dale

Shirley's Sewing Stuff Ⓠ Ⓔ Ⓨ Ⓝ Ⓒ
➡ SEE AD BELOW
11356 S. US 231
Between Dale and Huntingburg, 47523
(812) 683-3377 or (800) 375-2785
M-F 10-12, 1-5:30, Sa 9-12:30
Eastern Time
www.shirleyssewingstuff.com

Edinburgh

Martha's Quilts & Gift Shop Ⓠ
6463 E. Orchard Drive, 46124
(812) 526-2931

Edwardsville (Georgetown)

The Quilting Bee Quilt Shop Ⓠ
4904 Old Georgetown Road, 47122
(812) 542-1236
Tu-F 10-5, Sa 10-3
www.quiltingbeeshop.com

Elkhart

Sew Creative Threads Ⓠ Ⓜ
189 County Road 6 W, 46514
(574) 266-7397
MTuThF 10-6, W 12-7, Sa 10-3
www.sewcreativethreads.com

Evansville

Let's Sew Ⓠ Ⓔ Ⓜ
4406 E. Morgan Avenue, 47715
(812) 471-7945

SewTech Ⓠ
4651 Bayard Park Drive, 47714
(812) 477-8477

Stitches From The Heart LLC Ⓔ Ⓝ Ⓒ
2920 Oak Hill Road, 47711
(812) 437-1320

Fairmount

Knit 'n' Purl Ⓨ Ⓝ Ⓢ
5480 W 1100 S, 46928
(765) 551-7875
M-F 10-5 and by appt.
www.knitnpurlin.com

Ferdinand

Vaal's Furniture & Appliances & Fabric Ⓠ Ⓔ Ⓨ Ⓒ
515 Main Street, 47532
(812) 367-1750

Fishers

Quilt Expressions Ⓠ Ⓔ Ⓜ
12514 Reynolds Drive, 46038
(317) 913-1816

Ft. Wayne

Knitting Off Broadway Ⓨ Ⓢ
1309 Broadway, 46802
(260) 422-9276
Tu-F 11-5, Sa 11-3
www.knittingoffbroadway.com

Little Shop of Spinning Ⓨ Ⓦ Ⓢ
104 Three Rivers N, 46802
(260) 580-1811
By chance or by appt.
www.littleshopofspinning.com

Edwards Sewing Center Ⓠ Ⓜ
4114 N. Clinton Street, 46805
(260) 486-3003

Stitch 'N Frame Ⓒ
4220 Bluffton Road, 46809
(260) 478-1301

Gaston

Cotton Candy Quilt Shoppe Ⓠ
602 N. Main Street, 47342
(765) 254-1584

Goshen

Reverie Yarn Decor & Gifts ⓎⓌⓈ
201 S. Main Street, 46526
(574) 971-5129

Calico Point ⓆⒺⒸⓂ
24856 County Road 40, 46526
(574) 862-4065

Heartland Country Sewing ⓆⓂ
25630 County Road 36, 46526
(574) 862-4406

Granger

Sew Unique by Jackie ⓆⒺ
51095 Bittersweet Road, 46530
(574) 271-1775

Greenfield

Willowe's Basketry & Yarn Haus Ⓨ
226 W. Main Street, 46140
(317) 462-2026

Greensburg

Tree City Stitches Ⓠ
125 E. Main Street, 47240
(812) 222-0920

Greenwood

Back Door Quilts ⓆⒺ
2503 Fairview Place, Suite W, 46142
(317) 882-2120

Starstruck Cat Studio ⓎⓈ
3130 Meridian Park Drive, Suite M, 46142
(317) 889-9665

Griffith

Spinnin Yarns ⓎⓌⓈ
145 N. Griffith Blvd., 46319
(219) 924-7333
M 12-9, Tu-F 12-6, Sa 10-3
www.spinninyarns.com

Guilford

The Weavers Loft ⓎⓌ
24647 Zimmer Road, 47022
(812) 576-3904

Haubstadt

Quilts n' Bloom ⓆⒺ
879 W 1000 S, 47639
(812) 768-6009

Huntingburg

Serendipity Fibers ⒺⓎⓃⒸ
314 E. 4th Street, 47542
(812) 684-8033
TuWF 11-6, Th 12-7, Sa 11-4
www.serendipityfibers.com

Indianapolis

Broad Ripple Knits Ⓨ
6510 Cornell Avenue, 46220
(317) 255-0540

Crimson Tate Modern Quilter Ⓠ
845 Massachusetts Avenue, Suite A, 46204
(317) 426-3300

Mass Ave Knit Shop Ⓨ
862 Virginia Avenue, 46203
(317) 638-1833

The French Seam ⓆⓂ
9335 Castlegate Drive, 46256
(317) 841-1810

Kokomo

Khadija Knit Shop Ⓨ Ⓝ
➡ **SEE AD BELOW**
3712 S. Lafountain Street, 46902
(765) 453-4652
M-F 11-5, Sa 11-4
http://www.facebook.com/KhadijaYarnShopkokomo/

Guarantee Vacuum & Sewing Ⓜ
702 S. Reed Rd, 46901
(765) 452-0044
Handi Quilter® Authorized Retailer
Designed by a Quilter, for Quilters.®

La Porte

House of Stitches Ⓒ
1700 Lincolnway Place, Suite 4, 46350
(219) 326-0544 or (800) 455-8517
M-F 10-5:30, Sa 10-3 (CST)
www.houseofstitches.com

Lafayette

River Knits Ⓨ Ⓦ Ⓢ
846 Main Street, 47901
(765) 742-5648

Lawrenceburg

Quilters Garden Ⓠ
9 E. Center Street, 47025
(812) 539-4939

Liberty

Pohlar Fabrics Ⓠ Ⓔ Ⓜ
941 W. Coe Road, 47353
(765) 458-5466

Ligonier

Zinck's Fabric Outlet Ⓠ
1444 Lincolnway South, 46767
(260) 894-3000
M-Sa 8-5
www.zincksfabric.com

Lowell

Fox Farmhouse Quilting Ⓠ
15504 Morse Street, 46356
(219) 743-8570

K & S Sew -N- Quilt Ⓠ
304 E. Commercial Avenue, 46356
(219) 690-1695

Madison

Fabric Shop Ⓠ Ⓔ
220 E. Main Street, 47250
(812) 265-5828

L & L Yard Goods Ⓠ Ⓔ
1814 Taylor Street, 47250
(812) 273-1041

Margie's Country Store Ⓠ Ⓔ
721 W. Main Street, 47250
(877) 395-6263 or (812) 265-4429

Merrillville

Spyceware Sewing Center & Quilt Shop Ⓠ Ⓜ
1090 W. 84th Drive, 46410
(219) 663-6973

Middlebury

The Quilt Shop Ⓠ Ⓔ Ⓜ
240 US 20, 46540
(574) 825-9471 or (800) 455-9471
M-Sa 9-8 (seasonal - call for hours)
www.EssenhausQuiltShop.com

Mishawaka

Stone Soup Batiks Ⓠ Ⓔ Ⓜ
2520 Miracle Lane, 46545
(574) 400-0258
M-F 9-5, Sa 10-3
www.stonesoupbatiks.com

Montgomery

David V. Wagler's Quilts Ⓠ Ⓔ Ⓒ
4413 E 200 N, 47558
(812) 486-3836

Muncie

Elegant Needleworks, Inc. Ⓝ
7500 N. Janna Drive, 47303
(765) 284-9427

Nappanee

Heritage Fabric and General Store Ⓠ
25350 CR 52, 46550
(574) 773-2445

Nashville

The Clay Purl Ⓨ Ⓦ Ⓢ
92 W. Franklin Street, 47448
(812) 988-0336

New Carlisle

Yarn and More Ⓨ
106 S. Filbert Street, 46552
(574) 654-3300

New Castle

The Woolen Yurt Ⓨ
1435 N. Kennard Road W, 47362
(765) 465-6101

Newburgh

Red Rooster Stitchery Ⓝ
10044 State Route 662 W, 47630
(812) 853-9657 or (866) 200-4247

Sheepskeins Yarn Shop Ⓨ
1109 State Route 662 W, 47630
(812) 842-0200

Noblesville

Always In Stitches Ⓠ Ⓨ Ⓒ Ⓜ
➡ SEE AD AT RIGHT
1808 East Conner Street, 46060
(317) 776-4227
MWF 10-4:30, TuTh 10-7:30, Sa 9:30-4
www.alwaysinstitches1.com

The Black Sheep Yarn and Fiber Arts Ⓨ
1355 S. 8th Street, 46060
(317) 900-7117

North Vernon

Sharynn's Quilt Box Ⓠ Ⓔ Ⓜ
890 S. State Street, 47265
(812) 346-4731

Peru

The Knit Knack Shop Ⓨ
3378 W 550 N, 46970
(765) 985-3164

Plainfield

Nomad Yarns Ⓨ Ⓢ
218 E. Main Street, 46168
(317) 742-7456

Richmond

The Stitching Nook Q M
➡ **SEE AD BELOW**
4629 National Road E, 47374
(765) 962-7678
M-Sa 10-5
www.stitchingnook.com

Nancy's Fancys Sewing Corner Q M
1446 NW 5th Street, 47374
(765) 939-0465

Ply Fiber Arts Y W S
921 E. Main Street, 47374
(765) 966-5648

Roanoke

Fabric & Friends Quilt Shop Q E
126 W. 2nd Street, 46783
(260) 676-2149

Rome City

Caroline's Cottage Cottons Q E
195 Weston Street, 46784
(260) 854-3900

Rossville

Rossville Quilts and Mill House Retreat Center Q E M
356 W. Main Street, 46065
(765) 379-2900

Rushville

In Stitches Quilt Shop Q
837 W. 3rd Street, 46173
(765) 938-1818

Seymour

Small Town Stitches Q
1129 W. Tipton Street, 47274
(812) 271-1663

Shelbyville

Yarn on the Square* Y
13 Public Square, 46176
(317) 825-3099

Shipshewana

Lolly's Fabric & Quilts Q
255 E. Main Street, 46565
(260) 768-4703

Spector's Store Q E Y
305 S. Van Buren Street, 46565
(260) 768-4439

The Cotton Corner Q E M
350 S. Van Buren Street, 46565
(260) 768-7393

Yoder Department Store Q E Y
300 S. Van Buren Street, SR 5, 46565
(877) 768-1945 or (260) 768-4887

South Bend

Stitch 'N Time Fabrics Q
2305 Miami Street, 46614
(574) 234-4314

Thyme to Sew Q M
621 Lincolnway E, 46601
(574) 855-2297

Spencer

Unraveled Quilt Store Q
381 N. Fletcher Avenue, 47460
(812) 821-0309

Spiceland

Stitches Quilt Shop Q
109 N. Pearl Street, 47385
(765) 987-1188

St. Mary-of-the-Woods

The Farm Store at White Violet Center for Eco-Justice Y
1 Sisters of Providence, 47876
(812) 535-2936

Terre Haute

River Wools, Inc. Y W
671 Wabash Avenue, 47807
(812) 238-0090

Wabash Valley Fabrics Q M
1347 Wabash Avenue, 47807
(812) 232-0727

Topeka

Topeka Pharmacy & Sara's Attic Q M
101 N. Main Street, 46571
(260) 593-2252

Trafalger

Coffee Cup Quilting, LLC* Q
7 Trafalger Square, Suite A, 46181
(317) 878-5155

Twelve Mile

The Scarlet Thread Quilt Co. Q M
1974 E. CR 1000 S, 46988
(574) 709-3598 or (574) 709-3598

Valparaiso

Cotton Cottage Quilts Q M
831 E. Lincolnway, 46383
(219) 286-3929
MTuWF 10-5:30, Th 10-7, Sa 10-4
www.cottoncottagequilts.com

Joan's Flat Folds Q
821 E. Lincolnway, 46383
(219) 241-8572

Sheep's Clothing Knitting Supply Y
60 W. Lincolnway, 46383
(219) 462-1700

Versailles

The Quilter's Nook, Inc. Q M
82 Hill Street, 47042
(812) 689-0980

Vincennes

Atkinson Farm Yarns Y S
1061 N. Atkinson Road, 47591
(812) 316-0249

Wabash

Heaven on Earth Q E
4767 N. Road 15, 46992
(765) 833-5461

Nancy J's Fabrics Q
1604 S. Wabash Street, 46992
(260) 563-3505

Wanatah

Scrapyard Quilt Shop Q E
10501 W 1000 S, 46390
(219) 733-9980

Warsaw

Lowery's Sewing & Fabric Center Q C M
707 E. Winona Avenue, 46580
(574) 267-8631

Washington

The Stitching Post Q E C
401 E. Main Street, 47501
(812) 254-6063
M-Sa 10-5, EST
www.stitchingpostquilts.com

Wawaka

Ragtime Rugs W
1946 W 1050 N, 46794
(260) 215-2795

Zionsville

Persnickety Stitchers, Inc. N C
58 N. Main Street, Suite A, 46077
(317) 873-5010
TuWF 10-5, Th 2-8, Sa 10-4
www.persnicketystitchers.com

Village Yarn Company Y
209 S. Main Street, 46077
(317) 873-0004

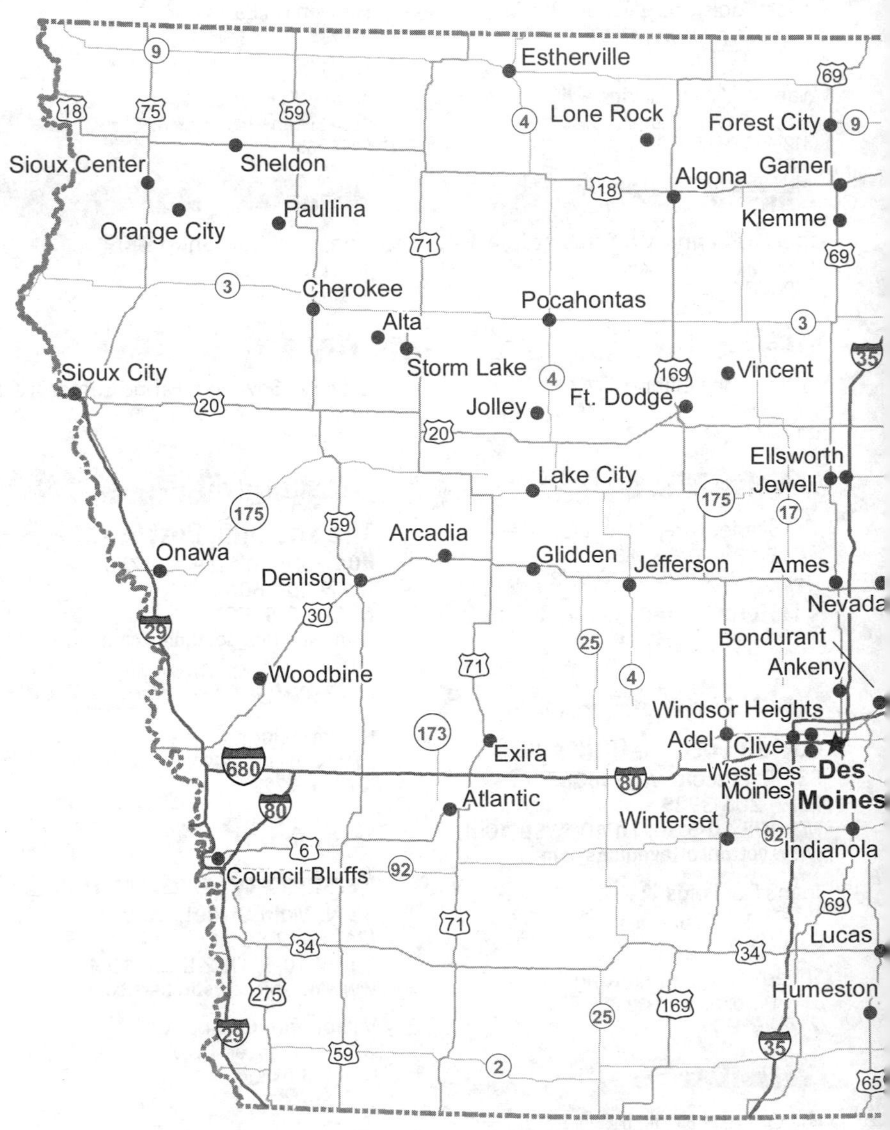

Estherville
Lone Rock
Forest City
Sioux Center
Sheldon
Garner
Algona
Klemme
Paullina
Orange City
Cherokee
Pocahontas
Alta
Storm Lake
Vincent
Sioux City
Jolley
Ft. Dodge
Ellsworth
Lake City
Jewell
Arcadia
Onawa
Glidden
Jefferson
Ames
Denison
Nevada
Bondurant
Woodbine
Ankeny
Windsor Heights
Adel
Clive
Exira
West Des Moines
Des Moines
Atlantic
Winterset
Indianola
Council Bluffs
Lucas
Humeston

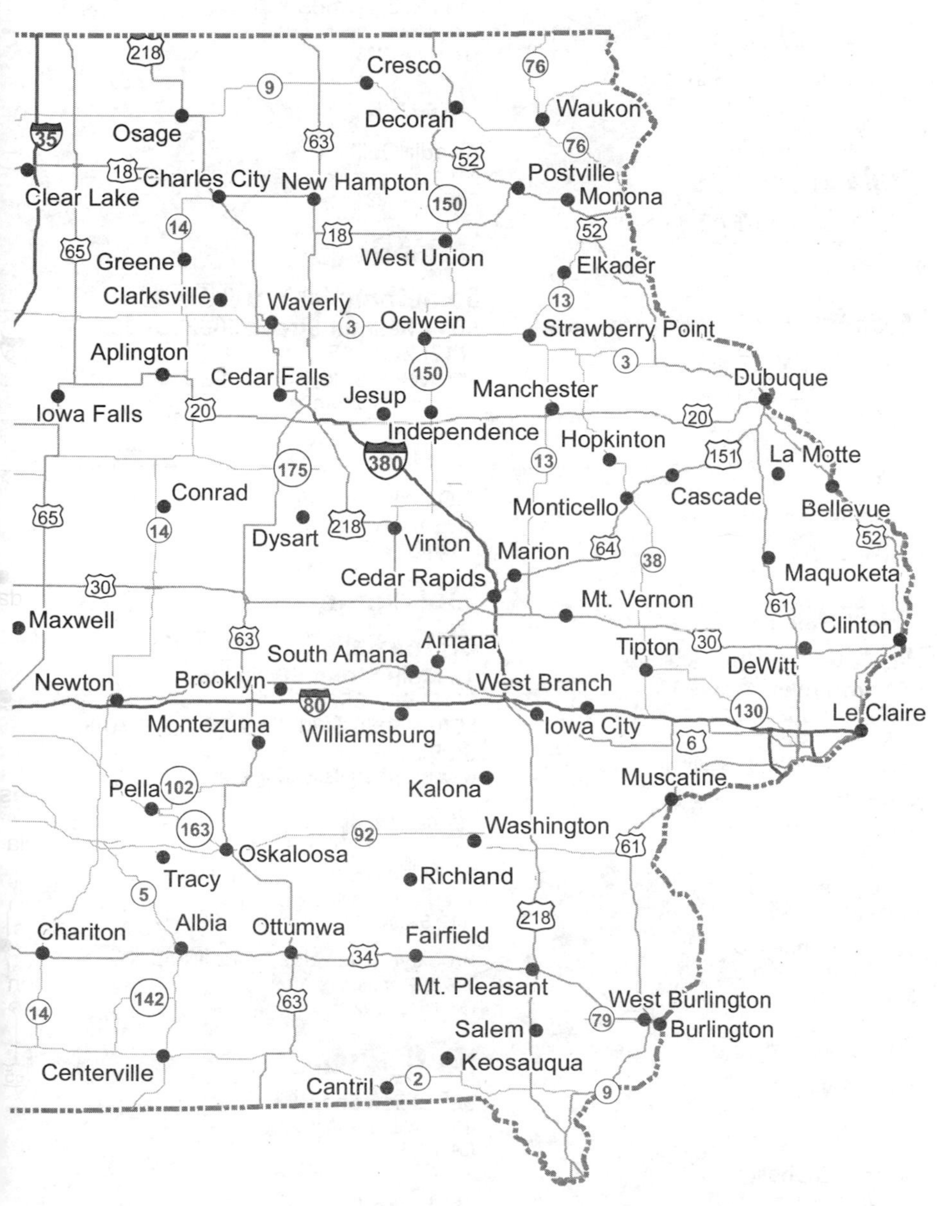
Cresco
Waukon
Osage
Decorah
Clear Lake
Charles City
New Hampton
Postville
Monona
Greene
West Union
Elkader
Clarksville
Waverly
Oelwein
Strawberry Point
Aplington
Cedar Falls
Jesup
Manchester
Dubuque
Iowa Falls
Independence
Hopkinton
La Motte
Conrad
Cascade
Monticello
Bellevue
Dysart
Vinton
Marion
Maquoketa
Cedar Rapids
Mt. Vernon
Maxwell
Clinton
Amana
Tipton
South Amana
DeWitt
Newton
Brooklyn
West Branch
Le Claire
Montezuma
Williamsburg
Iowa City
Muscatine
Pella
Kalona
Washington
Oskaloosa
Tracy
Richland
Chariton
Albia
Ottumwa
Fairfield
Mt. Pleasant
West Burlington
Burlington
Salem
Keosauqua
Centerville
Cantril

Iowa

Adel

Adel Quilting & Dry Goods Co. Q
909 Prairie Street, 50003
(515) 993-1170

Albia

Fiber Art Shoppe QYWS
5 Benton Avenue E, 52531
(641) 777-0465

Algona

Seams To Me QECM
17 E. State Street, 50511
(515) 295-5841

Alta

The Quilt Shoppe Q
206 S. Main Street, 51002
(712) 284-2724

Amana

Heritage Designs QEC
614 46th Avenue, 52203
(319) 622-3887
M-Sa 9-5, Su 11-4
www.heritagedesignsquiltshop.com

Amana Woolen Mill YWS
800 48th Avenue, 52203
(319) 622-3432

Ames

Quilting Connection QM
238 Main Street, 50010
(515) 233-3048

Ankeny

Knitting Next Door YWS
704 SW 3rd Street, 50023
(515) 963-0396

Quilter's Cupboard QEM
706 SW 3rd Street, 50023
(515) 963-8758

Aplington

Jen's Needleworks QY
900 Parriott Street, 50604
(319) 347-2793

Arcadia

Arcadia Quilts Q
201 S. Gault Street, Suite B, 51430
(712) 689-8888

Atlantic

Something for You QECM
501 Chestnut Street, 50022
(712) 243-4157
MTuWF 9-5:30, Th 9-7, Sa 9-4
www.sewsfy.com

Bellevue

JoQuilter Fabrics Q
128 S. Riverview, 52031
(563) 872-3473

Bondurant

Off the Rails Quilting QM
15 Main Street SE, 50035
(515) 967-3550
MTuW 9:30-5:30, Th 9:30-7, F 9:30-5, Sa 9:30-4
www.offtherailsquilting.com

Brooklyn

Brooklyn Fabric Company Q
121 N. Orchard Street, 52211
(641) 522-4766

Brooklyn True Value Fabric QEYNC
118 W. Front Street, 52211
(641) 522-7712

Burlington

Sew N Sew Shop QM
3206 Division Street, 52601
(319) 752-5733

Cantril

Dutchman's Store Q E Y C
103 Division Street, 52542
(319) 397-2322
M-F 8-6, Sa 8-5
www.dutchmansstore.com

Cascade

The Quilting Tree Q E
224 1st Avenue W, 52033
(563) 852-7765

Cedar Falls

Crazy to Quilt Q M
707 W. 1st Street, 50613
(319) 277-1360

Lulijune's Quilt Shop Q
14303 University Avenue, 50613
(319) 961-0705

Cedar Rapids

Delve / MIY Q M
➡ SEE AD PAGE 316
1101 3rd Street SE, 52401
(319) 200-4246

Inspired to Sew at Pine Needles Q M
1000 Old Marion Road NE, 52402
(319) 373-0334

West Side Sewing Q M
4100 1st Avenue NE, 52402
(319) 365-3075

Centerville

Shabby Chic Boutique* Q
313 N. 13th Street, 52544
(641) 895-0251

Chariton

Cindy Lou's Gifts and Quilt Shop Q
907 Braden Avenue, 50049
(641) 774-1215

Charles City

Stitches . . . Fabric & Yarn Shoppe* Q Y
715 Kelly Mall, 50616
(641) 228-3383

Cherokee

Quilt-N-Kaboodle Q E C M
420 W. Main Street, 51012
(712) 225-3600

Clarksville

Prairie Rose Fabrics Q
109 N. Main Street, 50619
(319) 278-4767

Clear Lake

Larson's Mercantile Q E Y N C
323 Main Avenue, 50428
(641) 357-7544

Clinton

Keeping You Sewing Q M
226 4th Avenue S, 52732
(563) 242-6135 or (844) 203-8739
M-F 10-5, Sa 10-3
www.keepingyousewing.com

Stitch'n & Stuff E C
242 6th Avenue S, 52732
(563) 243-2271 or (877) 641-2032

Clive

Creekside Quilting Q Y M
9926 Swanson Blvd., 50325
(515) 276-1977

Conrad

Hen & Chicks Studio Q E
101 N. Main Street, 50621
(641) 366-3336

Council Bluffs

Cut Up & Quilt! Q
303 McKenzie Avenue, 51503
(712) 256-5550

Cresco

Quilter's Garden Q E C
120 N. Elm Street, 52136
(563) 203-9266

Decorah

Blue Heron Knittery E Y W S C
➡ SEE AD BELOW
300 W. Water Street, 52101
(563) 517-1059
MTuWFSa 10-5, Th 10-8, Su 12-4
www.blueheronknittery.com

Blue Heron Knittery

300 W. Water Street
Decorah, IA
563.517.1059

Sunday 12-4p
Monday-Sat 10a-5p
Thurs 10a-8p

blueheronknittery.com

Red-Roxy Quilt Co. Q M
415 W. Water Street, 52101
(563) 382-4646

Denison

Wise Monkey Quilting Q E Y N C M
40 N. Main Street, 51442
(712) 393-7979

Des Moines

Woodside Quilting Q M
5360 NE 14th Street, Suite A, 50313
(515) 777-3500

DeWitt

Heartland Cottons Q E Y N C
615 10th Street, 52742
(563) 659-6200

Dubuque

The Cotton Cabin Quilt Shop Q E M
1075 Main Street, 52001
(563) 582-0800

Yarn Soup Y
1005 Main Street, 52001
(563) 587-8044

Dysart

Fiber Heart Y
323 Main Street, 52224
(319) 476-2437

Elkader

The Backstitch Q E C M
108 S. Main Street, 52043
(563) 245-2967 or (319) 331-7420

Ellsworth

Mended Hearts Quilting and Boutique Q E M
3212 330th Street, 50075
(515) 836-4280

Estherville

Homespun Quilt Shop Q
202 Central Avenue, 51334
(712) 362-5100

Wooden Thimble Q E C
17 S. 6th Street, 51334
(712) 362-2561

Exira

Log Cabin Quilting Q
111 W. Washington Street, 50076
(712) 268-2487

Fairfield

At Home Store Y
52 N. Main Street, 52556
(641) 472-1016

Forest City

The Quilted Forest Q E Y
205 N. Clark Street, 50436
(641) 585-2438

Ft. Dodge

The Family Quilt Shop Q
1200 A Street W, 50501
(515) 576-0295

Garner

Farm Chick Quilts Ⓠ Ⓔ
211 State Street, 50438
(641) 430-6341

Glidden

Threads Etc. Ⓠ Ⓔ Ⓒ
126 Idaho Street, 51443
(712) 659-2324

Greene

Dralles Department Store Ⓠ Ⓜ
122 E. Traer Street, 50636
(641) 816-4158

Hopkinton

Tipperary Fiber n Art Studio Ⓨ Ⓦ Ⓢ
2857 State Highway 38, 52237
(563) 920-7704

Humeston

Snips of Thread Quilt Shop* Ⓠ
124 S. Front Street, 50123
(515) 360-6901

Independence

Quilter's Quarters Ⓠ Ⓜ
213 1st Street E, 50644
(319) 334-4443
M-F 10-5, Sa 10-4
www.QuiltersQuartersonline.com

Indianola

The Stitching Place Ⓠ Ⓜ
➜ SEE AD BELOW
127 N. Buxton Street, 50125
(515) 961-5162
M-F 10-6, Sa 10-4, Su 1-4 (closed Su during summer)
www.thestitchingplace.com

Iowa City

Home Ec Workshop Ⓠ Ⓔ Ⓨ Ⓢ Ⓜ
424 E. Jefferson Street, 52245
(319) 337-4775

The Knitting Shoppe Ⓨ
2141 Muscatine Avenue, 52240
(319) 337-4920

Iowa Falls

Iowa Falls Sewing & Fabric Q
520 Washington Avenue, 50126
(641) 648-2379

Jefferson

the Stitch QM
217 E. Lincolnway, 50129
(515) 386-2014

Jesup

Merry's Stitchins Q
1923 Baker Road, 50648
(319) 827-6703

Jewell

Sew Bee It Quilt Shop Q
621 Main Street, 50130
(515) 290-0983

Jolley

Lee's Quilt Shed Q
2341 Inwood Avenue, 50551
(712) 297-8458

Kalona

Stitch N Sew Cottage QEC
207 4th Street, 52247
(319) 656-2923
M-Sa 9-5
www.stitchnsewcottage.com

Willow Creek Quilting & Gifts QEM
418 B Avenue, 52247
(319) 656-3939

Keosauqua

Bentonsport Quilt Company QE
21937 Marion Street, 52565
(319) 288-1042

Klemme

Wash Tub Quilts Q
101 E. Main Street, 50449
(641) 587-2014

La Motte

Irish Meadows Yarn Barn & Boutique YS
23477 Bellevue Cascade Road, 52054
(563) 543-1375
Sept.-March: ThFSa 10-5; and year round by appt.
www.irishmeadowsalpacafarm.com

Lake City

Towne Square Quilt Shoppe Q
103 E. Main Street, 51449
(712) 464-7477

Le Claire

Expressions In Threads QM
208 S. Cody Road, 52753
(563) 289-1447

Lone Rock

Sew and Sew Q
402 Front Street, 50559
(515) 925-3636

Lucas

Quilt with Us QE
100 E. Front Street, 50151
(641) 766-6486

Manchester

The Quiltmaker's Shoppe Q
110 E. Main Street, 52057
(563) 927-8017

Maquoketa

Hermes Auto & Upholstery, Inc. QM
1325 E. Platt Street, 52060
(563) 652-2279

Marion

Village Needlework (E)(Y)(N)(W)(S)(C)
➡ SEE AD BELOW
1129 7th Avenue, 52302
(319) 362-3271
MTh 10-8, TuWF 10-6, Sa 10-5
www.villageneedlework.com

Connie's Quilt Shop (Q)(M)
785 8th Avenue, 52302
(319) 373-9455

Maxwell

C & M Acres Fiber Mill (Y)(W)(S)
33707 663rd Avenue, 50161
(515) 387-8607

Monona

Suhdron Fabrics (Q)(E)(C)
120 W. Center Street, 52159
(563) 539-2135

Montezuma

3 Sisters Fabrics & Fashions (Q)(E)(C)(M)
305 E. Main Street, 50171
(641) 623-5640

Monticello

JT Hadherway Co (Q)(E)(N)(C)
23004 150th Avenue, 52310
(319) 465-5090

Mt. Pleasant

Quilters Paradise (Q)(E)
120 N. Main Street, 52641
(319) 385-1749

Mt. Vernon

Helios Stitches N Stuff (Q)
221 1st Street NE, 52314
(319) 512-3323

Muscatine

Neal's Vacuum & Sewing Center (Q)(M)
309 E. 2nd Street, 52761
(563) 263-4543

The Little Red Hen (Q)(E)(C)
612 Hope Avenue, 52761
(563) 262-5709

Nevada

Block Party Studios, Inc. (Q)
1503 W. K Avenue, 50201
(800) 419-2812 or (515) 382-3150

New Hampton

Quilter's Window (Q)(E)(M)
101 E. Main Street, 50659
(641) 394-6900

Newton

Crazy Redhead Quilting (Q)(M)
814 1st Avenue E, 50208
(641) 787-9122

Jan's Yarn Barn (Y)(S)
326 1st Avenue W, 50208
(641) 791-1173

Oelwein

LouAnn's Quilt Garden & Retreat (Q)
21 E. Charles Street, 50662
(319) 283-5165

Onawa

Susie's Quilts-N-More Q E
904 Iowa Avenue, 51040
(712) 423-9625

Orange City

Stitch Studio Q E Y W C
104 Central Avenue NW, 51041
(712) 737-9800

Osage

The Stitchery Nook E C
635 Main Street, 50461
(641) 732-5329
Tu-F 9:30-5, Sa 9:30-4
www.cross-stitch-usa.com

Debbie's Quilt Shop & Gifts Q E C M
605 Main Street, 50461
(641) 732-1474

Oskaloosa

Quilted Treasures & Retreats Q
3283 Merino Avenue, 52577
(641) 969-4444

Ottumwa

The Sewing House, LLC Q E M
220 E. Main Street, 52501
(641) 682-4995

Paullina

Prairie Woolens Quilt Shop Q
108 S. Main Street, 51046
(712) 229-0341 or (712) 949-7333

Pella

The Quilted Windmill Q
701 Franklin Street, 50219
(641) 628-3350

Pocahontas

Quilting on Main Q
229 N. Main Street, 50574
(712) 335-3969

Postville

Forest Mills Quilt Shop Q
650 Forest Mills Road, 52162
(563) 568-3807

Richland

The Red Hen Shop Q
30847 323rd Avenue, 52585
(319) 750-2631

Salem

Sistercraft Quilting & More Q E
1949 110th Street, 52649
(319) 850-0524

Sheldon

Ben Franklin Q E Y N C
912 3rd Avenue, 51201
(712) 324-3031

Sioux Center

Roelofs Fabric Q
24 3rd Street NW, 51250
(712) 722-2611

Sioux City

Granny's Stitches with Viking Q E N C M
3806 Floyd Blvd., 51108
(712) 239-0457

Heart & Hand Dry Goods Co.* Q
3011 Hamilton Blvd., 51104
(712) 258-3161

Tri-State Sew and Vac Q M
1551 Indian Hills Drive, Suite #5, 51104
(712) 258-1188

South Amana

Fern Hill Gifts and Quilts Ⓠ
103 220th Trail, 52334
(319) 622-3627
M-Sa 9:30-5, Su 11-4
www.fernhill.net

Storm Lake

Inspired By Time Quilts Ⓠ
516 Lake Avenue, 50588
(712) 213-1100

Strawberry Point

Quilted Strawberry Ⓠ Ⓔ
107 Commercial Street, 52076
(563) 920-1449

Tipton

The Fabric Stasher Ⓠ
505 Cedar Street, 52772
(563) 886-1600

Tracy

B & B Creations* Ⓠ
305 Parker Street, 50256
(641) 891-9507

Vincent

Mrs. T's Mercantile Ⓠ
100 Arthur Street, 50594
(515) 356-2230

Vinton

Viking Sewing Center Ⓠ Ⓜ
121 W. 4th Street, 52349
(319) 472-2660

Washington

Needle & Thread Ⓠ Ⓔ Ⓨ Ⓜ
122 W. Main Street, 52353
(319) 591-2009

Waukon

Queen Jean Quilting Ⓠ
708 2nd Avenue NW, 52172
(563) 217-0393

Waverly

Fiberworks Needlework Shop Ⓠ Ⓔ Ⓨ Ⓝ Ⓒ
108 E. Bremer Avenue, 50677
(800) 307-4103 or (319) 352-5464

Treasured Quilting and Gifts Ⓠ
115 W. Bremer Avenue, 50677
(319) 352-4355

West Branch

Cotton Creek Mill Quilt Shoppe Ⓠ Ⓜ
113 W. Main Street, 52358
(319) 643-3554

West Burlington

Ellen's Quilting Corner Ⓠ Ⓜ
123 Broadway Street, 52655
(319) 752-4288

West Des Moines

At The Heart of Quilting Ⓠ
315 5th Street, 50265
(515) 277-6497

The Quilt Block Ⓠ Ⓜ
325 5th Street, 50265
(515) 255-1010

Yarn Junction Co. Ⓨ Ⓦ
132 5th Street, 50265
(515) 277-2770

West Union

Moonlight Stitching Studio and Sisters Retreat Ⓠ
105 N. Vine Street, 52175
(563) 422-8212

One Block Over Ⓠ
322 E. Main Street, 52175
(563) 422-3822

Williamsburg

Rainbows and Calico Things Quilt Shop Ⓠ Ⓜ
2811 240th Street, 52361
(319) 668-1977

The Woolen Needle Ⓠ Ⓔ Ⓨ
225 W. Welsh Street, 52361
(319) 668-2642

Windsor Heights

Stitch 'n Frame Ⓔ Ⓨ Ⓝ Ⓒ
2201 68th Street, 50324
(515) 270-1066

Winterset

Heartland Fiber Company Ⓨ Ⓦ Ⓢ
112 N. 1st Avenue, 50273
(515) 468-8593
MTuWFSa 10-4, Th 10-8
www.heartlandfiber.net

Piece Works Quilt Shop Ⓠ Ⓜ
54 E. Court, 50273
(515) 493-1121
MTuWFSa 9:30-5:30,Th 9:30-8, Su 12-4
www.pieceworksquiltshop.com

Ben Franklin Ⓠ Ⓔ Ⓨ Ⓝ Ⓒ
72 Court Avenue, 50273
(515) 462-2062

Woodbine

Stitchin' Tree Quilts Ⓠ
3131 Highway 30, 51579
(712) 647-3161 or (877) 239-3655

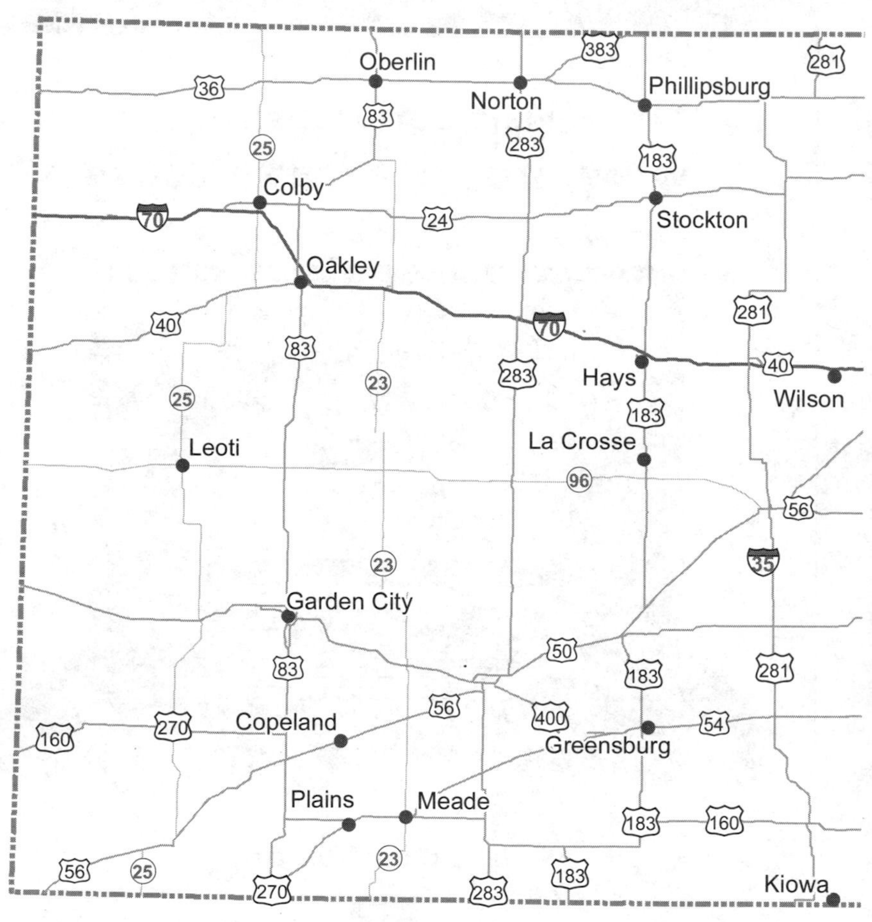

Oberlin
Norton
Phillipsburg
Colby
Stockton
Oakley
Hays
Wilson
Leoti
La Crosse
Garden City
Copeland
Greensburg
Plains
Meade
Kiowa
383
281
36
83
283
183
25
70
24
40
23
96
56
35
50
400
54
270
160

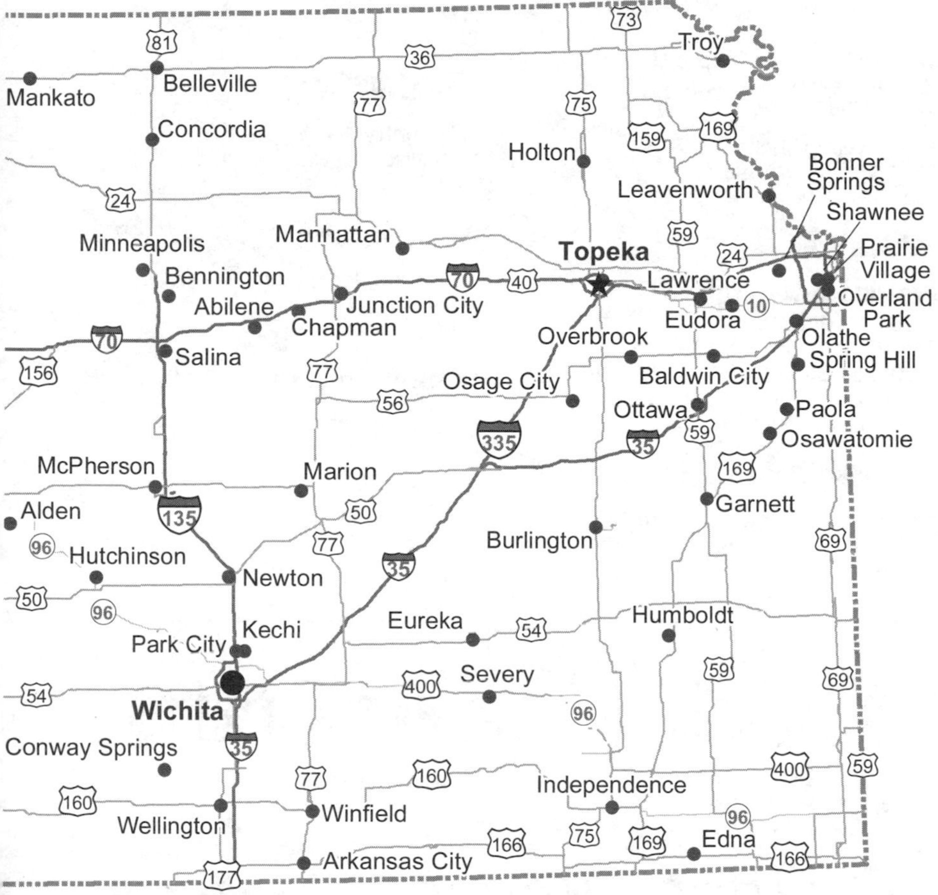
Mankato
Belleville
Concordia
Minneapolis
Bennington
Abilene
Salina
Manhattan
Junction City
Chapman
Holton
Troy
Leavenworth
Bonner Springs
Shawnee
Prairie Village
Overland Park
Topeka
Lawrence
Eudora
Olathe
Spring Hill
Overbrook
Baldwin City
Osage City
Ottawa
Paola
Osawatomie
McPherson
Marion
Alden
Hutchinson
Newton
Garnett
Burlington
Kechi
Park City
Eureka
Humboldt
Wichita
Severy
Conway Springs
Independence
Wellington
Winfield
Edna
Arkansas City

Kansas

Abilene

Material Girls Quilt Shop Q E
306 N. Buckeye Avenue, 67410
(785) 263-7787

The Shivering Sheep Y W S
308 N. Buckeye Avenue, 67410
(785) 263-7501 or (785) 479-0139

Alden

Prairie Flower Crafts Q
➡ SEE AD BELOW
205 Pioneer Street, 67512
(620) 534-3551 or (800) 527-3997
M-Sa 10-4:30
www.prairieflowercrafts.com

Arkansas City

McDonald's Sewing & Vacuum Q E M
222 S. Summit, 67005
(620) 441-0939

Baldwin City

Quilters' Paradise Q E Y
713 8th Street, 66006
(785) 594-3477

Belleville

Sew Country Q E C
1834 M Street, 66935
(785) 527-2332

Bennington

Kansas Troubles Quilters Q
103 N. Nelson, 67422
(785) 488-2120 or (785) 488-6214

Bonner Springs

Sunflower Embroidery, Quilting and Fabrics Q E
207 Oak Street, 66012
(913) 422-4501

Burlington

Silver Threads & Golden Needles Q E Y
321 Neosho, Highway 75, 66839
(620) 364-8233

Chapman

Lucky Charm Quilts Q
405 N. Marshall Street, 67431
(785) 922-6190
M-F 10-5, Sa 9-1
www.facebook.com/Lucky-CharM-Quilts-213829018660354/

Colby

Colby Sew & Vac Q E M
1015 Taylor Avenue, 67701
(785) 460-1900

Handi Quilter® Authorized Retailer
Designed by a Quilter, for Quilters.®

Quilt Cabin Q M
1525 S. Range Avenue, 67701
(785) 462-3375

Concordia

Fabric Essentials Q E
114 W. 6th Street, 66901
(785) 243-4044

Conway Springs

Old Town Quilts Q E C
101 E. Spring Avenue, 67031
(620) 456-3225

Copeland

Sunflower Creations, LLC Q E M
23403 2 Road, 67837
(620) 668-5584

Edna

The Quilters Patch Q
119 N. Marks Avenue, 67342
(620) 922-3129

Eudora

Quilting Bits and Pieces Q E
736 Main Street, 66025
(785) 542-2080

Eureka

Scraproom Q E Y N W S C
209 N. Main Street, 67045
(620) 583-7169

Garden City

A Quilted Crow, LLC Q
902 Stone Creek Drive, Suite C, 67846
(620) 805-5073

Handi Quilter® Authorized Retailer
Designed by a Quilter, for Quilters.®

Garnett

Country Fabrics Q E M
108 E. 5th Avenue, 66032
(785) 448-0003

Greensburg

Starla's Stitch 'N Frame E C
122 S. Main Street, 67054
(620) 723-3275

Hays

Quilt Cottage Company Q E Y W C M
2520 Vine Street, 67601
(785) 625-0080

Holton

Quilting on the Square Q
400 Pennsylvania Avenue, 66436
(785) 364-4050

The-Golden-Fleece Y W S
413 New York Avenue, 66436
(785) 362-7490

Humboldt

Heavenly Kneads & Threads LLC Q E Y N C
724 Bridge Street, 66748
(620) 473-2408

Hutchinson

Cottonwood Quilts Q
126 N. Main Street, 67501
(620) 662-2245

Country Fabrics Ⓠ Ⓔ
6411 W. Morgan Avenue, 67501
(620) 662-3681

Independence

Stella's Quilt-N-Fabrics Ⓠ
4530 County Road 6000, 67301
(620) 325-5378

Junction City

Quilter's Yard, LLC Ⓠ Ⓜ
722 N. Washington Street, 66441
(785) 307-0774

Kechi (Wichita)

Kechi Quilt Impressions Ⓠ Ⓔ
118 East Kechi Road, 67067
(316) 616-8036
WFSa 10-5, Th 10-9
www.kechiquilt.com

Kiowa

Clark's Fabric Shop Ⓠ
605 Main Street, 67070
(620) 825-4985

La Crosse

A Quilt Corral Ⓠ Ⓜ
812 Main Street, 67548
(352) 266-7108

Lawrence

Mea Bernina Ⓠ Ⓜ
2120 W. 25th Street, 66047
(785) 842-1595 or (800) 397-7750

Sarah's Fabrics Ⓠ
925 Massachusetts Street, 66044
(785) 842-6198

Stitch On Needlework Shop Ⓠ Ⓔ Ⓒ
926 Massachusetts Street, 66044
(785) 842-1101

Yarn Barn of Kansas Ⓨ Ⓦ Ⓢ
930 Massachusetts Street, 66044
(785) 842-4333 or (800) 468-0035

Leavenworth

First City Quilts LLC Ⓠ
200 S. 5th Street, 66048
(913) 682-8000

L.A.C. Quilt Shop Ⓠ Ⓨ Ⓒ
426 Miami Street, 66048
(913) 682-1916 or (913) 682-7873

Momo's Knitting Nook and Crochet Emporium Ⓨ
518 Delaware Street, 66048
(785) 766-2214

Leoti

Prairie Flower Quilt Co., LLC Ⓠ Ⓜ
102 S. Indian Road, 67861
(620) 375-2044

Manhattan

All About Quilts Ⓠ Ⓔ Ⓜ
8651 E. US Highway 24, 66502
(785) 539-6759

Weisners Sew Unique Ⓠ Ⓜ
314 Poyntz Avenue, 66502
(785) 776-6100

Mankato

Hidden Treasures Quilt Shop Ⓠ Ⓔ Ⓒ
101 N. Commercial Street, 66956
(785) 378-8020

Marion

Sew What Quilt Shop, LLP Ⓠ
329 E. Main Street, 66861
(620) 382-2020

McPherson

Stitches Quilt Shop Ⓠ
102 S. Main Street, 67460
(620) 241-2986
M-F 9-5:30, Sa 9-3
www.stitchesquiltshopmcp.com

Meade

Green Acres Quilt Shop Q
140 W. Carthage, Highway 54, 67864
(620) 873-5125

Minneapolis

No Place Like Home Quilt Shop Q
204 W. 2nd Street, 67467
(785) 392-9065
Tu-F 10-5:30, Sa 10-4
www.noplacelikehomequiltshop.com

Newton

Charlotte's Sew Natural Q
710 N. Main Street, 67114
(316) 284-2547

Norton

Stitch Up A Storm Q E
113 W. Main Street, 67654
(785) 874-5152

Oakley

Smoky River Quilt Shoppe Q E
307 Center Avenue, 67748
(785) 671-3070

Oberlin

Country Quilting & Keepsakes Q
310 W. Commercial Street, 67749
(785) 475-2411

Olathe

Quilters' Haven Q E M
116 N. Clairborne Road, #B, 66062
(913) 764-8600

Osawatomie

Happy Crafters Q E C
1935 Parker Avenue, 66064
(913) 755-4360

Ottawa

Chris' Corner Quilt Shop Q E
3593 Old Highway 59, 66067
(785) 242-1922

Overbrook

Overbrook Quilt Connection Q
500 Maple Street, 66524
(785) 665-7841
Tu-Sa 10-5
www.overbrookquilts.com

Overland Park

The Studio Knitting & Needlepoint Y N W S
9555 Nall Avenue, 66207
(816) 531-4466
MWFSa 10-5, TuTh 10-6, Su 12-4
www.thestudiokc.com

Addadi's Fabrics Q
9629 W. 87th Street, 66212
(913) 381-9705

Harper's Fabric & Quilt Co. Q E M
7918 Santa Fe Drive, 66204
(913) 648-2739

Quilted Memories Q E
11301-05 W. 87th Terrace, 66204
(913) 649-2704

Yarn Shop and More Y
7297 W. 97th Street, 66212
(913) 649-9276

Paola

Li'l Red Hen Quilt Shop Q
7 S. Agate Street, 66071
(913) 294-5230

Park City

Sewing & Embroidery Works Q E
1590 E. 61st Street N, 67219
(316) 337-5733

Phillipsburg

The Quilt Bugs Ⓠ
205 W. E Street, 67661
(785) 543-7905

The Shepherd's Mill, Inc. ⒺⓎⓌⓈⒸ
839 3rd Street, 67661
(785) 543-3128

Plains

Country Quiltin' by Design, LLC ⓆⒺ
410 Grand Avenue, 67869
(620) 563-7757

Prairie Village

Needle Fiber Arts, Inc. Ⓝ
4001 W. 87th Street, 66207
(913) 381-0722

Salina

Emporium, Inc ⓆⒺⓂ
1833 S. 9th Street, 67401
(785) 823-1515

Severy

Needle in a Haystack Ⓠ
207 Q Road, 67137
(620) 736-2942

Shawnee

Prairie Point Quilt & Fabric Shop ⓆⒺⓂ
11950 Shawnee Mission Parkway, 66216
(913) 268-3333

Spring Hill

The Quilted Sunflower ⓆⒺ
111 S. Main Street, 66083
(913) 592-0100
MWThF 9:30-5:30, Tu 9:30-7, Sa 9:30-2
www.thequiltedsunflower.com

Stockton

Stitch & Chatter ⓆⒺⓂ
320 Main Street, 67669
(785) 415-2015

Topeka

Yak 'n Yarn ⒺⓎⓌⒸ
5331 SW 22nd Place, 66614
(785) 272-9276
M 9:30-5, TuWF 11-5, Sa 11-2, 2nd and last W 6-8
www.yaknyarn.net

Stitching Traditions Quilt Shop Ⓠ
2900 SW Oakley Avenue, Suite H, 66614
(785) 266-4130

Troy

Out Back Quilt Shop Ⓠ
310 W. Locust Street, 66087
(785) 850-0375

Wellington

Beehive Quilt Shop ⓆⒺ
122 N. Washington Avenue, 67152
(913) 259-3346

Wichita

A-1 Singer Sewing Center (M)
1012 S. Oliver Street, 67218
(316) 685-0226

Attic Heirloom Designs (Q)(E)
1705 W. Douglas Avenue, 67213
(316) 265-4646

Heart's Desire (E)(C)
3210 E. Douglas Avenue, 67208
(316) 681-3369

Hen Feathers Quilt Shop (Q)
110 N. Rock Road, 67206
(316) 652-9599

Midwest Sewing & Vacuum Center* (M)
111 S. Pattie Street, 67211
(800) 848-6729 or (316) 262-3438

Handi Quilter® Authorized Retailer
Designed by a Quilter, for Quilters.®

Picket Fence Quilt Company (Q)(Y)
7011 W. Central, Suite 129, 67212
(316) 558-8899

The Sewing Center (Q)(M)
2407 W. 13th Street, 67203
(316) 832-0819

Wilson

Grandma J's* (Q)
106 23rd Street, 67490
(785) 658-2225

Winfield

Field to Fabric Quilt Company (Q)(E)
907 Main, 67156
(620) 229-8540

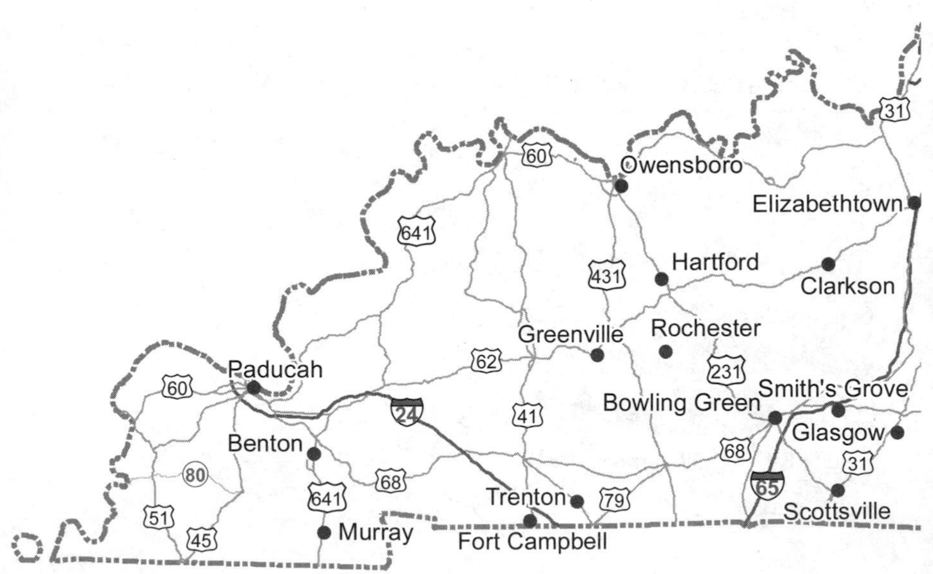

Owensboro
Elizabethtown
Hartford
Clarkson
Greenville
Rochester
Paducah
Bowling Green
Smith's Grove
Glasgow
Benton
Trenton
Scottsville
Murray
Fort Campbell
31
60
641
431
62
231
60
24
41
68
80
68
641
79
31
65
51
45

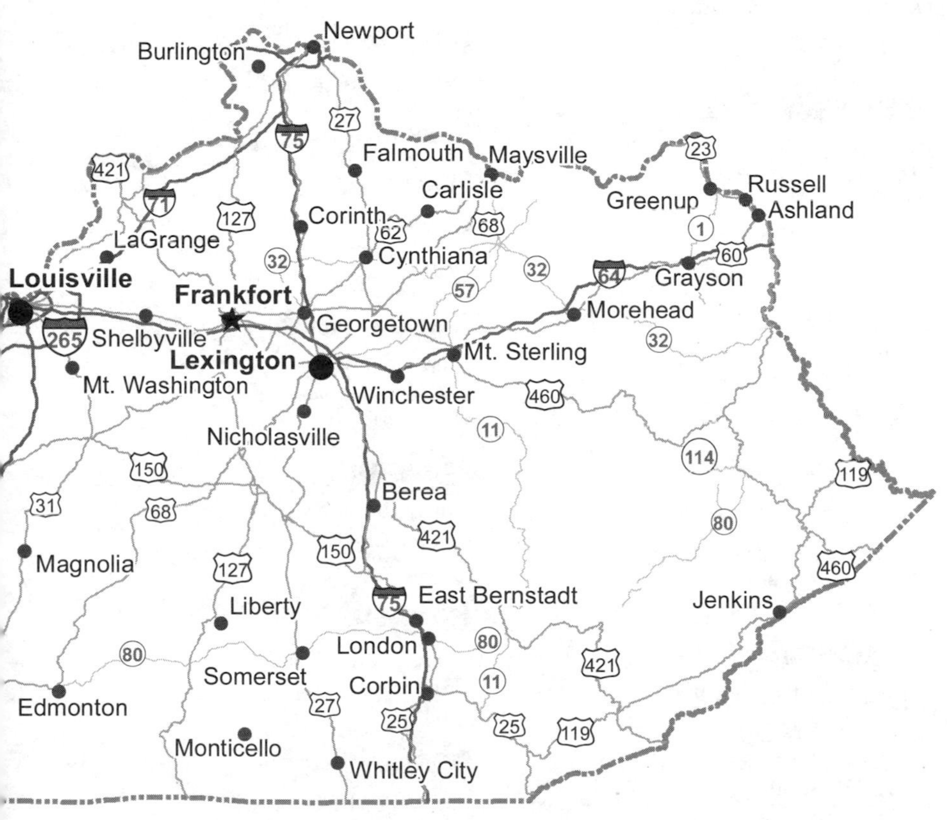
Newport
Burlington
Falmouth
Maysville
Russell
Ashland
Greenup
Carlisle
Corinth
LaGrange
Cynthiana
Grayson
Louisville
Frankfort
Morehead
Georgetown
Shelbyville
Mt. Sterling
Lexington
Mt. Washington
Winchester
Nicholasville
Berea
Magnolia
East Bernstadt
Jenkins
Liberty
London
Somerset
Corbin
Edmonton
Monticello
Whitley City

Kentucky

Ashland

Little Red Hen Quilt and Fabric Shop Q
1653 Greenup Avenue, 41101
(606) 329-2400

Benton

Odds & Ends Fabric & Crafts Q
95 Main Street, 42025
(270) 527-2250

Berea

Fiber Frenzy LLC Y S
137A N. Broadway Street, 40403
(859) 986-3832

Log House Craft Gallery Y
200 Estill Street, 40404
(859) 985-3226

Old Town Fabric Q E
132 N. Broadway Street, 40403
(859) 985-2538

Bowling Green

Elegant Traditions E N
1326 State Street, 42101
(270) 781-8547 or (270) 282-3907

The Kentucky Quilt Company Q
1575 Campbell Lane, 42104
(270) 842-2434

Burlington

Eagle Bend's Yarn & Fiber Shoppe Y W S
7812 East Bend Road, 41005
(859) 750-3560
Tu 1-7, W-Sa 10-4
www.eaglebendalpacas.com

Cabin Arts Q
5878 N. Jefferson Street, 41005
(859) 586-8021

Carlisle

Polka Dot Elephant Q Y
366 E. Main, 40311
(859) 473-4402

Clarkson

Sew Much More Sewing Center Q
120 W. Main Street, 42726
(270) 242-3349

Corbin

Fabric World and Quilting Q
33 Prestige Lane S (US HWY 25), 40701
(606) 526-1799

Corinth

Kokovoko Farm and B&B S
3240 Hinton Webber Road, 41010
(859) 420-5246

Cynthiana

Tay's Cloth Peddler Q E Y C
121 E. Pike Street, 41031
(859) 234-1846

East Bernstadt

Paula's Quilting Pantry Q
833 W. Highway 3094, 40729
(606) 231-3543

Edmonton

Marilyn's Q E N C
3917 Columbia Road, 42129
(270) 670-8827

Elizabethtown

Uniquely Yours Quilt Shop Q
2973 Rineyville Road, 42701
(270) 766-1456

Falmouth

Country Patchwork, LLC Q
101 W. Shelby Street, 41040
(859) 951-1118

Fort Campbell

Jenny's Y S
2840 Bastogne Avenue, 42223
(270) 872-7870

Frankfort

The Woolery Ⓨ Ⓦ Ⓢ Ⓜ
859 E. Main Street, Suite 1A, 40601
(800) 441-9665 or (800) 441-9665
M-F 10-6, Sa 10-3
www.woolery.com

Georgetown

Birdsong Quilting and Crafts, LLC Ⓠ Ⓜ
228 E. Main Street, 40324
(502) 603-8211

Glasgow

Creative Stitches by Linda* Ⓜ
77 Graham Road, 42141
(270) 404-3568

Grayson

Quilt Heaven Quilt Shop Ⓠ
5306 S. State Highway 7, 41143
(606) 475-0091

Greenup

Mom's Cotton Shop Ⓠ
2035 Ashland Road, 41144
(606) 473-2164

River Town Fabrics Ⓠ Ⓔ
420 Main Street, 41144
(606) 473-4589

Thomas Sewing Center* Ⓜ
2027 Ashland Road, 41144
(606) 473-3540

Greenville

Carroll's Quilting Ⓠ
115 W. Main Cross Street, 42345
(270) 338-2954

Hartford

Omadarlings Ⓠ Ⓜ
211 S. Main Street, 42347
(270) 256-9995

Quilts R Jewel's Ⓠ Ⓜ
483 Livermore Road, 42347
(270) 298-3507

Jenkins

Vintage Rose Fabrics & Gifts Ⓠ
12976 Highway 805, 41537
(606) 832-0311

La Grange

Friends & Fiber Ⓨ Ⓢ
106 E. Main Street, 40031
(502) 222-0658

Lexington

Eye of the Needle Ⓝ
3323 Partner Place, Suite 10, 40503
(859) 278-1401

M's Canvashouse Ⓝ
131 Kentucky Avenue, 40502
(859) 253-1302

Magpie Yarn Ⓨ
513 E. High Street, 40502
(859) 455-7437

Quilter's Square Ⓠ Ⓔ Ⓜ
3301 Keithshire Way, Suite 109, 40503
(859) 278-5010

ReBelle Ⓨ Ⓢ
225 Rosemont Garden, 40503
(859) 389-9750

Sandy's Sewing Center Ⓠ Ⓜ
436 Southland Drive, 40503
(859) 260-2003

Sew-A-Lot Ⓠ Ⓔ Ⓜ
2160 Sir Barton Way, Suite 148, 40509
(859) 264-7472

The Stitch Niche, Inc. Ⓔ Ⓨ Ⓝ Ⓒ
180 Moore Drive, 40503
(859) 277-2604

Liberty

The Quilter's Trunk Sewing Center, LLC Q E C M

➡ SEE AD BELOW

960 S. Fork Ridge Road, 42539
(606) 787-7648
MWThFSa 9-5
www.quilterstrunk.com

PRICES WORTH DRIVING FOR!

Authorized Sewing Machine Sales and Service

baby lock BERNINA accuquilt

606-787-7648

Monday-Saturday
9:00 am to 5:00 pm
Closed Sun

960 S. Fork Ridge Road,
Liberty, KY 42539
www.quilterstrunk.com

London

Sexton's Fabrics Q
2435 N. Laurel Road, 40741
(606) 843-6610

Louisville

Among Friends Quilt and Sewing Center Q E M

9537 Taylorsville Road, 40299
(502) 261-7377
MTuWF 9:30-6, Th 9:30-8, Sa 9:30-5
www.amongfriendsquiltshop.com

Handi Quilter® Authorized Retailer
Designed by a Quilter, for Quilters.®

Designs In Textiles Y N W S

1234 S. 3rd Street
Historic Old Louisville, 40203
(502) 212-7500 or (502) 558-6785
By appt. only
www.DesignsInTextiles.com

The Cozy Quilter Q

12204 Shelbyville Road, 40243
(502) 742-2699
MWThFSa 10-6, Tu 10-8, Su 12-4
www.thecozyquilter.com

Austin's Sewing Center Q E M
5640 Bardstown Road, 40291
(502) 239-2222

Beth's Needlepoint Nook N
10308 Shelbyville Road, 40223
(502) 244-0046

Little Loom House Y W S
328 Kenwood Hill Road, 40214
(502) 367-4792

Quilted Joy Q
10302 Bluegrass Parkway, 40299
(502) 718-7148

Stitch - a needlepoint shop N
215 Chenoweth Lane, 40207
(502) 384-3424

The Finishing Touch C
2004 Frankfort Avenue, 40206
(502) 893-3112

The Smocking Shoppe - St. Matthews Q M
3829 Staebler Avenue, 40207
(502) 893-3503

Magnolia

The Jewell Box Fabric & Upholstery Q
10075 N. Jackson Highway, 42757
(270) 528-3087

Maysville

Apron Strings Quilt Shop Q M
52 W. 2nd Street, 41056
(606) 584-7414

Monticello

Linda's Quilt Shop Etc. Q E
627 Michigan Avenue, 42633
(606) 340-1812

Morehead

A Good Yarn...Inside Coffee Tree Books Y
159 E. Main Street, 40351
(606) 784-8364

Calico Patch Designs Q M
155 Bluebank Road, 40351
(606) 784-7235

Quilter's Candy Shop Q
151 E. Main Street, 40351
(606) 356-0268

Mt. Sterling

Native Twist Ⓨ Ⓦ Ⓢ
31 S. Maysville Street, 40353
(859) 432-8133

Mt. Washington

Busy Lady Quilt Shop Ⓠ
223 B Delania Drive, 40047
(502) 538-8800

Murray

Murray Sewing Center / Kentucky Quilt Backings Ⓠ Ⓔ Ⓒ
942A S. 12th Street, 42071
(270) 759-8400

Red Bug Yarn & Gifts Ⓨ
102 S. 6th Street, 42071
(270) 761-2723

Newport

Knit On! Inc. Ⓨ Ⓦ Ⓢ
735 Monmouth Street, 41071
(859) 291-5648

Nicholasville

A Tangled Yarn and LunabudKnits Ⓨ Ⓦ Ⓢ
605 N. Main Street, 40356
(859) 885-5426

Owensboro

Simple Stitches Ⓠ
102 W. Byers Avenue, 42303
(270) 698-8320

Stychee Woman Studio Ⓠ
219 Williamsburg Square, 42303
(270) 686-7777

Paducah

Calico Country Sew & Vac Ⓠ Ⓜ
3401 Park Avenue, Suite 4, 42001
(270) 444-0301

Hancocks of Paducah Ⓠ
3841 Hinkleville Road, 42001
(800) 845-8723

Itty Bitty Knitty Shop Ⓨ
1920 Kentucky Avenue, 42003
(270) 709-3270

Jefferson Street Studios/ Helene Davis Hand-dye Fabric Ⓠ
1149 Jefferson Street, 42001
(270) 217-3976

Must Stitch Emporium Ⓠ Ⓒ
109 Market House Square, 42001
(270) 709-3331

Rochester

Sue's Quilting & Fabrics Ⓠ
223 Arndell Road, 42273
(270) 934-8401

Russell

Janis Campbell Knitting Studio Ⓨ
424 Bluebird Drive, 41169
(606) 494-2301

Scottsville

Valerie's Quilt Corner Ⓠ
104 S. Court Street, 42164
(270) 237-5429

Shelbyville

Needle Nest Ⓝ Ⓒ
702 Washington Street, 40065
(502) 633-4701
MTuWF 10-4:30, Th 10-8, Sa 10-4
www.needlenestky.com

Smiths Grove

Psycho Granny's Quilt Shop & More Ⓠ Ⓜ
101 Main Street, 42171
(270) 202-1889

Whittle's Fabrics Ⓠ
3784 Chalybeate Road, 42171
(270) 597-2987

Somerset

Blue Willow Mercantile Ⓠ Ⓨ Ⓜ
3311 S. Highway 27, Units 4 & 5, 42501
(630) 868-3833

Trenton

The Wooden Needle Ⓠ Ⓔ Ⓨ Ⓦ Ⓢ
118 S. Main Street, 42286
(270) 954-9005
MTuWF 10-5, Th 10-7, Sa 10-2
www.facebook.com/TheWoodenNeedle/

Quilt and Sew at Golden Threads Ⓠ
115 S. Main Street, 42286
(270) 466-5000

Whitley City

Agnes' Fabric Shop Ⓠ Ⓔ Ⓨ Ⓝ Ⓒ
66 N. Main Street, 42653
(606) 376-8773

Winchester

Judy's Stitch In Time Ⓠ Ⓔ Ⓨ Ⓒ
5839 Irvine Road, 40391
(859) 744-7404

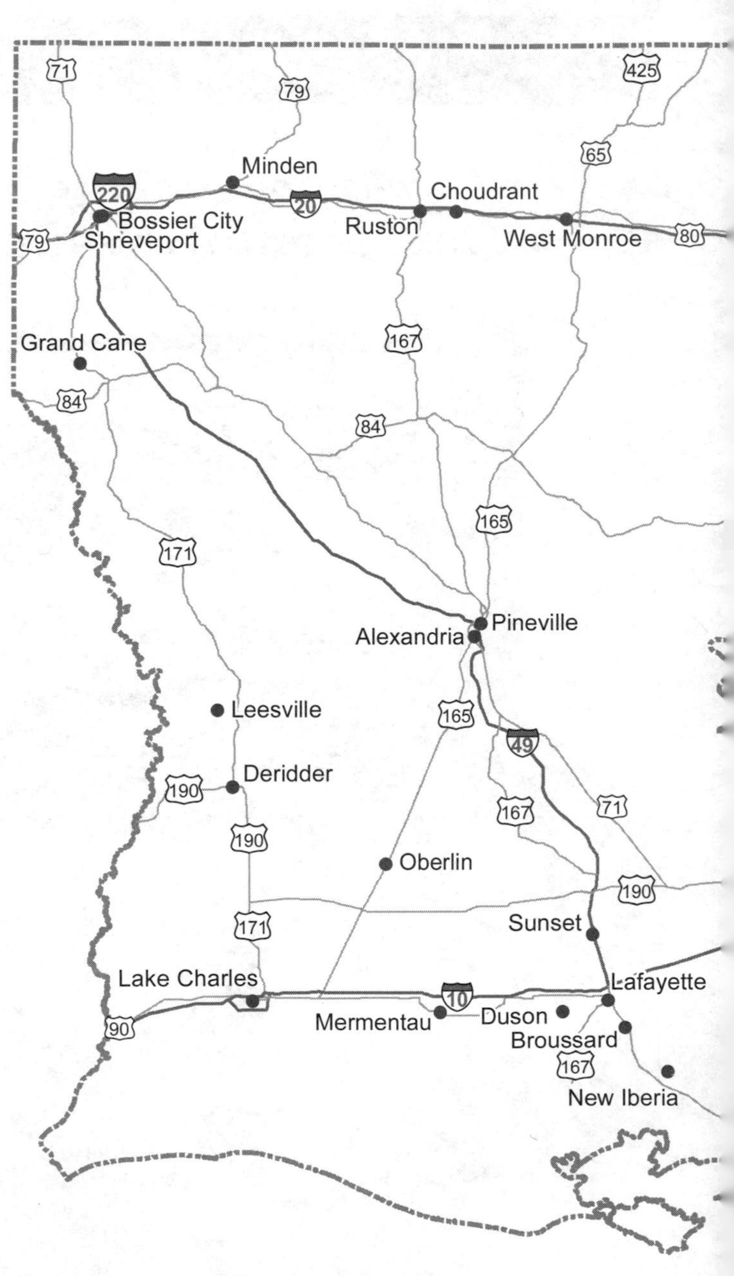

71
79
425
65
Minden
220
20
Choudrant
Bossier City
Shreveport
79
Ruston
West Monroe
80
Grand Cane
167
84
84
165
171
Pineville
Alexandria
Leesville
165
49
Deridder
190
190
167
71
Oberlin
190
171
Sunset
Lake Charles
10
Lafayette
Mermentau
Duson
90
Broussard
167
New Iberia

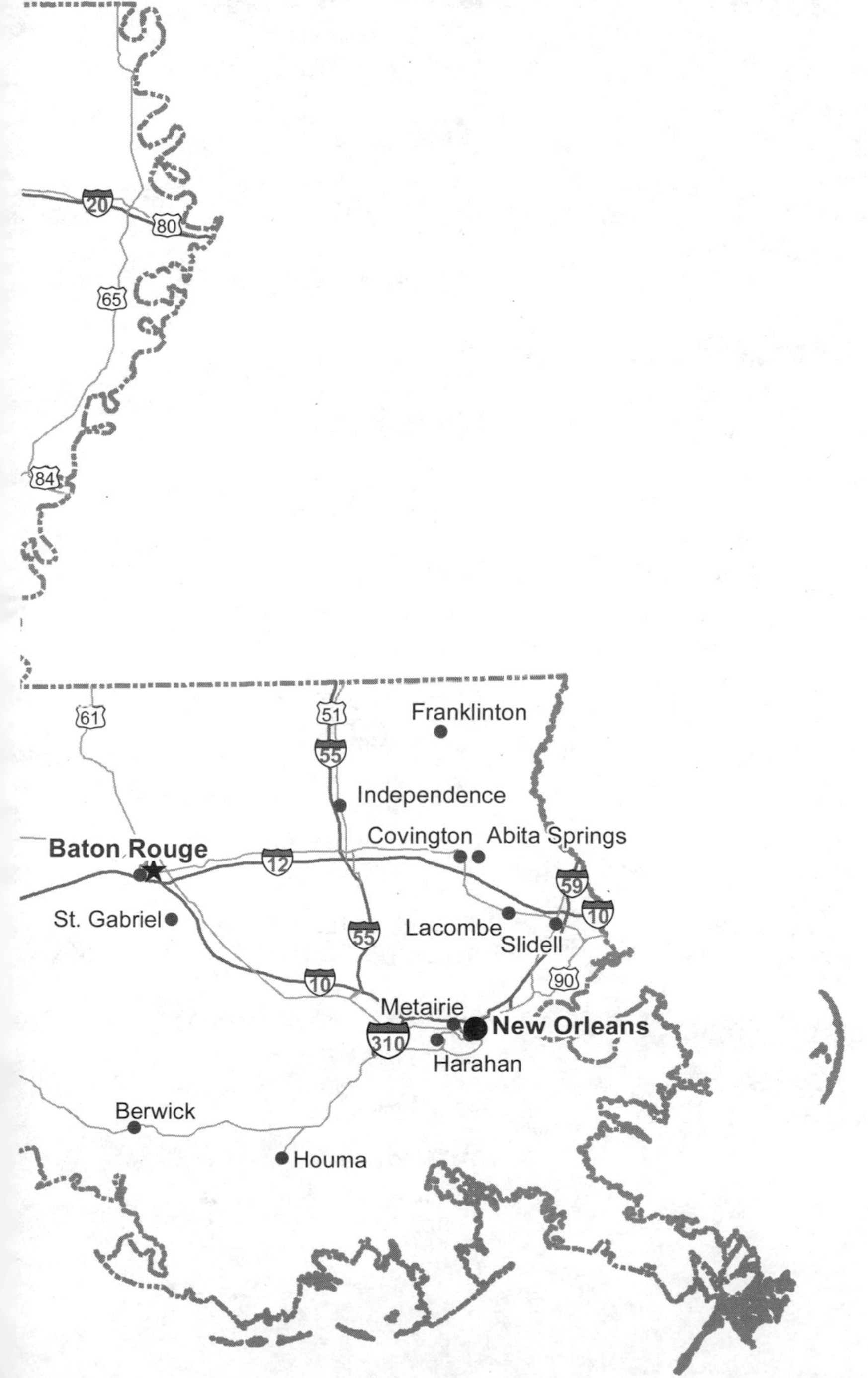
20
80
65
84
61
51
55
Franklinton
Independence
Baton Rouge
Covington
Abita Springs
12
59
10
St. Gabriel
55
Lacombe
Slidell
90
10
Metairie
310
New Orleans
Harahan
Berwick
Houma

Louisiana

Abita Springs

Sew This! Ⓠ Ⓜ
70117 Highway 59, Suite O, 70420
(985) 898-1112

Alexandria

Creative Quilting Ⓠ Ⓔ Ⓝ Ⓒ
2438 E. Texas Avenue, 71301
(318) 445-7793

Baton Rouge

MY Sewing Shoppe Ⓠ Ⓔ Ⓜ
7630 Old Hammond Highway, 70809
(225) 218-2250
M-F 10-5, Sa 10-3
www.mysewingshoppebernina.com

The Quilt Corner Ⓠ Ⓔ Ⓜ
13521 Hooper Road, 70818
(225) 315-7285
MWF 10-5, TuTh 10-6, Sa 10-2
www.quiltcorneronline.com

AllBrands.com Ⓠ Ⓔ Ⓜ
20415 Highland Road, 70817
(225) 923-1260

Knits By Nana* Ⓨ
7612 Old Hammond Highway, 70809
(225) 216-9460

The Elegant Needle Ⓝ
6641 Government Street, 70806
(225) 925-8920

Berwick

The Quilt Cupboard Ⓠ Ⓜ
101 Tournament Blvd., 70342
(985) 354-0030

Bossier City

Fabric Boutique Ⓠ Ⓔ Ⓜ
1701 Old Minden Road, Suite 11, 71111
(318) 742-0047

Broussard

A & A Sewing Center Ⓠ Ⓔ Ⓜ
817 Albertson Parkway, 70518
(337) 837-3444

Choudrant

Hannah's Quilts Ⓠ
402 St. Peters Road, 71227
(318) 251-0314 or (318) 245-9332

Covington

Precision Sewing Machine Co. Ⓠ Ⓔ Ⓜ
3997 Highway 190 E. Service Road, 70433
(985) 249-6156 or (800) 487-7397

Deridder

Country Lane Cross Stitch & Frame Ⓒ
2915 Glendale Road, 70634
(337) 463-2359

Countryside Crafts Ⓠ
214 Mahlon Street, 70634
(337) 221-3020

Duson

C'est Bon Stitches Ⓜ
108 Tunica Lane, 70529
(337) 278-5869

Franklinton

Jackie's Fabric Shop Ⓠ
1301 Greenlaw Street, 70438
(985) 839-9756

Grand Cane

Homemade Quilts n More Ⓠ
8370 Highway 171, 71032
(318) 858-0092

Harahan

All About Sewing Ⓠ Ⓔ
6005 Jefferson Highway, Suite E, 70123
(504) 739-9883

Houma

Mindy's Ⓒ
814 Grand Caillou Road, Suite 6, 70363
(985) 872-9404

Independence

Mama's Quilt Shop Ⓠ
15111 Catfish Farm Road, 70443
(985) 878-6396

Lacombe

McNeedles LLC Ⓨ
28120 Highway 190, 70445
(985) 882-7144

Lafayette

AllBrands.com Ⓠ Ⓔ Ⓜ
3541 Ambassador Caffery Parkway, 70503
(337) 981-2808

Heirloom Creations Fine Sewing Shop Ⓠ Ⓔ
431 Rena Drive, 70508
(337) 984-8949

Lola Pink Fabrics Ⓠ Ⓜ
123 Arnould Blvd., 70506
(337) 456-2364

Yarn Nook Ⓨ
1120 B Coolidge Blvd., 70503
(337) 593-8558

Lake Charles

AllBrands.com Ⓠ Ⓔ Ⓜ
2615 Dillard Loop, 70607
(337) 477-0492

Niche Fabric & Studio Ⓠ Ⓨ
4706 Common Street, 70607
(337) 477-3810

Leesville

Betty's All Wrapped Up* Ⓠ
223 Northrop Road, 71446
(337) 239-3136

Mermentau

Gale's Cajun Quilting Ⓠ
707 Railroad Avenue, 70556
(337) 250-7364

Metairie

Accents, Inc. (Accents in Stitches) Ⓔ Ⓒ
4500 Shores Drive, Suite 103, 70006
(504) 888-2458
Tu-F 10-5, Sa 10-3
www.accentsinc.com

All Stitched Up by Angela Ⓠ
3030 Severn Avenue, 70002
(504) 518-6628
M-F 10-5, Sa 10-4
www.allstitchedupbyangela.com

AllBrands.com Ⓠ Ⓜ
4029 Veterans Memorial Blvd., 70002
(504) 888-4952

Minden

The Little Country Quilt Shop Ⓠ
534 Old Arcadia Road, 71055
(318) 377-2462

New Iberia

Emily's Closet Ⓠ Ⓔ Ⓨ
699 E. St. Peter Street, 70560
(337) 364-9404

New Orleans

Mes Amis Quilt Shop Ⓠ
6505 Spanish Fort Blvd., 70124
(504) 284-3455
M-F 9:30-4:30, Sa 10-4
www.mesamisquiltshop.com

Bette Bornside Company Ⓨ
2733 Dauphine Street, 70117
(504) 945-4069

Chateau Sew & Sew Q E
2103 Magazine Street, 70130
(504) 533-9221

Needle Arts Studio Y N
5301 Canal Blvd., 70124
(504) 832-3050

Needlework Vault Y N C
1927 Sophie Wright Place, 70130
(504) 528-9797

Quilted Owl Q E
4600 Jefferson Highway, 70121
(504) 733-0993

The Quarter Stitch Y N C
629 Chartres Street, 70130
(504) 522-4451

Oberlin

Oberlin Quilt Company, LLC Q
116 W. Sixth Avenue, 70655
(337) 639-2900

Pineville

Aunt Nell's Quilt Shop Q
1634 Hyland Park Drive, 71360
(318) 640-5294

Ruston

QUILTEROO'S Q E M
1401 Farmerville Highway, 71270
(318) 255-0992

SheepDog Yarns Y
207 N. Trenton Street, 71270
(318) 302-0771

The Fabric Shop Q E M
100 W. Park Avenue, 71270
(318) 251-2400

Shreveport

Hanging By A Thread N
6505 Line Avenue, Suite 8, 71106
(318) 865-7878

PC Embroidery and Cottage Quilts Q E
9377 Mansfield Road, 71118
(318) 671-0331

Shreveport Sewing Center Q M
645 Bert Kouns Industrial Loop, 71118
(318) 688-2402

The Sewing Shop Q M
1275 Shreveport Barksdale Highway, 71105
(318) 869-1739

Yarn on Youree Y W S
3622 Youree Drive, 71105
(318) 210-0670

Slidell

All Stitched Up by Angela Q M
106 Gause Blvd. W, Suite A13, 70460
(985) 288-5050
M-F 10-5, Sa 10-4
www.allstitchedupbyangela.com

AllBrands.com Q E M
796 E. I-10 Service Road, Suite 100, 70458
(985) 643-4252

St. Gabriel

Cottage Creations & Quilts Q
7222 Bayou Paul Road, 70776
(225) 642-8166
Tu-F 10:30-5, Sa 10:30-3
www.cottagecreationsandquilts.com

Sunset

J & B Quilting and Fabrics Q
988 Napoleon Avenue, 70584
(337) 662-1183

West Monroe

Quilt 'N Stitch Q M
6049 Cypress Street, 71291
(318) 396-6020

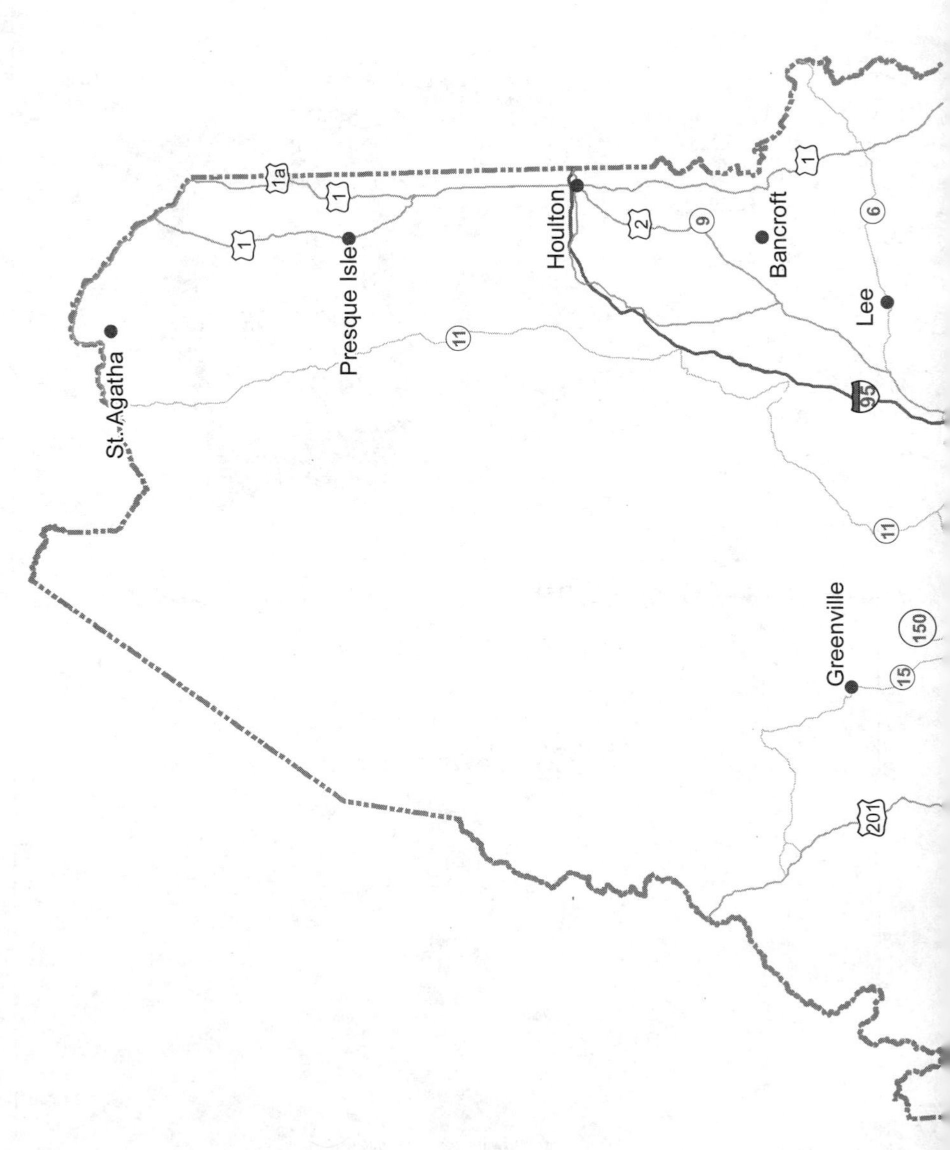
St. Agatha
Presque Isle
Houlton
Bancroft
Lee
Greenville
1a
1
2
9
6
11
95
150
15
201

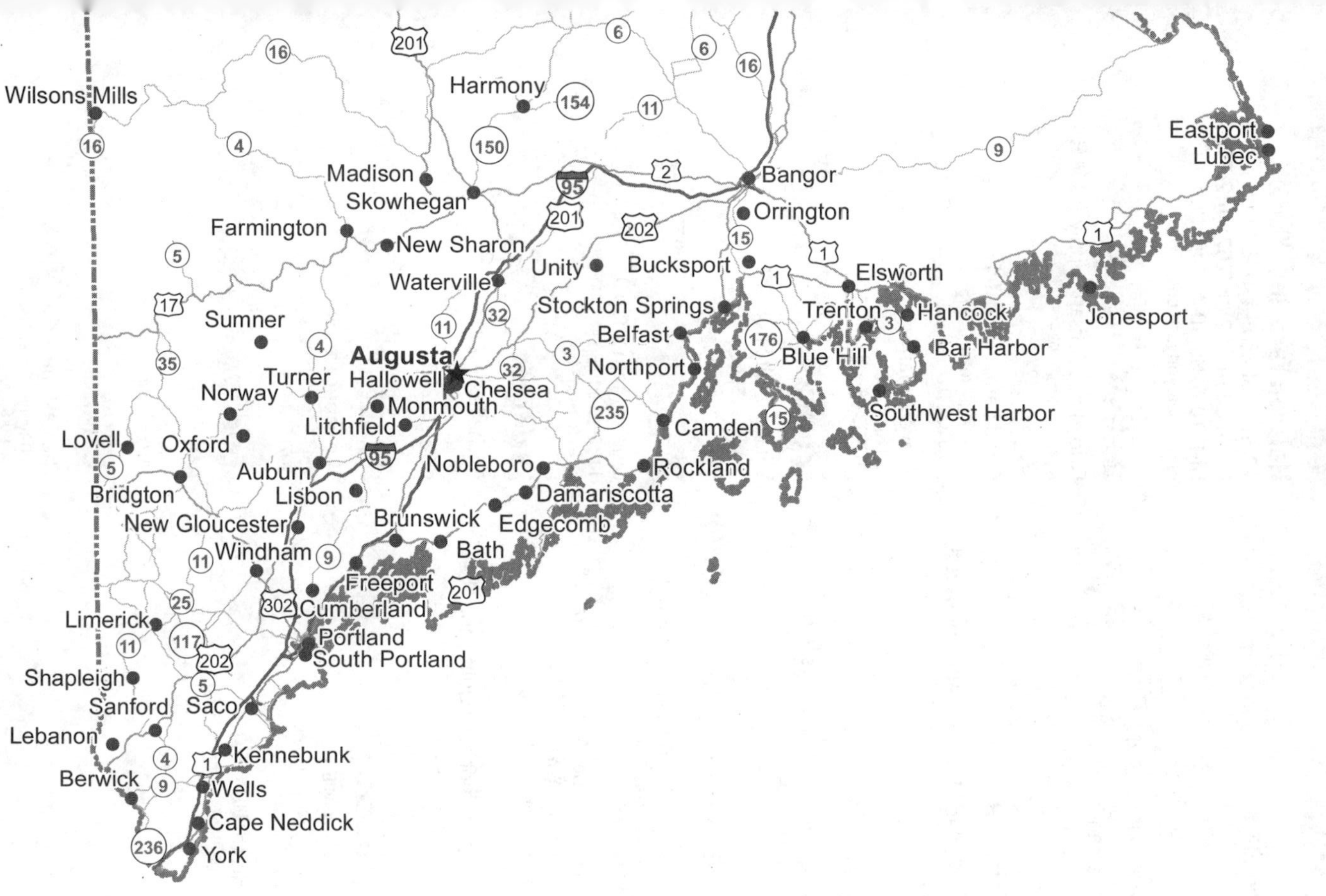
Wilsons Mills
Harmony
Madison
Skowhegan
Farmington
New Sharon
Waterville
Unity
Bucksport
Bangor
Orrington
Elsworth
Eastport
Lubec
Jonesport
Stockton Springs
Belfast
Trenton
Hancock
Bar Harbor
Blue Hill
Northport
Southwest Harbor
Camden
Rockland
Sumner
Augusta
Turner
Hallowell
Chelsea
Norway
Monmouth
Litchfield
Lovell
Oxford
Auburn
Nobleboro
Bridgton
Lisbon
Damariscotta
Brunswick
Edgecomb
New Gloucester
Windham
Bath
Freeport
Cumberland
Limerick
Portland
South Portland
Shapleigh
Sanford
Saco
Lebanon
Kennebunk
Berwick
Wells
Cape Neddick
York

Maine

Auburn

Fabric Warehouse Div. of Pinetree Industries, Inc. Ⓠ
104 Washington Street N, 04211
(207) 784-7151 or (877) 326-8172

Quiltessentials, Inc. ⓆⓎ
909 Minot Avenue, 04210
(207) 784-4486

Augusta

Cozy Cottage Fabrics & Alterations ⓆⓃ
22 Hummingbird Lane, 04330
(207) 512-8531

Bancroft

Spring Valley Yarn and Gifts ⓎⓌⓈ
248 Kelly Road, 04497
(207) 448-3226

Bangor

Essentially Felt Studio & Fine Yarn Ⓨ
865 Pushaw Road, 04401
(207) 942-0365

One Lupine Fiber Arts / Maine Yarn & Fiber Supply ⓎⓌⓈ
170 Park Street, 04401
(207) 299-6716

The Cotton Cupboard Quilt Shop ⓆⓂ
1213 Broadway, 04401
(207) 941-8900

Bar Harbor

Bee's, Inc. ⒺⓎⓃⒸ
59 Cottage Street, 04609
(207) 288-9046

Fabricate ⓆⒺⓎⓃⒸ
64 Mount Desert Street, 04609
(207) 288-5113

Bath

Halcyon Yarn, Inc. ⓎⓌⓈ
12 School Street, 04530
(800) 341-0282 or (207) 442-7909
M-F 10-6, Sa 10-4, Sun 11-4
www.halcyonyarn.com

Belfast

Fiddlehead Artisan Supply ⓆⒺⓃⓌⒸⓂ
64 Main Street, 04915
(207) 338-8422

Good Karma Farm ⓎⓈ
67 Perkins Road, 04915
(207) 322-0170

Heavenly Yarns Ⓨ
133 High Street, 04915
(207) 338-8388

Berwick

Village Quilt Shop ⓆⓎ
14 Wilson Street, 03901
(207) 698-4818

Blue Hill

Blue Hill Yarn Shop Ⓨ
141 Ellsworth Road, 04164
(207) 374-5631

Bridgton

Michelle's ⓆⒺⒸ
28 Forest Avenue, 04009
(207) 647-8828

Brunswick

The Fabric Den Ⓠ
124 Maine Street, #20, 04011
(207) 373-9090

Bucksport

Bolt Ⓠ
7 Third Street, 04416
(207) 702-9469

Camden

The Cashmere Goat ⓎⓌⓈ
20 Bayview Street, 04843
(207) 236-7236

Warner Graphics Ⓨ
22 Washington Street, 04843
(207) 236-2065 or (800) 875-2422

Cape Neddick

Knight's Quilt Shop Ⓠ
1901 Blue Star Memorial Highway, 03902
(207) 361-2500

Chelsea

Mystic Maine Quilts ⓆⒺⓂ
5 River Road, 04330
(207) 582-0312

Cumberland

The Elegant Knitter at Goose Pond ⓎⓌⓈ
176 Gray Road, 04021
(207) 829-2708

Damariscotta

Attic Heirlooms ⓆⒺⓎⓃⓌⒸ
157 Main Street, 04543
(207) 712-9914 or (207) 712-2280
MTuWFSa 10-5, Th 10-8, Su 12-4;
Winter: (Jan-March) Tu-Sa 10-4
www.attic-heirlooms.com

Eastport

Eastport Fabric Emporium* ⓆⓎ
106 Water Street, 04631
(207) 214-9280

Edgecomb

On Board Fabrics Ⓠ
660 Boothbay Road, Route 27, 04556
(207) 882-7536

Elsworth

Maine Alpaca Experience ⓎⓈ
112 Main Street, 04605
(207) 356-4146

Farmington

Pins & Needles ⓆⒺⓎⒸ
157 Main Street, 04938
(207) 779-9060

Freeport

Mother of Purl Yarn Shop Ⓨ
541 US Route 1, 04032
(207) 869-5280
MTuWFSa 10-5, Th 10-8, Su 11-4
www.motherofpurlyarn.com

Cotton Weeds Quilt Shop ⓆⒺⓂ
15 Main Street (Route 1), 04032
(207) 865-4600

Grace Robinson & Company ⒺⓎⓃⒸ
208 US Route 1, Suite 1, 04032
(207) 865-6110

Greenville

Crazy Moose Fabrics ⓆⓎ
16 Pritham Avenue, 04441
(207) 695-3600

Hallowell

WhipperSnappers Quilt Studio Ⓠ
103 Water Street, 04347
(207) 622-3458

Hancock

Shirley's Yarns And Crafts ⒺⓎⓃⒸ
677 US Highway 1, 04640
(207) 667-7158

Harmony

Bartlettyarns, Inc. ⓎⓌⓈ
20 Water Street, 04942
(207) 683-2251

Houlton

Rather-B-Quilting and County Yarn Basket ⓆⒺⓎⒸ
224 B Road, 04730
(207) 532-9229 or (207) 694-1500

Jonesport

Jolene's Originals* ⓆⓎ
560 Mason's Bay Road, 04649
(207) 497-2684

Kennebunk

Needlepoint America Website Ⓝ
173 Port Road, 04043
(207) 967-4900
M-F 10-4; weekends and holidays by appt. only. Closed 10/19- 5/23.
www.needlepointamerica.com

Camp Wool ⓆⒺⒸ
10 Main Street, 04043
(207) 985-0030

Lebanon

Footprints Quilt Shoppe ⓆⒺ
1498 Carl Broggi Highway, 04027
(603) 767-3624
MTu 12-6, Th 10-6, FSa 10-4
www.footprintsquilting.com

Lee

Amy's Sewing Room Ⓠ
110 Maxwell Road, 04455
(207) 794-4195
WF 9-6; call for addl. hours
www.amyssewingroom.com

Limerick

Annie's Teeny Tiny Quilt Shop Ⓠ
54 Central Avenue, 04048
(207) 793-9988

Lisbon

Spunky Eclectic* ⓎⓌⓈ
33 Webster Road, 04250
(207) 353-9665

Litchfield

Busy Thimble Quilt Shop* Ⓠ
2046 Hallowell Road, 04350
(207) 268-4581

Lovell

Hilltop Handspun ⓎⓈ
16 Lucy Lane, 04051
(207) 928-2000

Lubec

Wags and Wool Ⓨ
83 Water Street, 04652
(207) 733-4714

Madison

The Fabric Garden ⓆⒺⓂ
167 Lakewood Road, 04950
(207) 474-9628

Monmouth

Friends Folly Farm ⓎⓈ
319 Norris Hill Road, 04259
(207) 632-3115

New Gloucester

Acker's Acres Angoras ⓎⓈ
359 Gloucester Hill Road, 04260
(207) 926-4921

New Sharon

Imelda's Fabrics and Design ⓆⒺⓎⓃⓌⓈⒸⓂ
5 Starks Road, 04955
(207) 778-0665

Nobleboro

Alewives Fabrics ⓆⒺⓎⓃⒸ
10 Main Street, 04555
(207) 563-5002

Maine-ly Sewing Ⓠ
48 Atlantic Highway, 04555
(207) 563-8445

Northport

Maine Alpaca Experience ⓎⓈ
608 Atlantic Highway, 04849
(207) 356-4146

Norway

Fiber & Vine ⒺⓎⓈ
402 Main Street, 04268
(207) 739-2664

Sew Orchid Design, LLC Ⓠ
316 Main Street, 04268
(207) 739-2065

Orrington

A Straight Stitch Q
177 River Road, Suite 4, 04474
(207) 989-1234

Oxford

Oxford Mill End Store Q M
971 Main Street (Route 26), 04270
(207) 539-4451

Portland

KnitWit Yarn Shop Y
247A Congress Street, 04101
(207) 774-6444

PortFiber Y W S
50 Cove Street, 04101
(207) 780-1345

Tess' Designer Yarns Q Y
424 Fore Street, 04101
(207) 460-9276

Z Fabrics Q E Y M
477 Congress Street, 04101
(207) 773-1331

Presque Isle

Merchants on the Corner E Y
394 Main Street, 04769
(207) 764-1255

Rockland

clementine Q Y
428 Main Street, 04841
(207) 596-3905

Saco

Half Square Quilt Shop / Northern Comfort Quilts Q
15 Pepperell Square, 04072
(207) 494-7718

Sanford

Sanford Sewing Machines Q M
1923 Main Street, 04073
(207) 324-8375

Shapleigh

Primitive Quarters Quilt Shop Q
52 Jones Road, 04076
(207) 636-1571

Skowhegan

Happyknits LLC Y
42 Court Street, Suite C, 04976
(207) 474-7979

South Portland

Central Yarn Shop Y
868 Broadway, 04106
(207) 799-7789

Southwest Harbor

Quilt 'N' Fabric Q E Y N C
11 Seal Cove Road, 04679
(207) 244-1233

Under The Dogwood Tree Q
326 Main Street, 04679
(207) 244-3089

St. Agatha

Majestic Touch Quilt Shop Q
140 Main Street, 04772
(207) 543-2018

Stockton Springs

Purple Fleece* Ⓨ Ⓦ Ⓢ
103 School Street, 04981
(207) 323-1871

Sumner

A Wrinkle in Thyme Farm Ⓨ Ⓢ
106 Black Mountain Road, 04292
(207) 212-4058

Trenton

Sewing By The Sea Ⓠ Ⓔ Ⓜ
11 Periwinkle Lane, 04605
(207) 664-2558

Turner

Nezinscot Farm* Ⓠ Ⓨ Ⓝ Ⓦ Ⓢ
284 Turner Center Road, 04282
(207) 225-3231

Unity

Maine Alpaca Experience* Ⓨ Ⓢ
141 Crosby Brook Road, 04988
(207) 356-4146

Waterville

Yardgoods Center Ⓠ Ⓔ Ⓨ Ⓝ Ⓒ Ⓜ
60 Concourse W, 04901
(207) 872-2118

Wells

The Crafty Cat / Handmade by Janet* Ⓠ
Coles Corner on Route 1, 04090
(207) 351-6372 or (207) 457-1396

W. Cushing & Co. and Joan Moshimer's Studio Ⓠ Ⓨ Ⓝ Ⓒ
404 Littlefield Road, 04090
(207) 360-0792 or (800) 626-7847

Wilsons Mills

North Woods Quilting Ⓠ
346 Wilsons Mills Road, Route 16, 03579
(207) 486-9331

Windham

Calico Basket Quilt Shop Ⓠ Ⓔ
31 Page Road, 04062
(207) 892-5606

Rosemary's Gift and Yarn Shop Ⓨ Ⓦ Ⓢ
39 Roosevelt Trail, 04062
(207) 894-5770

York

The Yarn Sellar Ⓨ Ⓢ
264 US Route 1, 03909
(207) 351-1987

NeedleTravel

Download our App!

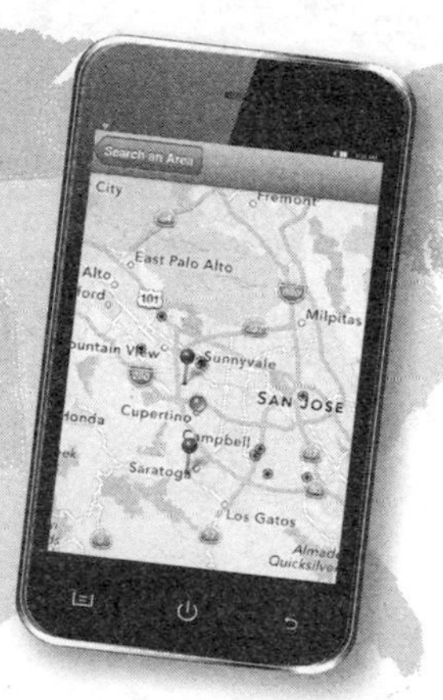

Find Shops From Your Phone

It's Free!

Check us out on:

www.facebook.com/Needletravel

http://www.pinterest.com/needletravel

https://twitter.com/Needletravel

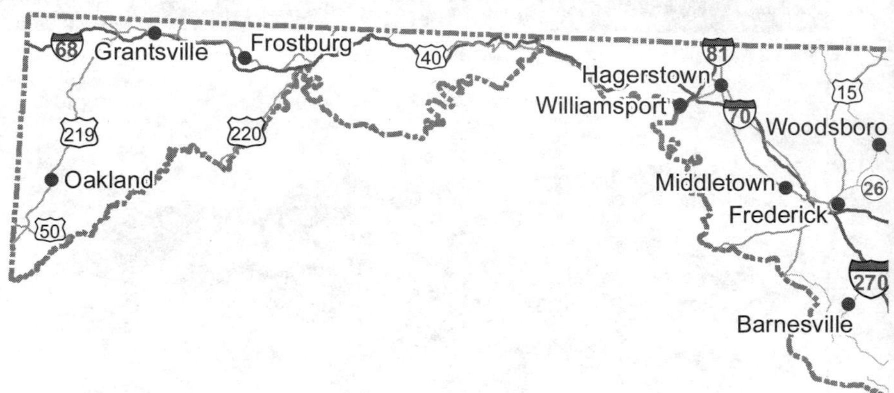
68
Grantsville
Frostburg
40
81
Hagerstown
15
Williamsport
70
Woodsboro
219
220
Oakland
Middletown
26
Frederick
50
270
Barnesville

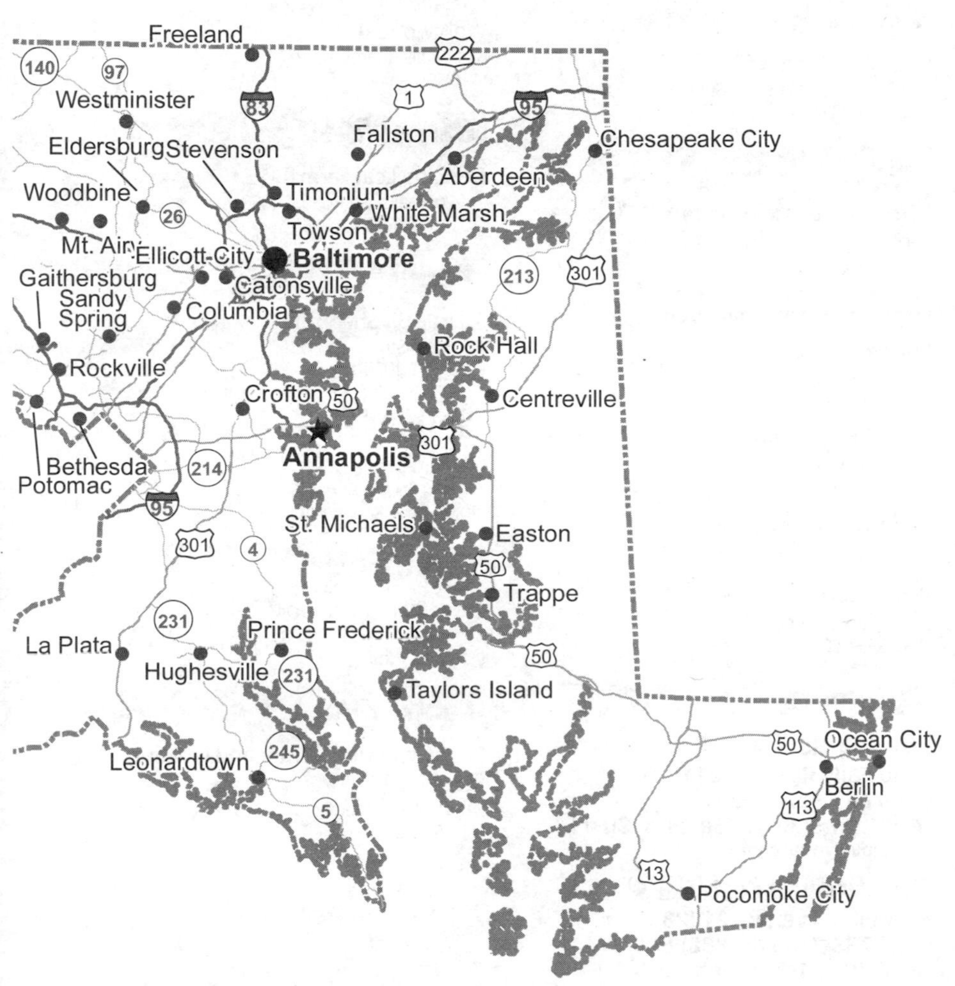

Freeland
140
97
222
Westminister
83
1
95
Fallston
Chesapeake City
Eldersburg
Stevenson
Aberdeen
Woodbine
Timonium
White Marsh
26
Towson
Mt. Airy
Ellicott City
Baltimore
213
301
Gaithersburg
Catonsville
Sandy Spring
Columbia
Rock Hall
Rockville
Crofton
50
Centreville
301
Annapolis
Bethesda
214
Potomac
95
St. Michaels
Easton
301
4
50
Trappe
231
Prince Frederick
La Plata
50
Hughesville
231
Taylors Island
245
50
Ocean City
Leonardtown
Berlin
113
5
13
Pocomoke City

Maryland

Aberdeen

Hoppin Bobbin Q
690 S. Philadelphia Blvd., Suite 100, 21001
(410) 272-2226

Annapolis

Woolwinders Yarn Shop Y
709 Skippers Lane, 21401
(410) 267-6564
Tu-Sa 11-6, Su 12-5
http://www.woolwinders.com

Knits & Pieces Y
626 Admiral Drive, Suite E, 21401
(410) 216-2897

The Crabby Quilter Q M
4 Annapolis Street, 21401
(410) 263-3897

Yarn Basket Inc. Y W S
53 Maryland Avenue, 21401
(410) 295-7000

Baltimore

Lovelyarns Y W S
3610 Falls Road, 21211
(410) 662-9276
MTuW 11-5:30, ThFSa 11-8, Su 11-5
www.lovelyarns.com

The Stitching Post E N C
67 Mellor Avenue, 21228
(410) 788-7760 or (888) 845-4744
M-Sa 10-4, 1st Su of month 1-4
www.the-stitching-post.com

Needlecraft Corner C
7905 Harford Road, 21234
(410) 668-3811 or (888) 396-8008

Neighborhood Fiber Co. Y W S
700 N. Eutaw Street, 21201
(410) 989-3770

Woolworks Y
6117 Falls Road, 21209
(410) 377-2060

Barnesville

Dancing Leaf Farm Y S
21920 Beallsville Road, 20838
(301) 801-6995

Berlin

A Little Bit Sheepish Y
1 S. Main Street, 21811
(410) 641-1080

Bethesda

Second Story Knits Y
4706 Bethesda Avenue, 20814
(301) 652-8688

Catonsville

Cloverhill Yarn Shop Y W S
77 Mellor Avenue, 21228
(410) 788-7262

Centreville

Peggy's Sewing Center and Quilting Studio Q
210 Pennsylvania Avenue, 21617
(410) 758-3827

Chesapeake City

Vulcan's Rest Fibers Y W S

➡ SEE AD BELOW

2728 Augustine Herman Highway, 21915
(410) 885-2890
Everyday 10-5
www.vulcansrest.com

Columbia

Spring Water Designs Quilting Q M

9691 Gerwig Lane, Suite G, 21046
(410) 381-0695
M-F 10-6, Sa 10-5, Su 12-4; check website for seasonal and holiday hours
www.springwaterdesigns.com

Crofton

Tomorrow's Treasures Q M
2110 Priest Bridge Drive, Suite 12, 21114
(410) 451-0400 or (301) 858-1705

Easton

Blue Heron Yarns Y W
125 Kemp Lane, 21601
(410) 829-5859

Frivolous Fibers Yarn Boutique Y S
31 N. Harrison Street, 21601
(410) 822-6580

Eldersburg

Knitters Nest Y
1431 Liberty Road, 21784
(410) 549-0709

Ellicott City

Ellicott City Sew Vac Q E M

8480 Baltimore National Pike, 21043
(410) 465-6366
MWF 10-6, TuTh 10-8, Sa 10-4, Su 12-4
www.sewfair.com

Fallston

Glory Bee's Sewing Center, LLC Q M
2112 Belair Road, Suite 5, 21047
(443) 981-3182

Frederick

Flying Goat Farm Y S

5241 Bartonsville Road, 21704
(443) 538-8303
F-Su 1:30-4:30, please call ahead
www.facebook.com/Flying-Goat-FarM-126228707403654/

Charlotte's Cottage Quilt Shop Q
122 N. East Street, 21701
(240) 815-6825

Primitive Homespuns Wool and Needleworks E C
120 N. East Street, 21701
(240) 608-2136

The Knot House Y
129 E. Patrick Street, 21701
(240) 357-4232

Freeland

Feederbrook Farm Ⓨ Ⓢ
1227 Morris Road, 21053
(410) 357-5336

Frostburg

Frostburg Fiber Depot Ⓨ Ⓢ
9 W. Main Street, 21532
(240) 284-2154

Gaithersburg

Capital Quilts Ⓠ Ⓔ Ⓜ
15926 Luanne Drive, 20877
(301) 527-0598
MTuWThSa 10-6, F 10-9, Su 12-5
www.capitalquilts.com

Knit Locally Ⓨ
1-D East Diamond Avenue, 20877
(301) 528-2800 or (240) 351-5118
WThF 12-6, Sa 10-5, Su 12-5. Please check website or FB as schedule is subject to seasonal change.
http://www.knitlocally.com

Grantsville

Four Seasons Stitchery Ⓠ Ⓔ Ⓒ
116 Main Street, 21536
(301) 895-5958

Shady Grove Market & Fabrics Ⓠ Ⓔ Ⓨ Ⓒ
1493 Springs Road, 21536
(301) 895-5660

Hagerstown

Traditions at the White Swan Ⓠ
16525 National Pike, 21740
(301) 733-9130

Wilson's, Your Favorite Quilt Shop Ⓠ
13516 Marsh Pike, 21742
(301) 790-3526

Hughesville

Michelle's Quilts Ⓠ Ⓔ Ⓒ
8132 Old Leonardtown Road, 20637
(301) 274-1919

La Plata

Material Girls Quilt Boutique Ⓠ Ⓔ Ⓜ
6750 Crain Highway, Suite B, 20646
(301) 392-9575

Leonardtown

New View FiberWorks, LLC Ⓨ Ⓦ Ⓢ
22696 Washington Street, 20650
(301) 475-3899
W-Sa 10-5, First Fri of the month 10-8
www.newviewfiberworks.com

Crazy for Ewe Ⓨ
22725 Washington Street, 20650
(301) 475-2744

Middletown

Kiparoo Farm Studio Ⓨ
3511 Bussard Road, 21769
(301) 371-7454

Mt. Airy

Patches Quilting & Sewing Ⓠ Ⓜ
308 S. Main Street, 21771
(301) 831-0366

Oakland

Yoder's Fabrics Ⓠ Ⓔ
4166 Mason School Road, 21550
(301) 334-4965

Ocean City

Salty Yarns Ⓔ Ⓨ Ⓝ Ⓒ
807 Atlantic Avenue, 21842
(410) 289-4667

Pocomoke City

The Pincushion Ⓠ Ⓔ
151 Market Street, 21851
(410) 957-4766

Potomac

From Start To Finish Ⓔ
8001 River Falls Drive, 20854
(301) 983-5017

Prince Frederick

Calvert Quilt Shop ⓆⒺⓂ
20 Industry Lane, 20678
(410) 535-0576
M-F 9:30-6, Sa 9:30-4
www.calvertquiltshop.com

Rock Hall

Village Quilting, LLC. ⓆⒺⒸ
5701 Main Street, 21661
(410) 639-4101

Rockville

Woolwinders Yarn Shop Ⓨ
404 King Farm Blvd., Suite 150, 20850
(240) 632-9276
Tu-Sa 11- 6, Su 12-5
www.woolwinders.com

G Street Fabrics ⓆⒺⓂ
12220 Wilkins Avenue, 20852
(301) 231-8998

Sandy Spring

SO Original ⓎⓃⓌ
900 Sandy Spring Road, 20860
(301) 774-7970

St. Michaels

B's Stitches Ⓝ
209 N. Talbot Street, 21663
(410) 745-6146

Stevenson

Hillside Needlepoint Ⓝ
10437 Stevenson Road, 21153
(443) 548-3691

Taylors Island

Kaire'je Studio* Ⓨ
4216 Robinson Neck Road, 21669
(410) 221-0299

Timonium

Black Sheep Yarn Shop Ⓨ
9602 Deereco Road, 21093
(410) 628-9276

Towson

Bear's Paw Fabrics ⓆⓂ
8812 Orchard Tree Lane, 21286
(410) 321-6730
M-F 10-5, Sa 9:30-4, Su 12-4
www.bearspawfabrics.com

Trappe

Quilt Vine Ⓠ
3987 Main Street, 21673
(410) 476-6166

Westminster

Blue House Fabrics ⓆⓂ
410 E. Main Street, 21157
(443) 289-9347

Jomax Sew & Vac Center ⓆⓂ
540A Jermor Lane, 21157
(410) 848-8080

White Marsh

Hooven Sewing Center ⓆⒺⓂ
11550 Philadelphia Road, Suite 108, 21162
(410) 529-7943 or (800) 354-0684

Williamsport

Williamsport Yarn Closet* Ⓨ
414 S. Conocheague Street, 21795
(240) 625-2944

Woodbine

Withers Wool / Unique Designs by Kathy Withers* ⓎⓌⓈ
6401 Woodbine Road, 21797
(410) 795-6070

Woodsboro

Forestheart Studio ⓎⓌⓈ
200 S. Main Street, 21798
(301) 845-4447 or (301) 663-3855

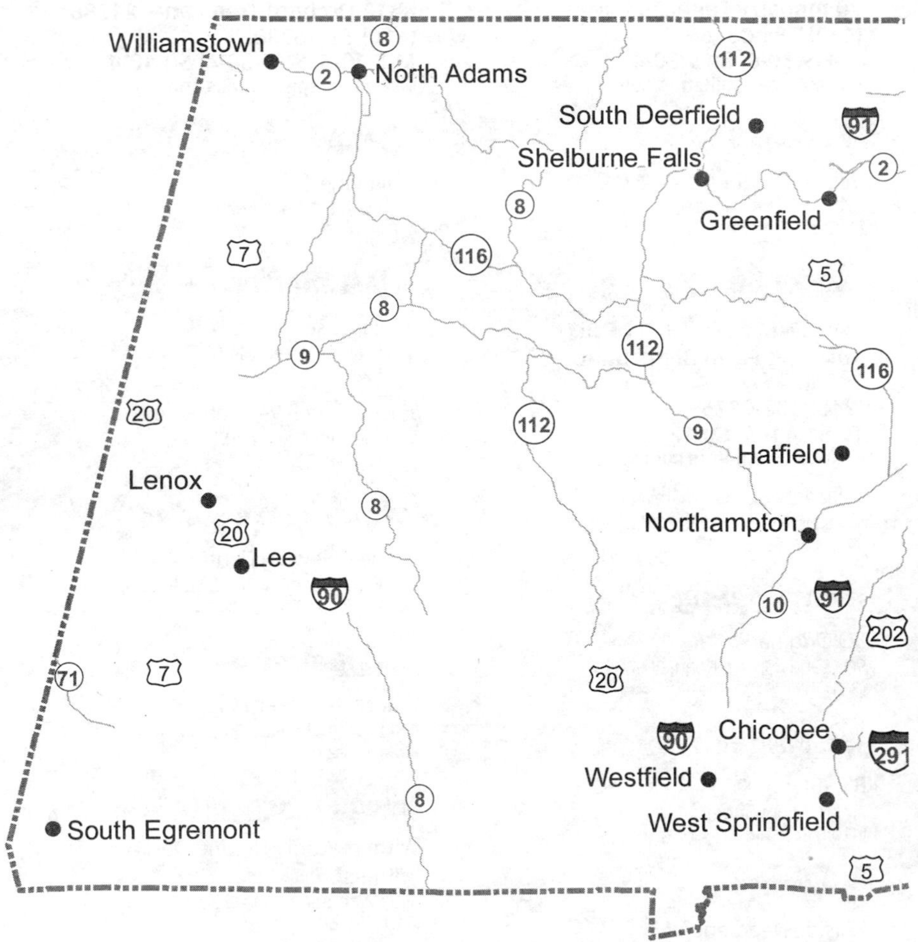
Williamstown
North Adams
South Deerfield
Shelburne Falls
Greenfield
Hatfield
Northampton
Lenox
Lee
Chicopee
Westfield
West Springfield
South Egremont

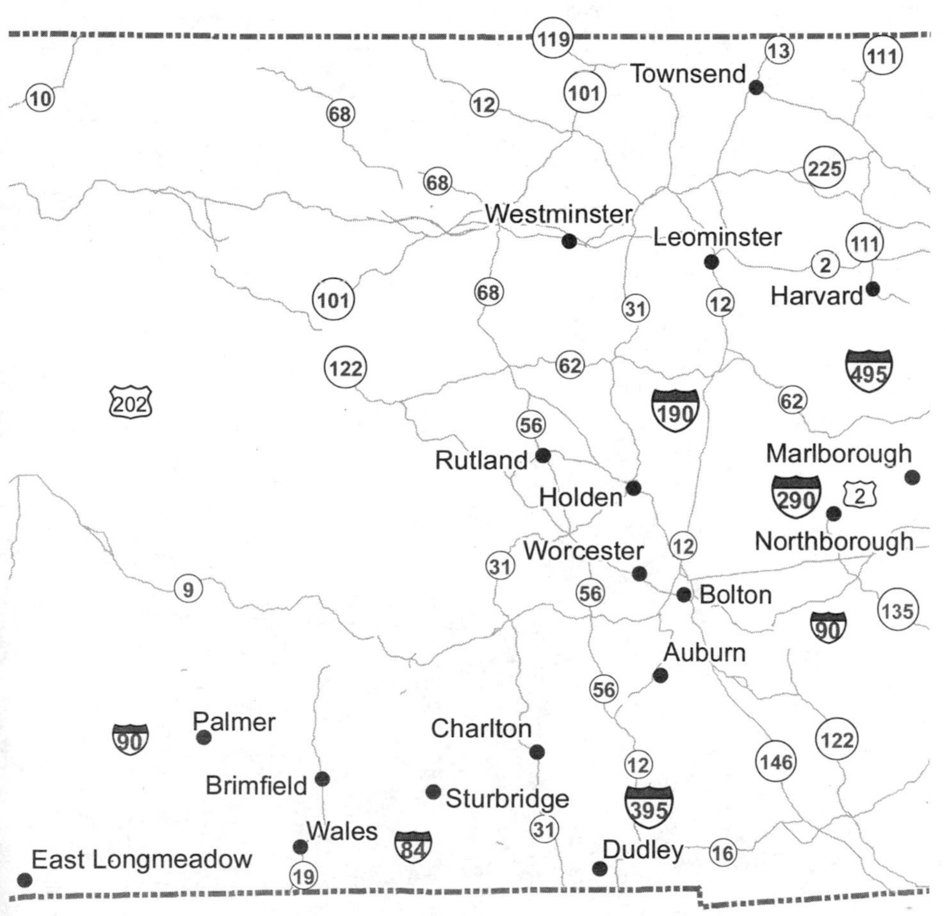
119
13
111
Townsend
10
68
12
101
225
68
Westminster
Leominster
111
2
101
68
31
12
Harvard
122
62
495
202
190
62
56
Marlborough
Rutland
Holden
290
2
Northborough
31
Worcester
12
9
56
Bolton
135
90
Auburn
56
Palmer
Charlton
122
90
12
146
Brimfield
Sturbridge
395
Wales
84
31
Dudley
16
East Longmeadow
19

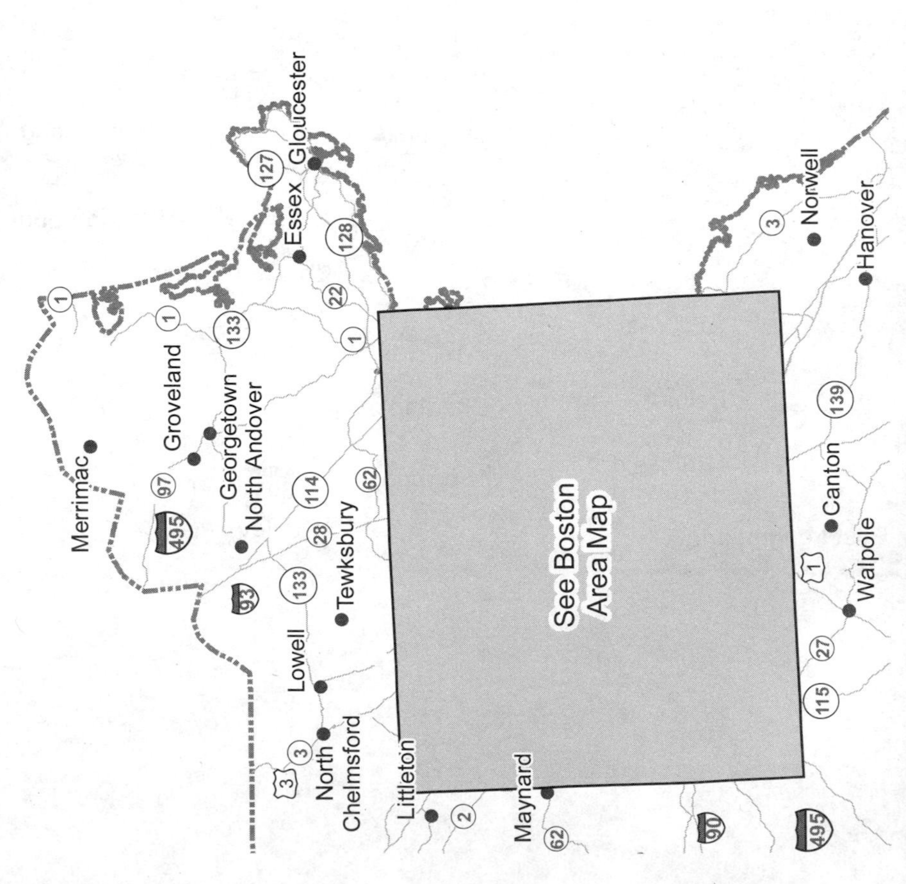
Merrimac
Groveland
Georgetown
North Andover
Essex
Gloucester
Lowell
Tewksbury
North Chelmsford
Littleton
Maynard
See Boston Area Map
Norwell
Hanover
Canton
Walpole

Bellingham
Franklin
95
1
27
North Easton
53
139
Provincetown
6
1
28
27
North Scituate
N. Attleboro
295
495
3
6
44
Middleboro
Rehoboth
3
Eastham
Lakeville
2
Orleans
Seekonk
Sandwich
Brewster
195
28
6
Dennis
134
137
28
195
West Barnstable
E. Harwich
6
Chatham
Fall River
Forestdale
28
6
West Dennis
Westport
Fairhaven
Mashpee
28
South Dartmouth
Vineyard Haven
Edgartown
Nantucket

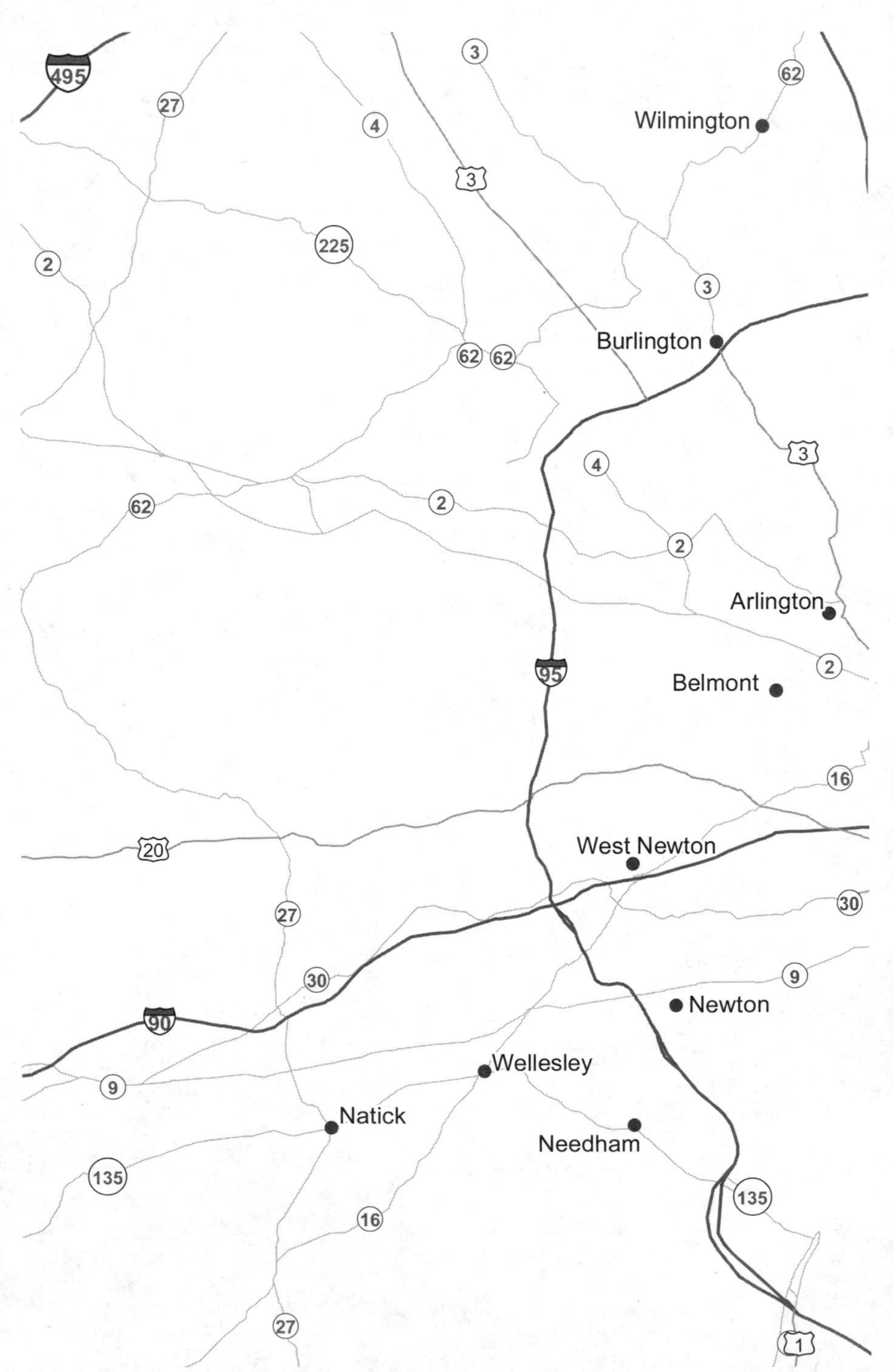
495
27
4
3
62
Wilmington
3
225
2
3
Burlington
62
62
4
3
62
2
2
Arlington
95
2
Belmont
16
20
West Newton
27
30
30
9
Newton
90
Wellesley
9
Natick
Needham
135
135
16
27
1

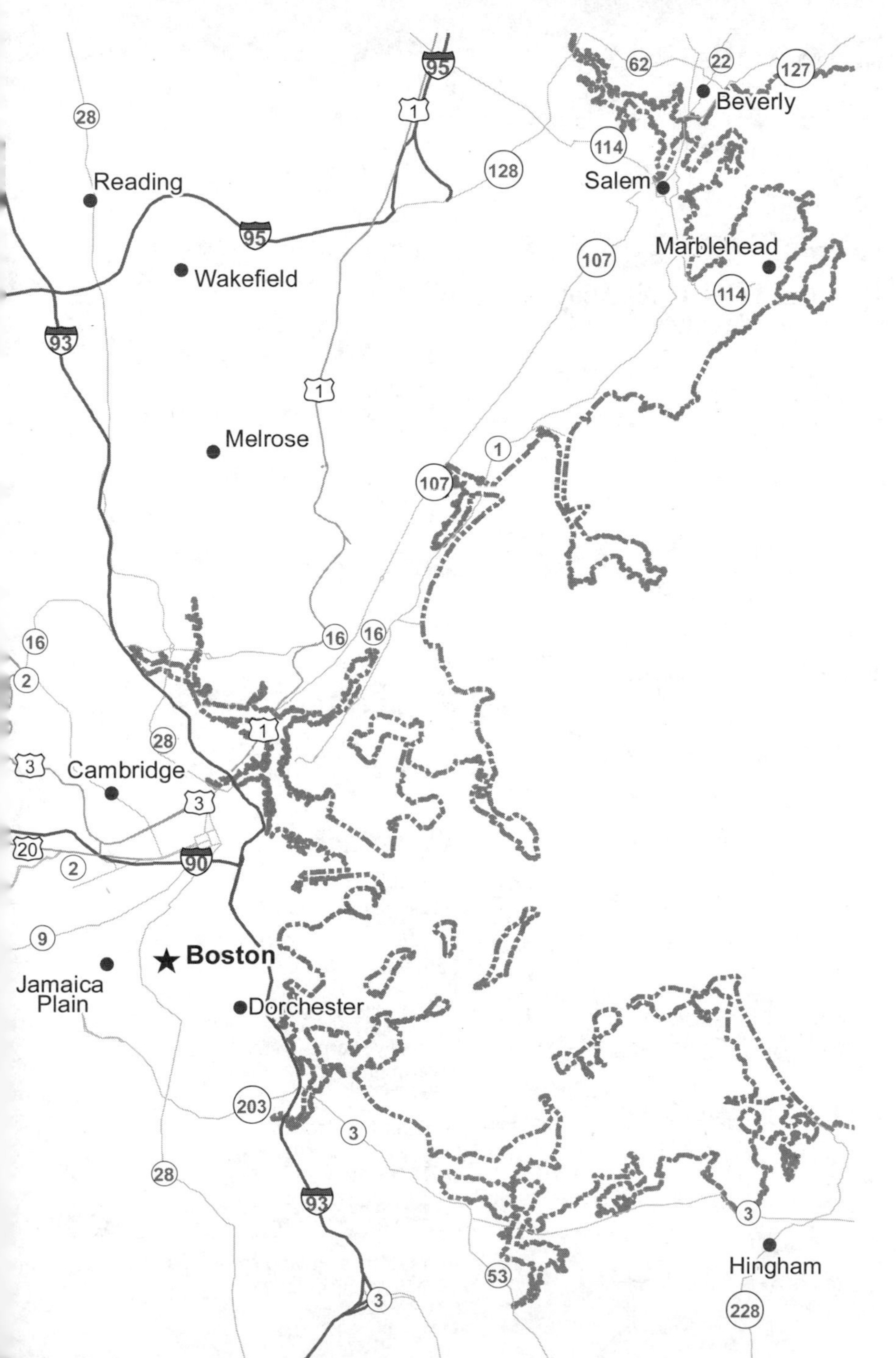

95
1
28
62
22
127
Beverly
114
128
Reading
Salem
95
107
Marblehead
Wakefield
114
93
1
Melrose
1
107
16
16
16
2
1
28
3
Cambridge
3
20
90
2
9
Boston
Jamaica Plain
Dorchester
203
3
28
93
3
53
Hingham
3
228

Massachusetts

Arlington

Fabric Corner Inc. Q
783 Massachusetts Avenue, 02476
(781) 643-4040

Auburn

Appletree Fabrics Quilt Shop Q
850 Southbridge Street, 01501
(508) 832-5562
M-W 10-6, Th-Sa 10-5, Su 12-4 (Please call ahead on Su)
www.appletreefabricsonline.com

Auburn Fabric Outlet Q
773 Southbridge Street, 01501
(508) 832-0330

Bellingham

Dragonfly's Quilt Shop Q M
799 S. Main Street, Unit 11A, 02019
(508) 360-6099

Handi Quilter® Authorized Retailer
Designed by a Quilter, for Quilters.®

Belmont

Hollingworth 5 & 10 Q E Y N C
89 Trapelo Road, 02478
(617) 484-6656

Beverly

Sew Creative Q M
14 Elliott Street, 01915
(978) 524-8848

Yarns in the Farms Y W
641 Hale Street, 01915
(978) 927-2108

Bolton

The Quilted Crow Q E
626 Main Street, 01740
(978) 266-9102

Boston

Bead & Fiber Y
460 Harrison Avenue, 02118
(617) 426-2323

Newbury Yarns Q Y
2 Milk Street, 02108
(617) 572-3733

Stitch Boutique of Boston N
231 Berkeley Street, 02116
(617) 236-4633

Brewster

Quilt-ish of Cape Cod Q
1357 Main Street, 02631
(703) 403-9771

Town-Ho Needleworks E N C
1912 Main Street, 02631
(508) 896-3000

Brimfield

Carolyn's Creations Q
149 E. Hill Road, 01010
(413) 245-3662

Burlington

Another Yarn Y
15 Cambridge Street, 01803
(781) 570-2134

Cambridge

Cambridge Quilt Shop Q
95 Blanchard Road, 02138
(617) 492-3279

Gather Here Q E Y C
1343 Cambridge Street, 02139
(617) 714-4880

Mind's Eye Yarns Y W S
22 White Street, 02140
(617) 354-7253

The Knittin' Kitten Y
93 Blanchard Road, 02138
(617) 491-4670

Canton

Ann's Fabrics Sewing Machine Center Q M
235 Turnpike Street, 02021
(781) 828-2201

Charlton

Charlton Sewing Center Q E M
12 Stafford Street (Route 31), 01507
(508) 248-6632

Handi Quilter® Authorized Retailer
Designed by a Quilter, for Quilters.®

The Fabric Stash Q
45A Sturbridge Road (Route 20), 01507
(508) 248-0600

Chatham

A Great Yarn Y
894 Main Street, 02633
(508) 348-5605

Chicopee

Bayberry Quilt and Gift Shoppe Q
137 Sheridan Street, 01020
(413) 592-9653

Dennis

Salt Yarn Studio Y
620 Main Street (Route 6A), 02638
(508) 694-6189

Dorchester

Stitch House Q E Y
846 Dorchester Avenue, 02125
(617) 265-8013

Dudley

Quilter's Loft LLC Q Y
26 Mill Road, 01571
(508) 949-9095
Sa 10-6, Su 10-3, evenings by appt.
http://www.quiltersloft.com

East Harwich

Adventures In Knitting Y
105 Route 137, Suite B, 02645
(508) 432-3700

East Longmeadow

Quilts & Treasures, Inc. Q M
➡ SEE AD BELOW
56 Shaker Road, 01028
(413) 525-4789 or (413) 525-6647
M-Th 10-8:30, FSa 10-5
www.quiltsandtreasuresinc.com

Eastham

Quilter's Palette Q
45 Gingerplum Lane, 02642
(508) 255-4038

Yarn Basket Y
4205 County Road, 02642
(508) 255-3557

Edgartown

Needleworks N
12 N. Summer Street, 02539
(508) 627-6027 or (914) 238-8809

Essex

Hooked Knitting Y
65 Eastern Avenue, 01929
(978) 768-7329 or (978) 471-9993

Fairhaven

Eva's Yarn Shop Y
42 Main Street, 02719
(508) 996-5648

Fall River

K G Krafts Q E Y N W C
260 New Boston Road, 02720
(508) 676-3336

Forestdale

Sew Pro of Cape Cod Q E M
337 Cotuit Road, 02644
(508) 759-2222

Franklin

Franklin Mill Store Q Y
305 Union Street, 02038
(508) 528-3301
MFSa 10-5, TuWTh 10-8
www.franklinmillstore.com

Emma's Quilt Cupboard and Sewing Center Q E M
12 Main Street, 02038
(508) 520-0234

Georgetown

Quilters' Quarters Q E
59 North Street, 01833
(978) 352-2676
Th-Sa 12-5, and by appt.
www.atquiltersquarters.blogspot.com

Gloucester

Coveted Yarn Y S
127 Eastern Avenue, Suite 4, 01930
(978) 282-8809

Greenfield

The Textile Company, Inc. Q
21 Power Square, 01301
(413) 773-7516

Groveland

Merrimack Yarn Y
908 Salem Street, Unit 2, 01834
(978) 641-3639

Hanover

American Folk Art & Craft Supply Q E M
1415 Hanover Street, Route 139, 02339
(781) 871-7277

Harvard

The Fiber Loft Y W S
9 Massachusetts Avenue, Route 111, 01451
(978) 456-8669

Hatfield

The Yellow Quilt Shop Q
131 Main Street, Suite 107, 01038
(413) 247-6481 or (413) 247-6481
Th 10-8, FSa 10-5
http://www.theyellowquiltshop.com

Hingham

Hingham Square Needlepoint Ⓝ
132 North Street, 2nd Floor, 02043
(781) 836-5200

Holden

The Sheep Shack Ⓨ
787 Main Street, 01520
(508) 829-5811

Jamaica Plain

J.P. Knit & Stitch ⓆⒺⓎ
461 Centre Street, 02130
(617) 477-3707

Lakeville

Homestead Quilting and Fabrics ⓆⓂ
54 Main Street, #20, 02347
(774) 419-3984

Lee

Pumpkin Patch ⓆⓂ
43 Main Street, 01238
(413) 243-1635

Lenox

Colorful Stitches Fine Yarn Ⓨ
48 Main Street (Rear Suite), 01240
(800) 413-6111 or (413) 637-8206

Leominster

The Merry Weaver ⓎⓌ
244 Grove Avenue, 01453
(978) 467-6541

Littleton

The World In Stitches ⒺⓎⓃⒸ
256 Great Road, Unit 16, 01460
(978) 486-8330

Lowell

New England Quilt Museum Ⓠ
18 Shattuck Street, 01852
(978) 452-4207

Marblehead

Marblehead Knits Ⓨ
152 Washington Street, 01945
(781) 990-1722

Marlborough

Wayside Sewing ⓆⒺⒸⓂ
1021 Boston Post Road E, 01752
(508) 481-2088

Mashpee

Osterville Needlepoint Ⓝ
17A Trinity Place, 02649
(508) 428-4455

Yarn Basket Ⓨ
681 Falmouth Road, 02649
(508) 477-0858

Maynard

The Island Yarn Company ⓎⓌⓈ
189 Main Street, 01754
(978) 331-0009

Melrose

Crosscut Sewing Co. ⓆⓂ
200 Green Street, 02176
(781) 620-1896

Lucky Cat Yarns Ⓨ
167 W. Emerson Street, 02176
(781) 590-4940

Merrimac

Red Barn Sewing & Yarn Center ⓆⓎⓂ
116 W. Main Street, 01860
(978) 346-9292

Middleboro

The Wool Patch Ⓨ
446 Wareham Street, 02346
(508) 923-6029

Nantucket

Erica Wilson Needle Works Ⓝ Ⓒ
25 Main Street, 02554
(508) 228-9881

Flock Ⓨ
79 Orange Street, 02554
(508) 228-0038

Weatherly Design, LLC Ⓠ
1 Federal Street, 02554
(508) 228-3846

Natick

Fabric Place Basement Ⓠ Ⓨ
321 Speen Street, 01760
(508) 655-2000

Iron Horse Ⓨ Ⓦ Ⓢ
3 Pond Street, 01760
(508) 647-4722

Needham

Black Sheep Knitting Ⓨ
1500 Highland Avenue, 02492
(781) 444-0694

Elissa's Creative Warehouse Ⓔ Ⓨ Ⓝ Ⓦ Ⓢ Ⓒ
220 Reservoir Street, Suite 10, 02494
(781) 444-9341

Newton

Knits & Pieces Ⓨ
293A Elliot Street, 02464
(617) 969-8879

North Adams

The Spin-Off Yarn Shop Ⓨ
60 Roberts Drive, Suite 302, 01247
(413) 344-6257

North Andover

A Garden For Knitters Ⓨ
52 Water Street, 01845
(978) 682-3297

North Attleboro

Yarn It All Ⓨ
1 Bank Street, 02760
(508) 695-3331

North Chelmsford

Aunt Margaret's Ⓨ
165 Princeton Street, 01863
(978) 251-2272

North Easton

Auntie Zaza's Fiber Works Ⓨ Ⓢ
104 Main Street, 02356
(774) 269-6899

North Scituate

Yarns In The Square Ⓨ
363 Gannett Road, 02060

Northampton

WEBS - America's Yarn Store Ⓨ Ⓦ Ⓢ
75 Service Center Road, 01060
(800) 367-9327 or (413) 584-2225
MTuWF 10-6, Th 10-8, Sa 10-5:30
www.yarn.com

Northampton Wools Ⓨ
29 Pleasant Street, 01060
(413) 586-4331

Northborough

Craftworks Ⓨ Ⓦ Ⓢ
➡ SEE AD BELOW
243 W. Main Street, 01532
(508) 393-9435
M 10-8, TuWF 10-5, Th 10-6, Sa 10-4, Su 12-4; closed Sundays July & Aug
www.craftworkscoop.com

Norwell

yarn's end Ⓨ Ⓦ Ⓢ
376 Washington Street, 02061
(781) 924-5549

Orleans

Murray's Fabrics Ⓠ
11 Route 28, 02653
(508) 255-0653

Palmer

Sew Bizzie Quilting Ⓠ
4109 Main Street (Thorndike), 01069
(413) 283-4422

Provincetown

Pürl Ⓨ Ⓦ Ⓢ
349 Commercial Street, Unit D, 02657
(508) 456-7875
Winter: W-Sa 11-5; Summer: (June-Sept.) Everyday 10-6
www.ptownpurl.com

Reading

Mary Rose's Quilts and Treasures Ⓠ
4 Brande Court, 01867
(781) 942-9497

Rehoboth

Loraine's Stitch 'n' Crafts Ⓠ Ⓔ Ⓜ
235 Winthrop Street, 02769
(508) 252-5640

Rutland

Knit N Stitch* Ⓨ
10 Phillips Road, 01543
(508) 886-6167

Salem

BF Goodstitch Ⓔ Ⓝ Ⓒ
18 Front Street, 01970
(978) 740-8986

Circle of Stitches Ⓔ Ⓨ Ⓦ Ⓢ Ⓒ
66 Wharf Street, 01970
(978) 745-9276

Sandwich

Black Purls Yarn Shop Ⓨ
201 Route 6A, 02563
(508) 362-8880

Seekonk

The Calico Cottage Quilt Shop Ⓠ
1460 Fall River Avenue, Suite 10, 02771
(888) 403-5809

Shelburne Falls

Vävstuga Weaving School Ⓨ Ⓦ Ⓢ
16 Water Street, 01370
(413) 625-8241

South Dartmouth

Needleworker* Ⓝ
1 Bridge Street, 02748
(508) 999-2477 or (800) 598-2477

South Deerfield

Sheep & Shawl Ⓨ Ⓢ
265 Greenfield Road, 01373
(413) 397-3680

South Egremont

Brookside Quiltworks Ⓠ Ⓜ
2 Sheffield Road, 01258
(413) 528-0445

Sturbridge

The Quilt and Cabbage Ⓠ Ⓨ
538 Main Street (Route 20), 01566
(508) 347-3023
MW-Sa 9:30-4:30, Su 11-3; call ahead for M and W hours
https://www.facebook.com/TheQuiltAndCabbage/

Tewksbury

Sew-Together Quilt Shop Ⓠ
2297 Main Street, 01876
(978) 203-0291
M 6-9 PM, WFSa 10-4, Th 10-9, Su 12-4
www.sew-together.com

Townsend

Cobblestone Quilts Q
10 Elm Street (Route 13), 01469
(978) 597-0091

Vineyard Haven

The Heath Hen Yarn and Quilt Shop Q E Y
455 State Road, 02568
(508) 693-6730

Vineyard Knitworks E Y N W S
10 State Road, 02568
(508) 687-9163

Wakefield

Quilters Common Q M
364 Main Street (rear of building), 01880
(781) 587-0360
M-Sa 9-5, Su 12-4
www.quilterscommon.com

Wales

Meeting House Fabric & Trim Q E
83 Main Street, 01081
(413) 245-1235

Walpole

All About Quilts Q
958 Main Street, 02081
(508) 668-0145 or (877) 789-8957

Dee's Nimble Needles & Yarn Shop Y
15 West Street, 02081
(508) 668-8499

Wellesley

The Wellesley Needlepoint Collection N
22 Grove Street, 02482
(781) 235-2477

West Barnstable

Tumbleweed Quilt Shop Q
1919 Main Street, 02668
(508) 362-8700
M-Sa 10-5:30, Su 12-5
www.tumbleweedquilts.com

West Dennis

Cape Cod Quilts and Cottages Q
109 Main Street (Route 28), 02670
(508) 760-4524

West Newton

Putting On The Knitz Y
1282 Washington Street, 02465
(617) 969-8070

West Springfield

Osgood Textile Company Q
333 Park Street, 01089
(413) 737-6488 or (888) 674-6638

Westfield

The Spare Room Q
77 Mill Street, Unit 15, 01085
(413) 642-6987

Westminster

Appleberry Fabrics Q E
23 Village Inn Road, Suite A, 01473
(978) 874-0400

Westport

Sisters Of The Wool Y
782 Main Road, 02790
(774) 264-9665

Westport Yarns & Art Supplies E Y N C
1099 State Road, 02790
(508) 994-7845

Williamstown

Karen's Quilting Corner Q
723 Cold Spring Road, 01267
(413) 884-6200

Wilmington

The Crafting Closet Q E Y N C
1 Church Street, #103, 01887
(978) 909-3221

Worcester

Knitscape Y
1116 Pleasant Street, 01602
(508) 459-0557

41
Houghton
26
Tapiola
45
28
Wakefield
Ironwood
41
Marquette
28
Au Train
141
41
2
Norway
2
41
Menominee

Paradise
123
Sault Sainte Marie
28
75
123
2
Manistique
Hessel
134
St. Ignace
75
Carp Lake
Cross Village
31
Alanson
Burt Lake
Indian River
Charlevoix
23
66
Northport
East Jordan
Hillman
Alpena
88
32
Gaylord
32
Suttons Bay
Bellaire
75
22
37
Alden
Frederic
Cedar
Williamsburg
72
Traverse City
72
Grayling
131
Interlochen
18
Fife Lake
Roscommon
22
31
66
27
Lake City
Houghton Lake
East Tawas
Manistee
Cadillac
55
55
West Branch
Tawas City

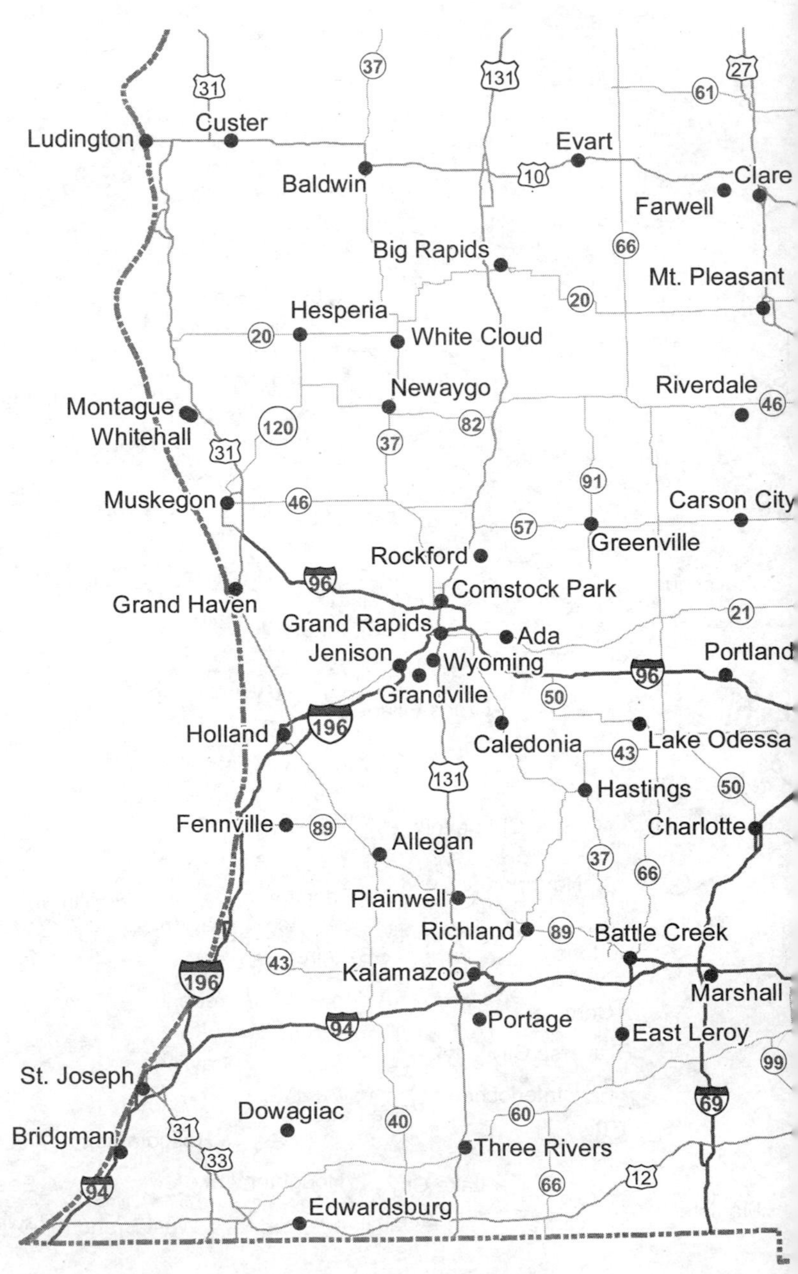

Ludington
Custer
Baldwin
Evart
Clare
Farwell
Big Rapids
Mt. Pleasant
Hesperia
White Cloud
Newaygo
Riverdale
Montague
Whitehall
Muskegon
Carson City
Greenville
Rockford
Comstock Park
Grand Haven
Grand Rapids
Ada
Portland
Jenison
Wyoming
Grandville
Holland
Caledonia
Lake Odessa
Hastings
Fennville
Allegan
Charlotte
Plainwell
Richland
Battle Creek
Kalamazoo
Marshall
Portage
East Leroy
St. Joseph
Dowagiac
Bridgman
Three Rivers
Edwardsburg

Gladwin
Beaverton
Pinconning
Midland
Bay City
Caro
Snover
St. Louis
Merrill
Saginaw
Frankenmuth
Croswell
St. Charles
Brown City
Perrinton
Ovid
Lansing
Haslett
East Lansing
Williamston
Howell
Mason
Chelsea
Pinckney
Leslie
Stockbridge
See Detroit Area Map
Tecumseh
Hillsdale
Adrian
Monroe
Ottawa Lake

75
Davison
21
69
15
24
475
Grand Blanc
75
Ortonville
10
Fenton
Lake Orion
Clarkston
Waterford
Hartland
Township
1
96
Birmingham
Berkley
Brighton
Farmington Hills
Southfield
696
Farmington
36
102
Livonia
Whitmore Lake
96
Plymouth
23
275
Wayne
Ann Arbor
94
12
94
24
75
Saline
12
275

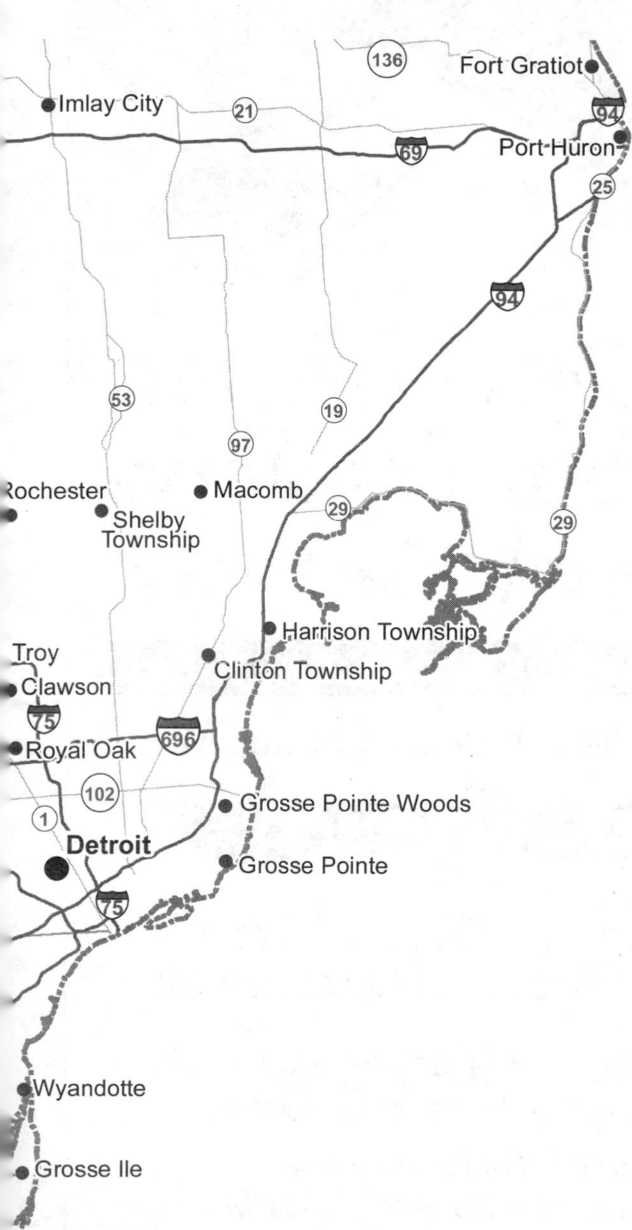

136
Fort Gratiot
Imlay City
21
94
69
Port Huron
25
94
53
19
97
Rochester
Macomb
29
Shelby Township
29
Harrison Township
Troy
Clinton Township
Clawson
75
696
Royal Oak
102
Grosse Pointe Woods
1
Detroit
Grosse Pointe
75
Wyandotte
Grosse Ile

Michigan

Ada

Peacock Alley Needlepoint N
452 Ada Drive SE, Suite 120, 49301
(616) 682-9854 or (877) 550-9898

Adrian

Ann's By Design Q E Y
118 W. Maumee Street, 49221
(517) 438-8459

Yarn Hoppers Y S
136 E. Maumee, Suite 5, 49221
(517) 759-3240

Alanson

Dutch Oven Yarn Shop Y
7611 Burr Avenue U.S. 31, 49706
(231) 548-2700

Alden

The Warm Fuzzy Y
9046 Helena Road, 49612
(231) 944-0757 or (231) 331-4000

Allegan

Baker Allegan Studios Y W S
148 Mill District Road, 49010
(269) 903-6883

Sharon's Quilts & More, Inc. Q
128 Hubbard Street, 49010
(269) 686-9579

Alpena

Stitches n' Blooms E N C
2205 US 23 S, Suite 132, 49707
(989) 354-3739

Yarns to Go & Fabrics Q E Y W S
127 N. 2nd Avenue, 49707
(989) 356-4119

Ann Arbor

Ann Arbor Sewing and Quilting Center Q M
5235 Jackson Road, 48103
(734) 761-3094

Leabu Sewing Center Q E
1960 S. Industrial Highway, Suite C, 48104
(734) 663-3033

Pink Castle Fabrics Q E C M
1915 Federal Blvd., 48103
(877) 808-8695

Spun Y
407 N. Fifth Avenue, 48104
(734) 780-7867

Au Train

Whispering Pines Quilt Shop Q
N7037 Forest Lake Road, 49806
(906) 202-3612

Baldwin

Fabric Peddler Q E C
815 Michigan Avenue, 49304
(231) 745-4500

Battle Creek

Sew Unique Threads Q E
7175 Tower Road, Suite F, 49014
(269) 317-3022

Bay City

A Piece of Ewe Inc. Y
506 Columbus Avenue, 48708
(989) 892-6400

Between Patches Q
470 Chip Road, 48706
(989) 297-6722

Bonnie's Sewing Center Q M
3557 Wilder Road, 48706
(989) 686-8180

Stitchin' at the Bay Q M
132 Uptown Drive, 48708
(989) 778-1900

The Stitching Well Q E Y N C
78 State Park Drive, 48706
(989) 684-0231 or (800) 746-1916

Beaverton

Pieces of Thyme Q
3037 Shock Road, 48612
(989) 435-9230

Bellaire

Cousins' Quilt Shop Q M
732 E. Cayuga Street, 49615
(231) 533-4661

Berkley

...Have You Any Wool Y
3455 Robina Avenue, 48072
(248) 541-9665

Big Rapids

Creative Loop* Q
18841 Northland Drive, 49307
(231) 629-8228

Birmingham

The Needleworks N
725 S. Adams Road, Suite 178, 48009
(248) 645-1180
MTuThF 10-4, W 10-4 & 6-8:30; Sa 10-2, closed M and W evenings in the summer
http://www.eneedleworks.com

Woolly&Co. Y
147 Pierce Street, 48009
(248) 480-4354

Bridgman

The Sandpiper Y S
4217 Lake Street, 49106
(269) 465-5936

Brighton

Unwind Yarn Shop Y
9912 E. Grand River Avenue, Suite 1300, 48116
(810) 229-5579

Brown City

Ann's Fabric Shop Q
5044 Bailey Road, 48416
(810) 346-3237

Burt Lake

Estelle Knit Shop Y N W S
10249 E. West Resort Road, 49717
(231) 881-0251

Cadillac

Northern Hearth Quilting & Sewing Center Q E C M
115 N. Mitchell Street, 49601
(231) 942-4800

Caledonia

Henny's Yarn Shop Y
131 E. Main Street, 49316
(616) 891-2406

Caro

Back Alley Fibers Y
142 N. State Street, 48723
(989) 672-2144

Carp Lake

Quilting & Crafts by Mercer Q
8815 Paradise Trail, 49718
(231) 537-2180

Carson City

Miner Road Fabrics Q
9617 Miner Road, 48811
(989) 584-2163

Seven Sisters Quilt Shop Q
210 W. Main Street, 48811
(989) 584-3300

Cedar

Wool & Honey Ⓨ Ⓢ
9031 S. Kasson Street, 49621
(231) 228-2800

Charlevoix

Barnhart Studios/Mother of Purl Ⓨ Ⓦ Ⓢ
1207 Bridge Street, 49720
(231) 437-3808

Hearts to Holly Quilt Shop Ⓠ Ⓔ
207 Ferry Avenue, 49720
(231) 547-2729

Charlotte

The Hen House Ⓠ Ⓔ Ⓨ Ⓦ Ⓢ
211 S. Cochran Avenue, 48813
(517) 543-6454

Yarn Garden, LLC Ⓨ
131 S. Cochran Avenue, 48813
(517) 541-9323

Chelsea

Artisan Knitworks Ⓨ Ⓢ
105 N. Main, 48118
(248) 427-0804

Chesaning

Creative Passions Retreat Center
➡ SEE AD PAGE 220
203 Pearl Street
(989) 845-2159
www.creativepassionsllc.com

Clare

Apple Tree Lane* Ⓨ
520 N. McEwan Street, 48617
(989) 386-2552

Surrey Road Quilt Shop Ⓠ
3681 E. Surrey Road, 48617
(989) 386-3043

Clarkston

Basketful of Yarn Ⓨ
5 S. Main Street, 48346
(248) 620-2491

The Knitter's Nest Ⓨ
5922 S. Main Street, 48346
(248) 707-6442

Clawson

The Yarn Stop Ⓨ
➡ SEE AD BELOW
25 S. Main Street, 48017
(248) 808-6630
Tu 11-9, W-F 11-7, Sa 10-5
www.theyarnstop.com

Clinton Township

Sew Many Things Sewing Center Ⓠ Ⓔ
35486 Groesbeck Highway, 48035
(586) 790-5601

Comstock Park

Attic Window Quilt Shop Ⓠ
5363 Alpine Avenue NW, 49321
(616) 785-3357
M 10-8, Tu-Th 10-6, F 10-5, Sa 10-4
www.westmichquilter.blogspot.com

Cross Village

Three Pines Studio Y
5959 W. Levering Road, 49723
(231) 526-9447

Croswell

Victorias LLC Q Y M
5458 Peck Road, 48422
(810) 359-5940

Custer

Pig Patch Farm Quilts Q
3007 E. Hansen Road, 49405
(231) 757-2812

Davison

Elaine's Yarns Y
219 E. Flint Street, 48423
(810) 653-9010

Linda's Country Quilt Shop Q
3058 N. State Road, Unit F, 48423
(810) 658-9051

Dowagiac

Yarn on Front Y
122 S. Front Street, 49047
(269) 462-9094

East Jordan

Stonehedge Fiber Mill and Yarn Shop Y S
2246 Pesek Road, 49727
(231) 536-2779

East Lansing

Country Stitches Q E M
2200 Coolidge Road, 48823
(517) 351-2416 or (800) 572-2031
M-F 10-8, Sa 10-5
http://www.countrystitches.com

Woven Art Y W S
325 B Grove Street, 48823
(517) 203-4467

East Leroy

Quilt N Go Q
7212 6-1/2 Mile Road, 49051
(269) 979-2347

East Tawas

Mooney's Ben Franklin Q E N C
138 Newman Street, 48730
(989) 362-2751
Winter: M-Sa 9-6, Su 11-4; Summer: (June) M-Sa 9-8, Su 10-5 (July) M-Sa 9-9, Su 10-8
www.facebook.com/Mooneys-Ben-Franklin-in-East-Tawas-120081611348259/

Tawas Bay Yarn Co. Y
1820 E. US 23, 48730
(989) 362-4463
M-Sa 11-5
www.tawasbayyarn.com

Edwardsburg

Robin's Nest: Quilts & More Q Y
26848 Main Street (US Highway 12), 49112
(269) 663-3303

Evart

Juneberry Cottage Q M
147 N. Main Street, 49631
(231) 734-5863

Farmington

The Rocking Horse C
33305 Grand River Avenue, 48336
(248) 474-3113

Farmington Hills

Fun With Fiber Y Y W
33304 W. 12 Mile Road, 48334
(248) 553-4237 or (248) 553-2624

Farwell

Elm Creek Q E Y N C
2609 W. Surrey Road, 48622
(989) 588-6061

Fennville

Custom Quilts Unlimited Q E
6184 Quilters Court, 49408
(269) 561-6214 or (866) 561-6214

Fenton

Stitches 'N Things C
➡ SEE AD BELOW
14288 N. Fenton Road, 48430
(810) 629-3333 or (877) 325-4060
M-Sa 10-5
www.stitchesnthings.com

Fife Lake

The Quilter's Clinic Q Y
108 W. State Street, 49633
(231) 879-4115

Frankenmuth

Rapunzel's Boutique Y
664 S. Main Street, 48734
(989) 652-0464

The Front Porch Quilt Shop Q M
305 S. Franklin Street, 48734
(989) 652-8050

Frederic

OOOO La La Fiber Creations Q
11686 Old 27 N, 49733
(989) 731-5166

Ft. Gratiot

Sew Elegant Q E M
3909 Pine Grove Avenue, 48059
(810) 982-6556

Gaylord

Delphine's Quilt Shop LC Q E
114 N. Otsego Avenue, 49735
(989) 732-1252
M-Sa 10-6
www.delphinesquiltshop.com

Gladwin

Yarn for Ewe Y S
320 W. Cedar Avenue, 48624
(989) 709-5149

Grand Blanc

Beyond the Rainforest Y W
12830 S. Saginaw Street, Suite E, 48439
(810) 953-0089

Homestead Needle Arts, LLC N
8185 Holly Road, Suite 4, 48439
(810) 694-3040 or (888) 694-3040

Grand Haven

Needlesmith Y C
109 N. 7th Street, 49417
(616) 844-7188
MThF 10-5, Tu 10-8, Sa 10-1
www.theneedlesmith.com

Grand Rapids

Gall Sewing & Vac Center* M
3933 Plainfield NE, 49525
(616) 363-1911

Have Company* Y
136 Division Avenue S, 49503
(616) 426-9132

Lakeshore Sewing Q
1971 E. Beltline Avenue NE, Suite 108, 49525
(616) 365-8282

Michigan Fibre Studio Y W S
1503 Lake Drive SE, 49506
(616) 551-1273

Queen Bee Quilt Shoppe Q E
6703 Division Avenue S, 49548
(616) 827-8911

Smith-Owen Sewing & Quilting Q M
4051 Plainfield NE, 49525
(616) 361-5484

Grandville

Threadbender, Inc. Y W S
5570 Wilson Avenue SW, Suite B, 49418
(616) 531-6641

Grayling

AuSable Fabrics & More* Q E Y
108 E. Michigan Avenue, 49738
(989) 745-2988

Greenville

Forever Fabrics Q E
117 W. Cass Street, 48838
(616) 225-8486

Grosse Ile

Island Stitchery & Studio E N C
8242 Sarah Court, 48138
(734) 675-8708
TuWTh 9:30-6, F 9:30-5, Sa 10-4 or by appt.
www.islandstitchery.com (Under Construction)

Grosse Pointe

The Wool & The Floss Y N
397 Fisher Road, 48230
(313) 882-9110

Grosse Pointe Woods

The Knotted Needle Y N
20229 Mack Avenue, 48236
(313) 886-2828

Harrison Township

City Knits Y S M
26050 Crocker Blvd., 48045
(586) 469-9665

Hartland Township

Rockin' Bobbins Quilt Shop Q E
10199 Bergin Road, 48843
(248) 245-4391

Haslett

Custom Quilts & Sewing Center Q
5676 Okemos Road, 48840
(517) 339-7581
MWF 10-6, TuTh 10-8, Sa 10-5
www.quiltsgalore.com

Hastings

Walker Music & Textiles Co. Ⓨ Ⓦ Ⓢ

➡ SEE AD BELOW
131 W. State Street, 49058
(269) 804-6024
M-F 10-6
www.walkermt.com

Jami's Craft Supplies Ⓠ Ⓔ Ⓨ Ⓝ Ⓒ
116 E. State Street, 49058
(269) 945-4484

Sisters Fabrics Ⓠ Ⓔ
218 E. State Street, 49058
(269) 945-9673

Hesperia

Fanna's Mercantile Ⓠ Ⓔ Ⓨ Ⓒ
151 Spruce Street, 49421
(231) 854-0612

Hessel

Pickle Point Ⓔ Ⓨ Ⓝ Ⓢ Ⓒ

138 S. Pickford Avenue, 49745
(906) 484-3479
Jan - April WThFSa 11-4; May - Dec Everyday 10-5
www.facebook.com/picklepoint

Hillman

Sandy Dee's Sewing Ⓠ
1015 Hawley Road, 49746
(989) 379-2406

Hillsdale

Trevathan's Sweep and Sew Shoppe, LLC Ⓠ Ⓜ
47 N. Broad Street, 49242
(517) 437-5555

Holland

GarenHuis Yarn Studio, LLC Ⓨ Ⓦ Ⓢ
27 W. 9th Street, Suite 110, 49423
(616) 294-3492

Pressing Matters Quilt Shoppe Ⓠ Ⓔ
399 E. 32nd Street, 49423
(616) 392-9700

Houghton

Portage Quilt House Ⓠ Ⓔ
46509 US Highway 41, 49931
(906) 487-5500

Sew Irresistible Ⓠ Ⓨ
407 Shelden Avenue, Suite A, 49931
(906) 482-1722

Houghton Lake

AJ's Quiltery & Gifts Ⓠ
4532 W. Houghton Lake Drive, 48629
(989) 422-5276

AJ's Quiltery West Ⓠ
6230 W. Houghton Lake Drive, 48629
(989) 302-8040

Arnie's Arts and Crafts Ⓔ Ⓨ Ⓝ Ⓒ
3741 W. Houghton Lake Drive, 48629
(989) 366-8794

Howell

Stitch In Time Ⓔ Ⓨ Ⓝ Ⓦ Ⓒ
722 E. Grand River Avenue, 48843
(517) 546-0769
M 10-8, Tu-Th 10-6, FSa 10-5
www.stitchintimemi.com

The Stitchery Ⓠ
1129 E. Grand River Avenue, 48843
(517) 548-1731

Imlay City

Stitchin' at the Barn Ⓠ Ⓜ
2648 S. Van Dyke Road, 48444
(810) 721-7037

The Pincushion Ⓠ
113 E. 3rd Street, 48444
(810) 724-7065

Indian River

The Quilt House Ⓠ
4819 S. Straits Highway, 49749
(231) 238-4339

Interlochen

InterQuilten Ⓠ Ⓔ Ⓜ
2323 M 137, 49643
(231) 276-9100

Ironwood

The Fabric Patch Ⓠ Ⓜ
100 W. McLeod Avenue, 49938
(906) 932-5260

Jenison

Country Needleworks, Inc. Ⓨ Ⓒ
584 Chicago Drive, 49428
(616) 457-9410
M-F 9:30-8, Sa 9:30-5
www.countryneedleworks.net

Kalamazoo

Lucy in The Sky Quilts Ⓠ
839 Gull Road, 49048
(269) 381-7242 or (269) 381-7643
Tu-Sa 12-5:30
www.lucyintheskyquilts@etsy.com

Bernina Sewing Center & Quilt Shop Ⓠ Ⓔ Ⓜ
4205 Portage Road, 49001
(269) 383-1244

Great Northern Weaving Ⓨ Ⓦ
451 E. D Avenue, 49009
(269) 341-9752 or (800) 446-5977

Quilts Plus, Inc. Ⓠ
3314 Stadium Drive, 49008
(269) 383-1790

Lake City

Cardinal Creations, Inc. Ⓠ
7451 W. Blue Road (M-55), 49651
(231) 839-5570

Loney's Alpaca Junction* Ⓨ Ⓢ
3109 N. 7 Mile Road, 49651
(231) 229-4530

Lake Odessa

Friends Quilting Basket Ⓠ Ⓜ
1001 4th Avenue, Suite 2, 48849
(616) 374-3060

Handi Quilter® Authorized Retailer
Designed by a Quilter, for Quilters.®

Lake Orion

Heritage Spinning & Weaving Ⓨ Ⓦ Ⓢ
47 E. Flint Street, 48362
(248) 693-3690

Lansing

Sticks & Strings Ⓨ Ⓦ
1107 N. Washington Avenue, 48906
(517) 372-1000

Leslie

Sittin' On Pins Ⓠ Ⓨ
110 S. Main Street, 49251
(517) 589-8802

Livonia

Michigan Fine Yarns Ⓨ Ⓦ Ⓢ
37519 Ann Arbor Road, 48150
(734) 462-2801

Sandy's Make It Sew Ⓠ Ⓜ
28790 Plymouth Road, 48150
(734) 266-2491

Ludington

Nautical Yarn Ⓔ Ⓨ Ⓝ Ⓦ Ⓒ
108 S. Rath Avenue, 49431
(231) 845-9868
Winter: M-F 10-5, Sa 10-4, Su 12-4;
Summer: M-F 10-5, SaSu 10-4
www.nauticalyarn.com

Macomb

Crafty Lady Trio Ⓠ Ⓨ
15401 Hall Road, 48044
(586) 566-8008 or (800) 455-9276

The Yarn and I Ⓨ Ⓦ
48218 Roosevelt Drive, 48044
(586) 532-8384

Time Remembered Quilting Ⓠ Ⓜ
16701 21 Mile Road, 48044
(586) 221-1954

Manistee

Northern Spirits Ⓨ
389 River Street, 49660
(231) 398-0131

Sunrise Fabric Ⓠ Ⓜ
354 River Street, 49660
(231) 398-3795

TK Quilting & Design LLC Ⓠ Ⓜ
166 Cleveland Street, 49660
(231) 299-1333

Manistique

Ben Franklin Ⓠ Ⓔ Ⓨ Ⓝ Ⓒ
239 S. Cedar Street, 49854
(906) 341-5911

Marquette

Alley Kat's Quilt Shop Ⓠ Ⓜ
623 W. Washington Street, 49855
(906) 315-0050
Handi Quilter Authorized Retailer
Designed by a Quilter, for Quilters.

Ben Franklin Craft Center Ⓠ Ⓔ Ⓨ Ⓒ
100 Coles Drive, 49855
(906) 226-9613

Marshall

Quilts at the Marshall House Ⓠ Ⓔ
100 Exchange Street, 49068
(269) 781-9450

The Handmade Hive Ⓠ
209 W. Michigan Avenue, 49068
(269) 224-1402

Mason

Kean's Store Company Ⓠ
406 S. Jefferson Street, 48854
(517) 676-5144

Yards of Fabric Ⓠ
116 E. Ash Street, 48854
(517) 676-2973

Menominee

Quilter's Haven, Ltd. Ⓠ
447 1st Street, 49858
(906) 864-3078

The Elegant Ewe Ⓔ Ⓨ Ⓝ Ⓒ
400 1st Street, 49858
(906) 863-2296 or (888) 336-0449

Merrill

Miles of Stitches Ⓠ
123 N. Midland Street, 48637
(989) 643-5566

Twisted Warp & Skeins Ⓨ Ⓦ Ⓢ
240 E. Saginaw, 48637
(989) 643-0108

Midland

Material Mart Ⓠ Ⓜ
86 Ashman Circle, 48640
(989) 835-8761

Park Bench Quilt Shop Ⓠ
1613 E. Wheeler Street, 48642
(989) 832-5722

Monroe

Lake Erie Mercantile Q E Y M
15555 S. Telegraph Road, Suite 10, 48161
(734) 682-3945

Montague

Quilted Memories, Inc. Q M
9919 US 31, 49437
(231) 893-0096

Mt. Pleasant

Keepsake Quilts, Inc. Q E
4585 E. Pickard, Suite K, 48858
(989) 317-8700

Stitches Y
615 S. Anna Street, 48858
(989) 772-4562

Muskegon

Abbi May's Q Q
1500 Whitehall Rd, Suite A, 49445
(231) 563-6861
M-Sa 10-5
www.abbimays.com

Apple Knits & Purls Y
2033 Lakeshore Drive, 49441
(231) 780-5648 or (231) 780-KNIT
TuThF 12-6, W 12-7, Sa 10-4
www.appleknitsandpurls.com

Lakeshore Sewing Q
1848 E. Sherman Blvd., Suite R, 49444
(231) 288-1263

Newaygo

New Ewe Yarn & Quilt Shoppe Q Y W
59 State Road, 49337
(231) 652-5262
MTuThFSa 10-5, W 10-7
www.newewe.com

Northport

Dolls & More Q Y
102 W. Nagonaba, 49670
(231) 386-7303

Norway

Jeri's Quilt Patch Q
703 Brown Street - US2, 49870
(906) 563-9620

Rainbow's Gifts & Yarn Y
W6139 US 2, 49870
(906) 563-7034

Ortonville

Mabelena Quilting Supplies & Comforts Q
470 Mill Street, 48462
(248) 627-9100

Ottawa Lake

Yarn Envy Y
4570 Sterns Road, Suite 1, 49267
(734) 856-1015

Ovid

Elaine's Too Q
122 S. Main Street, 48866
(989) 834-2538

Paradise

Village Fabrics & Crafts Q E Y C M
32702 W. Highway M-123, 49768
(906) 492-3803

Perrinton

Calico Cupboard Q
4625 MacArthur Road, 48871
(989) 236-7728

Pinckney

S & B Quilting Studio Q M
1210 E. Main Street, 48169
(734) 648-0188
Tu-F 10-5, Sa 10-2
http://www.sbquiltingstudio.com

Handi Quilter® Authorized Retailer
Designed by a Quilter, for Quilters.®

Jennifer's Quilt Shop Q E
149 N. Howell Street, 48169
(734) 878-6188

Pinconning

Bittersweet Quilt Shop & Home Decor Q E
624 W. 5th Street, 48650
(989) 879-1900

Plainwell

Dancing Dogs Quilt Shop Q
119 N. Main Street, 49080
(269) 685-3647

Stitching Bits and Bobs C
211 E. Bannister Street, Suite A9, 49080
(269) 685-9418

Plymouth

Old Village Yarn Shop Y
42307 E. Ann Arbor Road, 48170
(734) 451-0580

Port Huron

RMC Quilts Q
3561 Gratiot Avenue, 48060
(810) 985-3668

Portage

Stitching Memories Y N C
5401-3 Portage Road, 49002
(269) 552-9276

Portland

MO's Needle & Thread Q N C M
120 Maple Street, 48875
(517) 647-5430

Richland

Fabrications Y
8860 N. 32nd Street, 49083
(269) 629-0190 or (877) 629-0190

Riverdale

Sheila's Fabric Shop Q
11995 NW Monroe Road, 48877
(989) 833-7147

Rochester

2nd Street Quilt Shop Q E
116 W. 2nd Street, 48307
(248) 601-6565

Skeins on Main Yarn Company Y
428 S. Main Street, 48307
(248) 656-9300

Rockford

J.T. Stitchery Y
30 E. Bridge Street, 49341
(616) 866-2409

Luv 2 Quilt Q
10580 Northland Drive, Suite A, 49341
(616) 951-7156

Roscommon

Michigan Warm Hugs Quilts LLC Q
402 Lake Street, 48653
(989) 281-1621

Royal Oak

Ewe-nique Knits Y W S
515 S. Lafayette Street, 48067
(248) 584-3001

Ladybug Craft Shoppe C
123 Catalpa Drive, 48067
(248) 545-3200

Saginaw

Speedy Sew Q M
3210 Tittabawasee Road, 48604
(410) 263-3897

Stitch'N Time E N C
7579 Gratiot Road, 48609
(989) 781-5209

The Little Yarn Shoppe Y S
203 S. Washington Avenue
1st Level, 48607
(989) 274-8571

Saline

The Quilting Season Q E
7025 E. Michigan Avenue, Suite A3, 48176
(734) 429-2900

Sault Sainte Marie

The Quilted Moose Q E
1812 Ashmun Street, 49783
(906) 253-9886

Shelby Township

Decorative Stitch, LLC Q M
48814 Van Dyke, 48317
(586) 799-7507

Sewing Products Inc. Q M
50304 Schoenherr Road, 48315
(586) 566-4500

Snover

County Treasures Q
2509 Ubly Road, 48472
(810) 672-9422

Southfield

Rachel's Needlepoint Y N
29260 Franklin Road, #103, 48034
(248) 352-5622

St. Charles

The Silver Thimble Q E
200 S. Saginaw Street, 48655
(989) 865-5555 or (989) 326-0547

St. Ignace

Georgia B's Quilts Q
W1044 Old Portage Trail, 49781
(906) 643-7726

St. Joseph

At the Heart of Quilting Q M
2603 S. Cleveland Avenue
Suite 2, 49085
(269) 408-8442

St. Louis

Common Threads Quilt Shop Q
109 N. Mill Street, 48880
(989) 681-5082

Stockbridge

Quality Quilting Q
4983 Bird Drive, 49285
(517) 851-6325

Suttons Bay

Cherry Country Quilters Q
310 N. Saint Joseph Street (M-22), 49682
(231) 271-0117

Leelanau Fiber Y W S
310 N. St. Joseph Street, 49682
(231) 271-9276

Tapiola, Otter Lake, Chassell

Calico Bass Quilting Studio Q
20091 Aldrich Road, 49916
(906) 334-2441

Tawas City

Cotton Patch Quilt Shop Q
685 N. McArdle Road, 48763
(989) 362-6779

Tecumseh

The Quilt Patch Q
112 N. Evans Street, Suite 5, 49286
(517) 423-0053

Timeless Stitches E Y N S C
112 N. Evans Street, Suite 3, 49286
(517) 423-0808

Three Rivers

Karen's Fabric Shop Q E
57501 N. Main Street, 49093
(269) 279-9391

Traverse City

CS Sewing* M
1425 S. Airport Road, Suite D, 49686
(231) 946-9751 or (866) 309-4700

Knitology Ⓨ
300 US 31 S, 49685
(231) 492-0193

Lost Art Yarn and Needlepoint Shoppe ⓎⓃ
733 Woodmere Avenue, 49686
(231) 941-1263

Quilt-N-Bee ⓆⒺ
1425 S. Airport Road, Suite G, 49686
(231) 922-6766

Troy

Fabric Affair ⓆⒺⓂ
4972 John R Road, 48085
(248) 457-9320

Front Porch Quilts Ⓠ
1790 Livernois Road, 48083
(248) 795-4876

Needlepoint For You Ⓝ
1969 South Blvd. W, 48098
(248) 828-8020

Wakefield

Nanette's Knits and Gifts Ⓨ
501 Sunday Lake Street, 49968
(906) 364-4752

Waterford

A Little Quilt Shop ⓆⒸ
5721 Elizabeth Lake Road, 48327
(248) 681-1107

Wayne

Bits 'n Pieces ⓆⓂ
34629 W. Michigan Avenue, 48184
(734) 641-4970

West Branch

Aunt Effy's Craft Closet Ⓠ
205 W. Houghton Avenue, 48661
(989) 312-3373

Caroline's Sewing Ⓠ
3100 W. Houghton Avenue, 48661
(989) 345-9180

North Woods Knit & Purl ⓎⓈ
103 Plaza Drive, 48661
(989) 701-2725

White Cloud

Quilt Something New Ⓠ
28 S Charles (M-37), 49349
(231) 408-1309

Whitehall

The General Store Ⓠ
103 E. Colby Street, 49461
(231) 894-2164

Whitmore Lake

Forma* ⓎⓌⓈ
111 E. Northfield Church Road, 48189
(734) 761-1102

Williamsburg

Renee's House of Quilting, Inc. Ⓠ
8995 M-72 E, 49690
(231) 267-5895

Williamston

Knitters' Nook* Ⓨ
120 High Street, 48895
(517) 899-6759

Wyandotte

Sew What! Ⓠ
1128 Eureka Street, 48192
(734) 281-1344

Wyoming

Lakeshore Sewing Ⓠ
1011 Gezon Parkway SW, 49509
(616) 531-5561

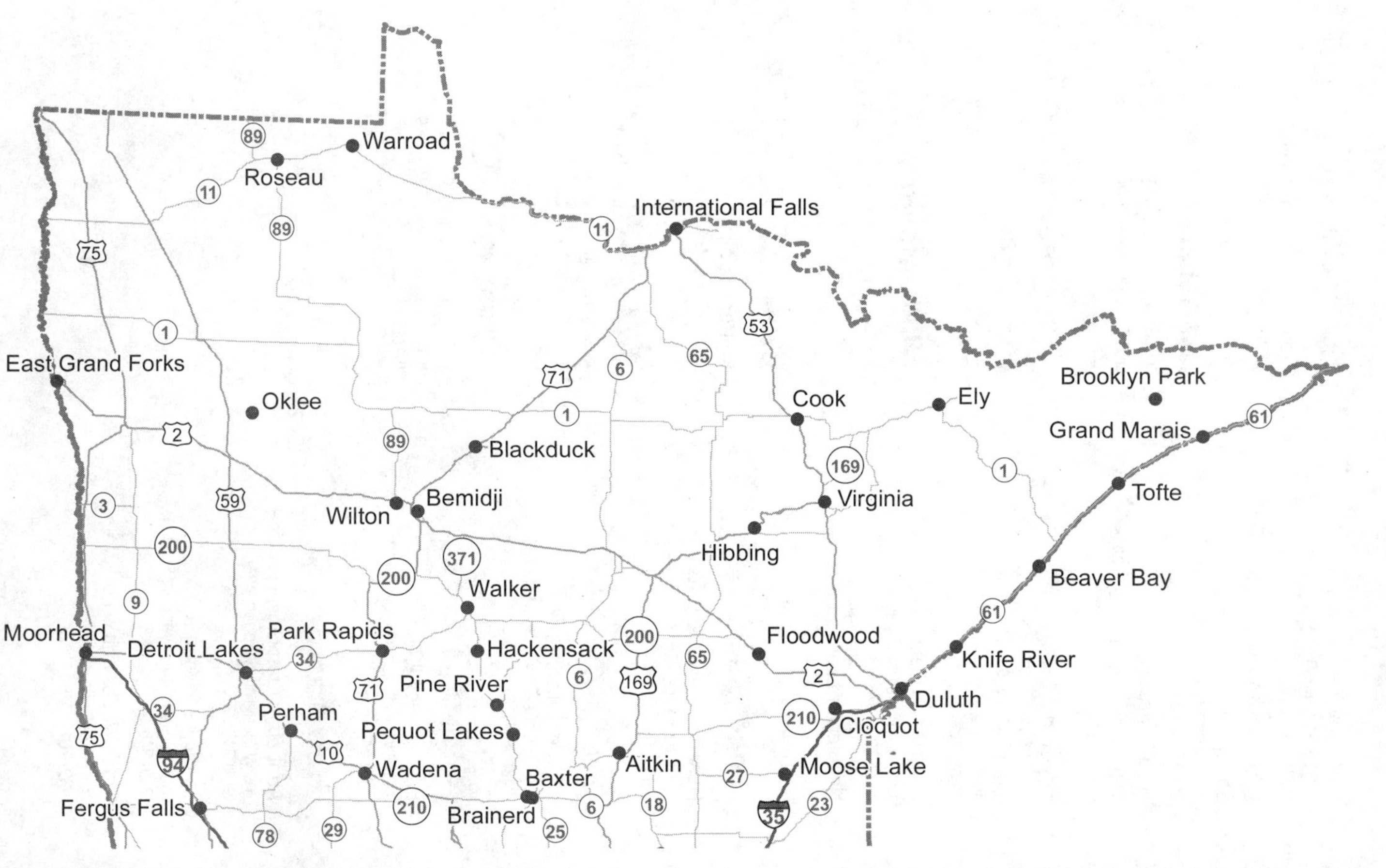
Warroad
Roseau
International Falls
East Grand Forks
Oklee
Cook
Ely
Brooklyn Park
Grand Marais
Blackduck
Bemidji
Wilton
Virginia
Tofte
Hibbing
Walker
Beaver Bay
Moorhead
Detroit Lakes
Park Rapids
Hackensack
Floodwood
Knife River
Pine River
Duluth
Perham
Pequot Lakes
Cloquot
Wadena
Baxter
Aitkin
Moose Lake
Fergus Falls
Brainerd
89
11
75
1
2
3
59
200
9
34
71
10
94
210
78
29
6
371
25
18
169
65
53
27
35
23
61

Randall
Wahkon
Isle
Sandstone
Alexandria
Sauk Centre
Morris
See Minneapolis Area Map
Willmar
Granite Falls
Marshall
New Ulm
St. Peter
Zumbrota
Mankato
Kasson
Rochester
Winona
Windom
Luverne
Sherburn
Hayward
Worthington
Kiester
Mabel
Caledonia
94
10
35
75
59
212
14
63
52
71
90
65
218

10
52
94
23
Foley
169
Sauk Rapids
95
75
St. Cloud
Princeton
Waite Park
25
23
55
15
Paynesville
94
10
52
Kimball
Elk River
Buffalo
12
55
25
Minnetrista
Excelsior
7
Hutchinson
15
41
Bird Island
212
Norwood
Young America
25
5
21
19
19
Montgomery
15
169

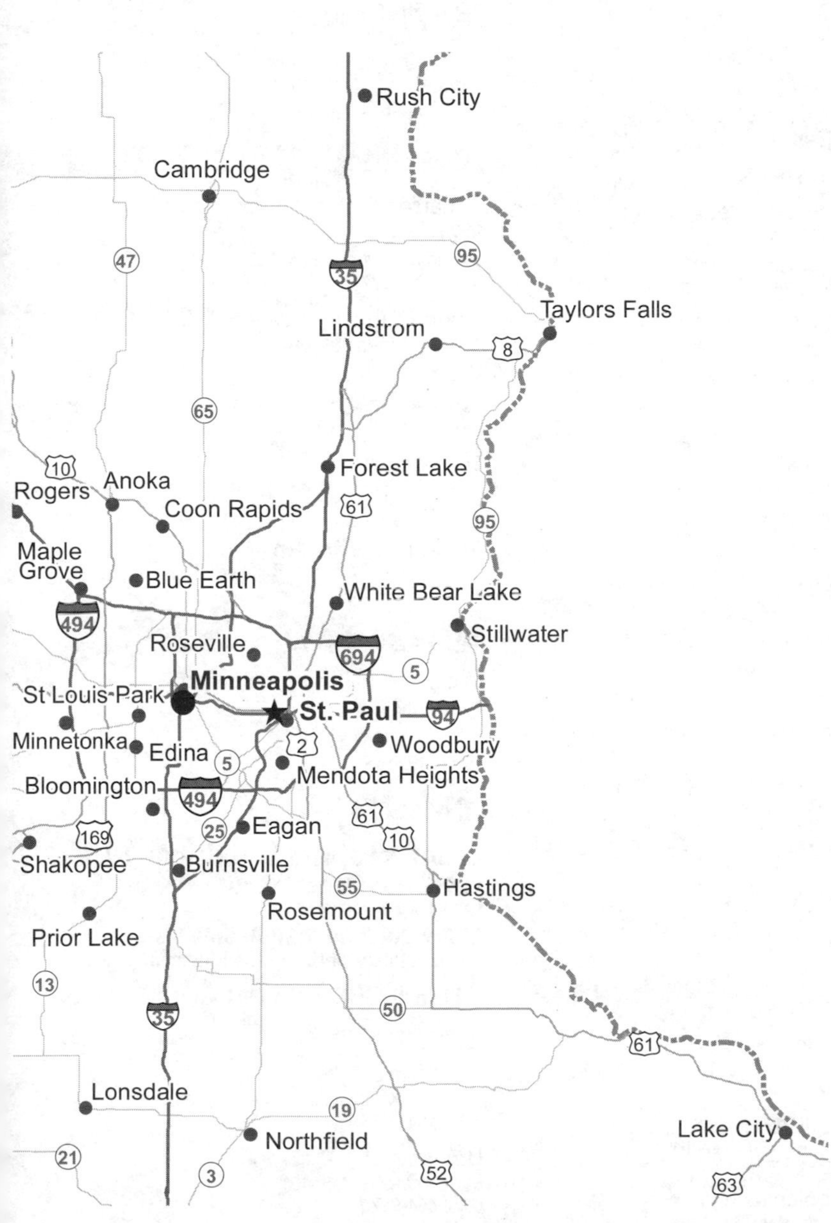
Rush City
Cambridge
Taylors Falls
Lindstrom
Forest Lake
Rogers
Anoka
Coon Rapids
Maple Grove
Blue Earth
White Bear Lake
Stillwater
Roseville
Minneapolis
St Louis Park
St. Paul
Minnetonka
Edina
Woodbury
Mendota Heights
Bloomington
Eagan
Shakopee
Burnsville
Hastings
Rosemount
Prior Lake
Lonsdale
Lake City
Northfield
47
95
35
8
65
10
61
494
694
5
94
2
25
169
55
13
50
19
21
3
52
63

Minnesota

Aitkin

Aitkin Quilts & Fabric Q
936 2nd Street NW, 56431
(218) 429-0057

Alexandria

Dawn's Quilt Shop Q
522 Broadway Street, 56308
(320) 763-7011
M-F 10-5, Sa 10-4
www.dawnsquiltshop.com

Community Vacuum & Sewing Center Q E M
1321 Broadway Street, 56308
(320) 762-1412

Anoka

Millie P's Q E
219 E. Main Street, 55303
(763) 421-0367

Baxter

Cherrywood Hand Dyed Fabrics Q
7882 College Road, 56425
(218) 829-0967

Colorz Quilt Shop / The Cherrywood Store Q
14091 Baxter Drive, Suite 112, 56425
(218) 825-9101

Beaver Bay

Quilt Corner Q
1007 Main Street (Highway 61), 55601
(218) 226-6406

Bemidji

A Stitch in Time Inc. M
219 Third Street NW, 56601
(218) 444-7727

Handi Quilter® Authorized Retailer
Designed by a Quilter, for Quilters.®

Bemidji Woolen Mills Y S
301 Irvine Avenue NW, 56601
(888) 751-5166 or (218) 751-5166

Sadie Rae's Quilt Shop Q E
405 Beltrami Ave NW, 56601
(218) 444-2387

Bird Island

Gathering Friends Quilt & Gift Shop Q
101 S. Main Street, 55310
(320) 365-4670

Blackduck

Anderson Factory Outlet and Quilt Shop Q
24 Summit Avenue E, 56630
(218) 835-6377 or (800) 638-8921

Moon Pharmacy & Variety Q E Y N C
17 Main Street, 56630
(218) 835-7740

Bloomington

1st Sewing Center* M
7971 Southtown Center, 55431
(952) 884-1938

Blue Earth

Michele's Quilting and Sewing Center Q E M
120 N. Main Street, 56013
(507) 526-3295

Brainerd

Country Fabrics & Quilting Q E M
909 S. 6th Street, 56401
(218) 829-7273
M-F 9:30-5, Sa 9:30-4, Su 11-3
www.countryfabricsandquilting.com

A2Z Yarn, LLC Y
1001 Kingwood Street, Suite 115, 56401
(218) 454-0133

Utrinkets, LLC Y
617 Laurel Street, 56401
(218) 454-9276

Brooklyn Park

SR Harris Fabric Outlet Q
8865 Zealand Avenue N, 55445
(763) 424-3500

Buffalo

Silver Creek Cabin Y W S
3 Division Street W, 55313
(763) 684-0554

Burnsville

SR Harris Fabric Outlet Q
3715 Highway 13 W, 55337
(952) 222-5676

Unwind Yarn Shop Y
14617 County Road 11, 55337
(952) 303-6617

Caledonia

Just Stitch It Q Y
14574 County 12, 55921
(507) 725-2708

Cambridge

Quilterati Q E
236 Adams Street S, 55008
(763) 552-6080

Cloquet

The Quilted Dog Q
274 Highway 33 N, 55720
(218) 879-3577

Columbia Heights

Daisy Knits Knitting Machines Y
819 49th Avenue NE, 55421
(763) 571-8724

Cook

Cabin Quilting Q
227 1st Street SW, 55723
(218) 666-3146

Coon Rapids

All About Yarn Y
455 99th Avenue NW, Suite 180, 55433
(763) 785-4900

Anoka Fiber Works Y W S
4153 Coon Rapids Blvd., 55433
(763) 479-9626

Detroit Lakes

Hometown Crafts and Fabrics Q E Y N C
824 Washington Avenue, 56501
(218) 844-5840

Red Pine Quilt Shop Q E
915 Washington Avenue, 56501
(218) 844-5260

Duluth

Creations Quilt Shop Q
2904 W. 3rd Street, 55806
(218) 628-1687

Hannah Johnson Fabrics Q
4511 E. Superior Street, 55804
(218) 525-7800

Yarn Harbor, Inc. Y W S
4629 E. Superior Street, 55804
(218) 724-6432

Duluth

Sew with Me Q M
2826 Piedmont Avenue, 55811
(218) 522-4540

Eagan

Quilt Cove Q
1960 Cliff Lake Road, Suite 134, 55122
(651) 452-8891

East Grand Forks

Quilter's Eden Q
223 DeMers Avenue, 56721
(218) 773-0773

Edina

Harriet & Alice Y
3922 W. 50th Street, Suite 105, 55424
(952) 500-9724

The Picket Fence, Inc. N
3907 W. 54th Street, 55424
(952) 920-7888

Elk River

The Noble Quilter Q E
19570 Holt Street NW, 55330
(763) 633-4669

Ely

Sisu Designs Yarn Y
31 W. Chapman Street, 55731
(218) 365-6613

Excelsior

Lakeside Yarn Y
347 Water Street, 55331
(952) 401-7501

Fergus Falls

Quilters Cottage Q
1701 W. Lincoln Avenue, 56537
(218) 739-9652

Floodwood

Hingeley Road Quilt Shop Q
11284 Highway 2, 55736
(218) 476-3139

Foley

Quilts on Broadway Q E
320 Dewey Street, 56329
(320) 968-9929

Forest Lake

Country Loft Quilt & Design Q M
15161 Feller Street NE, 55025
(651) 464-6260 or (877) 778-4586

Grand Marais

That Little Red House Yarn Shop* Y
113 1st Avenue W, 55604
(218) 387-1094

Granite Falls

Heather's Book Nook & Sew Much More Q Y
682 Prentice Street, 56241
(320) 564-0074

Hackensack

Piecemaker's Quilt Shop Q
313 State Highway 371, 56452
(218) 675-6271

Hastings

Rach-Al-Paca Farm Q Y W S
18495 Goodwin Avenue, 55033
(651) 485-7916

Hayward

Calico Hutch Q E M
20520 810th Avenue, 56043
(507) 377-1163

Hibbing

Knitting Knight Y S
113 E. Howard Street, 55746
(218) 262-5764

Quilts Around The Corner Q
12150 Old Highway West 169, 55746
(218) 263-9078

Hutchinson

Quilt Haven on Main Q E
7 N. Main Street, 55350
(320) 587-8341 or (888) 843-8215
M 10-7, Tu-Sa 10-5
www.quilthavenonmain.com

International Falls

Studio 53 Fabric and Gifts Q
2030 2nd Avenue, 56649
(218) 285-9962

Up North Quilt Shop Q
4062 Highway 11, 56649
(218) 285-7704

Isle

The Tinshack Co. Y S
250 W. Main Street, 56342
(320) 279-9359

Kasson

Kasson Variety Fabrics, Crafts & More Q E Y N C
207 W. Main Street, 55944
(507) 634-6521

Kiester

Quilter's Cottage Q
119 S. Main Street, 56051
(507) 294-3700

Kimball

Gone to Pieces Quilt Shop Q
70 S. Main Street, 55353
(320) 398-5300

Knife River

Playing With Yarn E Y W S
276 Scenic Drive, 55609
(218) 834-5967

Lake City

Pumpkinberry Stitches Q
108 E. Lyon Avenue, 55041
(651) 345-2573

Rather Bee Quilting Q
106 S. Lakeshore Drive, 55041
(651) 345-3958 or (877) 233-9549

Lindstrom

Cottage Gifts / Miss Elsie's Yarnery Y S
12710 Lake Blvd., 55045
(651) 257-6199

Lonsdale

Quilting by the Hearth Q E
208 Main Street S, 55046
(507) 744-4284

Luverne

The Sewing Basket Q M
204 E. Main, 56156
(507) 283-9769

Mabel

Krazy Kwiltz Q Y
416 N. Maple Street (Highway 44), 55954
(507) 493-5893

Mankato

Mary Lue's Yarn and Ewe Y W S
605 N. Riverfront Drive, 56001
(507) 388-9276

River City Quilts Q
529 N. Riverfront Drive, 56001
(507) 625-8135

Maple Grove

Amazing Threads Y W S
11262 86th Avenue N, 55369
(763) 391-7700

Four Seasons Quilts Q
9708 63rd Avenue N, 55369
(763) 557-5899

Marshall

Fabrics Plus Q M
307 W. Main Street, 56258
(507) 537-0835

Mendota Heights

3 Kittens Needle Arts E Y N W
750 Main Street, Suite 112, 55118
(651) 457-4969

Minneapolis

Glad Creations Inc. Q
3400 Bloomington Avenue, 55407
(612) 724-1079
MWThFSa 9:30-5, Tu 9:30-8:30
www.gladcreationsquilts.com

Digs Q E Y
3800 Grand Avenue S, 55409
(612) 827-2500

Ingebretsen's Scandinavian Center E Y C
1601 E. Lake Street, 55407
(612) 729-9333 or (800) 279-9333

Knit & Bolt Q E Y
2833 Johnson Street NE, 55418
(612) 788-1180

StevenBe Y W S
3448 Chicago Avenue, 55407
(612) 259-7525

Textile Center Q E Y W S
3000 University Avenue SE, 55414
(612) 436-0464

The Linden Tree Q
4404 Beard Avenue S, 55407
(612) 961-7623

Minnetonka

Stitchville USA E N C
12945 Ridgedale Drive, 55305
(952) 474-1700 or (888) 232-9403
M-F 10-8, Sa 10-5
www.stitchville.com

Minnetrista

Gale Woods Farm Y W S
7210 County Road 110 W, 55364
(763) 694-2001

Montgomery

Quilter's Dream Q
116 1st Street S, 56069
(507) 364-5130

Moorhead

Prairie Fiber Arts Center Y W S
127 4th Street S, 56560
(218) 284-0004
MWFSa 10-5, TuTh 10-7
www.prairiefiberarts.com

The Quilted Ladybug Q
420 Center Avenue, Suite 2, 56560
(218) 284-5239

Moose Lake

Kathy's Country Square Q E Y S
100 Hillside Terrace, 55767
(218) 485-8231

Morris

Helen's Fabrics Q E Y
1001 Atlantic Avenue, 56267
(320) 589-1735

New Ulm

Nadelkunst E Y C
212 N. Minnesota Street, 56073
(507) 354-8708

Sewing Seeds Quilt Company Q
1417 S. State Street, 56073
(507) 354-8801

Spinning Spools Quilt Shop Q
106 S. Minnesota Street, 56073
(507) 359-2896

The Thimble Box Q
10 N. Minnesota Street, 56073
(507) 354-6721

Northfield

Northfield Yarn Q E Y N S C
314 Division Street S, 55057
(507) 645-1330

Reproduction Fabrics Q
105 E. 4th Street, Suite 205, 55057
(507) 664-1447

Norwood Young America

The Quilting Grounds Q
224 W. Elm Street, 55368
(952) 467-2757

Oklee

Oklee Quilting Supply Q
128 S. Main Street, 56742
(218) 796-5151 or (800) 777-7403

Park Rapids

Ben Franklin Q E Y N
208 Main Street, 56470
(218) 732-4426

Monika's Q Y
210 S. Main Street, 56470
(218) 732-3896

Paynesville

Sweetwater Cotton Shoppe Q E C
122 W. James Street, Suite 1, 56362
(320) 243-4436

Pequot Lakes

Mother Originals Quilt Shop Q
29514 Patriot Avenue, 56472
(218) 568-6924

Perham

Bay Window Quilt Shop Q E
116 2nd Avenue SW, 56573
(218) 346-7272 or (888) 346-7275

Princeton

Princeton Weaving and Fabrics* Q W
34301 Puma Street NW, 55371
(763) 389-4156

Prior Lake

Twisted Loop Yarn Shop Y
16210 Eagle Creek Avenue, 55372
(952) 240-8550

Whispering Oaks Alpacas Y S
21851 Calmor Avenue, 55372
(952) 412-0345

Randall

The Old Creamery Quilt Shop Q E Y
120 Superior Avenue, 56475
(320) 749-2420

Rochester

Kelleys Quality Sewing Center Q E Y M
3432 55th Street NW
NW Plaza, near Sam's Club, 55901
(507) 288-9051
M-Th 9:30-8, F 9:30-6, Sa 9:30-5
www.kqsc.net

Pine Needles Quilt & Sew Q E M
1300 Salem Road SW, Suite 250, 55902
(507) 226-8480

The Quilting Cupboard Q W
1611 N. Broadway, 55906
(507) 281-9988

Rogers

Quilted Treasures Q
14178 Northdale Blvd., 55374
(763) 428-1952

Roseau

Quilt S'more Q M
209 2nd Avenue NE, 56751
(218) 463-3867

Rosemount

Quilter's Haven Q E M
2930 146th Street, Suite 108, 55068
(651) 322-7071
M-F 10-8, Sa 10-6, Su 12-5
www.quiltershavenmn.com

Roseville

Twin Cities Quilting Q
1085 Dionne Street, 55113
(651) 340-8263

Rush City

Fabric, Fashions and More Q M
485 S. Dana Avenue, 55069
(320) 358-3693

Sandstone

Quarry Quilts & Yarns, LLC Q Y
326 Quarry Place, 55072
(320) 216-7639
M-Sa 9-5
http://www.qqyonline.com

Sauk Centre

Family Fabric Shop Q E Y C
306 Main Street South, 56378
(320) 351-2739

Sauk Rapids

Bound in Stitches Q E
2078 45th Street NE, 56379
(320) 255-9021

Shakopee

Eagle Creek Quilt Shop Q E
333 2nd Avenue W, 55379
(952) 233-3774

Sherburn

Old Alley Quilt Shop Q
115 N. Main Street, 56171
(507) 764-4088
M-F 10-5, Sa 9-4
www.oldalleyquiltshop.com

St. Cloud

Bonnie's Spinning Wheel Ⓨ
16 21st Avenue S, 56301
(320) 253-2426

Carole's Country Knits at Rocking Horse Farm ⓎⓌⓈ
25636 County Road 74, 56301
(320) 252-2996

St. Cloud Sewing Center Ⓜ
3603 W. Division Street, 56301
(320) 251-6540

St. Louis Park

Needle & Skein Ⓨ
5814 Excelsior Blvd., 55416
(952) 303-3895

St. Paul

The Yarnery* ⓎⓌⓈ
840 Grand Avenue, 55105
(651) 222-5793

Treadle Yard Goods Ⓠ
1338 Grand Avenue, 55105
(651) 698-9690

St. Peter

St. Peter Woolen Mill ⓆⓈ
101 W. Broadway Avenue, 56082
(507) 934-3734
M-F 9-5
www.woolenmill.com

Stillwater

Darn Knit Anyway ⓎⓈ
423 S. Main Street, Suite 423B, 55082
(651) 342-1386

Sew With Me ⓆⓂ
1815 Greeley Street, 55082
(651) 342-2126

Tofte

The Tall Tale Studio Ⓨ
7197 Bayview Drive (Highway 61), 55615
(218) 663-7557

Virginia

Material Girl Fabric & Crafts ⓆⒺⓎⓃⒸ
309 Chestnut Street, 55792
(218) 749-1390

Wadena

Hometown Crafts and Fabrics ⓆⒺⓎⓃⒸ
111 S. Jefferson Street, 56482
(218) 631-3141

Wahkon

Country Caboose Quilts ⓆⒺ
108 S. Main Street, 56386
(320) 495-3658

Waite Park

Crafts Direct ⓆⒺⓎⓃⒸ
620 Sundial Drive, 56387
(320) 654-0907

Grubers Quilt Shop ⓆⒺⓎ
310 4th Avenue NE, 56387
(320) 259-4360

Walker

Front Porch Quilts of Walker, Inc. ⓆⒺ
613 Michigan Avenue W, 56484
(218) 547-1122

White Bear Lake

Rosebud's Cottage ⓆⒺⒸ
4715 Banning Avenue, 55110
(651) 426-1885

Sheepy Yarn Shoppe Ⓨ
2185 3rd Street, 55110
(651) 426-5463 or (800) 480-5462

Windom

Prairie Quilting Ⓠ
1293 Hale Place, 56101
(507) 831-2740
M-F 9-5, Sa 9-3
www.prairiequiltingmn.com

Winona

Bluffview Quilt Shop Ⓠ
1671 W. 5th Street, 55987
(507) 458-8539

Yarnology Ⓨ
65 E. 3rd Street, 55987
(507) 474-9444

Woodbury

Knitting From the Heart Ⓨ
1785 Radio Drive, 55125
(651) 702-0880
M 12-8, TuWF 10-5:30, Th 10-8, Sa 10-5
www.heartknits.com

Sew With Me ⓆⓂ
1750 Weir Drive, 55125
(651) 600-3258

Worthington

Crafty Corner Quilt & Sewing Shoppe ⓆⓂ
1820 Oxford Street, 56187
(507) 372-2707
M-F 9-5:30, Sa 9-4
www.craftycornerquiltandsewingshoppe.com

Zumbrota

All in Stitches ⓆⒺ
308 S. Main Street, Highway 58, 55992
(507) 732-4101

Ellison Sheep Farm ⓎⓌⓈ
15775 Highway 60 Blvd., 55992
(507) 732-5281

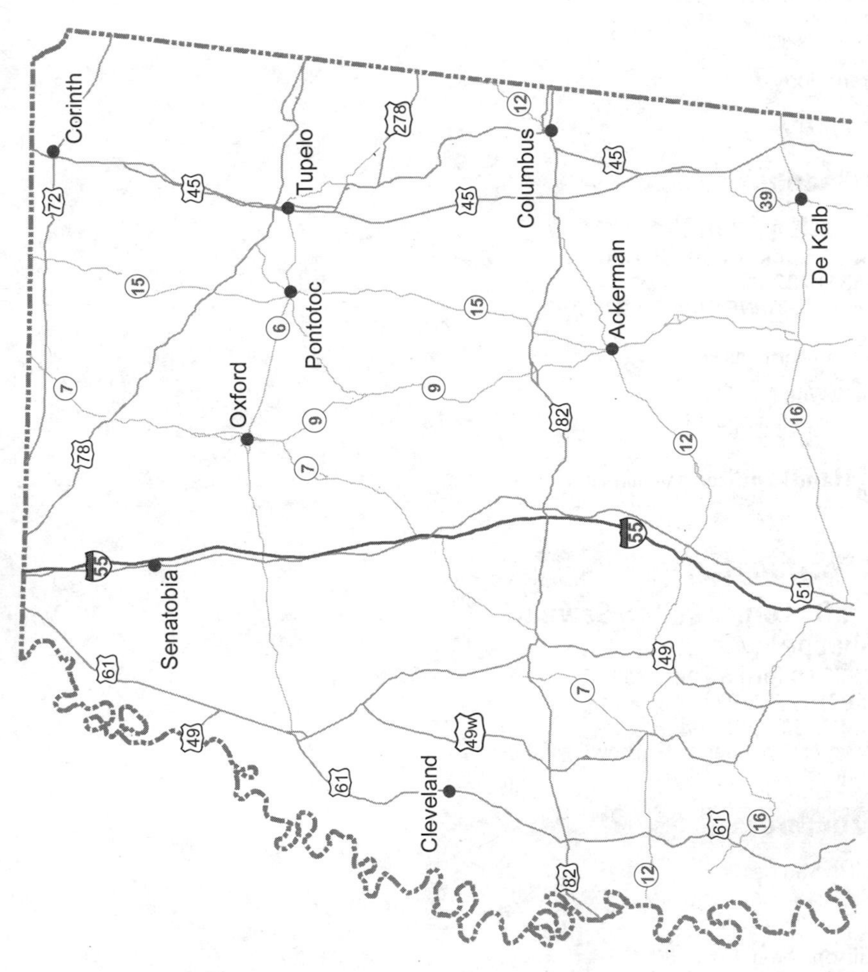
Corinth
Tupelo
Columbus
De Kalb
Pontotoc
Ackerman
Oxford
Senatobia
Cleveland
72
45
278
12
39
15
6
7
9
82
16
78
55
51
61
49
49W

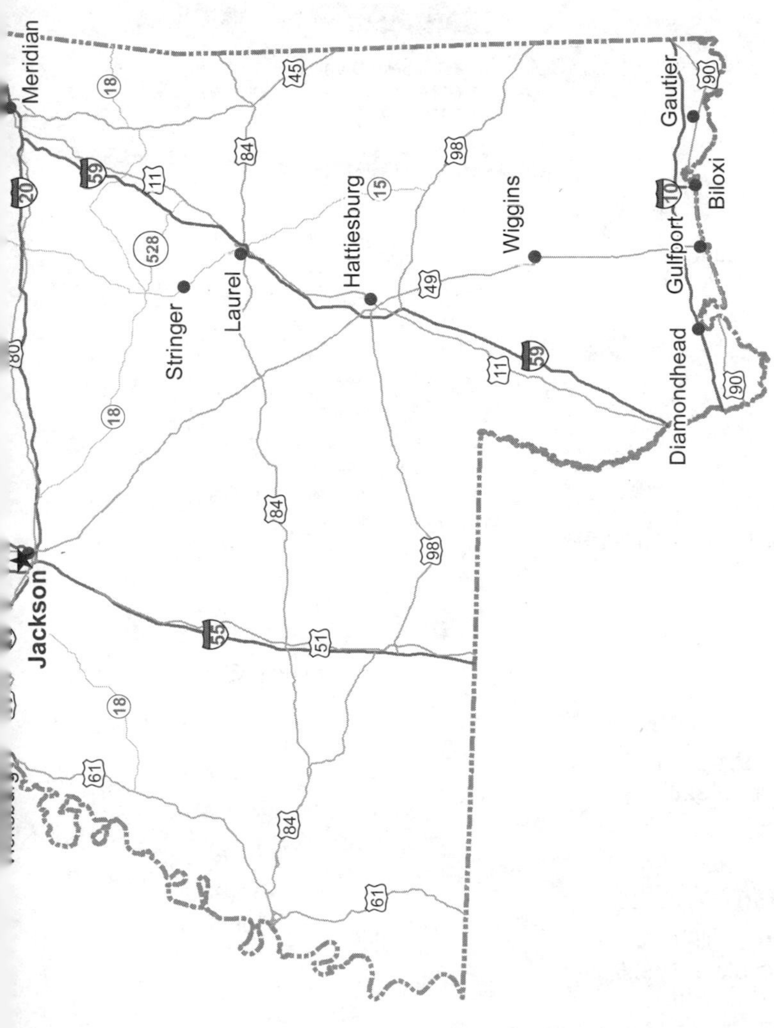
Meridian
Jackson
Stringer
Laurel
Hattiesburg
Wiggins
Gautier
Biloxi
Gulfport
Diamondhead

Mississippi

Ackerman

Main Street Fabrics QEC
93 E. Main Street, 39735
(662) 285-6241

Biloxi

Peace by Piece LLC* Q
1013 Howard Avenue, 39530
(228) 207-0425

Cleveland

Ella Rose Fabrics & Boutique* QYM
158 N. Sharpe Avenue, 38732
(662) 843-4800

Columbus

Figg Fabrics & Studio* Q
59 Old Swan Lane, 39702
(662) 549-4318

Corinth

Treasure Chest Quilting & More* QEM
202 Highway 72 E, 38834
(662) 594-1055

De Kalb

Village Cloth Shoppe QE
302 Main Avenue, 39328
(601) 743-5638
MTuWF 9:30-5, Sa 9:30-1

Diamondhead

The French Knot YN
5401 Indian Hills Blvd., 39525
(228) 255-3100
Tu 10-6, W-F 10-4:30, Sa 10-3
www.frknot.com

Gautier

Block Therapy Quilt Shop & Sewing Center* QEM
4353 Gautier VanCleave Road, 39553
(228) 202-1493

Gulfport

Coastal Sew & Vac QM
12100 Highway 49, Suite 200, 39503
(228) 831-4771

Hattiesburg

Sew Select* QEM
4400 Hardy Street, Suite B9, 34902
(601) 268-0739

The Stitchin Post LLC QEM
5039 Old Highway 11, 39402
(601) 268-5545

Jackson

Continental Sewing* QEM
5068 Parkway Drive, 39211
(601) 956-6376 or (866) 956-6376

The Knit Studio Y
1481 Canton Mark Road, Suite B, 39211
(601) 991-3092

Laurel

Let's Make Something LLC* Q
1317 Highway 15 N, Suite E, 39440
(601) 340-3143

Meridian

The Sewing and Vacuum Center Ⓠ Ⓜ
525 22nd Avenue S, 39301
(601) 693-1863

Handi Quilter® Authorized Retailer
Designed by a Quilter, for Quilters.®

Oxford

Knit1 Oxford* Ⓨ Ⓢ
303 Heritage Drive, 38655
(662) 238-2829

Pontotoc

Mulberry Cottage Industries Ⓨ
204 S. Main Street, 38863
(662) 509-2091

Ridgeland

BERNINA Sewing, Etc.* Ⓠ Ⓔ Ⓜ
665 S. Pear Orchard Road, Suite 104, 39157
(601) 991-2120

Cotton Blossom Fabric Shop* Ⓠ Ⓜ
670 Highway 51, Suite A, 39517
(601) 427-5214

The Southern Needle Ⓨ Ⓦ Ⓢ
500 Highway 51N, Suite T, 39157
(601) 919-7118

Senatobia

Cotton Treasures* Ⓠ
218 E. Main Street, 38668
(662) 562-4422

Stringer

A Stroka Gene Us Alpacas Ⓨ Ⓢ
383 County Road 155, 39481
(716) 863-4366

Tupelo

Heirlooms Forever* Ⓠ Ⓜ
3112 Cliff Gookin Blvd., 38801
(662) 842-4275 or (800) 840-4275

Vicksburg

Fabs & More and the Whole 9 Yarns Ⓨ
3040 Halls Ferry Road, 39180
(601) 636-0510

Stitch-N-Frame* Ⓠ Ⓔ Ⓜ
31 Willow Creek Drive, 39183
(601) 634-0243 or (877) 634-1462

Wiggins

The Fabric Dock* Ⓠ Ⓜ
2118 S. Azalea Drive (Highway 49), 39577
(601) 928-1904

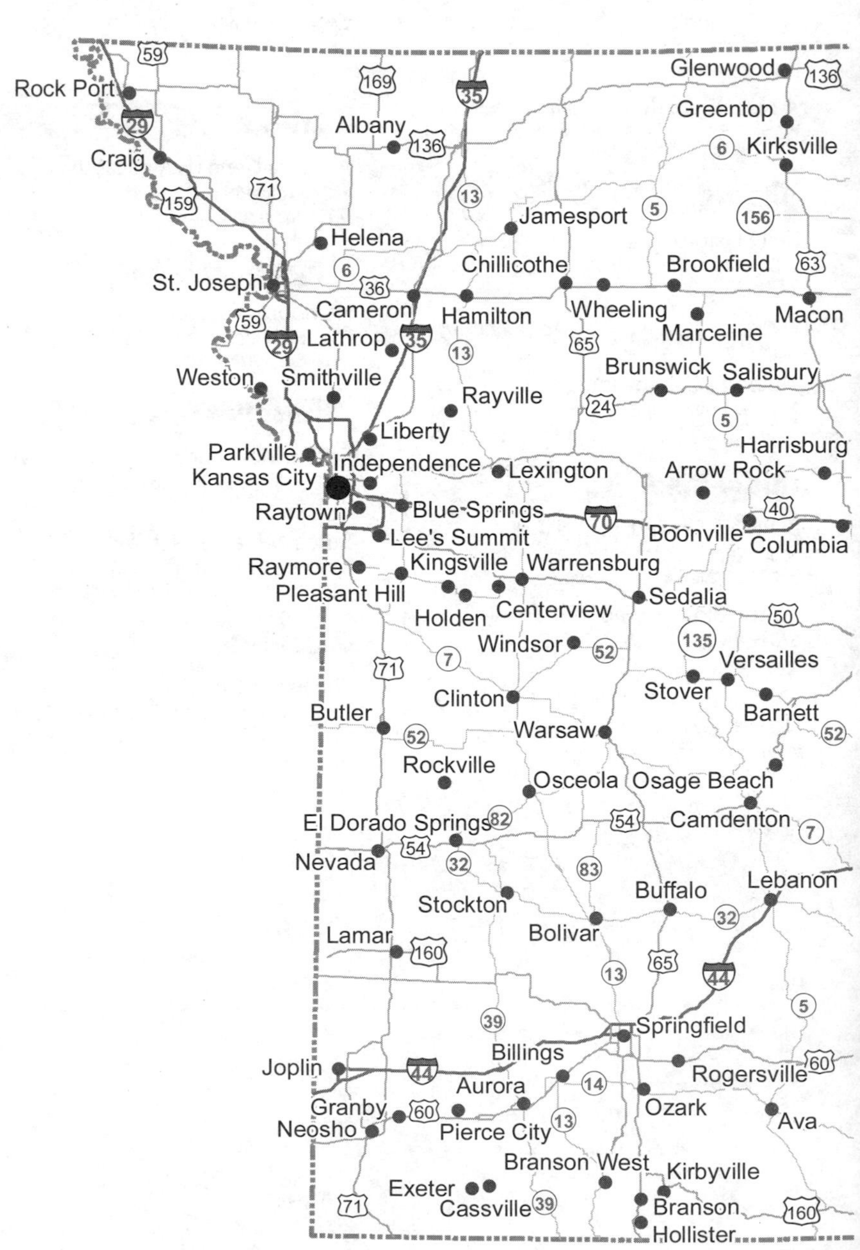

Rock Port
Craig
Albany
Glenwood
Greentop
Kirksville
Jamesport
Helena
St. Joseph
Chillicothe
Brookfield
Cameron
Hamilton
Wheeling
Marceline
Macon
Lathrop
Weston
Smithville
Brunswick
Salisbury
Rayville
Liberty
Parkville
Kansas City
Independence
Lexington
Harrisburg
Arrow Rock
Raytown
Blue Springs
Boonville
Columbia
Lee's Summit
Raymore
Kingsville
Warrensburg
Pleasant Hill
Holden
Centerview
Sedalia
Windsor
Versailles
Stover
Clinton
Butler
Barnett
Warsaw
Rockville
Osceola
Osage Beach
El Dorado Springs
Camdenton
Nevada
Stockton
Buffalo
Lebanon
Bolivar
Lamar
Springfield
Billings
Joplin
Aurora
Rogersville
Ozark
Ava
Granby
Neosho
Pierce City
Branson West
Kirbyville
Exeter
Cassville
Branson
Hollister

Memphis
136
Kahoka
Rutledge
61
156
6
36
Shelbina
Hannibal
Monroe City
24
19
61
151
54
22
Mexico
61
19
70
New Florence
Wentzville
54
19
O'Fallon
Florissant
Holts Summit
Valley Park
St. Louis
Jefferson City
Fenton
Arnold
50
St. Clair
Bland
Sullivan
Vienna
47
28
21
44
185
28
Potosi
Bonne Terre
Rolla
8
32
66
68
19
Park Hills
St. Robert
Viburnum
61
55
Salem
49
32
63
19
67
Cape Girardeau
Mountain Grove
106
49
Birch Tree
57
Willow Springs
60
19
Poplar Bluff
Dexter
14
21
West Plains
55
160
160
63
Doniphan
67
62
61
7
412

Missouri

Albany

Locklar's Crafts & Quilting* Ⓠ Ⓝ Ⓒ
115 S. Polk Street, 64402
(660) 726-3140

Arnold

Your Quilt Shop Ⓠ Ⓨ Ⓜ
2051 Southway Drive, 63010
(636) 464-2929 or (866) 520-3764

Arrow Rock

A Grand Yarn* Ⓨ Ⓢ
302 Main Street, 65340
(660) 837-3111

Aurora

Quilted Garden Fabric Shop Ⓠ Ⓜ
620 McNatt Avenue, 65605
(417) 678-1600

Ava

Dogwood Quilting Ⓠ Ⓔ
808 S. Jefferson, Suite 1, 65608
(417) 683-4700

Barnett

Pleasant Valley Quilts * Ⓠ Ⓔ Ⓒ
15050 Hopewell Road, 65011
(573) 378-4447

Billings

Fox Pen Quilting Ⓠ Ⓔ
154 NE Elm Street (Highway 60), 65610
(417) 695-3031

Birch Tree

Hideaway Quilt Shop* Ⓠ Ⓔ
3217 W. 1st Street, 65438
(573) 292-1008

Bland

Satches, LLC* Ⓠ
895 CR 703, 65014
(573) 263-8019

Blue Springs

CC and Company Ⓒ
1701 SW US Highway 40, Suite 102, 64015
(816) 229-2950
Tu-F 9:30-5, Sa 9:30-3
http://www.ccandcompanybluespgs.com

Bolivar

Margie Pearl's Fabrics* Ⓠ Ⓔ
4743 S. 131st Road, 65613
(417) 777-4913

Bonne Terre

Cutt N Sew* Ⓠ
27 W. School Street, 63628
(573) 358-7887

Boonville

Missouri Country Quilts Q M
➡ SEE AD BELOW. 24298 HIGHWAY 98
Exit 111 - I 70, 65233
(660) 537-3541
M-Sa 9:30-5
www.missouricountryquilts.com

Missouri Country Quilts
3,000 Bolts Fabric
Bargain Section
Authorized Dealers
Janome & Grace (Q'nigue)
Sewing, Quilting & Embroidery
10% off First Order
Must present this ad at time of purchase
Not valid on Janome/Grace Products
660-537-3541
24298 Highway 98
Boonville, Mo. 65233
Exit 111 off I-70
½ mile west of
Budweiser Clydesdale Ranch

Branson

Cecilia's Samplers E Y C
2652 Shepherd of the Hills Expressway, 65616
(417) 336-5016
M-F 8-4:30, Sa 10-4
www.ceciliassamplers.com

Quilts & Quilts The Fabric Shoppe Q E
3500 N. Gretna Road, 65616
(417) 334-3243
Winter:(Jan-Feb) M-Sa 9-5; Summer Hours: (Mar-Dec): M-Sa 9:30-5:30
www.quiltsandquilts.com

Branson Sewing Center Q E N C M
4520 Gretna Road, 65616
(417) 320-6090

canfieldcreations & The Yarn Patch* Y W S
Inside Silver Dollar City Amusement Park, 65616
(417) 294-0067 or (417) 338-3854

Miss Kate's at Silver Dollar City* Q
399 Silver Dollar Parkway, 65616
(417) 338-8216

Branson West

The Quilted Cow Q E
18593 Business 13, Suite 203, 65737
(417) 272-0000

Brookfield

Hueffmeier's Fine Pines* Q E
27905 Highway FF, 64628
(660) 258-3244

Brunswick

Sew Sweet Quilt Shop* Q E M
207 E. Broadway Street, 65236
(660) 548-3056

Buffalo

Maw & Paw Fabrics & More LLC Q E
800 S. Ash, 65622
(417) 345-4414

Butler

Rocking Chair Quilts Q E C
21 N. Main Street, 64730
(660) 200-2226

Camdenton

Fleeces to Pieces Y W S
138 W. Highway 54, 65020
(573) 836-0105

Cameron

Crossroads Quilting* Q
1720 N. Walnut Street, Suite D, 64429
(816) 649-0550

Cape Girardeau

The Golden Needle Sewing Basket* Q M
330 S. Kings Highway, 63703
(573) 339-0494

Yearning 4 Yarn* Y W S
5 N. Spanish Street, 63701
(573) 579-7679

Cassville

Stitches Fine Fabrics & Notions Q E C
24493 State Highway 76, 65625
(417) 858-2990

Centerview

Hunter Heirloom Quilting* Q
573 NW US Highway 50, 64019
(660) 656-3325

Chillicothe

Cuts & Bolts Fabrics Q
24 S. Washington Street, 64601
(660) 240-0120
M-Sa 9-5
www.cutsandboltsfabrics.com

Clinton

White Flower Quilt Shop LLC Q
140 W. Jefferson Street, 64735
(660) 492-5379

Columbia

Appletree Quilting Center Q M
2541 Bernadette Drive, 65203
(573) 446-2655 or (800) 269-2655

Handi Quilter® Authorized Retailer
Designed by a Quilter, for Quilters.®

Carol Leigh's Hillcreek Fiber Studio Y W S
7001 S. Hill Creek Road, 65203
(573) 874-2233 or (800) 874-9328

Hillcreek Yarn Shoppe Y
4093 E. Ketterer Road, 65202
(573) 449-5648

Quilt 4 U* Q C M
908 Rain Forest Parkway, Suite E, 65202
(573) 443-7858

Satin Stitches Sewing & Embroidery Q E M
705D Vandiver Drive, 65202
(573) 817-0006

Craig

Fabrics Unique* Q E
11290 Highway 59 N, 64437
(660) 683-5757

Dexter

Treasured Threads Quilting Q
14605 US Highway 60, 63841
(573) 624-4042
Tu-F 10-5, Sa 10-2
www.treasuredthreadsquilting.com

Doniphan

Current River Fabrics and Quilting Q E C
103 Washington Street, 63935
(576) 996-1888

El Dorado Springs

Material Matters Quilting Shop Q
105 E. US Highway 54, 64744
(417) 876-2606

Exeter

P-Dub's Quilt Stuff Q
12203 Highway 76, 65647
(417) 847-9276

Fenton

Fenton Sew-N-Vac Q E M
180A Gravois Bluffs Circle, 63026
(636) 343-8088

Florissant

Weaving Department / Myers House* Y W S
180 W. Dunn Road, 63031
(314) 921-7800

Glenwood

Bri-Lee Quilting, Batting & Fabric Shop Q
16596 Johnson Drive, 63541
(660) 216-4383

Granby

Heavenly Notions* Q Y
312 N. Main Street, 64844
(417) 389-9472

Greentop

Wildflower Quilting Q
309 E. 1st Street, 63546
(208) 280-1141

Hamilton

Missouri Star Quilt Co. Q Y
114 N. Davis Street, 64644
(888) 571-1122 or (816) 368-8670

Hannibal

Bits and Pieces Q
221 N. Main Street, 63401
(573) 603-1279

Hickory Stick Quilt and Gift Shop Q E
326 N. Main Street, 63401
(573) 221-4538

Harrisburg

Spindleweb Yarn & Pottery Shop Y W S
14851 N. Highway NN, 65256
(573) 874-1005

Helena

Top Stitch Quilt Shop Q M
14000 Highway 169, 64459
(816) 369-2425

Holden

Patchwork Pals Quilt Shop Q M
1469 SW 800 Road, 64040
(816) 838-4473

Hollister

Homestead Fabric & Woolens Q

215 Gage Street, 65673

Holts Summit

Rooster Creek Q
176 W. Simon Blvd., 65043
(573) 896-8025

Independence

Yarn Mercantile Knitcraft's & Angelika's Y M
500 N. Dodgion, 64050
(816) 461-1248 or (816) 461-5505
Tu-Sa, please call ahead
www.yarnmercantile.com

Knitcraft Yarn Shop* Y
500 N. Dodgion Street, 64050
(816) 461-1248

Jamesport

Sue's Soft Stuff Q Y W S
205 S. Broadway Street, 64648
(660) 684-6205
M-Sa 10-5
www.facebook.com/suessoftstuff/

Shearwood Quilts & Fabrics Q
1091 HWY U, 64648
(660) 684-6121

Jefferson City

Specialty Quilts & Fabrics, LLC* Q
2709 Industrial Drive, Suite D, 65109
(573) 761-7313

Joplin

Bittersweet Quilts* Q
8133 W. Highway 86, 64804
(417) 627-9555

The Fabric Merchant* Q
120 S. Main Street, 64801
(417) 622-0012

Kahoka

DB's Quilters & Supplies* Q E
115 W. Main Street, 63445
(660) 727-1208

Kansas City

KC Needlepoint Ⓝ
➡ SEE AD BELOW
105 E. Gregory Blvd., 64114
(816) 599-7331
Tu-F 10-4, Sa 10-3
http://www.kcneedlepoint.com

The (New) Dime Store Ⓨ
314 W. 63rd Street, 64113
(816) 523-3140

Kingsville

Liberty Homestead* Ⓠ
115 SW 1991 Road, 64061
(816) 597-9402

Kirbyville

Yarn Diva ⓆⓎ
5439 E. Highway 76, 65679
(417) 334-1586

Kirksville

Quilted Square* ⓆⒺⓂ
511 S. Baltimore Street, Suite 10, 63501
(660) 665-7533

Lamar

Blue Top Quilt Shop ⓆⒺ
61 SE 1st Lane, 64759
(417) 681-0330
M-F 9-5, Sa 9-2
www.bluetopquiltshop.com

Lathrop

Sisters Fabric Farm Ⓠ
6320 NE 272nd Street, 64465
(816) 528-3626 or (816) 628-4515
Th 9-4, Call for other times
www.facebook.com/pages/Sisters-Fabric-Farm/825257047491719

Lebanon

Buckles Bobbins and Bolts LLC Ⓠ
22476 Highway MM, 65536
(417) 650-5043

Lee's Summit

Quilter's Station ⓆⒺⒸⓂ
3680 NE Akin Drive, 64064
(816) 525-8955

Zoelee's Fabrics Ⓠ
1329 NE Deer Valley Drive, 64086
(816) 524-7217

Lexington

All About Quilting Ⓠ
912 Main Street, 64067
(816) 868-5246

Liberty

Quilting Is My Therapy* ⓆⓂ
2 E. Franklin Street, 64068
(816) 679-8810
Handi Quilter® Authorized Retailer
Designed by a Quilter, for Quilters.®

Macon

Wavering's Ben Franklin* ⓆⓎ
103 N. Rollins, 63552
(660) 385-5751

Marceline

Rosie's Quilts & Things ⓆⒺ
11526 Long Branch Avenue, 64658
(660) 376-2593

Memphis

Green Acres Sew & Vac ⓆⒺⓂ
221W Grand Avenue, 63555
(660) 465-7131

Mexico

Homestead Hearth* Q E
105 N. Coal Street, 65265
(573) 581-1966

Monroe City

Wavering's Ben Franklin Q E Y
100 S. Main, 63456
(573) 735-4395

Mountain Grove

Ozarks Patchwork Peddler Q E C
106 E. 17th Street, 65711
(417) 926-0844

Neosho

The Quilted Swan / N Stitches* Q
108 W. Main Street, 64850
(417) 455-0999

Nevada

Nine Patch Quilt & Fabrics Q
129 E. Walnut Street, 64772
(417) 667-7100

New Florence

All N Stitches Q E C
352 Booneslick Road, 63363
(573) 564-4050

O'Fallon

O'Sewpersonal Fabric Shop Q M
1157 Bryan Road, 63366
(636) 294-7922

Osage Beach

Love to Sew Boutique & Fabrics Q E C M
877 Highway 42, Suite B, 65065
(573) 348-1972

Osceola

Brenda's Quilt Stop & More Q
785 SW Highway 54, 64776
(417) 876-9997

Ozark

Sew Simple Quilt Shoppe* Q M
5241 N. 17th Street, 65721
(417) 582-8383

Park Hills

Mad Monk's Fabric Warehouse* Q E C
204 E. Main Street, 63601
(573) 431-1677

Parkville

Peddler's Wagon Q E
115 Main Street, 64152
(816) 741-0225

Pierce City

The Thistle Quilt Shop* Q
102 W. Commercial Street, 65723
(417) 476-5844

Pleasant Hill

Kathy's Quilts Plus Q
32001 E. State Route P, 64080
(913) 486-2822

Poplar Bluff

Sew Much More Q E C
1103 Cherry Street, 63901
(573) 727-9898

Potosi

Pieces Patches N Lace* Q E N C M
201 E. High Street, 63664
(573) 438-6718

Raymore

Creative Hands Quilt Shop and Decorative Painting Q E C
1907 W. Foxwood Drive, 64083
(816) 331-1992

Raytown

Show-Me Quilting* Q E
6221 Blue Ridge Blvd., 64133
(816) 313-8225

Rayville

By The Yard Q
16587 Highway C, 64084
(816) 470-6703

Rock Port

Quilters Boutique LLC Q
300 W. US Highway 136, 64482
(660) 744-2528

Rockville

DbarJ Quilts etc. Q E Y C
405 1st Street, 64780
(660) 598-2222

Rogersville

One City Market* Y
214 Beatie Street, 65742
(417) 753-7100

Rolla

The Stitch Niche Q E Y N W S C
634 S. Bishop Avenue, 65401
(573) 458-6995

Uniquely Yours Knitting & Quilting Center Q E Y S C M
404 E. State Route 72, 65401
(573) 364-2070

Rutledge

Zimmerman's Store* Q
29229 First Street, 63563
(660) 883-5766

Salem

Quilter's Journey* Q
1424 Highway 68, 65560
(573) 453-2100

Salisbury

Sew Creative* Q
407 E. Patterson Street, 65281
(660) 388-6287

Sedalia

D & T Quilt Shop* Q E C
3620 S. Marshall Avenue, 65301
(660) 826-4788

Shelbina

Midwest Quilt Company Q
102 Hall Street, 63468
(573) 588-7000

Smithville

Cornerstone Fabric* Q E
108 S. Bridge Street, 64089
(816) 873-0005

Springfield

F. M. Stores* Q
2814 S. Fremont, 1E, 65804
(417) 882-9244

Fabric Outlet* Q
1241 E. Republic Road, 65804
(417) 889-0528

Fabric Outlet* Q
1333 S. Glenstone Avenue, 65804
(417) 881-4966

Merrily We Quilt Along* Q E M
1718 S. Ingram Mill Road, 65804
(417) 890-9000

Quilt Sampler* Q M
1802 S. Glenstone Avenue, 65804
(417) 886-5750

Shawn's Sewing Center* M
1500 S. Glenstone Avenue, 65804
(417) 885-1242

Handi Quilter Authorized Retailer
Designed by a Quilter, for Quilters.

The Village Yarnery Y
2134 W. Chesterfield Blvd., 65807
(417) 882-1662

St. Clair

R&R Ace* Q
845 N. Commercial Avenue, 63077
(636) 629-4300

St. Joseph

Glenda's Sewing Cupboard Ⓠ
18255 County Road 349, 64505
(816) 662-3105 or (816) 294-2781

St. Louis

Sign of the Arrow Ⓝ
➡ SEE AD ABOVE
9814 Clayton Road, 63124
(314) 994-0606
M-Sa 9:30-5
www.signofthearrow.com

Heyde Sewing Machine Company ⓆⒺⓂ
5451 S. Lindbergh Blvd., 63123
(314) 843-1168 or (877) 245-8100
M-F 10-6, Sa 10-4, Su (only November and December) 11-4
http://www.heydesewing.com

Handi Quilter® Authorized Retailer
Designed by a Quilter, for Quilters.®

Quilted Fox Ⓠ
10403 Clayton Road, 63131
(314) 993-1181

Batiks Plus* ⓆⓂ
1322 Ashby Road, 63132
(800) 756-1223 or (314) 432-1223

Jackman's Fabrics Ⓠ
1234 N. Lindbergh Blvd., 63132
(314) 994-1060

Kirkwood Knittery* ⓎⓈ
10404 Manchester Road, 63122
(314) 822-7222

Knitorious* ⓎⓌⓈ
3268 Watson Road, 63139
(314) 646-8276

The First and Last Stitch* Ⓝ
8988 Manchester Road, 63144
(314) 961-8157

The Needlepoint Clubhouse* Ⓝ
717 N. New Ballas Road, 63141
(314) 432-2555

St. Robert

Michels Frames & Things E C
690 Missouri Avenue, Suite 21, 65584
(573) 336-8666
M-F 10-5, Sa 10-2
www.michelsframesandthings.com

Stockton

Creative Notions* Q E
211 East Street, 65785
(417) 276-4216

Stover

Nustyle Quilting Machines & Supplies* Q
309 W. 4th Street, Highway 52, 65078
(573) 377-2244 or (800) 821-7490

Stover Quality Quilting* Q E
606 N. Ash Street, 65078
(573) 377-2303 or (800) 521-4171

Sullivan

Devine Quilts, Fabrics & Hobbies Q E M
➡ SEE AD BELOW
33 N. Clark Street, Suite A, 63080
(314) 378-3868
Tu-Sa 10—5

Valley Park

Merrily We Sew Along* Q E M
932 Meramec Station Road, Unit H, 63088
(636) 220-7738

Versailles

Excelsior Fabrics* Q E
39990 Excelsior Drive, 65084
(573) 378-7448

Viburnum

Seams Sew Sweet Designs* Q E
60 Walnut Street, 65566
(573) 233-4380

Vienna

Leisure Time Sewing & Fabrics* Q E C
410 8th Street, 65582
(573) 422-3500

Warrensburg

Primitive Stitches Q E
34 SW 365 Road, 64093
(660) 747-7787

Sew Good Quilting* Q
126 SW Highway 13, 64093
(660) 580-0033

Warsaw

City's Edge Q M
616 W. Main Street, 65355
(660) 438-3177

Saltbox Primitive Woolens* Q E Y
30148 W. Dam Access Road, 65355
(660) 438-6002

Wooden Wagon* Q
242 W. Main Street, 65355
(660) 438-6400

Wentzville

Susie Q Quilting Q
119 W. Pearce Blvd., 63385
(636) 272-7455

West Plains

The Sewing Connection Q M
2122 State Route CC, 65775
(417) 293-8732

Weston

Florilegium* Ⓠ Ⓔ Ⓨ Ⓝ Ⓦ Ⓢ
367 Main Street, 64098
(816) 746-6164

Wheeling

The Quilt Shoppe Ⓠ
10650 Highway B, 64688
(660) 659-2469

Willow Springs

Stitchin' Post* Ⓠ Ⓔ Ⓒ
224 E. Main Street, 65793
(417) 469-5806

Windsor

Countryview Fabrics* Ⓠ
1291 SE 1300, 65360

Our Industry Sponsors

Please patronize them.
They make this book possible.

WHOLESALERS

MANUFACTURERS

DESIGNERS

The goal of this travel guide is to list every NeedleArts shop in the country, regardless of whether they buy anything from us. This would not be possible without the generous support of our sponsors. So, please look through this section and support our sponsors when you can.

Listings by Merchandise

Listings by Merchandise

Organizations/Services:

Publications/Websites:

Sewing Machines/Accessories:

Retreats/Events:

Yarn:

Sponsor Listings – Alphabetical

COTTON
COUTURE
38 NEW COLORS

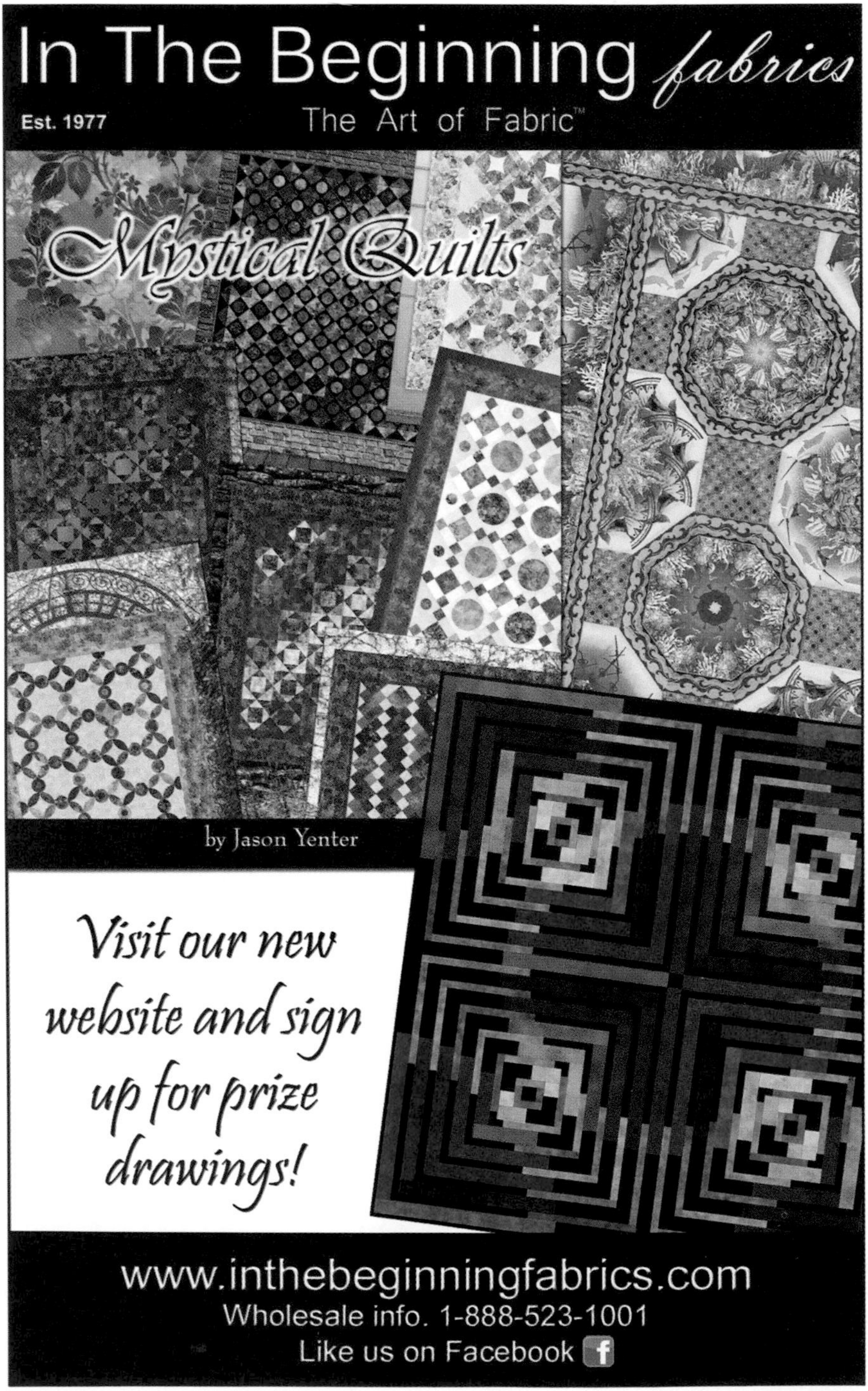

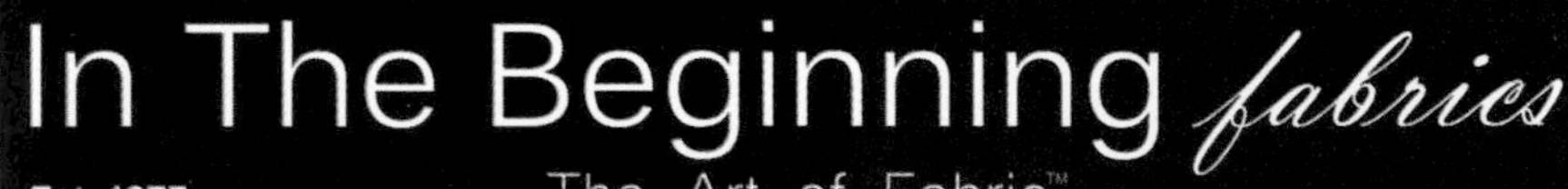

In The Beginning fabrics
Est. 1977
The Art of Fabric™
Mystical Quilts
by Jason Yenter
Visit our new website and sign up for prize drawings!
www.inthebeginningfabrics.com
Wholesale info. 1-888-523-1001
Like us on Facebook

CREATING QUALITY TOOLS FOR CREATIVE MINDS

For almost 20 years, Famore has been offering its customers sharpening and reconditioning on all their Famore branded products for FREE. We have also offered this service for other brands at a low cost per scissors. Due to our extensive knowledge of scissors reconditioning we have come up with a new category of "Scissors Care". With this new category comes 3 new items, two of which are bundled.

FAMORE RUST ERASER

The first is our own Famore Rust Eraser. The rust eraser is not something our products will ever need but we all have a pair of rusted knives, tools or scissors in our workshop. This small block works like an eraser and literally erases the rust right before your eyes, leaving a brushed satin finish. This new product retails for $8.50

FAMORE BLADE CARE KIT

Famore's next product is a two-item bundle. ALL metal tools and scissors need to be oiled from time to time. The reason tools with pivot points like scissors, plyers, and hemostats get tight is from the wear and tear. Cutting instruments debris gets trapped around the screw, then attracts moisture which inevitably ends in rust. Our Famore Lubricating oil will remove debris and coat your screw to keep your scissors from rusting or seizing up. Our oil will also slow down existing rust from spreading. Lastly this kit contains one reusable polishing cloth. The cloth works on steel and fine metals like scissors or jewelry. This kit retails for $19.99.

---

www.famorecutlery.com • 678-971-4438 • info@famorecutlery.com

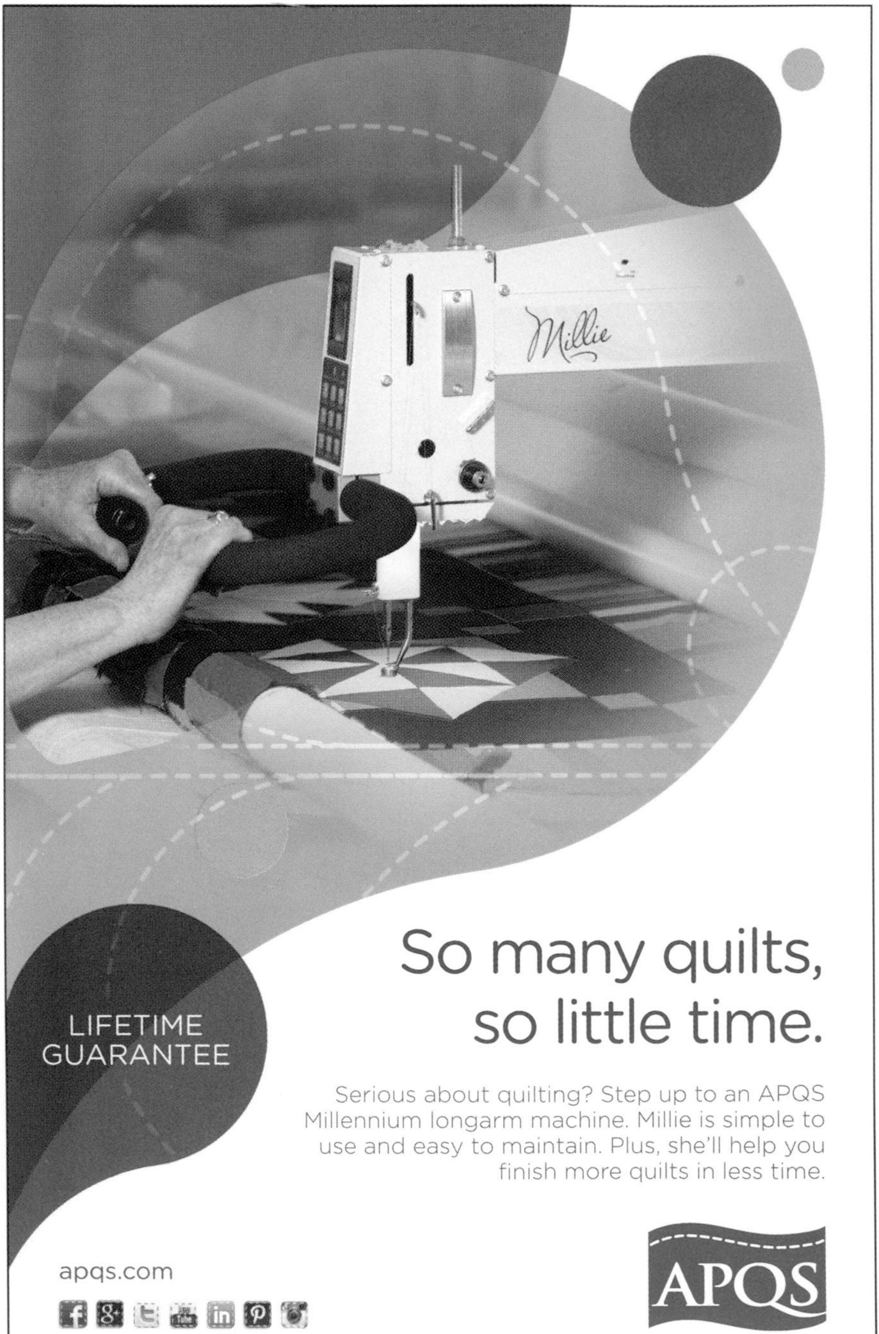

Millie

LIFETIME GUARANTEE

So many quilts, so little time.

Serious about quilting? Step up to an APQS Millennium longarm machine. Millie is simple to use and easy to maintain. Plus, she'll help you finish more quilts in less time.

apqs.com

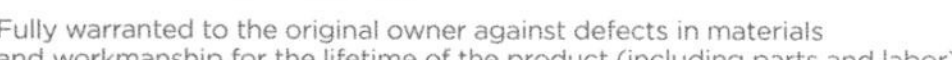

QUILT FOREVER!

1924: Hoffman Fabrics is a 4th generation family business celebrating 95 years beginning in 1924.

1950'S: We created the surf wear craze in the 1950's by introducing aloha prints.

1987: We are the *first* and *finest* in batiks introducing quilting and home-sewing to their beauty in 1987.

1990'S: We've perfected the metallic touch in screen prints specializing in holiday fabrics since the 1990's.

2001: *We care.* With an eye on sustainability, we built our water reclamation facility at our factory in Bali in 2001.

2012: We are the leaders in innovation as we raise the bar and set the standard in digitally printed fabrics since 2012.

2015: We are continuing our quest for quality with the launch of our modern division, ME+YOU in 2015.

TODAY: We are continually striving to produce and provide the highest quality designs and fabrications.

Celebrating

95 • YEARS

Tour our Certified Shops...It's time to check this adventure off your bucketlist! Our **Certified Shops** are exclusive dealers of the our *Technique of the Month Programs* which means they're trained teachers of Judy's techniques, authorities on our product line, they have living galleries of completed quilts, and are committed to kitting to meet your needs. The states with quilts displayed below have Certified Shops in them!

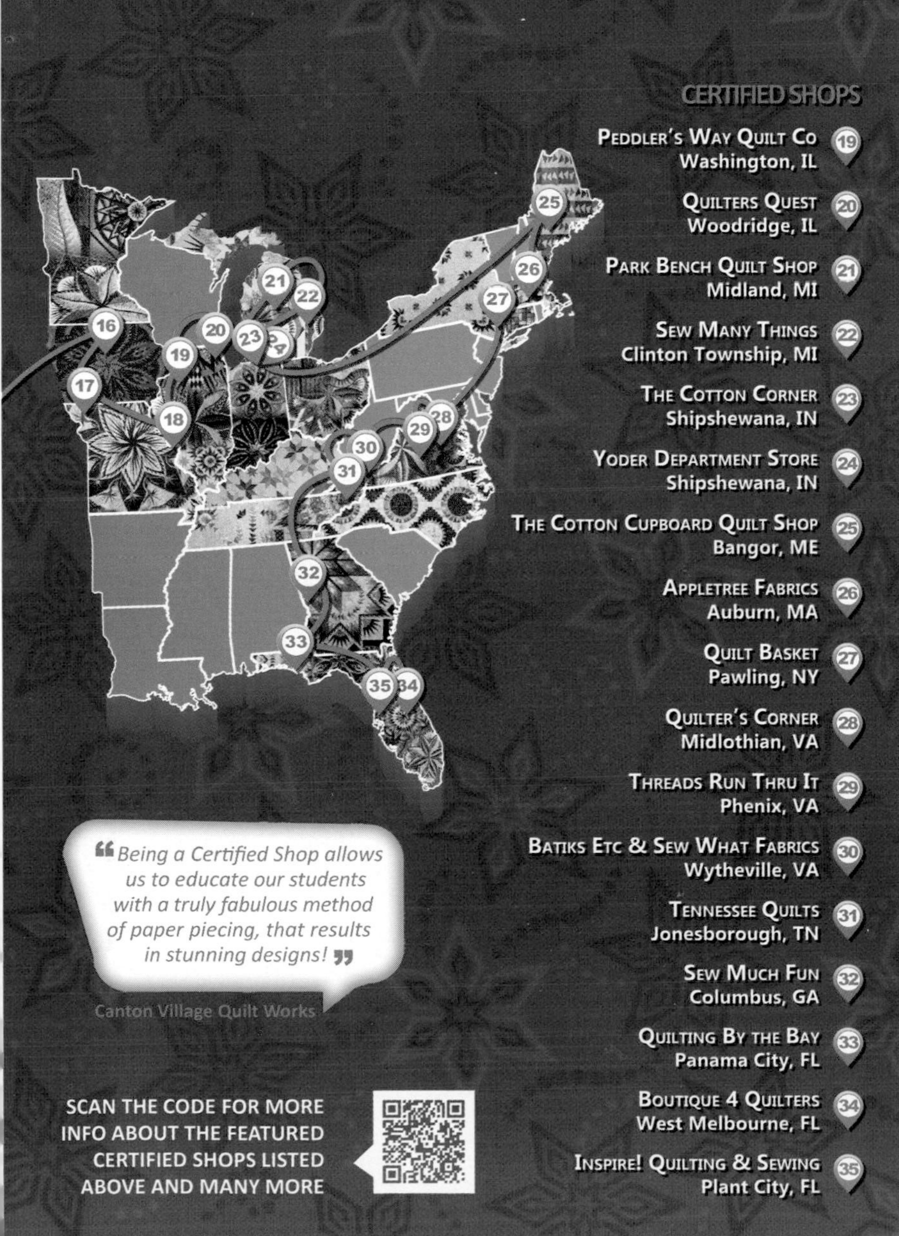

SCHMETZ
5 SUPER NONSTICK NEEDLES
Aiguilles Super Antiadhésives
Agujas Super Antiadherentes
SCHMETZ
NonStick Needles
Available in sizes:
70/10, 80/12, 90/14, 100/16
HOT PICKS!
BOBBINSAVER2™
(BobbinSaver® Squared™)
Sewing Essentials in Every Workspace!
Grabbit SEWING TOOLS ®
www.SCHMETZneedles.com

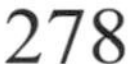

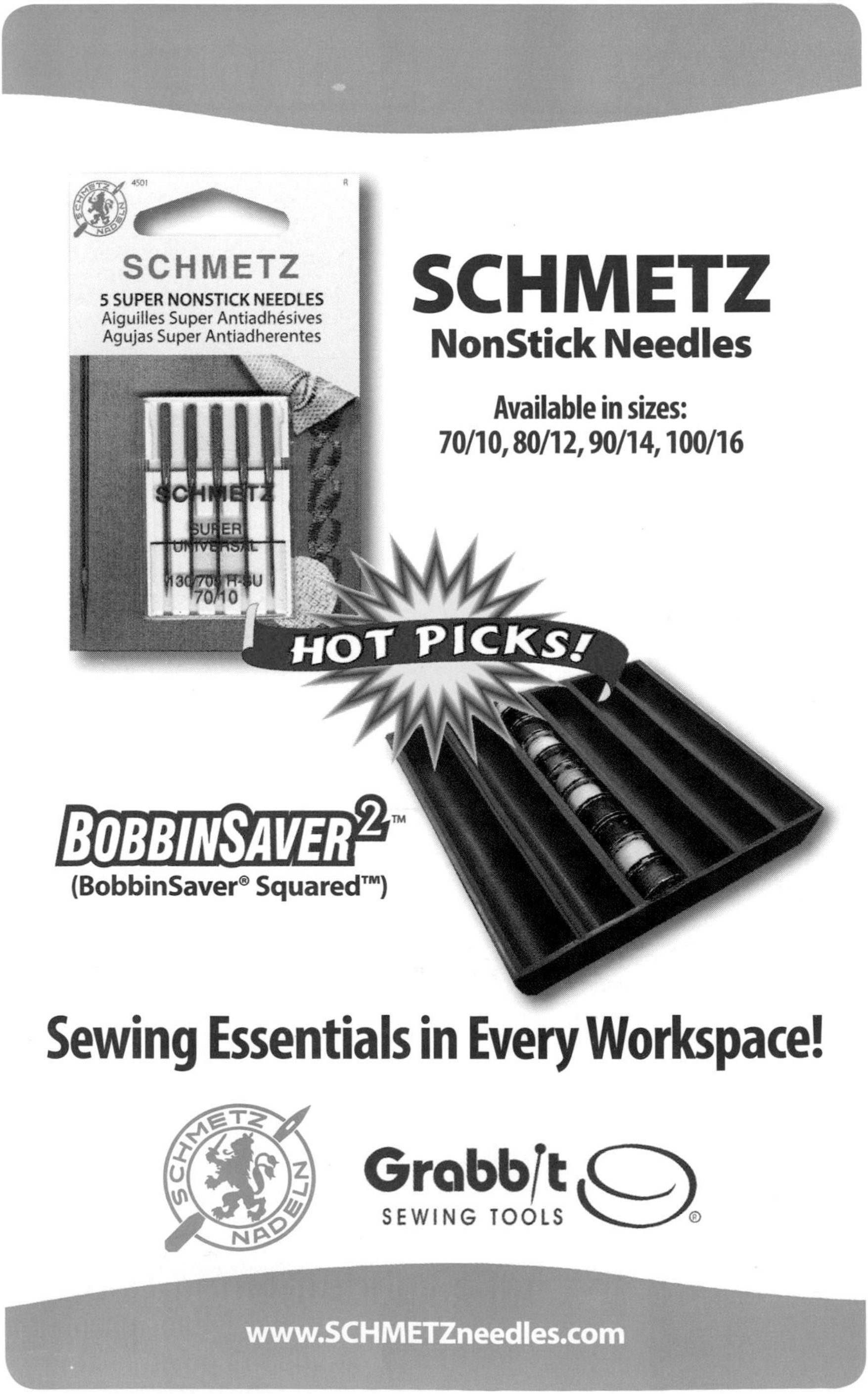

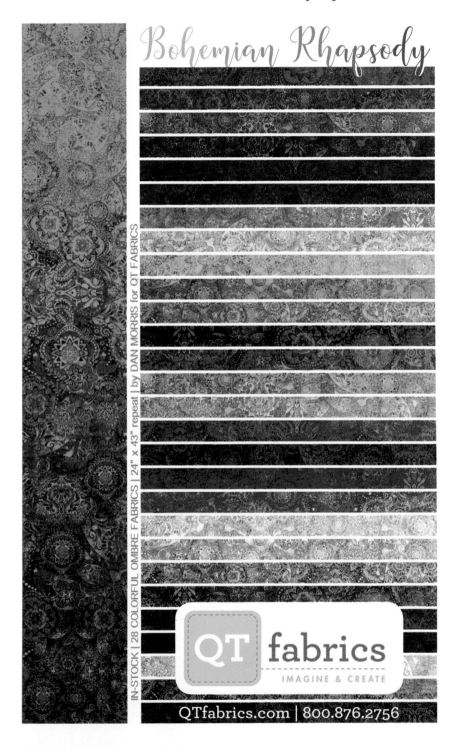

Bohemian Rhapsody
IN-STOCK | 28 COLORFUL OMBRE FABRICS | 24" x 43" repeat | by DAN MORRIS for QT FABRICS
QT fabrics
IMAGINE & CREATE
QTfabrics.com | 800.876.2756

Anzula
luxury fibers
Saltmarsh Shell
by Laura Crowley
design includes
sizes 33–45½"
all sizes use just
3 skeins of Anzula Vera
Saltmarsh Shell
find a shop near you at
www.anzula.com

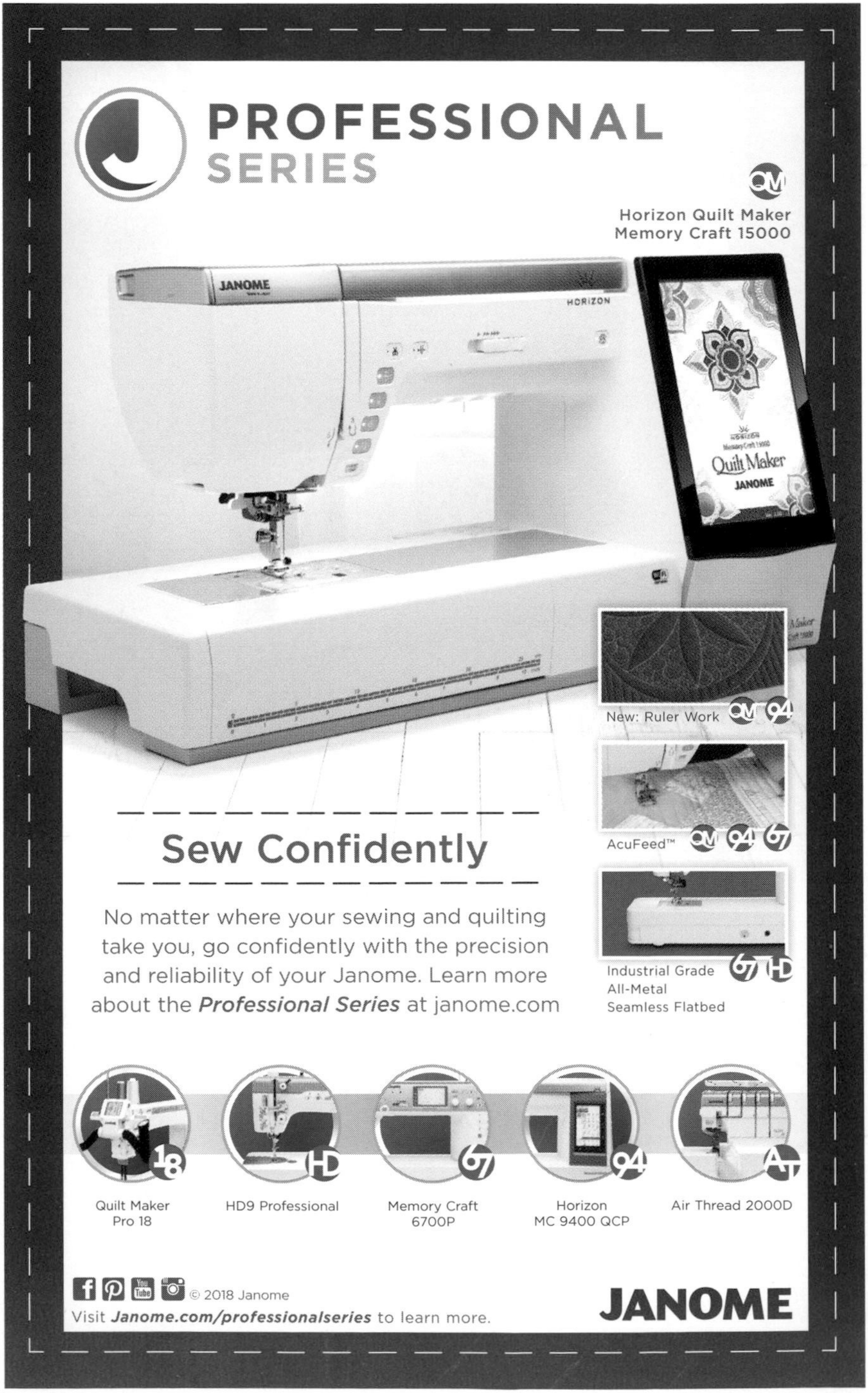
PROFESSIONAL
SERIES
Horizon Quilt Maker
Memory Craft 15000
New: Ruler Work
AcuFeed™
Industrial Grade
All-Metal
Seamless Flatbed
Sew Confidently
No matter where your sewing and quilting take you, go confidently with the precision and reliability of your Janome. Learn more about the *Professional Series* at janome.com
Quilt Maker Pro 18
HD9 Professional
Memory Craft 6700P
Horizon MC 9400 QCP
Air Thread 2000D
© 2018 Janome
Visit *Janome.com/professionalseries* to learn more.
JANOME

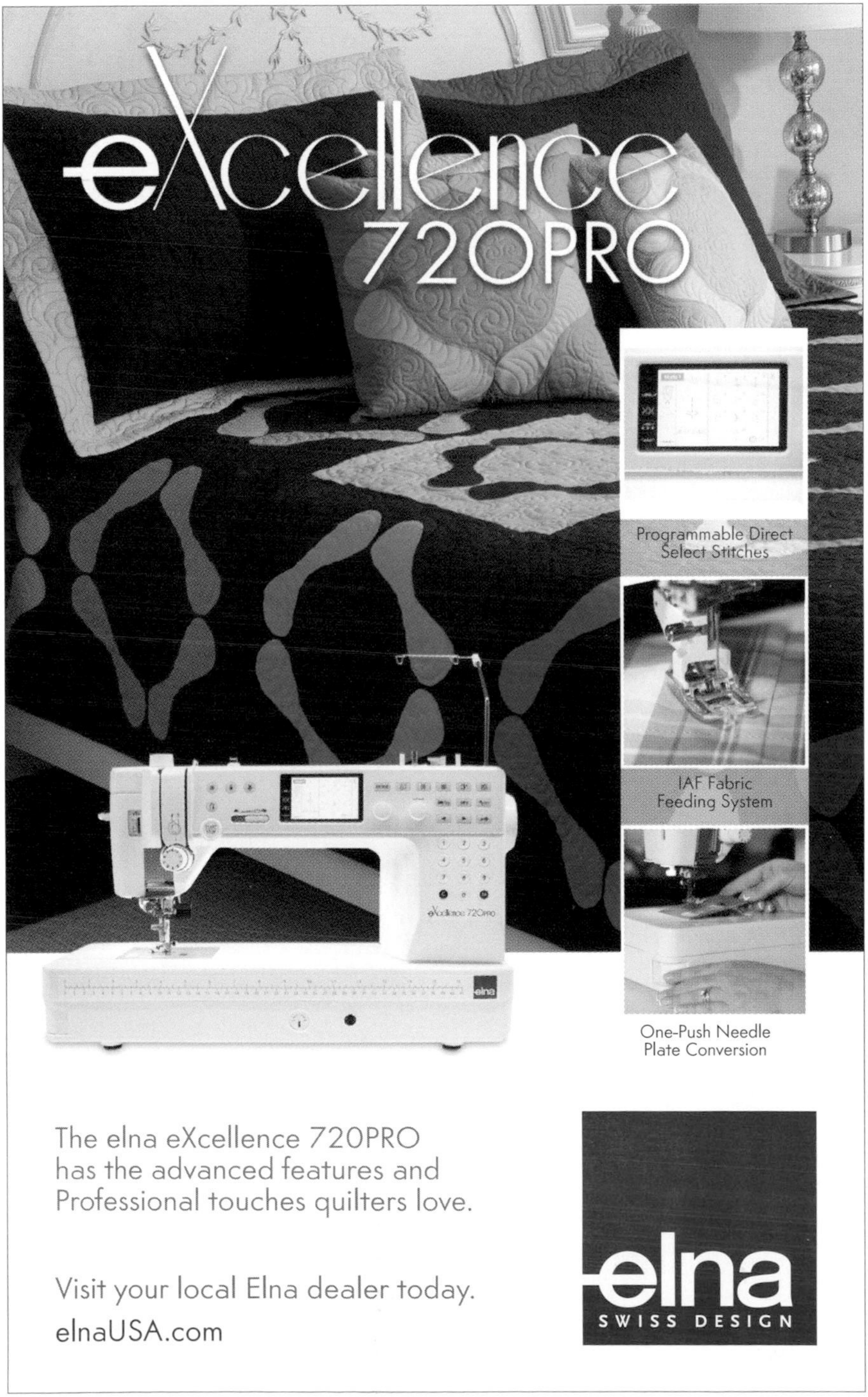
eXcellence
720PRO
Programmable Direct Select Stitches
IAF Fabric Feeding System
One-Push Needle Plate Conversion
The elna eXcellence 720PRO has the advanced features and Professional touches quilters love.
Visit your local Elna dealer today.
elnaUSA.com
elna
SWISS DESIGN

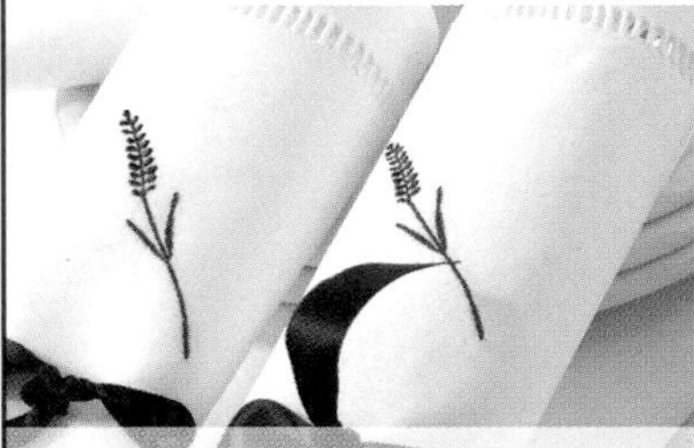

www.SeewWhatMaterializes.com/Brands/Gutermann

  GutermannOfAmerica

 SeeWhatMaterializes

STONEHENGE
10TH ANNIVERSARY
LIMITED EDITION
Solstice
by Deborah Edwards and Linda Ludovico
2019 marks the 10th Anniversary of the Stonehenge fabric brand! We have lots of exciting events happening in 2019 and 2020 to celebrate! Participating shops will be hosting an International Block Party event and local shop challenge. There are lots of ways to win great prizes - like a trip to visit Stonehenge in England!
Visit www.northcott.com for full details and a list of participating shops.
NORTHCOTT
Cottons that feel like silk

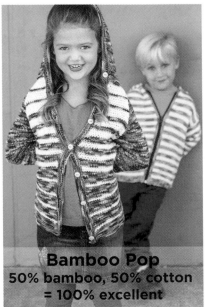

GLOBAL
ON THE ROAD
ARTISANS
www.globalartisans.shop
Hand
Crafted.
Fairly
Traded.
Your source for
House of Embroidery
www.globalartisans.shop

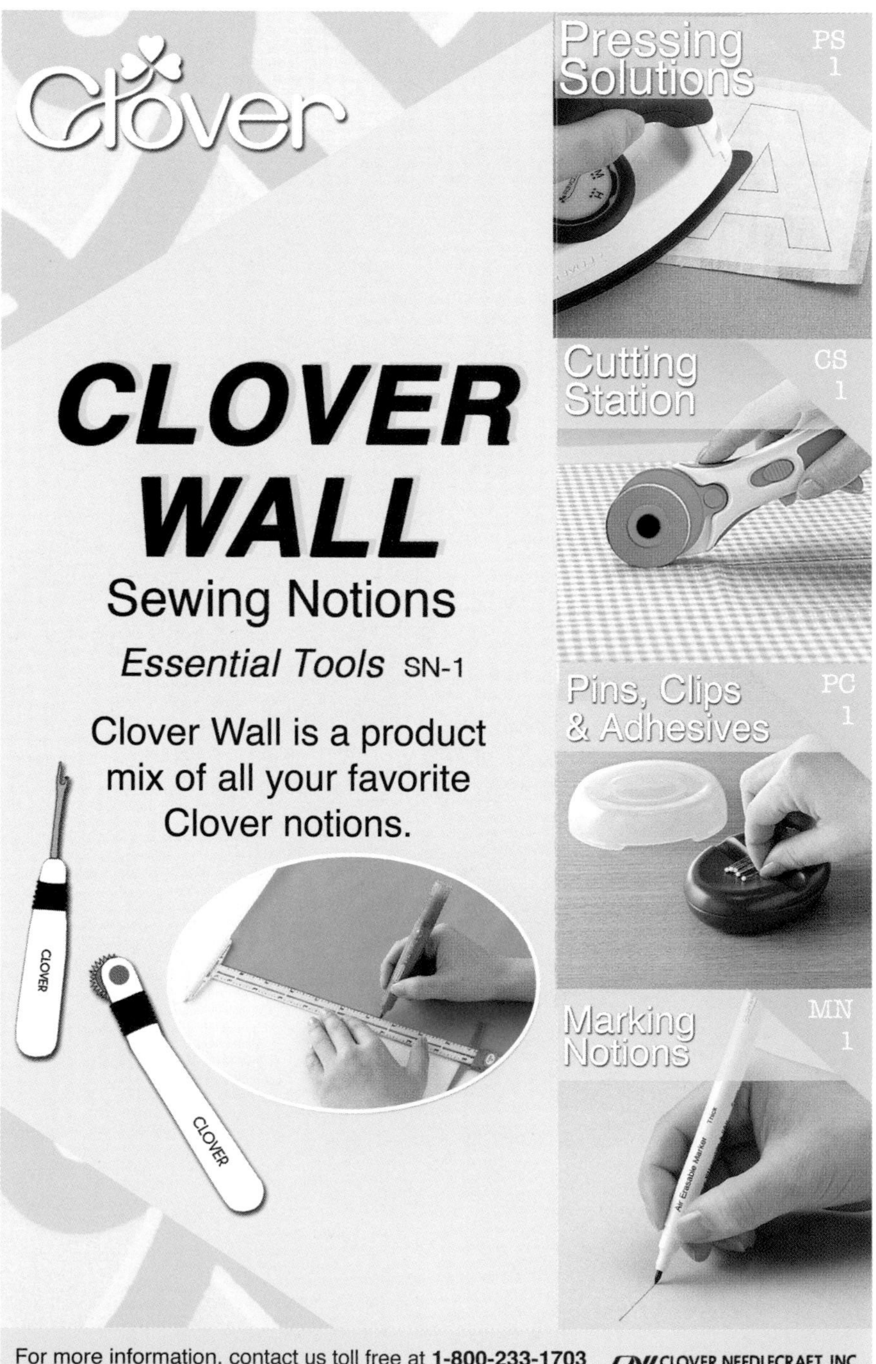
Clover
CLOVER WALL
Sewing Notions
Essential Tools SN-1
Clover Wall is a product mix of all your favorite Clover notions.
Pressing Solutions PS 1
Cutting Station CS 1
Pins, Clips & Adhesives PC 1
Marking Notions MN 1
CLOVER
CLOVER
Air Erasable Marker
For more information, contact us toll free at 1-800-233-1703 or e-mail us at info@clover-usa.com
CLOVER NEEDLECRAFT, INC.
www.clover-usa.com

Q Snap™

Q Snap Floor Model

The lightweight baste it, quilt it, tie it frame! Not only for quilting, the Q-Snap Floor Model may also be used for large needlepoint tapestries and large counted cross stitch works. Stands 32" tall, is 28" wide, and 38" long when assembled so you have lots of room to stitch. Tubes are 1½" diameter. Comes in a suitcase style carton which is great for storage when you are not using your Q-Snap Floor Model. Also known as Floor Stand or Quilt Stand. Weighs under 8 pounds. Extension and Tilt Kits are also available. Genuine Q-Snaps are made in the USA by Yarn Tree.

7785 Q Snap Floor Model

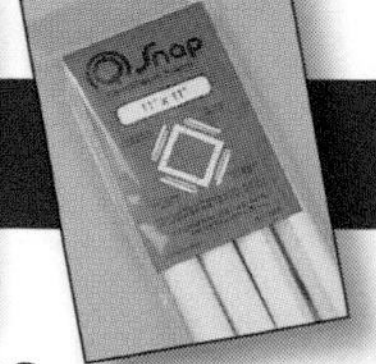

Q-Snap Frames

Unique method to hold fabric taut while stitching. Four ribbed plastic C-shaped clamps hold the fabric onto the bars. Tension is easy to adjust. You have a smooth stitching surface around ntire frame without "hoop inkles". The Q-snap frame es apart in seconds to store arry in practically any tote. n the USA by Yarn Tree. uine Q-Snaps at your eedlework store.

" Q-Snap

Q-Snap

Q-Snap

)-Snap

Snap

Yarn Tree

1-800-247-3952

117 Alexander Avenue, Ames, Iowa 50010

Fax 1-800-291-0789

e-mail info@yarntree.com

ph 515-232-3121 fax 515-232-0789

http://yarntree.com

Remember Yarn Tree for all your Zweigart, Fabric Flair, and Charles Craft Fabrics, too.

ore's Best Source For Cross Stitch

FABRIC
EMBROIDERY & MORE !
LoralieDesigns.com
THEY JUST MAKE YOU SMILE !

BIG CONTROL FOR THE SMALLEST PROJECTS
Regalia
Designing a quilt is just the beginning. Giving it a beautiful finish is why I use the Baby Lock Regalia. This 20" longarm gives me plenty of room to work more comfortably and efficiently than ever. The built-in stitch regulator keeps pace with me, creating consistent even-length stitches. Regalia even makes free motion quilting smoother than ever – the handles are independently adjustable and extendable! Top it off with an elegant frame that supports even my largest quilts, and you can see why Regalia is my machine of choice.
Amy Ellis
Amy's Creative Side
Regalia
baby lock
Kinetic
www.BabyLock.com
baby lock
FOR THE LOVE OF SEWING

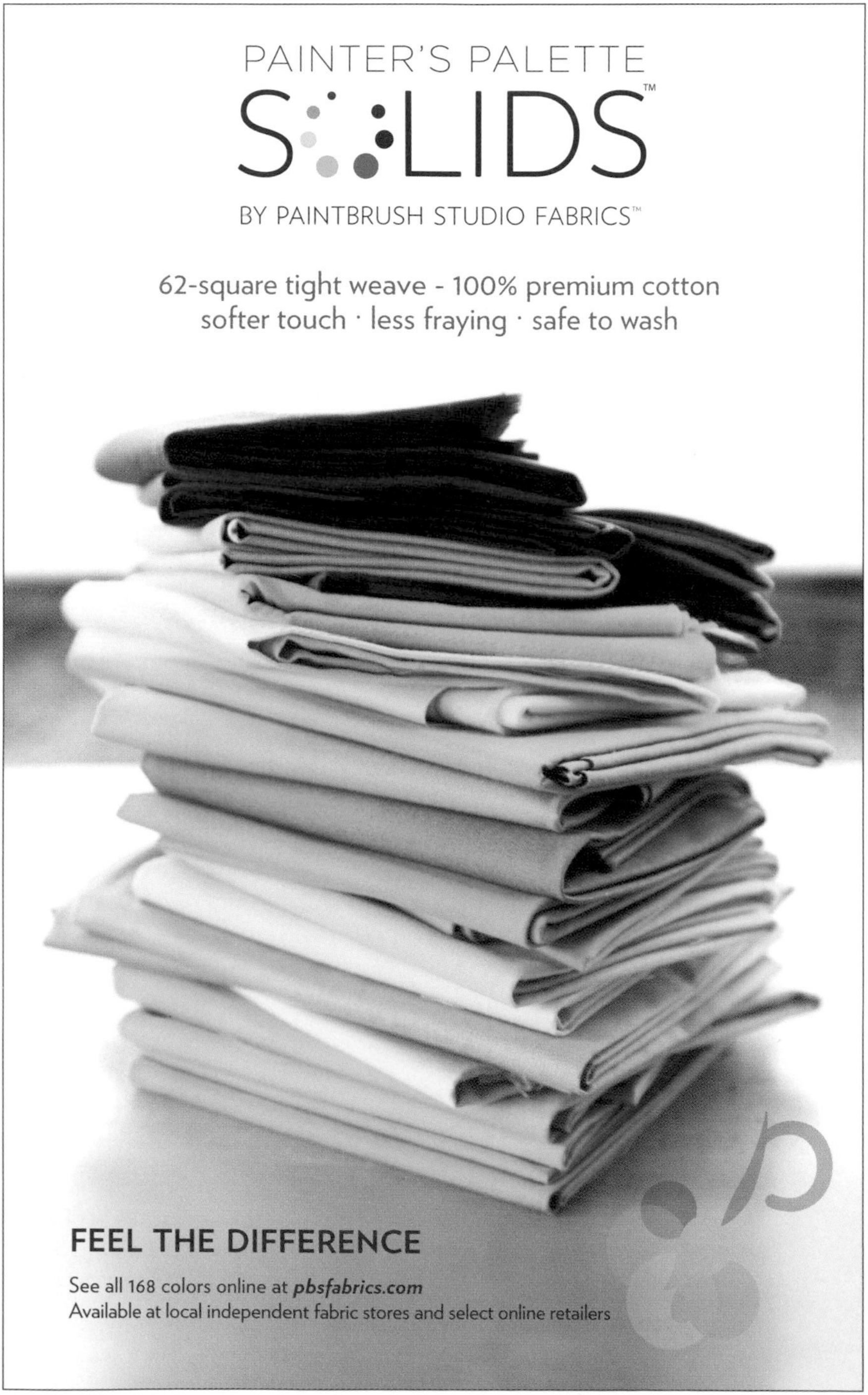
PAINTER'S PALETTE
SOLIDS™
BY PAINTBRUSH STUDIO FABRICS™
62-square tight weave - 100% premium cotton
softer touch · less fraying · safe to wash
FEEL THE DIFFERENCE
See all 168 colors online at pbsfabrics.com
Available at local independent fabric stores and select online retailers

SQUARE™

Knitting Needles & Crochet Hooks

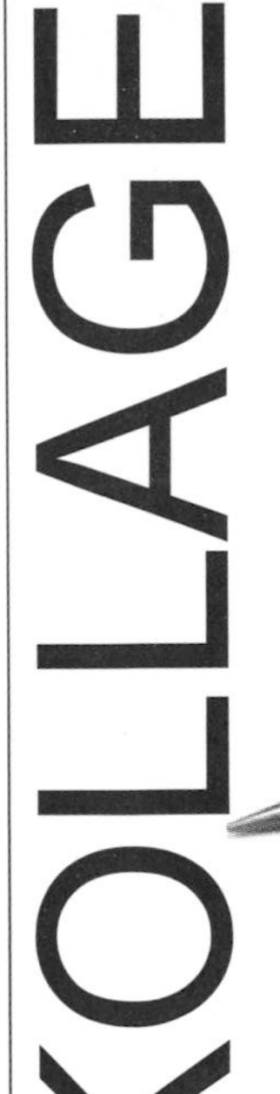

LIFETIME WARRANTY

MADE IN NORTH AMERICA

ERGONOMIC: EASY ON HANDS & WRISTS

Try them at an LYS near you!

www.louet.com

(& click 'find a retailer')

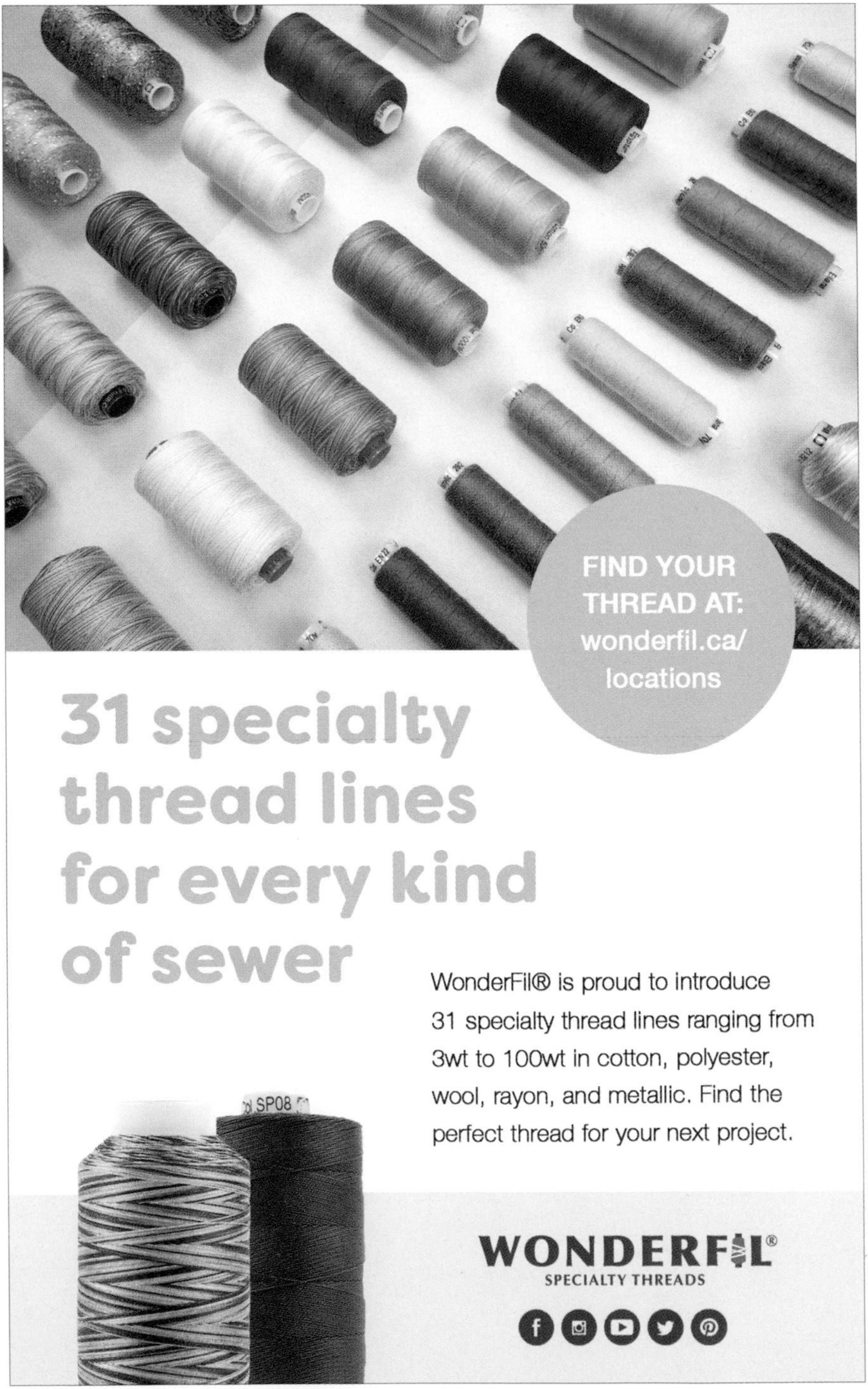
FIND YOUR THREAD AT:
wonderfil.ca/ locations
31 specialty thread lines for every kind of sewer
WonderFil® is proud to introduce 31 specialty thread lines ranging from 3wt to 100wt in cotton, polyester, wool, rayon, and metallic. Find the perfect thread for your next project.
WONDERFIL®
SPECIALTY THREADS

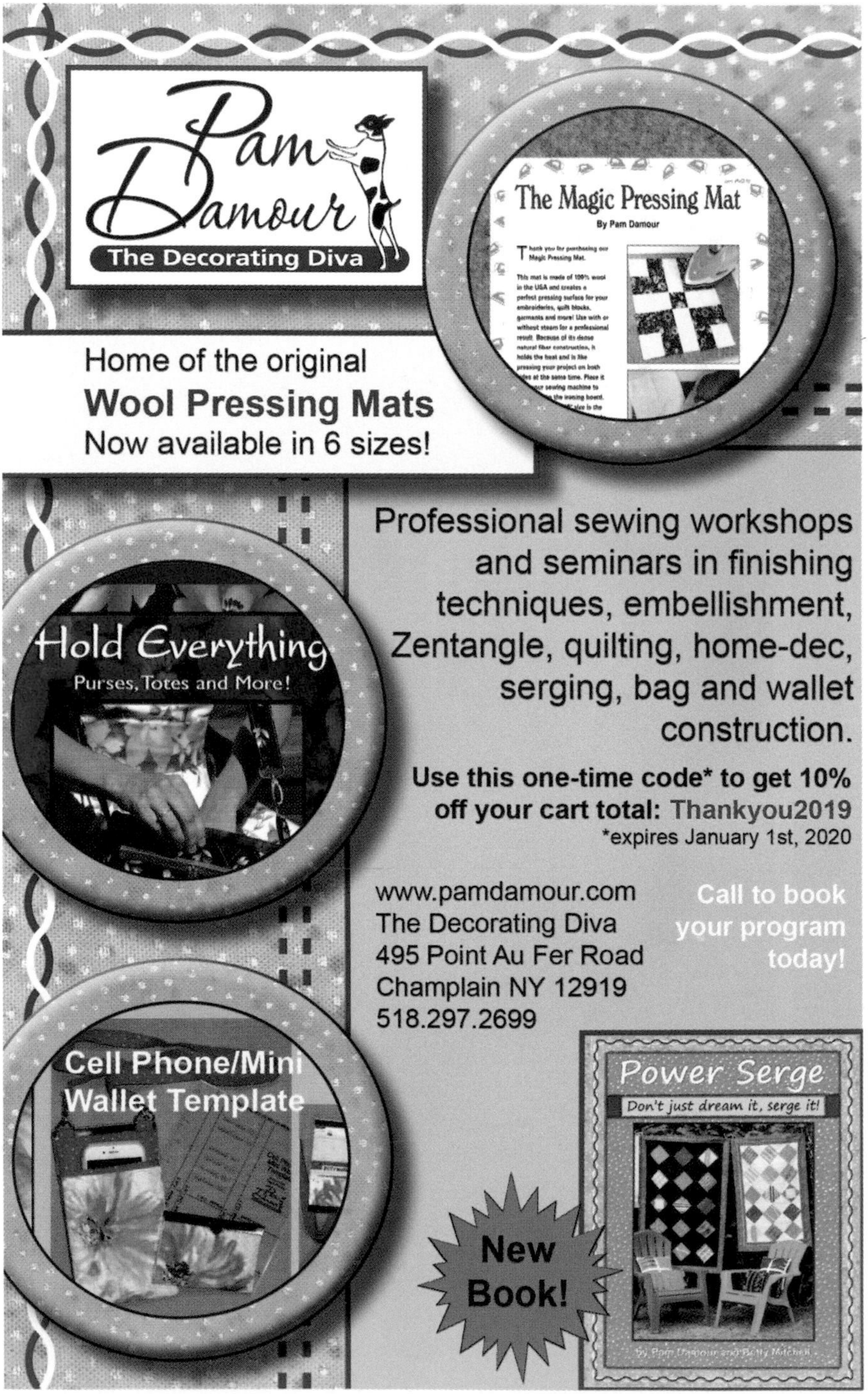
Pam Damour
The Decorating Diva
The Magic Pressing Mat
By Pam Damour
Home of the original
Wool Pressing Mats
Now available in 6 sizes!
Professional sewing workshops and seminars in finishing techniques, embellishment, Zentangle, quilting, home-dec, serging, bag and wallet construction.
Use this one-time code* to get 10% off your cart total: Thankyou2019
*expires January 1st, 2020
www.pamdamour.com
The Decorating Diva
495 Point Au Fer Road
Champlain NY 12919
518.297.2699
Call to book your program today!
Hold Everything
Purses, Totes and More!
Cell Phone/Mini Wallet Template
New Book!
Power Serge
Don't just dream it, serge it!

THE NATIONAL QUILT MUSEUM
Paducah, KY
"The Museum is where the 'best of the best' is preserved and displayed and can be seen all year long."
—Caryl Bryer Fallert-Gentry
Award Winning Fiber Artist
Quilt: The Beatles Quilt by Pat Holly & Sue Nickels
Quilt: Forest Walk by Pat Durbin
HALL of FAME
2014 2015 2016 2017
2018
CERTIFICATE of EXCELLENCE
tripadvisor
• Open Year-Round
• Special Group Rates
• Van and RV Parking
• Award Winning Gift Shop
• 6 Restaurants within 3 Blocks
Background Quilt: Sun-Bathing Blue Tit by Inge Mardal & Steen Hougs
215 Jefferson Street, Paducah, KY 42001 • QuiltMuseum.org

Landscape Medley
Our Landscape Medley collection features:
Morning Skies • Evening Skies • Constellations
Seashells • Sea Glass • Pebbles • Sand
Water • Grass • Bamboo • Barn Wood
Bark • Pinecones • Fern • Leaves • Trees
Wildflowers • Bees and Honey
Ask for Landscape Medley at your local independent quilt store.
elizabeth's studio llc
www.elizabethsstudio.com

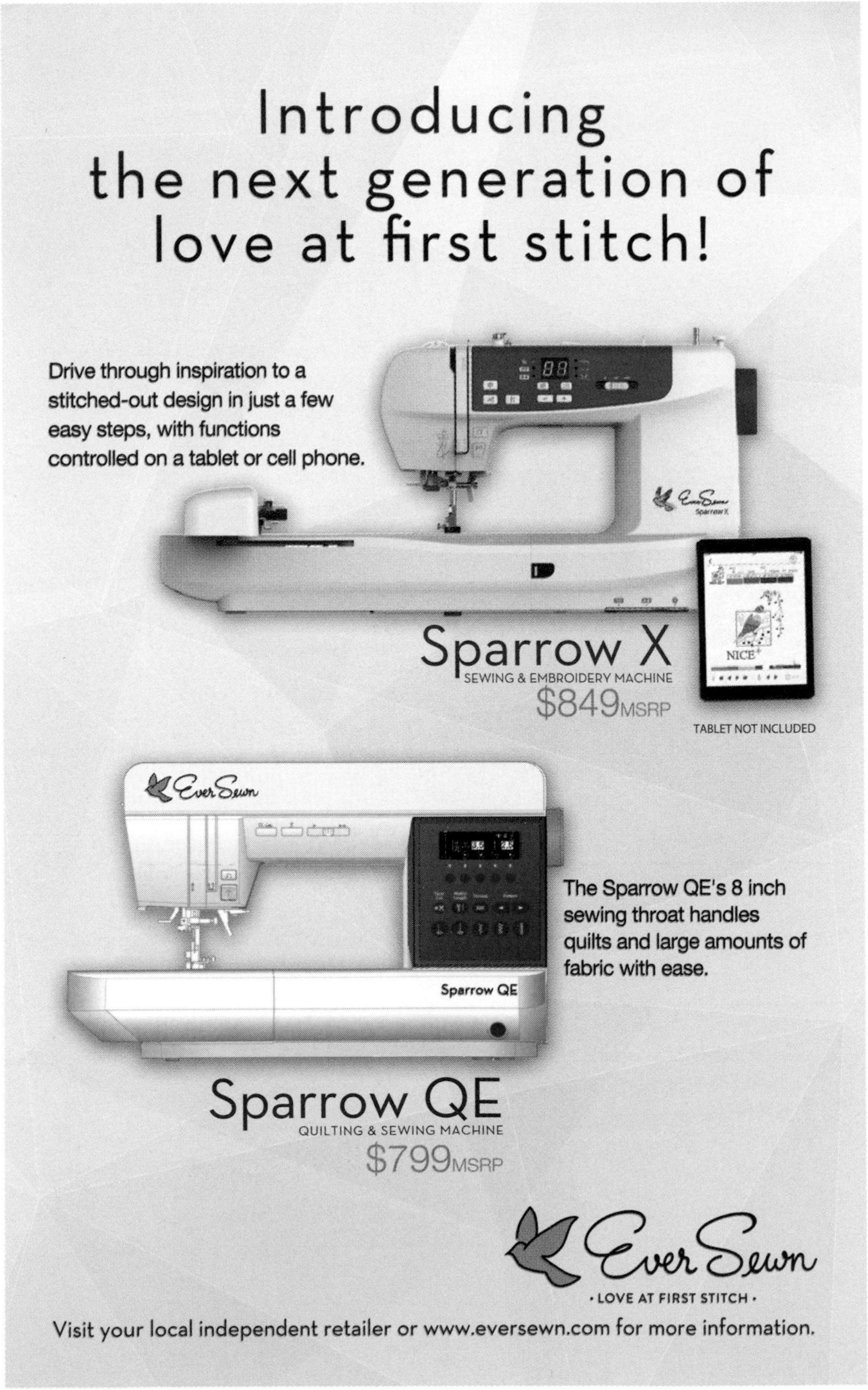

Introducing
the next generation of
love at first stitch!
Drive through inspiration to a stitched-out design in just a few easy steps, with functions controlled on a tablet or cell phone.
Sparrow X
SEWING & EMBROIDERY MACHINE
$849MSRP
TABLET NOT INCLUDED
EverSewn
Sparrow QE
The Sparrow QE's 8 inch sewing throat handles quilts and large amounts of fabric with ease.
Sparrow QE
QUILTING & SEWING MACHINE
$799MSRP
EverSewn
• LOVE AT FIRST STITCH •
Visit your local independent retailer or www.eversewn.com for more information.

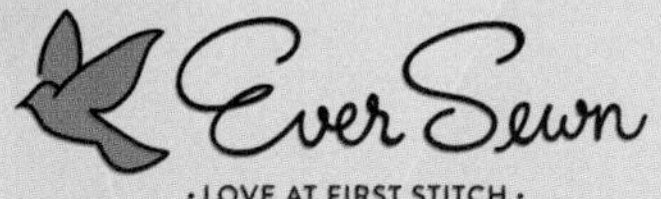

stof fabrics
Danish Design
AVALANA
KNIT
US distributor: Blank quilting
US distributor: Brewer
www.stoffabrics.com
the blog

"My grandmother always told me, finish what you start and never be ashamed if you gave it your best!"
Beverly Ray
Handi Quilter®
Designed by a Quilter, for Quilters.®
Celebrating 20 YEARS
Quilt your desire...
Beverly has embraced quilting as a way to contemplate, create, and send good intentions. She is grateful for the connection it provides to the memory of her grandmother, as well as the freedom of expression it represents.
Quilt your desire, finish as inspired.
QUILT BY BEVERLY RAY
Read, watch, and learn more from the Quilt Your Desire Inspiration Squad at www.HandiQuilter.me/QuiltYourDesire.
AMARA
The HQ Amara® 20-inch longarm
WWW.HANDIQUILTER.COM • 1.877.MY.QUILT (697.8458)
CONNECT WITH US
Visit your local Handi Quilter retailer for a test drive. www.HandiQuilter.me/locations/

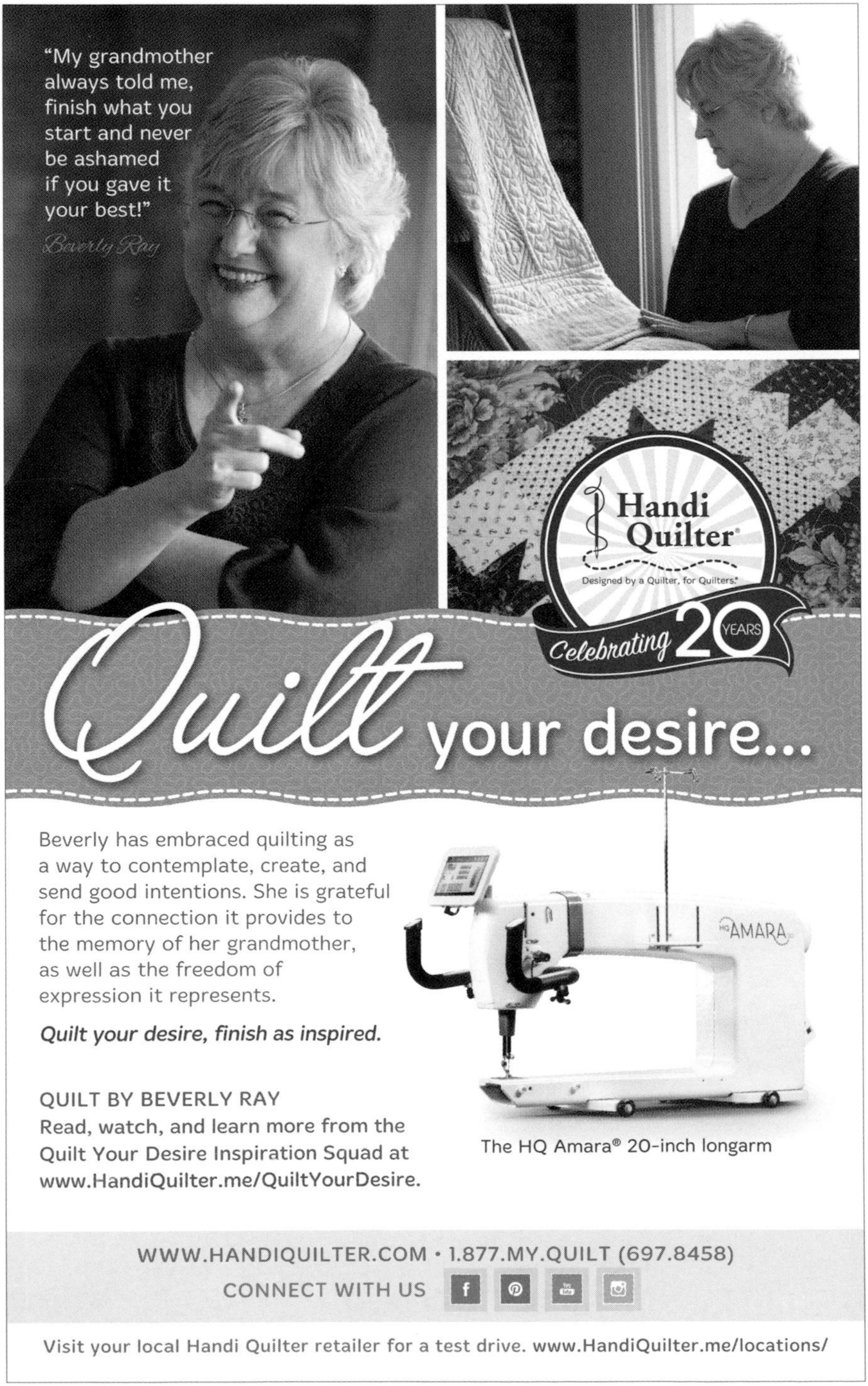

Tone and Tone Collection
www.fabricsrepublic.com
stitch & sparkle
100%Cotton Print.
High quality flannel,
baby Bamboo and nice
fleece.
Nursery Flannel Collection
Paul Brent Watercolor Collection
RTC Fabrics

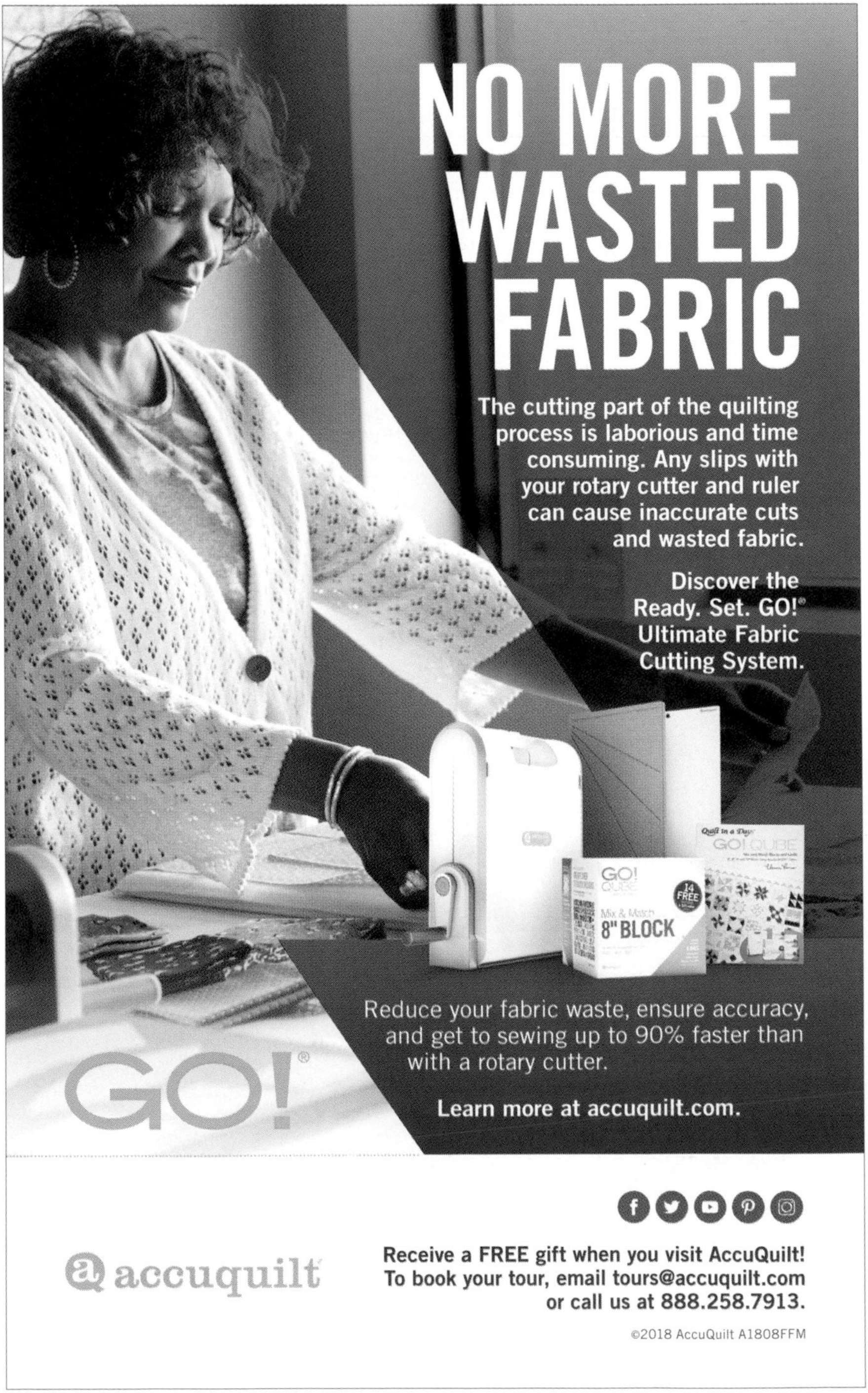

NO MORE WASTED FABRIC
The cutting part of the quilting process is laborious and time consuming. Any slips with your rotary cutter and ruler can cause inaccurate cuts and wasted fabric.
Discover the Ready. Set. GO!® Ultimate Fabric Cutting System.
GO! QUBE
Mix & Match 8" BLOCK
14 FREE
Reduce your fabric waste, ensure accuracy, and get to sewing up to 90% faster than with a rotary cutter.
Learn more at accuquilt.com.
GO!®
accuquilt
Receive a FREE gift when you visit AccuQuilt!
To book your tour, email tours@accuquilt.com
or call us at 888.258.7913.
©2018 AccuQuilt A1808FFM

frond
SHOP + STUDIO.

Diana Collection
Silk & Merino
Xtrafine Merino
from Italy

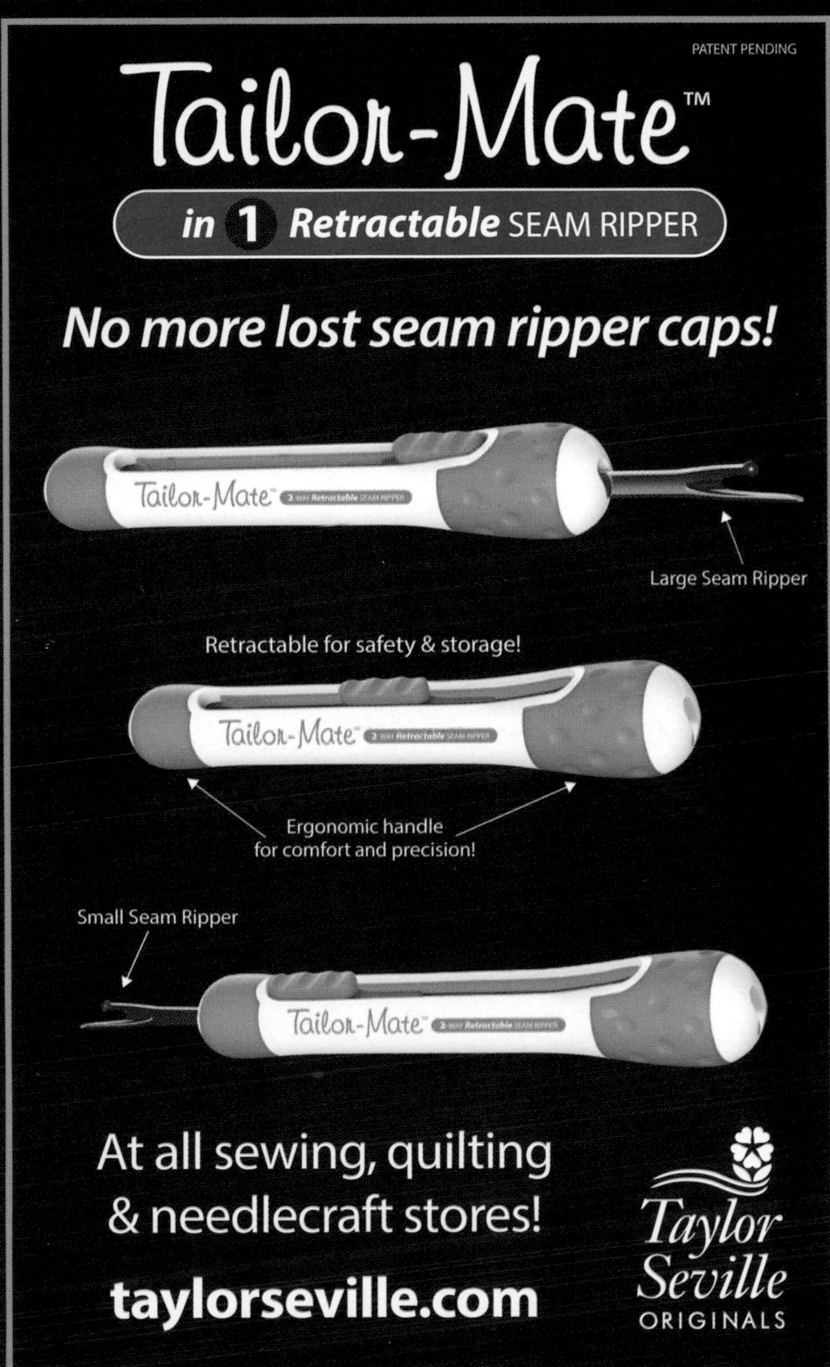
PATENT PENDING
Tailor-Mate™
in 1 Retractable SEAM RIPPER
No more lost seam ripper caps!
Large Seam Ripper
Retractable for safety & storage!
Ergonomic handle
for comfort and precision!
Small Seam Ripper
At all sewing, quilting
& needlecraft stores!
taylorseville.com
Taylor
Seville
ORIGINALS

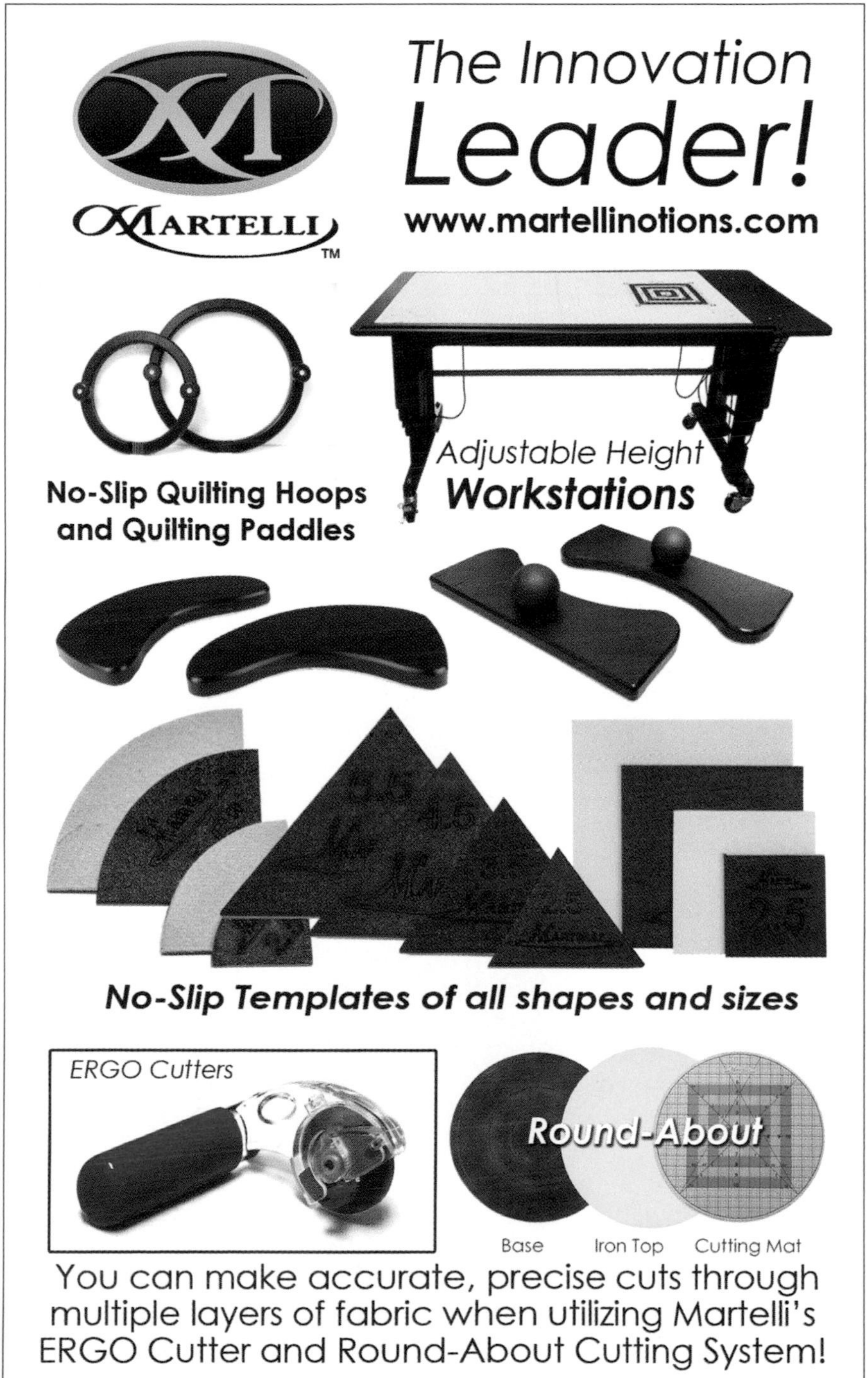
MARTELLI
TM
The Innovation
Leader!
www.martellinotions.com
No-Slip Quilting Hoops
and Quilting Paddles
Adjustable Height
Workstations
No-Slip Templates of all shapes and sizes
ERGO Cutters
Round-About
Base
Iron Top
Cutting Mat
You can make accurate, precise cuts through
multiple layers of fabric when utilizing Martelli's
ERGO Cutter and Round-About Cutting System!

posim | retail power.
Point of Sale and
Inventory Management.
Designed specifically for fabric, sewing,
yarn, and needleart shops.
Integrated eCommerce
Serialized Inventory
Cutting Table
Event & Class Management
Kit Building
Short Bolt & Fat Quarter Tracking
Service & Repair
Accounting Integration
Custom Reporting
Recurring Billing
Marketing Integration
Dye Lots & Product Matrix
Contact us today to see how POSIM can
make your business more successful.
posim 800.409.7678 | posim.com | info@posim.com

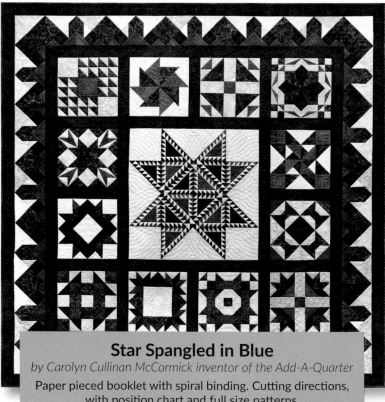

Star Spangled in Blue

by Carolyn Cullinan McCormick inventor of the Add-A-Quarter

Paper pieced booklet with spiral binding. Cutting directions, with position chart and full size patterns.
This booklet is designed as a block of the month program using your own fabrics and at your own pace.

CM Designs, Inc
www.cmdesignsonline.com | 303-841-5920
Facebook: CM Designs Inc | Instagram: add_a_quarter

INNOVA

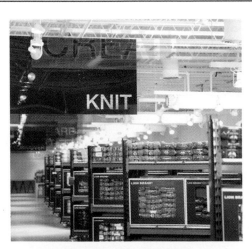

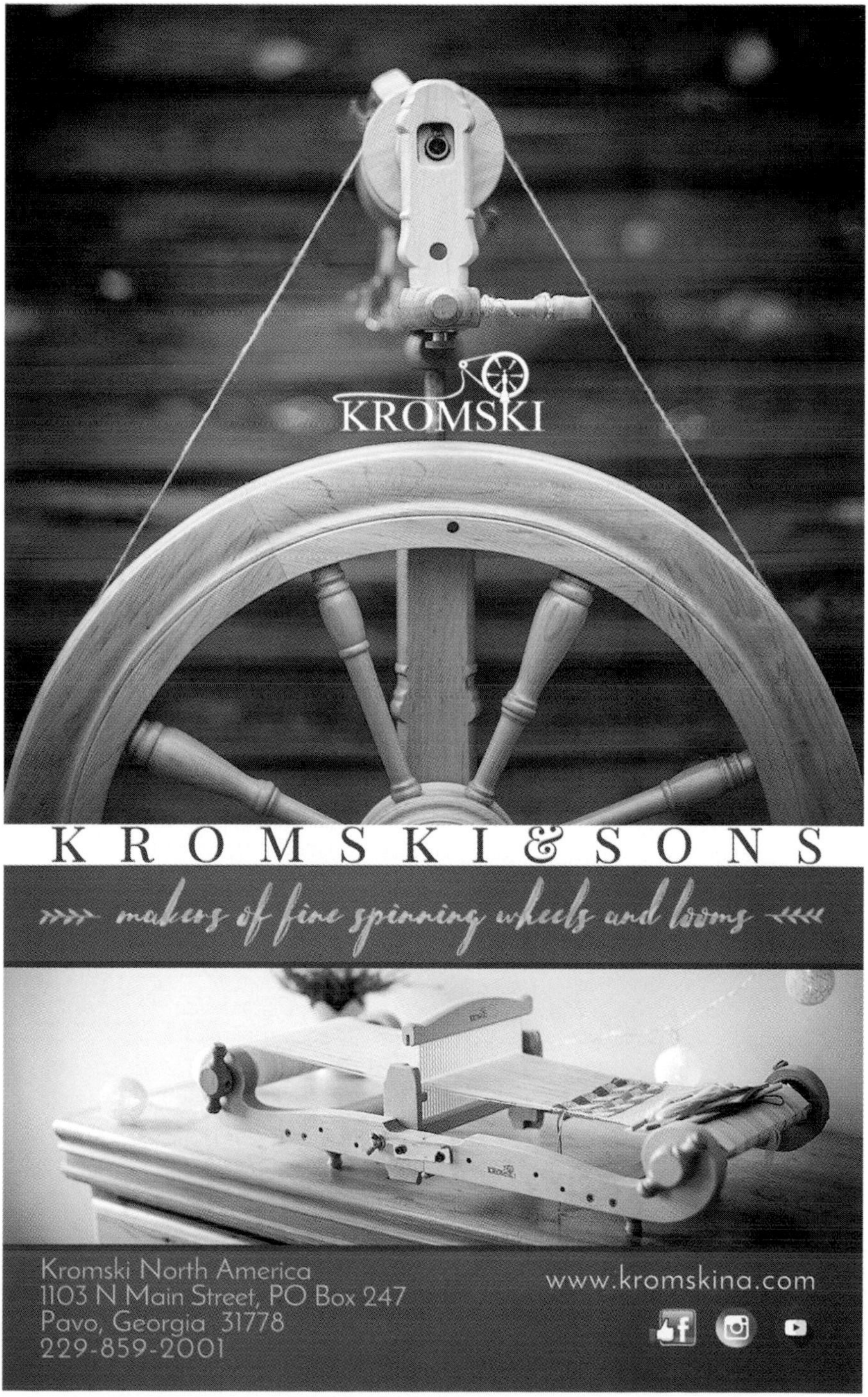

Comfort in Quilting

Real tools that help you become really good!

Teach them to Dream,

Teach them to Create ...

Teach them to Sew!

Made in the U.S.A.

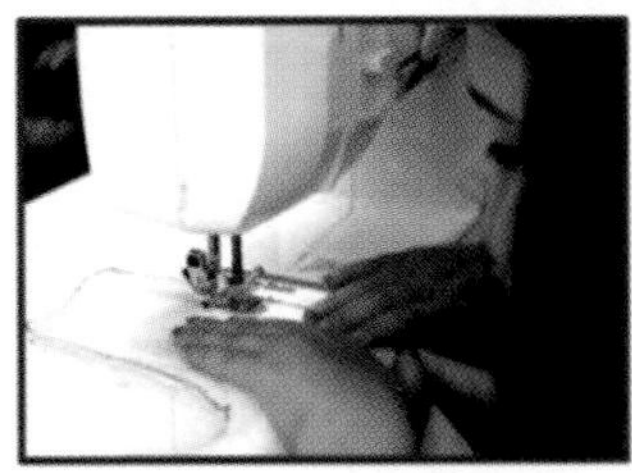

Student Edition

Made in the USA with Sew-Tacky Technology™ Repositionable, washable and affordable for beginners and advanced fabric artists.

Ideal Quilt Guide

Effortlessly Straight!

"...one of the best new quilting notions on the market..."

AQ Magazine September 2014

Reusable sewing tools, essential for straight seams and ***"Practical Perfect Piecing."***

Luxurious Sewing Surface polish

Fabric seems to float!

Comfort in Quilting

Sew-Tacky Technology™

sewverysmooth.com

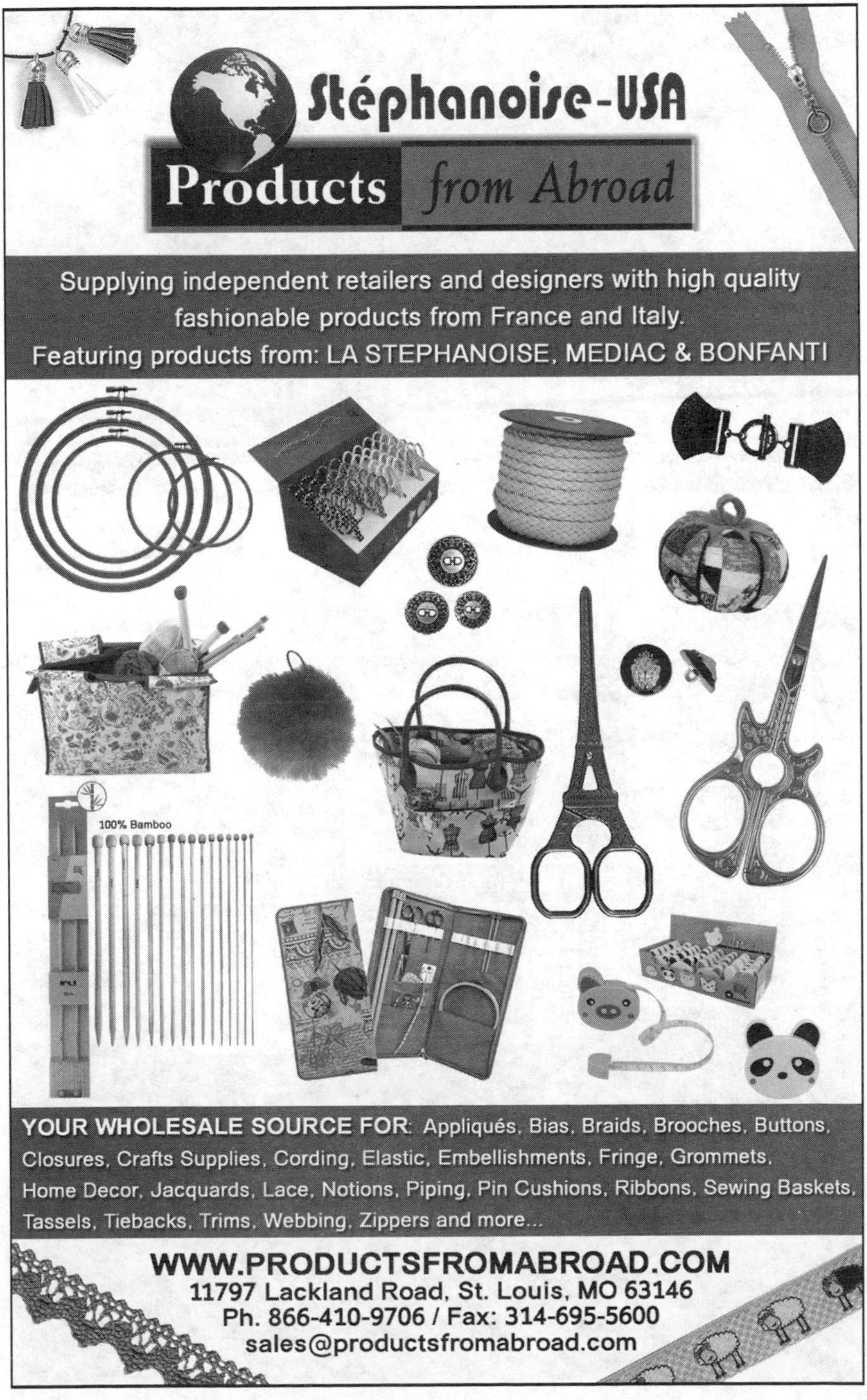

Stéphanoise-USA
Products from Abroad
Supplying independent retailers and designers with high quality fashionable products from France and Italy.
Featuring products from: LA STEPHANOISE, MEDIAC & BONFANTI
100% Bamboo
YOUR WHOLESALE SOURCE FOR: Appliqués, Bias, Braids, Brooches, Buttons, Closures, Crafts Supplies, Cording, Elastic, Embellishments, Fringe, Grommets, Home Decor, Jacquards, Lace, Notions, Piping, Pin Cushions, Ribbons, Sewing Baskets, Tassels, Tiebacks, Trims, Webbing, Zippers and more...
WWW.PRODUCTSFROMABROAD.COM
11797 Lackland Road, St. Louis, MO 63146
Ph. 866-410-9706 / Fax: 314-695-5600
sales@productsfromabroad.com

Tradition Meets Modern Production

Dill Button Factory — Bavaria/Germany

Manufacturing high-quality, fashion buttons since 1924

As a partner for fabric, knitting, haberdashery, notions, quilting and craft stores but also for fashion studios and designers, our main focus is supplying our customers with high-quality, innovative and fashionable buttons. We make full use of our own expertise at all stages of production and button design, with decades of experience and the skills of our experts help make this possible. As a reliable and loyal supplier to retailers and designers, we have also established a worldwide sales network.

Dill Buttons of America Inc
50 Choate Circle, Montoursville PA 17754
888-460-7555
www.dill-buttons.com

Stitch
Sprouts

Spring
apr
7 | 8 | 9 | 10 | 11 | 12
2019

A week of
friendship,
laughter,
and sharing a
passion
for the art of
quilting.

Fall
oct
13 | 14 | 15 | 16 | 17 | 18
2019

For information, please visit
www.quiltcampcedarlakes.com
email quiltcampcedarlakes@gmail.com or call 330.620.9825

Quilters Dream Batting ❤ J.N. Harper Co. ❤ Aurifil USA, Inc. ❤ Dragon Threads

Judy Martin Books ❤ Kimberbell Designs ❤ Minick and Simpson ❤ Nestlings by Robin ❤ PRYM Consumer USA/Dritz Quilting ❤ Perkins Dry Goods

Quilters Travel Companion ❤ Quilters World Magazine ❤ Raggedy Ruth Designs/Forevers in Stitches LLC

Shannon Fabrics ❤ Siesta Silver Jewelry ❤ Stitch Publications ❤ Straight Stitch Society ❤ Swan Amity Studios ❤ Suzn Quilts ❤ The Wooden Bear ❤ YLI Threads

Quilters Dream Batting®
Presents the Annual
HOPES & DREAMS™
QUILT CHALLENGE FOR ALS

Please give the gift of a quilt to warm the life, the heart and the lap of an ALS patient, and help raise awareness and research money for ALS – Lou Gehrig's disease.

For Entry Forms, Rules, Grand Sponsors, Prize Categories, and our Facebook Page Please Visit:

www.QuiltersDreamBatting.com
Call Toll Free: 1-888-268-8664
QuiltersDreamBatting@juno.com

Please Send Quilts with Entry Forms to:

HOPES & DREAMS
c/o Quilters Dream Batting®
589 Central Drive
Virginia Beach, VA 23454

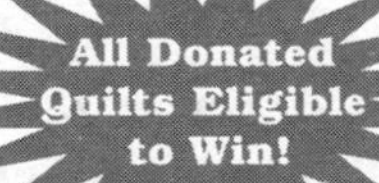

To Give a Handmade Quilt Is to Give a Gift of Love

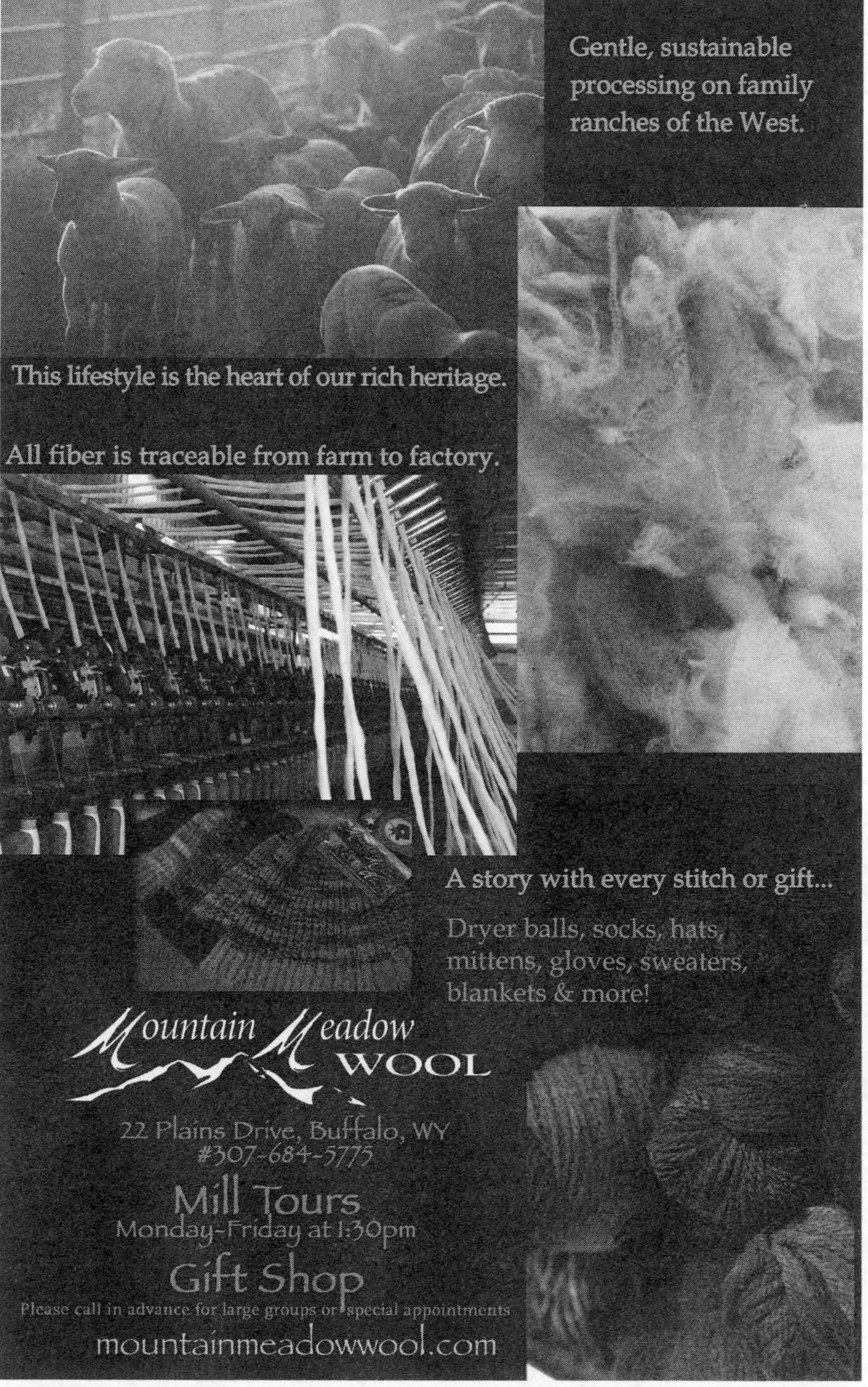
Gentle, sustainable processing on family ranches of the West.
This lifestyle is the heart of our rich heritage.
All fiber is traceable from farm to factory.
A story with every stitch or gift...
Dryer balls, socks, hats, mittens, gloves, sweaters, blankets & more!
Mountain Meadow WOOL
22 Plains Drive, Buffalo, WY
#307-684-5775
Mill Tours
Monday-Friday at 1:30pm
Gift Shop
Please call in advance for large groups or special appointments
mountainmeadowwool.com

Transforming fabrics into patchwork quilts that comfort children in need.

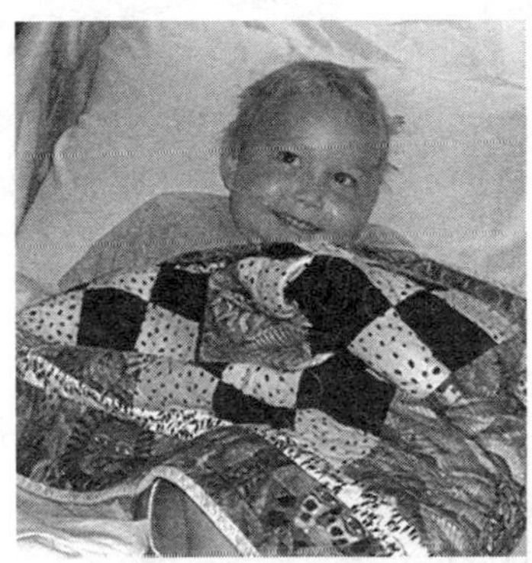

Goal: Bring comfort to children in need who are fighting a life battle with an illness, poverty or abuse. We strive to turn tears to smiles in about 30,000 children each year. We'd love your help.

Your fabric destination! All fabric sales proceeds go to the cause-wrapping children in need in a quilt.

Quilts for Kids has created and distributed tens of thousands of quilts worldwide. We are a 501(C) 3 non profit. Stop by our store and visit or take a class if you're in our area.

Help us turn tears to smiles in these children today.

To participate please visit our website at:
www.quiltsforkids.org or email info@quiltsforkids.org
Write: Quilts for Kids, 494 Lincoln Highway, Fairless Hills, PA 19030
Call: 215-295-5484

Join us at our shop for free quilt workshops Mon-Fri, 10:00 – 3:00

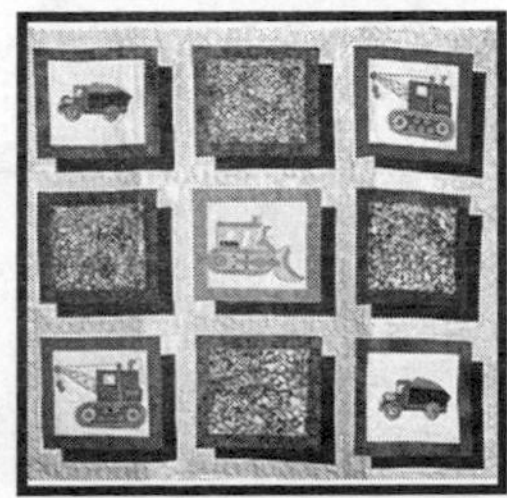

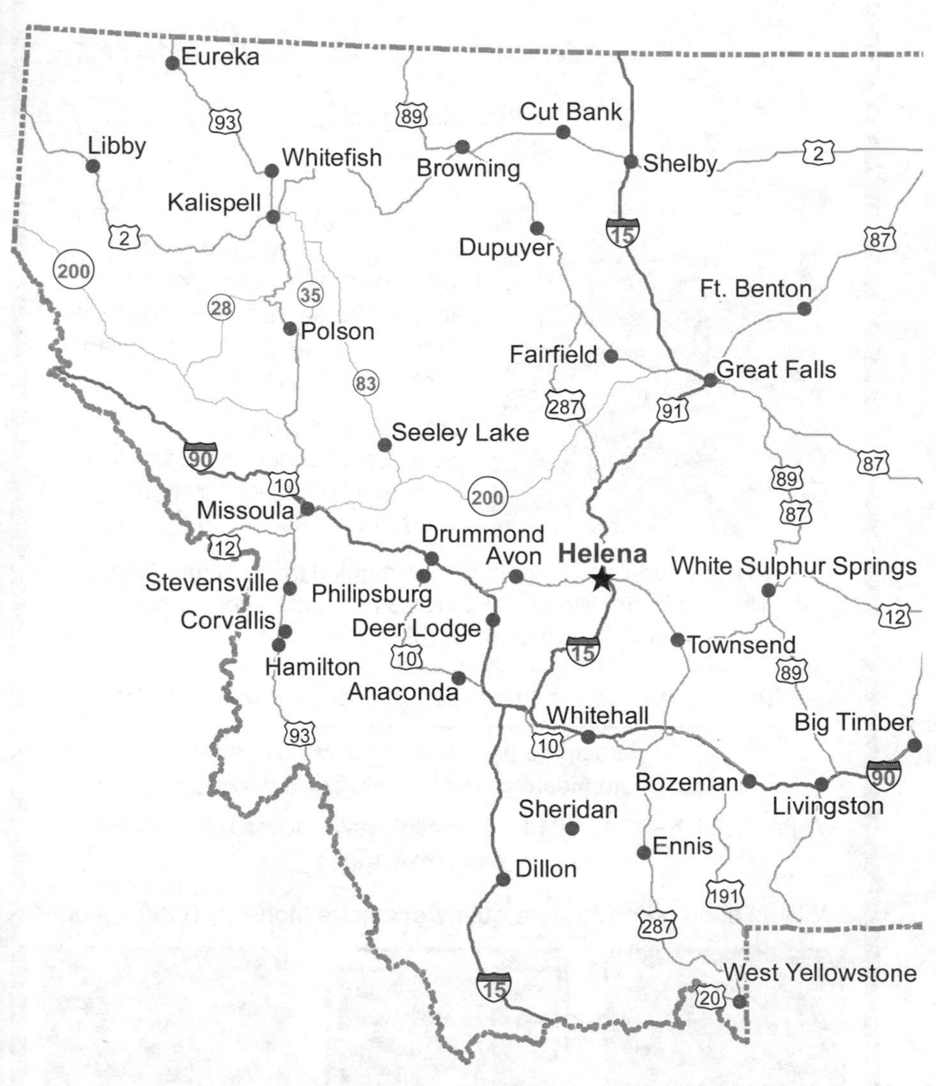
Eureka
93
Libby
Whitefish
89
Cut Bank
Browning
Shelby
2
Kalispell
2
Dupuyer
15
87
200
35
28
Ft. Benton
Polson
Fairfield
Great Falls
83
287
91
90
Seeley Lake
87
10
89
200
Missoula
87
Drummond
12
Helena
Avon
White Sulphur Springs
Stevensville
Philipsburg
Corvallis
12
Deer Lodge
Townsend
15
10
Hamilton
89
Anaconda
Whitehall
Big Timber
93
10
90
Bozeman
Livingston
Sheridan
Ennis
Dillon
191
287
West Yellowstone
15
20

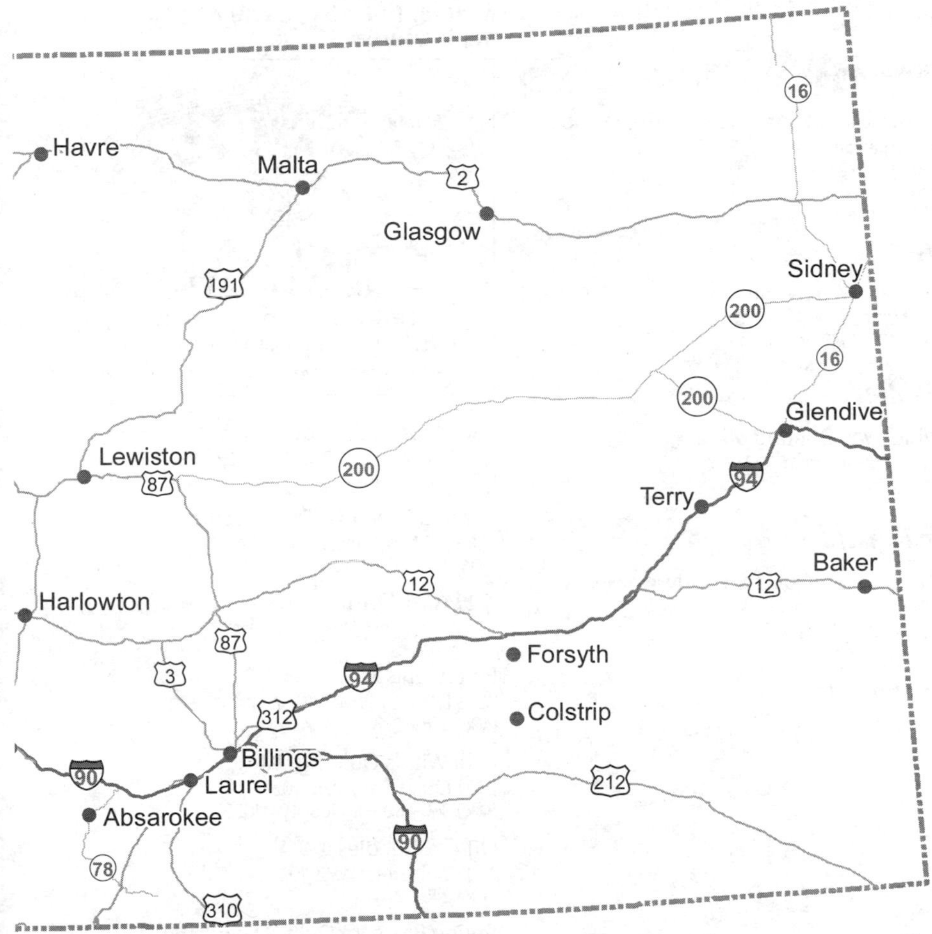
Havre
Malta
2
Glasgow
16
191
Sidney
200
16
200
Glendive
Lewiston
87
200
94
Terry
Baker
12
12
Harlowton
87
Forsyth
3
94
312
Colstrip
Billings
90
Laurel
212
Absarokee
90
78
310

Montana

Absarokee

Cloud Nine Quilts Q
15 S. Woodard Avenue, 59001
(406) 328-4032

Anaconda

Upper Thread Embroidery / The Fabric Room Q E
119 E. Park Avenue, 59711
(406) 563-7871

Avon

Birdseye Mercantile Q Y
105 Main Street W, 59713
(406) 492-7070 or (406) 492-7091

Baker

Whichway Quilting Q
7 W. Sewall Avenue, 59313
(406) 778-3008

Big Timber

Little Timber Quilts & Candy Q E M
108 McLeod Street, 59011
(406) 932-6078

Billings

Yarn Bar Y W S
➡ SEE AD BELOW
1940 Grand Avenue, 59102
(406) 534-4032
M 10-8, Tu-F 10-6, Sa 10-4
https://yarn.bar

Backdoor Quilt Shoppe Q E
712 Carbon Street, Suite A, 59102
(406) 655-1001

Bernina Sewing & Fabric Center Q M
1505 Rehberg Lane, Suite A, 59102
(406) 656-4999

Handi Quilter® Authorized Retailer
Designed by a Quilter, for Quilters.®

Fiberworks Q
3213 Henesta Drive, 59102
(406) 656-6663

Four Winds Quilting Q E
2101 Grand Avenue, 59102
(406) 860-4529 or (406) 694-1025

Off The Needles Y W S
1206 24th Street W, 59102
(406) 245-2224

Spring Blossom Quilt N Sew Q E Y M
1327 Main Street, Unit 9, 59105
(406) 252-4188

Treasured Times Quilting and Gifts Q M
2750 Old Hardin Road, Suite J, 59101
(406) 698-7281

Bozeman

Main Street Quilting Company Q E M
128 E. Main Street, 59715
(406) 586-6097

Stix Ⓨ
23 W. Main Street, 59715
(406) 556-5786

The Critting Bag, LLC Ⓔ Ⓨ
3 Cloninger Lane, 59718
(406) 587-2770

The Silver Thimble, Inc. Ⓠ Ⓜ
1008 N. 7th Avenue, Suite G, 59715
(406) 587-0531

Yarn Scout Ⓨ
1203 N. Rouse, Suite 3C, 59715
(406) 577-2088

Browning

Native Life Fabrics & Gifts Ⓠ
414 Central Avenue W, 59417
(406) 338-7888
M-F 9-6, Sa 11-5
www.nativelifestore.com

Colstrip

Taylor's Ace Hardware Ⓠ
6141 Homestead Blvd., 59323
(406) 748-3450

Corvallis

Mountain Colors Studio Ⓨ Ⓦ Ⓢ
1200 Eastside Highway, 59828
(406) 961-1900

Cut Bank

Coulee Quilts Ⓠ
317 E. Railroad Street, 59427
(406) 873-2685

Deer Lodge

Quilter's Corner, Etc. Ⓠ
401 Main Street, 59722
(406) 846-3096 or (877) 646-3096

Dillon

The Daily Yarn Ⓨ
36 N. Idaho Street, 59725
(406) 660-0597

The No. 1 Ladies Quilt Shop / Veva La Stitchin Ⓠ
34 N. Idaho Street, Suite 3, 59725
(406) 683-5884

Drummond

The Cotton Patch Ⓠ Ⓔ
38 E. Front Street, 59832
(406) 288-3154

Dupuyer

Beaverslide Dry Goods Ⓨ Ⓢ
307 Montana Street, 59432
(406) 472-3272 or (406) 472-3283

Dupuyer Cache Ⓨ
307 Montana Street, 59432
(406) 472-3272

Ennis

Stitches That Bind* Ⓠ Ⓔ Ⓒ
111 W. Main Street, 59729
(406) 682-3166

Eureka

Woolery Mammoth Ⓨ Ⓦ Ⓢ
401 2nd Ave West, 59917
(406) 297-7403

Fairfield

Berry Patch Quilt n' Coffee Ⓠ
424 Central Avenue, 59436
(406) 467-2298

Forsyth

Corner Craft Fair Ⓠ Ⓨ
1401 Front Street, 59327
(406) 346-9276

Ft. Benton

Stitch Away* Ⓠ Ⓨ
1510 Front Street, 59442
(406) 622-4244

Glasgow

Crazy Woman Quilts Ⓠ Ⓔ
27 US Highway 2 E, 59230
(406) 228-9665

Glendive

The Enchanted Room Ⓠ Ⓔ
222 W. Towne Street, 59330
(406) 377-4745 or (866) 377-4745

Great Falls

Fibre House ⒺⓎⓃⒸ
➡ **SEE AD BELOW**
205 9th Avenue S, Suite 102, 59405
(406) 761-4652
Tu 10-7, WF 10-5, Th 10-6, Sa 10-3
www.fibrehouse406.com

When you visit Fibre House, you'll be inspired to get your needles and nest!

(406)761-4652
Tues, 10-7
Wed & Fri, 10-5
Thurs,10-6; Sat 10-3
Mon-Closed

205 9th Avenue South, Suite 102
Great Falls, Montana 59405

info@fibrehouse406.com
www.fibrehouse406.com

Bernina Silver Thimble ⓆⓂ
3301 10th Avenue S, #1, 59405
(406) 452-7222

Big Sky Quilts ⓆⓂ
101 Central Avenue, 59401
(406) 727-1757

Handi Quilter® Authorized Retailer
Designed by a Quilter, for Quilters.®

Old MacDonald's Craft Barn Ⓨ
140 Wilson Butte Road, 59405
(406) 788-1314 or (406) 454-2077

Quilts Galore & More* Ⓠ
104 Truman Avenue, 59404
(406) 836-9552

The Quilt-A-Way ⓆⒺⓃⓂ
222 13th Street S, 59405
(406) 453-2788

Hamilton

Patchwork Quilts ⓆⒺ
1720 N. 1st Street, Suite E, 59840
(406) 363-5754

The Yarn Center ⒺⓎⓃⒸ
110 Pinckney Street, 59840
(406) 363-1400

Harlowton

Diana's Quilts-n-Things Ⓠ
10 1st Street SE, 59036
(406) 632-4861

Havre

Bearly Square Quilting ⓆⓂ
109 1st Street W, #3, 59501
(406) 265-4424

Ben Franklin Crafts ⓆⒺⓎⓃⒸ
631 1st Street W, 59501
(406) 265-3290

Helena

Creative Stitches ⓆⓂ
3710 N. Montana Avenue, 59602
(406) 443-7540

Handi Quilter® Authorized Retailer
Designed by a Quilter, for Quilters.®

Prickly Pear Quilts ⓆⒺⓂ
1200 Cedar Street, 59601
(406) 442-7327

The Sewing Palace ⓆⒺⓂ
124 E. Lyndale Avenue, 59601
(406) 443-5724

Y'arnings Ⓨ
36 S. Last Chance Gulch, 59601
(406) 443-8073

Kalispell

A-1 Vacuum & Sewing Ⓠ
140 W. Center Street, 59901
(406) 755-1871

Camas Creek Cottage ⒺⓎⓃⓌⓈⒸ
338 Main Street, 59901
(406) 755-9276

Glacier Quilts ⓆⒺ
125 Hutton Ranch Road, 59901
(406) 257-6966

Quilt Gallery ⓆⒺⓂ
1710 US Highway 93 S, 59901
(406) 257-5799

Authorized Retailer

Woolen Collectibles Ⓨ
904 7th Avenue E, 59901
(406) 756-8746

Laurel

Trackside Quilting Q M
109 E. Main Street, 59044
(406) 628-7051

Lewistown

Lewistown's Sew Pieceful Q E
214 W. Main Street, 59457
(406) 535-3122 or (406) 366-3941

Libby

Cultured Purl Yarn Shop Y
507 Mineral Avenue, 59923
(406) 293 9111

The Quilt Cottage Q
907 Mineral Avenue, 59923
(406) 293-5999

Livingston

Back Porch Quilts Q Y
5237 US Highway 89 S, Suite 14, 59047
(406) 222-0855
M-F 10-5:30, Sa 10-5
www.backporchquilter.com

Thimbelina's Quilt Shop Q E Y N C M
118 N. B Street, Suite B, 59047
(406) 222-5904

Malta

Gone To Pieces Q
135 S. 2nd Street E, 59538
(406) 654-1649

Missoula

Joseph's Coat Y W S
➡ SEE AD BELOW

115 S. 3rd Street W, 59801
(406) 549-1419
M-Sa 10:30-5:30
www.josephscoatyarn.com

A-1 Vacuum & Janitorial Supply Q
1900 Russell Street, 59801
(406) 543-8757

Beads, Yarns and Threads E Y N C
2100 Stephens Avenue, Suite 109, 59801
(406) 543-9368

Goin' Quilting Q
425 N. 5th Street W, #4, 59802
(406) 541-7111

The Confident Stitch Q E
139 W. Front Street, 59802
(406) 540-4068

Timeless Quilts and Friends* Q M
2412 River Road, Suite F, 59804
(406) 542-6566

Vicki's Quilts Down Under Q E
2425 W. Central Avenue, Suite B, 59801
(406) 728-9446

Philipsburg

Sew Unique Custom Quilting & Retreat* Q
130 E. Broadway, Suite A, 59858
(406) 859-7858

Polson

All In Stitches Q
210 Main Street, 59860
(406) 883-3643

Seeley Lake

Deer Country Quilts* Q E M
3150 Highway 83 N, 59868
(406) 677-2730

Shelby

Quilt With Class Q
131 4th Avenue S, 59474
(406) 434-5801

The Creative Needle Q M
325 Main Street, 59474
(406) 434-7106 or (800) 377-0145

Sheridan

Timeless Treasures Quilt Gallery Q
28 Rustic Trail, 59749
(406) 842-5001

Sidney

Quilts & More Q
12653 County Road 352, 59270
(406) 482-3366

Stevensville

Daydream Fabrics Q E
304 Main Street, 59870
(406) 777-7195

Terry

Creative Cottage* Q M
415 S. Logan Avenue, 59349
(406) 635-5606

Townsend

Creative Closet Q
222 Broadway Street, 59644
(406) 266-4555

J. L. Wrights Trading Post Q E Y
119 Broadway Street, 59644
(406) 266-3032

West Yellowstone

Send It Home Q Y S
30 Madison Avenue, 59758
(406) 646-7300

White Sulphur Springs

Good Looks Unlimited E Y C
804 1st Avenue SE, 59645
(406) 547-2146

Whitefish

Gwen Carreon Designs Q
1064 Creekwood Drive, 59937
(406) 862-6173 or (877) 702-1992

Knit 'N Needle Yarn Shoppe Y
14 Lupfer Avenue, 59937
(406) 862-6390

Quilt Kits To Go Q
903A Wisconsin Avenue, 59937
(406) 863-9773

Whitefish Quilts and Gifts Q
131 Central Avenue, 59937
(406) 730-2207

Whitehall

The Dysfunctional Quilter Q E
7 Sowden Lane, 59759
(406) 287-9237

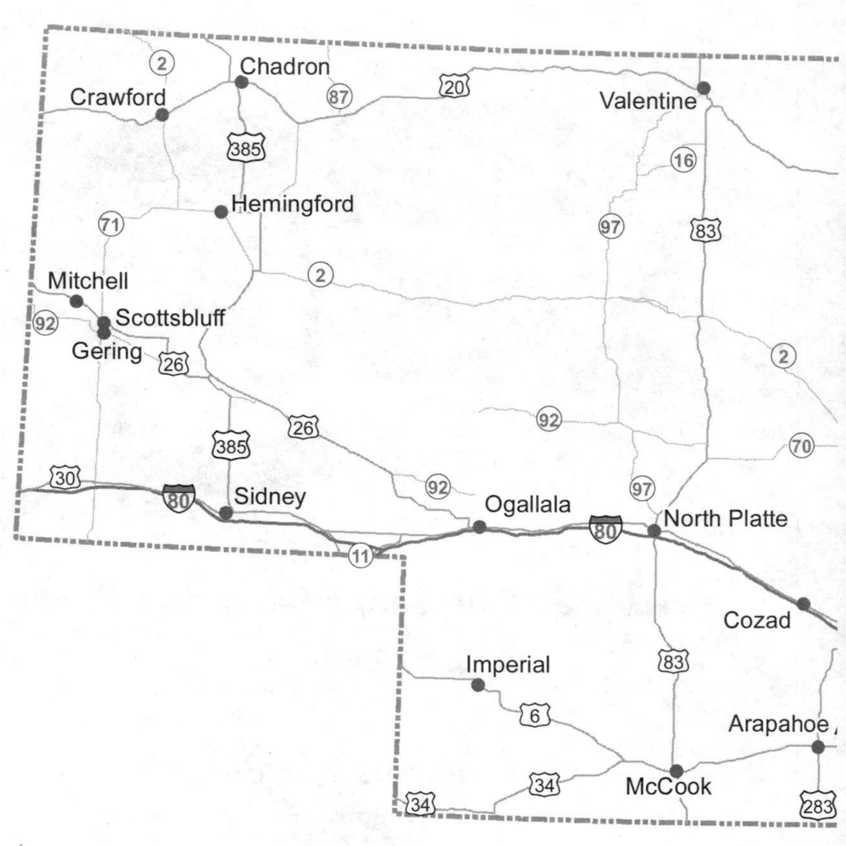

Chadron
Crawford
Valentine
Hemingford
Mitchell
Scottsbluff
Gering
Sidney
Ogallala
North Platte
Cozad
Imperial
Arapahoe
McCook
2
87
20
385
16
71
97
83
92
26
2
92
70
30
80
11
6
34
283

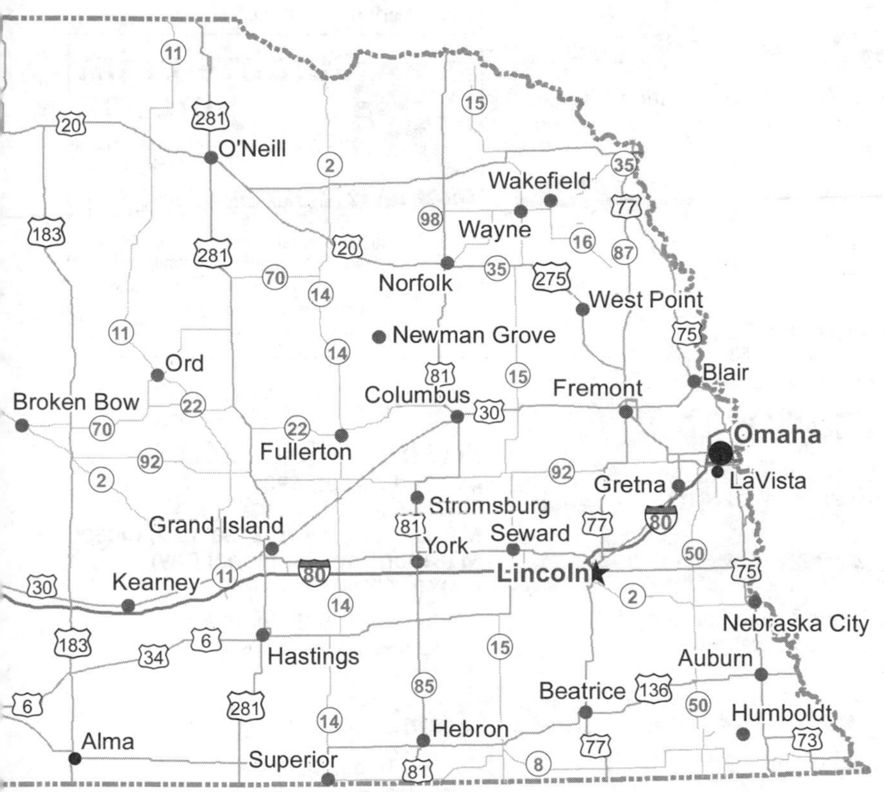
O'Neill
Wakefield
Wayne
Norfolk
West Point
Newman Grove
Ord
Blair
Broken Bow
Columbus
Fremont
Omaha
Fullerton
LaVista
Gretna
Stromsburg
Grand Island
Seward
York
Lincoln
Kearney
Nebraska City
Hastings
Auburn
Beatrice
Humboldt
Hebron
Alma
Superior

Nebraska

Alma

Butterfield Alpaca Ranch Y S
612 Main Street, 68920
(308) 920-5000

Arapahoe

Wagner's Quilts & Conversation Q E
404 Chestnut Street, 68922
(308) 962-8458

Auburn

Needles I Q
72896 638th Avenue, 68305
(402) 274-3339

The Fabric Fairie Q
900 Central Avenue, 68305
(402) 274-4454

Beatrice

Quilt Stitches Q E
505 Court Street, Suite B, 68310
(402) 223-1916

Blair

Acme Fabric & Quilt Company Q E
1716 Washington Street, 68008
(402) 533-1015

Broken Bow

The Quilting Shack Q E C M
518 E. South E Street, 68822
(308) 872-6221

Chadron

Ta-Da! Quilt Shop Q Y
223 Main Street, 69337
(308) 432-3565

Columbus

Claus'en Paus Quilt Shop Q
2510 13th Street, 68601
(402) 564-1618

Sew What Needle Arts & Quilting* Q E C
3415 21st Street, 68601
(402) 563-3900

Cozad

Prairie Point Junction Q
➡ SEE AD BELOW
124 E. 8th Street, 69130
(308) 784-2010
M-F 10-5, Sa 10-4
www.prairiepointjunction.com

Crawford

Pine Needle Quilts LLC Q E
413 2nd Street, 69339
(308) 665-1107
MTuThF 10-5, W 10-8, Sa 10-2, Closed M (Labor Day - Memorial Day)
www.pineneedlequilts.com

Stitches Fabric & Notions* Q
120 McPherson Street, 69339
(308) 665-5069

Fremont

Country Traditions Q E M
330 N. Main Street, 68025
(402) 721-7752

Fullerton

Calico Annie's Quilt Shop Q E
210 Broadway Street, 68638
(308) 536-2925

Gering

Prairie Pines Quilt Shop Q E M
1270 Tenth Street, Suite B, 69341
(308) 436-5152

Grand Island

Material Girl Q E C
3415 W. State Street, 68803
(308) 381-6675

Gretna

The Quilted Moose Q M
109 Enterprise Drive, 68028
(402) 332-4178

Hastings

Calico Cottage Q
743 W. 2nd Street, 68901
(402) 463-6767

Kitty Rose* Y
237 N. St. Joseph Avenue, 68901
(402) 705-7747

The Plum Nelly & Julie's Xpressions E Y W S
743 W. 2nd Street, 68901
(402) 462-2490

Hebron

Sew Bee It Quilt Shop* Q
341 Lincoln Avenue, 68370
(402) 768-6980

Hemingford

Pat's Creative Q E M
7355 Gage Road, 69348
(308) 487-3999
M-F 10-5, Sa 10-4
www.patscreative.com
Handi Quilter® Authorized Retailer
Designed by a Quilter, for Quilters.®

Humboldt

Creative Collectible Quilts and Crafts Q E N
332 East Square, 68376
(402) 862-4001

Imperial

Prior's New Generations Fabrics Q E
525 Broadway, 69033
(308) 882-4354

Kearney

Kearney Quality Sew & Vac Q E M
712 E. 25th Street, 68847
(308) 234-4304

The Quilters Cottage Q E M
2216 Central Avenue, 68847
(308) 237-2701

LaVista

Reflections Framing & Stitching C
7314 Harrison Street, 68128
(402) 331-1740

Lincoln

Cosmic Cow Q
6136 Havelock Avenue, 68507
(402) 464-4040

Crafthouse Q Y W
3520 Village Drive, Suite 600, 68516
(402) 261-4453

Knit-Paper-Scissors Y
6701 Vanderslice Circle, 68516
(402) 429-8029

Sew Creative Q M
5143 S. 48th Street, 68516
(402) 489-6262

The Calico House Q
5221 S. 48th Street, Suite 4, 68516
(402) 489-1067

The Yarn Shop Y
5221 S. 48th Street, 68516
(402) 489-9550

Yarn Charm Y S
5930 S. 58th Street, Suite N, 68516
(402) 858-6300

McCook

Quacky Quilter Haberdashery Q E
112 W. C Street, 69001
(402) 525-9523

Sew Blessed Q E
402 Norris Avenue, Suite 103, 69001
(308) 344-9389

Mitchell

Brown Sheep Company, Inc. (Y)(N)(W)(S)

➡ **SEE AD BELOW**

100662 County Road 16, 69357
(308) 635-2198
M-F 8-5
www.brownsheep.com

Nebraska City

Sew Enchanting (Q)
616 1/2 Central Avenue, 68410
(402) 873-1009

Sewing Basket* (Q)(E)(Y)(C)
805 Central Avenue, 68410
(402) 873-3955

Newman Grove

Betz's Little Shoppe (Q)(E)(Y)
505 Hale Avenue, 68758
(402) 447-6048

Norfolk

I Bee Quiltin (Q)
322 W. Norfolk Avenue, 68701
(402) 371-0045

North Platte

Prairie Hand Knits (Y)(W)
508 S. Dewey Street, 69101
(308) 534-4272

The Quilt Rack & Wool Cubby (Q)(E)(C)
101 W. Front Street, 69101
(308) 532-2606

O'Neill

Quilters Candy Shoppe (Q)
420 E. Douglas Street, 68763
(402) 336-1953

Ogallala

Silver Thimble Sewing Center (Q)(M)
108 N. Spruce Street, 69153
(308) 284-6838

Omaha

ImagiKnit Yarn Shop, LLC (Y)(S)

➡ **SEE AD BELOW**

#602 Bel Air Plaza
12100 W. Center Road, 68144
(402) 932-9525
M 5-9, Tu-F 10-6, Sa 10-4
www.facebook.com/pages/ImagiKnit-Yarn-Shop/263171999129

Country Sampler (Q)(E)
11928 W. Center Road, 68144
(402) 333-6131

David M. Mangelsen's (Q)(E)(Y)(C)
3457 S. 84th Street, 68124
(402) 391-6225

Modern Quilter Q
4429 S. 50th Street, 68117
(402) 934-4750

Personal Threads Boutique Q Y N
8600 Cass Street, 68114
(402) 391-7733 or (800) 306-7733

Sew Creative Q M
2809 S. 125th Avenue, Suite 385, 68144
(402) 334-0121

The Quilt Studio/Modern Quilter Q
4429 S 50th Street, 68117
(402) 934-4750

Village Needleworks N
8709 Shamrock Road, 68114
(402) 391-1191 or (800) 391-0603

Wooly Mammoth Yarn Shop Y W
5096 S. 108th Street, 68137
(402) 932-2157

Ord

MidWest Quilting and Embroidery Q
1433 M Street, 68862
(308) 728-7811

Scottsbluff

Platte Valley Vac and Sew Q M
1804 Broadway, 69361
(308) 632-3734

The Quilt Stop Q
1609 1/2 Broadway, 69361
(308) 632-7028

Seward

Cosmic Cow - The Udder Store Q
636 Seward Street, 68434
(402) 646-1000

Sidney

Laughing Lamb Fibers W S
925 Illinois Street, 69162
(866) 582-0058

More Than Quilts Q Y S
1044 Illinois Street, 69162
(308) 203-1600

Stromsburg

Spindle, Shuttle, and Needle Yarn Shop Y W S
117 E. 4th Street, 68666
(402) 405-1971
Tu-F 10-5, Sa 10-12
www.spindleshuttleandneedle.com

Superior

Quilter's Nook Q E
214 N. Central Avenue, 68978
(402) 879-5431

Valentine

Country Fabric & Crafts Q E Y C M
148 N. Main Street, 69201
(402) 376-3544 or (866) 228-6987

Wakefield

The Quilt Shop Q E C
314 Main Street, 68784
(402) 287-2325

Wayne

Just Sew Q E C
512 E. 7th Street, 68787
(402) 375-4697

West Point

Creative Notions Q E N C M
107 N. Main Street, 68788
(402) 372-2004

York

The Quilt Basket Q E C M
718 N. Lincoln Avenue, 68467
(402) 362-5737

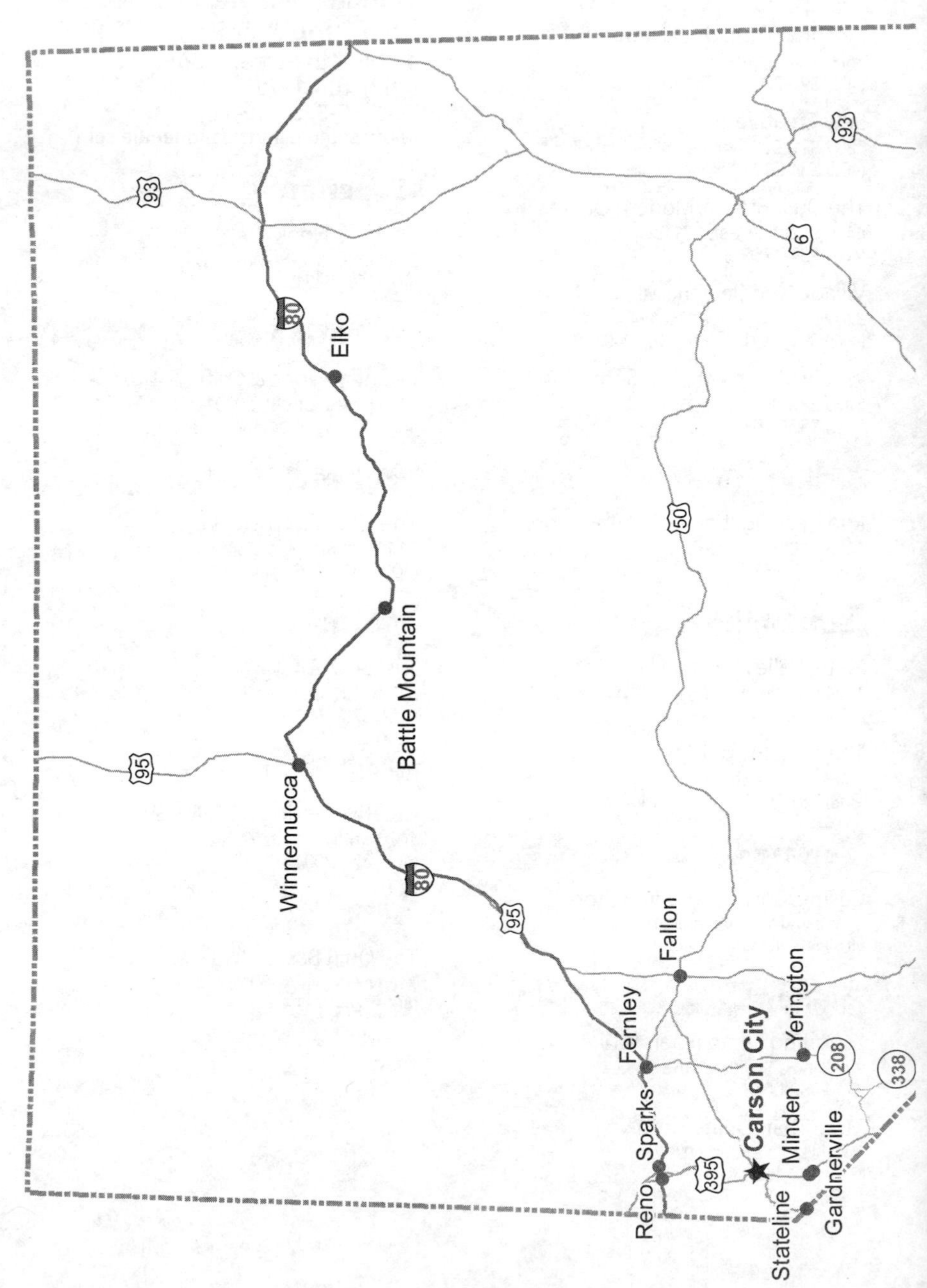
93
93
6
80
Elko
50
Battle Mountain
95
Winnemucca
80
95
Fallon
Fernley
Yerington
Carson City
208
338
Sparks
Minden
Gardnerville
395
Reno
Stateline

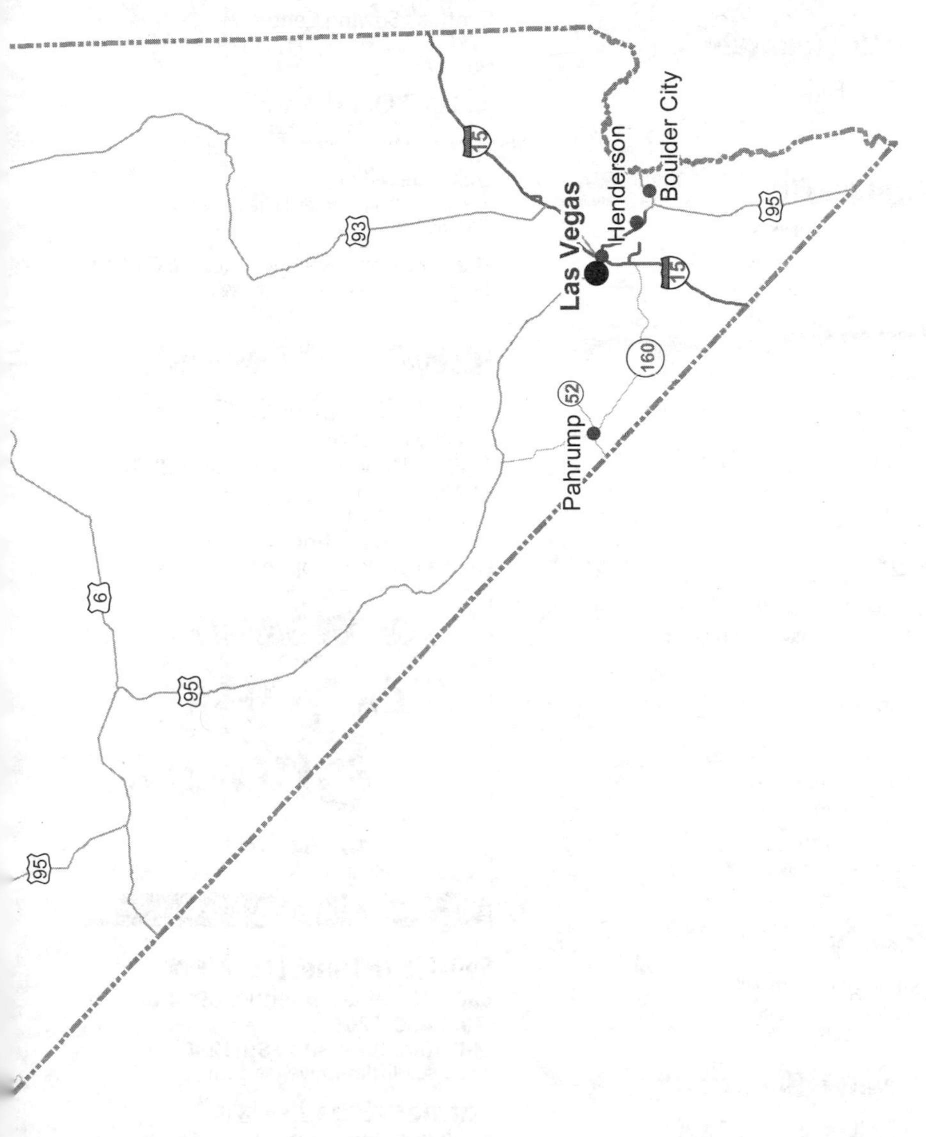
Las Vegas
Henderson
Boulder City
Pahrump
15
15
93
95
95
95
160
52
6

Nevada

Battle Mountain

The Quilt Parlor Q
147 E. Front Street, 89820
(775) 635-2600

Boulder City

Craft Cottage E Y N C
1326 Wyoming Street, 89005
(702) 294-4465

Carson City

Out of My Mindesigns Q
411 Hot Springs Road, Suite 2, 89706
(775) 882-8247

Sierra Sewing Center Q M
911 Topsy Lane, Suite 222, 89705
(775) 267-6694

Elko

Elko Sew Vac Q E M
1250 Lamoille Highway, #940, 89801
(775) 778-6763

Fallon

The UnCommon Thread Q
1525 W. Williams Avenue, Suite L, 89406
(775) 867-4225

Workman Farms Q E
4990 Reno Highway, 89406
(775) 867-3716

Fernley

A Stitch of Country Q
15 E. Main Street, Suite 1, 89408
(775) 835-0558

Gardnerville

The Quilt House, Inc. Q E M
1328 US Highway 395 N, Suite 105, 89410
(775) 782-8845

Henderson

Cynthia's Sewing Center* M
1570 W. Horizon Ridge Parkway, Suite 120, 89012
(702) 897-7155

Handi Quilter® Authorized Retailer
Designed by a Quilter, for Quilters.®

Quiltique Q E M
213 N. Stephanie Street, Suite E, 89074
(702) 563-8600

The Downtown Sewing Machine Co. Q M
155 S. Water Street, Suite 130, 89015
(702) 457-9600

Las Vegas

Sin City Knit Shop Y S
➡ SEE AD BELOW
2165 E. Windmill Lane, Suite 200, 89123
(702) 641-0210
Please call for hours
www.sincityknitshop.com

Sew Little Time, LLC Q E M
6360 W. Sahara Avenue, 89146
(702) 450-6766
M-F 10-4, Sa 9:30-2, Su 12-4
www.sewlittletimevegas.com

Stitcher's Paradise N C
2550 S. Rainbow Blvd., Suite E25, 89146
(702) 227-9735
MTuWF 10-6, Th 10-8, Sa 10-4
www.stitchersparadiseinc.com

Golden Needle Arts LLC Ⓔ Ⓨ Ⓝ Ⓦ Ⓢ Ⓒ
4855 W. Desert Inn Road, Suite 101, 89102
(702) 362-6252

Sew Yeah Quilting Ⓠ
3690 N. Rancho Drive, 89130
(702) 586-8687

The Christmas Goose Ⓠ Ⓔ Ⓜ
2988 S. Durango, Suite 109, 89117
(702) 877-1158

Minden

Fabric-Chicks Creative Oasis Ⓠ
1166 Annie Court, #C, 89423
(775) 267-0204

Pioneer Yarn Company Ⓨ
1653 Lucerne Street, Suite B, 89423
(775) 392-3336

Pahrump

Bernina Sewing Center Ⓠ Ⓜ
4920 Pahrump Valley Blvd., 89048
(775) 727-3633

The Quilted Dragon Ⓠ
2890 S. Yucca Terrace Avenue, 89048
(775) 751-9033

Reno

Yarn Refuge Ⓨ
3368 Lakeside Court, 89509
(775) 384-1600
M-Sa 11-6
http://www.yarnrefuge.com

Going Batty Quilt Shop Ⓠ Ⓔ Ⓜ
9744 S. Virginia Street, Suite C, 89511
(775) 351-2424

Jimmy Beans Wool Ⓨ Ⓦ Ⓢ
4850 Joule Street, Suite A1, 89502
(877) 529-5648

Mill End Fabrics Ⓠ
1745 Kuenzli Street, 89502
(775) 322-5844

Sierra Sewing, Quilting, and Vacuums Ⓠ Ⓜ
8056 S. Virginia Street, Suite 6, 89511
(775) 823-9700

Stitch In Time, Inc. Ⓝ Ⓒ
5000 Smithridge Drive, Suite A15, 89502
(775) 829-9222

Windy Moon Quilts Ⓠ Ⓔ Ⓜ
440 Spokane Street, 89512
(775) 323-4777

Handi Quilter® Authorized Retailer
Designed by a Quilter, for Quilters.®

Sparks

Windy Moon Quilts Sewing Center Ⓠ Ⓔ Ⓜ
406 Pyramid Way, 89431
(775) 870-4031

Stateline

The Knitting Nest Ⓨ
472 Needle Peak Road, 89449
(775) 588-4015
Call for hours
www.tahoeknittingnest.com

Winnemucca

Mad Hatter Quilt Shoppe Ⓠ Ⓜ
346 S. Bridge Street, 89445
(775) 623-2521

Yerington

Sylvia's Quilter's Quarters Ⓠ Ⓔ Ⓒ
120 Bovard Street, 89447
(775) 463-7036

The WorkShop In The Back Ⓠ Ⓔ Ⓨ Ⓝ Ⓦ Ⓢ Ⓒ
27 Broadway Avenue, 89447
(775) 463-9492

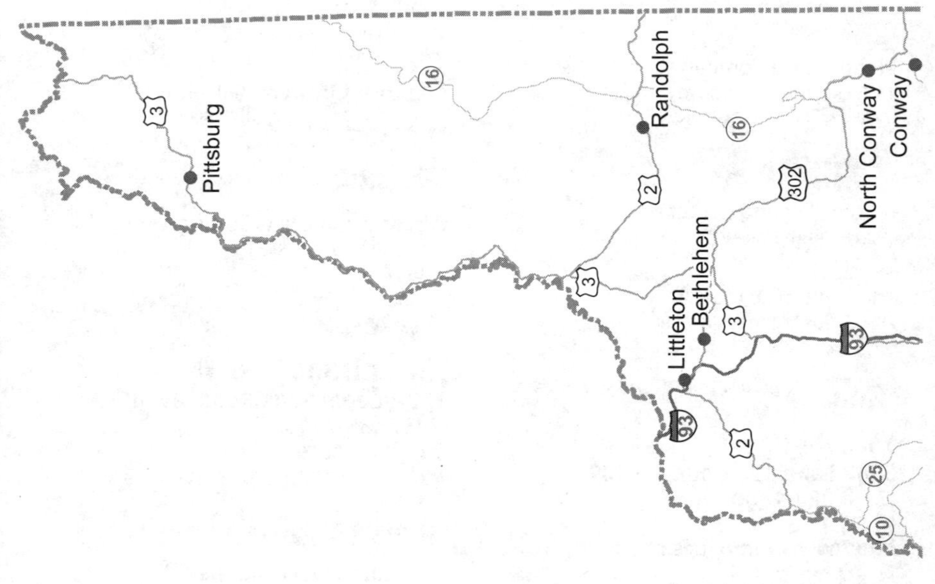
Pittsburg
Randolph
North Conway
Conway
Littleton
Bethlehem
3
16
2
302
93
25
10

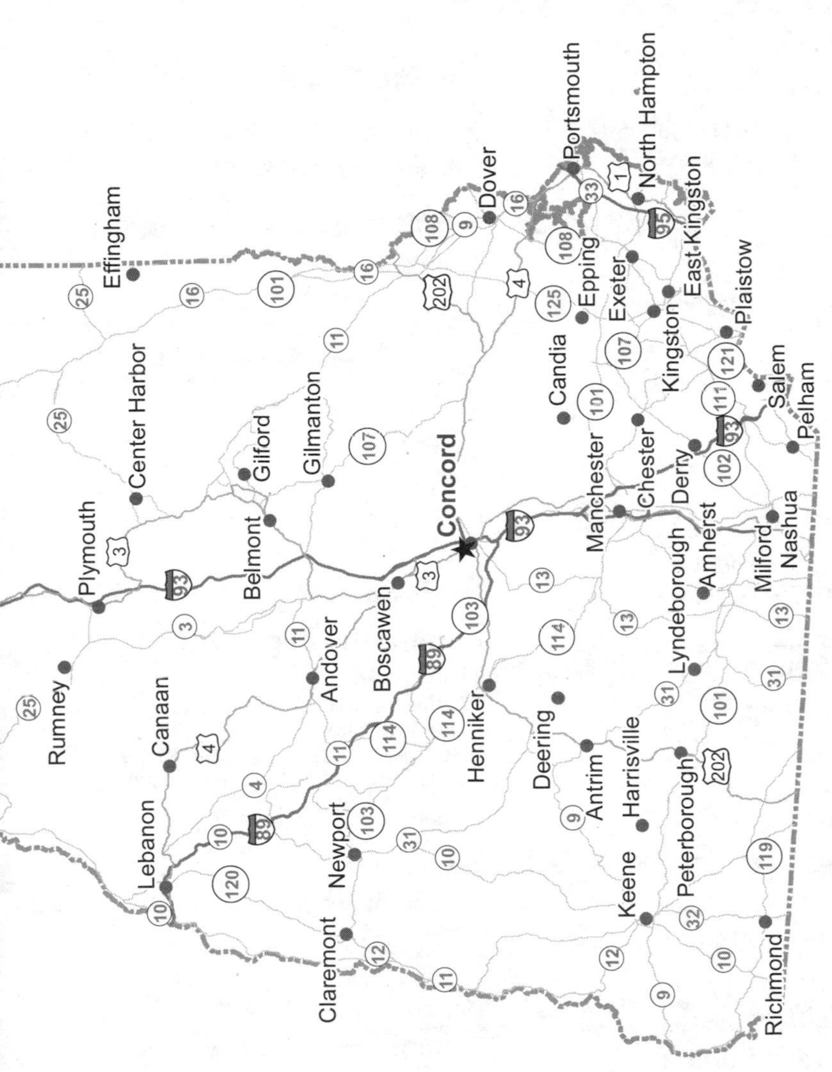
Effingham
Center Harbor
Plymouth
Rumney
Canaan
Lebanon
Gilford
Belmont
Gilmanton
Andover
Boscawen
Concord
Newport
Claremont
Henniker
Deering
Antrim
Harrisville
Keene
Dover
Portsmouth
North Hampton
Epping
Exeter
East Kingston
Kingston
Plaistow
Candia
Manchester
Chester
Derry
Salem
Pelham
Amherst
Lyndeborough
Milford
Nashua
Peterborough
Richmond

New Hampshire

Amherst

Covered Bridge Creations, LLC Ⓨ Ⓝ
141 Route 101A, Heritage Place M7, 03031
(603) 889-2179

Quilting A Way To A Pieceful Life Ⓠ Ⓜ
17 Old Nashua Road, Unit 2, 03031
(603) 721-2356

Andover

The Constant Quilter Ⓠ
139 Pancake Road, 03216
(603) 735-4100

Antrim

Artful Alpaca@Hidden Hill Farm* Ⓨ Ⓢ
27 Mattheson Road, 03440
(603) 588-3370

Belmont

Vacman and Bobbin Ⓠ Ⓔ Ⓜ
225 Daniel Webster Highway, 03220
(603) 528-6759

Bethlehem

Love Yarn Shop Ⓨ
2050 Main Street, 03574
(603) 869-2600
Tu-Sa 10-5
www.loveyarnshop.com

Boscawen

Bittersweet Fabric Shop Ⓠ Ⓜ
8 Cottage Street, 03303
(603) 753-4920

Canaan

Haphazard Quilting Ⓠ
49 NH Route 118, 03741
(603) 523-2029
M-Sa 9-5
www.haphazardquilting.com

Conwell Corners* Ⓠ
9 Funny Cide Drive, 03741
(603) 523-4861

Candia

Thread In Hand Ⓠ Ⓔ
143 Raymond Road, Unit 10, 03034
(603) 587-0425

Center Harbor

Keepsake Quilting, Inc. Ⓠ
12 Main Street, 03226
(603) 253-4026 or (800) 865-9458

Chester

A Knitter's Garden Ⓨ
58 Derry Road, 03036
(603) 887-8550

Claremont

Four Pines Quilting Ⓠ Ⓜ
367 Washintgon Street, 03743
(603) 543-3311

Frank's Bargain Center Ⓠ Ⓔ Ⓨ Ⓝ Ⓦ Ⓢ Ⓒ
Route 11/12 Charlestown Road, 03743
(603) 542-2218

Concord

Paradise Quilting and Gift Studio Ⓠ Ⓜ
75 Allison Street, 03301
(603) 493-6389
MTuThF 9:30-8, W 10-6, Sa 10-4:30
www.facebook.com/paradisequilting/

Golden Gese Quilt Shop* Ⓠ
22 Liberty Street, 03301
(603) 228-5540

The Elegant Ewe Ⓨ Ⓦ Ⓢ
75 S. Main Street, Unit 1, 03301
(603) 226-0066

Conway

The Quilt Shop at Vac n Sew Ⓠ Ⓔ Ⓜ
290 E. Side Road, 03818
(603) 447-3470

Deering

Clark Summit Alpacas* Ⓨ Ⓦ Ⓢ
Call for address, 03244
(603) 464-2910

Derry

Aunt Mary's Quilting Ⓠ
43 Stark Road, 03038
(603) 845-9380

The Yarn and Fiber Company ⓆⓎⓈ
14 E. Broadway, 03038
(603) 505-4432

Dover

Spinning Yarns Ⓨ
511 Central Avenue, 03820
(603) 740-6476

E. Kingston

Compass Point Quilt Shop & CPQ Studio Ⓠ
➡ **SEE AD BELOW**
59 Sanborn Road, 03827
(973) 214-6784
Sa 10-4, Tu 6:30 pm-9 pm or by appt.
www.compasspointquilts.com

Effingham

The Attic Cat Quilting Ⓠ
661 Townhouse Road, 03882
(603) 539-4669

Epping

Riverslea Farm ⓎⓈ
362 North River Road, 03042
(603) 679-2629

Exeter

Charlotte's Web, Inc. Ⓨ
137 Epping Road, 03833
(603) 778-1417 or (888) 244-6460

Gilford

Lamb's Ear Yarns Ⓨ
3 Waterford Place, 03249
(603) 528-4333

Gilmanton

Badger Brook Farm Ⓠ Ⓔ Ⓨ Ⓢ Ⓒ
170 Province Road, 03237
(603) 267-1200

Camelot Alpaca Farm* Ⓨ
528 Meadow Pond Road, 03237
(603) 267-8251

Harrisville

Harrisville Designs Retail Store Ⓨ Ⓦ Ⓢ
4 Mill Alley, 03450
(603) 827-3996

Henniker

Quilted Threads Ⓠ Ⓜ
116 Main Street, 03242
(603) 428-6622

Keene

New England Fabrics Ⓠ Ⓔ Ⓨ Ⓜ
55 Ralston Street, 03431
(603) 352-8683

The Wooly Lamb Knitting Company * Ⓨ
305 Marlboro Street, 03431
(603) 762-5737

Kingston

Stitched In Stone Ⓠ Ⓔ Ⓨ Ⓜ
53 Church Street, 03848
(603) 642-4220

Lebanon

Scratch, Inc. Ⓔ Ⓨ Ⓒ
1 Court Street, 03766
(603) 727-9528 or (844) 406-6046

Littleton

One Stitch, Two Stitch Ⓠ Ⓔ
81 Main Street, Suite 200, 03561
(603) 444-5284

Lyndeborough

The Bunkhouse Quilt Shop Ⓠ Ⓔ
350 Center Road, 03082
(603) 654-6734

Manchester

Patches Quilt Loft & Embroidery Ⓠ Ⓔ Ⓜ
649 E. Industrial Park Drive, Unit 17, 03109
(603) 206-5490

Milford

Twill Fabric and Yarn Ⓠ Ⓨ
20 Middle Street, 03055
(603) 213-6365

Nashua

All American Quilt Co. Ⓠ
3 Pine Street, Unit C, 03060
(603) 689-3652

Newport

Hodge Podge Yarns and Fibers Ⓨ Ⓢ
59 Belknap Avenue, 03773
(603) 863-1470

North Conway

Nancy's Alterations and Yarn Shop Ⓨ
9 Norcross Circle, 03860
(603) 356-7344 or (603) 986-1900

North Hampton

Pintuck & Purl Ⓠ Ⓨ Ⓜ
69 Lafayette Road, 03862
(603) 418-7157

Pelham

Bits N Pieces Quilt Shop Ⓠ Ⓜ
70 Bridge Street, Unit 6, 03076
(603) 635-9705
MTuWF 10-6, Th 10-8, Sa 9-5, Su 10-5
http://www.bnpquilts.com

Peterborough

Knitty Gritty Yarn Shop Ⓨ
16 Depot Street, Unit 20, 03458
(603) 924-2028

Pittsburg

Moose Country Quilting, LLC Q
23 Lisa Lane, 03592
(603) 538-6671

Plaistow

D&D Sewing Q M
160 Plaistow Road, 03865
(603) 382-1122

YarnSong Y
160 Plaistow Road, Unit 18, 03865
(603) 974-7372

Plymouth

Inspire 2 Knit & Tea Y
72 Yeaton Road, 03264
(603) 536-5648

Portsmouth

Merristitches Inc. Q M
72 Mirona Road, Suite 15, 03801
(603) 431-9922

Portsmouth Fabric Co. Q M
112 Penhallow Street, 03801
(603) 436-6343

Seacoast Sewing & Quilting LLC Q E Y W M
755 Banfield Road, 03801
(603) 373-0151

Randolph

Grand View Country Store Y
89 US Route 2, 03593
(603) 466-5715 or (800) 898-5715

Richmond

Pickering Farm Quilt Shop Q
19 Fitzwilliam Road, 03470
(603) 239-7550

Rumney

North Country Quilters & Sew 'n Vac Q E C M
15 Depot Street, 03266
(603) 786-6118

Authorized Retailer

Salem

Angels Sewing and Vacuum Center Q E M
236 N. Broadway, 03079
(603) 898-0777

Pine Tree Quilt Shop Q
224 N. Broadway, 03079
(603) 870-8100

The Victorian Cupboard Sewing Studio Q E M
401 Main Street, Suite 111, 03079
(603) 458-1320

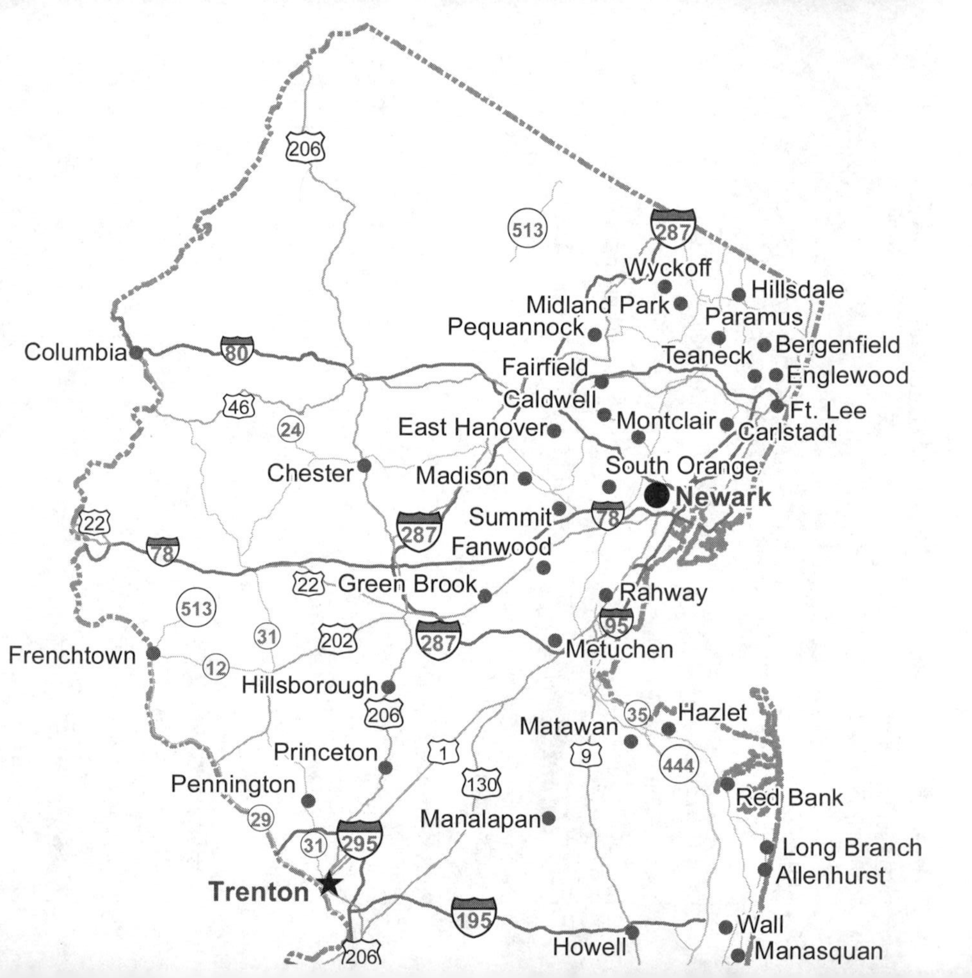

Hillsdale
Paramus
Bergenfield
Englewood
Ft. Lee
Carlstadt
Wyckoff
Teaneck
Midland Park
Montclair
South Orange
Newark
Pequannock
Fairfield
Caldwell
East Hanover
Madison
Summit
Fanwood
Rahway
Metuchen
Green Brook
Hazlet
Matawan
Red Bank
Long Branch
Allenhurst
Wall
Manasquan
Howell
Manalapan
Chester
Hillsborough
Princeton
Pennington
Trenton
Columbia
Frenchtown
287
513
206
80
46
24
78
22
202
31
12
29
295
1
130
195
9
35
444
95

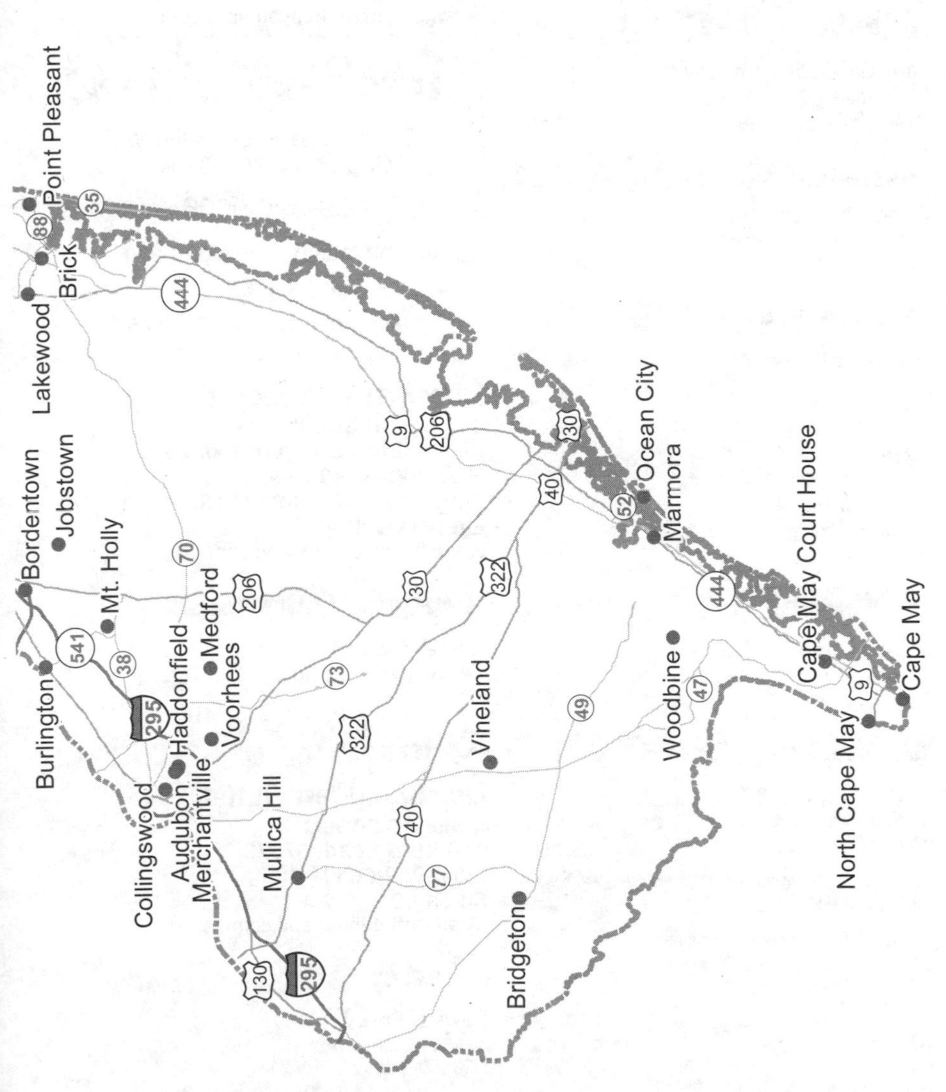

Point Pleasant
Brick
Lakewood
Bordentown
Jobstown
Mt. Holly
Burlington
Medford
Voorhees
Haddonfield
Collingswood
Audubon
Merchantville
Mullica Hill
Vineland
Bridgeton
Ocean City
Marmora
Woodbine
Cape May Court House
Cape May
North Cape May
35
88
444
9
206
30
40
52
70
206
541
38
295
73
322
49
47
77
130

New Jersey

Allenhurst

Needles & Threads LLC Ⓨ Ⓝ
411 Main Street, 07711
(732) 493-4300

Audubon

Early Girl Quilt Company Ⓠ Ⓔ
235 S. White Horse Pike, 08106
(856) 429-7573

Bergenfield

Gone Stitching Ⓔ Ⓝ Ⓒ
31 S. Washington Avenue, 07621
(201) 385-2100

Bordentown

Just Make It Sew Ⓠ
316 Farnsworth Avenue, 08505
(609) 386-4218

Brick

Crafty Fabrics Ⓠ
750 Mantoloking Road, 08723
(732) 920-6220

Bridgeton

Broad Meadows Country Fabrics Ⓠ
100 Mary Elmer Drive, 08302
(856) 332-7269

Burlington

Olde City Quilts Ⓠ Ⓔ Ⓜ
339 High Street, 08016
(609) 747-0075

Caldwell

Beyond Knits & Needles* Ⓝ
339 Bloomfield Avenue, 07006
(973) 226-4242

Cape May

Stitch By Stitch Ⓔ Ⓝ Ⓒ
➡ **SEE AD BELOW**
315 Ocean Street, Suite 9, 08204
(609) 898-9606
Every Day 10-5, Winter hours (Jan-Apr) SaSu 10-5
www.stitchbystitchcapemay.com

Fiber Arts Yarn Shop Ⓨ Ⓦ Ⓢ
315 Ocean Street, #23
Washington Commons, 08204
(609) 898-8080
Winter: SuMThFSa 10-5; Summer: Every Day 10-6
www.fiberartsyarnshop.com

Cape May Court House

Home Made* Ⓠ Ⓨ
1761 N. Route 9, 08210
(609) 536-2940

Carlstadt

Lion Brand Yarn Outlet Ⓨ Ⓦ
➡ **SEE AD PAGE 328**
140 Kero Road, 07072
(201) 939-0611
Su-Th 10-5, F 9-4
http://outlet.lionbrand.com

Chester

Rows of PurL Ⓨ
44 Main Street, 07930
(908) 879-0403

Collingswood

The Quilted Nest Q E M
823 Haddon Avenue, 08108
(856) 240-1410

Authorized Retailer

Columbia

Winterberries Yarn Y W S
468 Route 94, 07832
(908) 496-8353

East Hanover

Sew Jersey Q E M
136 Route 10, 07936
(973) 585-7282

Englewood

Expression Yarn Studio* Y
13 E. Ivy Lane, 07631
(201) 569-4111

Fairfield

The Edwardian Needle N
390 Fairfield Road, 07004
(862) 210-8839
W-Sa 11-4
www.theedwardianneedle.com

Fanwood

Do Ewe Knit? Y
42B S. Martine Avenue, 07023
(908) 654-5648

Frenchtown

The Spinnery Y W S
33 Race Street, 08825
(908) 996-9004
Every Day 10-4
http://www.spinnery.net

Ft. Lee

Pat's Yarn Boutique Y
807 Abbott Blvd., Suite B, 07024
(201) 224-7771

Green Brook

Fabricland Q
270 US Highway 22, 08812
(908) 755-4700

Haddonfield

Hooked Fine Yarn Boutique Y S
411 N. Haddon Avenue, 08033
(856) 428-0110

Hazlet

Moore Yarn Y
1340 Route 36, Suite 14, 07730
(732) 847-3665

Hillsborough

Swallow Hill Farm Y W S
583 Montgomery Road, 08844
(908) 369-7091

The Yarn Attic Y
406 Route 206, 08844
(908) 864-5311

Hillsdale

Yarn Diva and More Y
428 Hillsdale Avenue, 07642
(201) 664-4100

Howell

Mouse Creek Quilts Q E N C
2212 Route 9 S, 07731
(732) 294-7858

Handi Quilter Authorized Retailer
Designed by a Quilter, for Quilters.

Jobstown

The Yarn Shop At Alma Park * Y
2800 Monmouth Road, 08041
(732) 620-1052

Lakewood

Stitch 'N Sew Centre Q
123 E. County Line Road, 08701
(732) 363-2220

Long Branch

SM Stitches Ⓝ
1191 Lincoln Square, 07740
(848) 303-8686

Madison

The Blue Purl Ⓨ
60 Main Street, 07940
(973) 377-5648

Manalapan

Knit's Fabulous! Ⓨ
337 US 9 S, Suite B14
Summerton Plaza, 07726
(732) 677-2020

Manasquan

House of Yarn and Needlecraft Ⓨ
227 E. Main Street, 08736
(732) 223-9788

Marmora

Dollard Baker Sew & Vac* Ⓜ
232 S. Shore Road, Suite 2, 08223
(609) 390-0343

Matawan

Bernina Sewing Center ⓆⒺ
443-K Highway 34, 07747
(732) 566-2121

Medford

Cattell's Sew and Vac* ⓆⓂ
1 Tomlinson Mill Road, 08055
(856) 334-8139

Merchantville

Nimble Needle ⒺⓃⒸ
45 S. Centre Street, 08109
(856) 354-8100

Metuchen

Needleworker's Delight / Silkweaver Fabrics / Zweigart USA ⒺⓃⒸ
181 US Highway 1 S, 08840
(732) 388-4545 or (800) 931-4545

Midland Park

Close Knit Ⓨ
22 Paterson Avenue, 07432
(201) 891-3319

Montclair

Yarnia ⓎⓈ
147 Valley Road, 07042
(973) 572-9276

Mt. Holly

The Village Quilter ⓆⒺ
10 Charles Street, 08060
(609) 265-0011

Woolbearers ⓎⓌⓈ
90 High Street, 08060
(609) 914-0003

Mullica Hill

Needles & Pins Quilt & Fabric Shop ⓆⓂ
533 Mullica Hill Road, 08062
(856) 218-7467

North Cape May

Enchanted Fiber ⓆⓎⓈ
3704 Bayshore Road, Unit 3, 08204
(609) 600-1041

Ocean City

Scrim Discovery Needlepoint Ⓝ
924 Haven Avenue, 08226
(609) 398-6659

The Knitting Niche Ⓨ
1330 Asbury Avenue, 08226
(609) 399-5111

Paramus

Paramus Fabric Center Ⓠ
70 N. Route 17, 07652
(201) 843-7640

Pennington

Knit One Stitch Too Y N
16 N. Main Street, 08534
(609) 737-2211

Pennington Quilt Works Q M
7 Tree Farm Road, 08534
(609) 737-4321

Pequannock

Acme Country Fabrics Q Y M
24-26 Newark Pompton Turnpike, 07440
(973) 696-1784

Point Pleasant

Frame & Fiber Q Y
1004 Trenton Avenue, 08742
(732) 892-6207

Princeton

Pins & Needles Y N
8 Chambers Street, 08542
(609) 921-9075

Rahway

The Fabric Warehouse Q
970 New Brunswick Avenue, 07065
(732) 882-0007

Red Bank

Chelsea Yarns Y
25 Mechanic Street, 07701
(732) 637-8600

South Orange

The Local Yarn Store Y S
15 Village Plaza, 07079
(973) 821-5005

Summit

Wool & Grace Y N
102 Summit Avenue, 07901
(908) 277-1431

Teaneck

Yarn DezVous Y
495 Cedar Lane, 07666
(201) 357-4710

Vineland

A Fabric Outlet & Gifts, LLC Q
2644 N. West Blvd., 08360
(856) 690-8633

The Pin Cushion Q E Y N C
657 N. Delsea Drive, 08360
(856) 692-5460

Voorhees

Needlepoints & Framing 4 U N
2999 Evesham Road, 08043
(856) 424-7962

Wall

Arrow Acres Farm* Y
2021 Bentz Road, 07719
(732) 974-8696

Woodbine

North Country Knits Y W S
551 Hands Mill Road, 08270
(609) 861-0328

Wyckoff

Ridgewood Needlepoint N
391 Clinton Avenue, 07481
(201) 612-7770

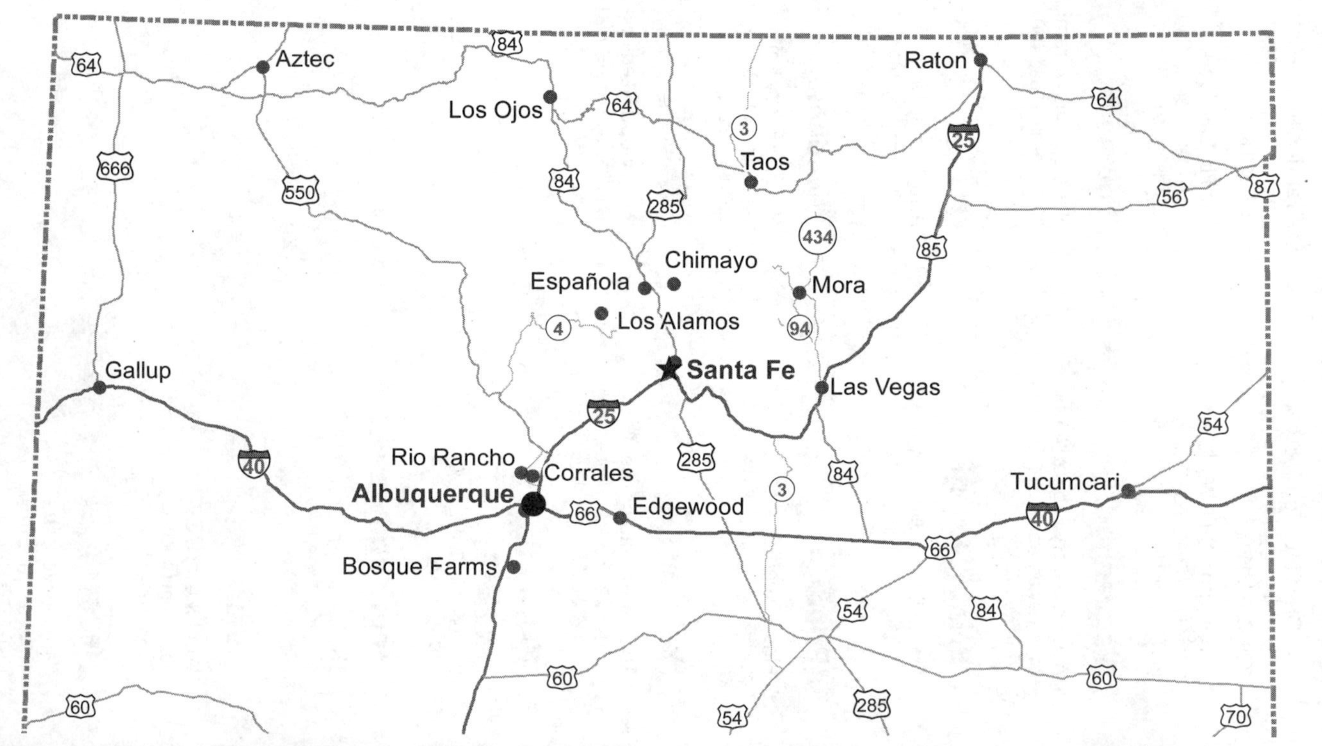
Aztec
Los Ojos
Taos
Raton
Chimayo
Española
Mora
Los Alamos
Gallup
Santa Fe
Las Vegas
Rio Rancho
Corrales
Albuquerque
Edgewood
Tucumcari
Bosque Farms
64
84
666
550
285
3
434
25
85
56
87
4
94
40
66
54
60
70

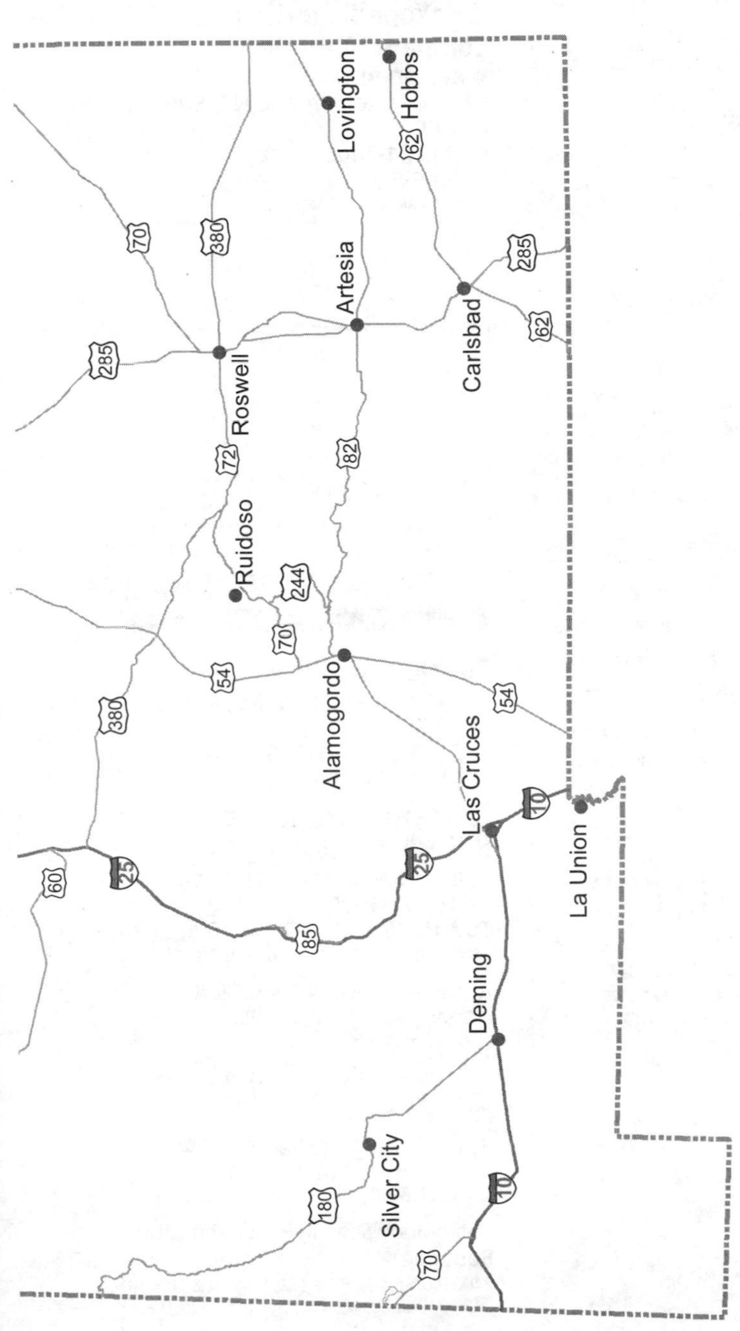

Hobbs
Lovington
62
70
380
Artesia
285
Carlsbad
62
285
Roswell
72
82
Ruidoso
244
70
54
Alamogordo
54
380
Las Cruces
10
La Union
25
60
25
85
Deming
Silver City
10
180
70

New Mexico

Alamogordo

Homestead Quilting Q Y W S
2701 Highland Drive, 88310
(575) 434-2009

Albuquerque

Hip Stitch Q E Y M

➡ SEE AD BELOW
2320 Wisconsin Street NE, 87110
(505) 821-2739
M-Sa 9-6, Su 12-5
http://www.hipstitchabq.com

Southwest Decoratives & Kokopelli Quilting Company Q E C M

➡ SEE AD BELOW
5711 Carmel Avenue NE, Suite B, 87113
(505) 821-7400
M-Sa 9-5
www.swdecoratives.com

The Quilt Works Q

11117 Menaul Blvd. NE, 87112
(505) 298-8210
M-F 9-5:30, Sa 9-5, Su 1-4:30
www.quiltworksabq.com

The Yarn Store at Nob Hill E Y N W S

120 Amherst Drive NE, 87106
(505) 717-1535
TuWTh 10-6, F 10-7, Sa 10-5, Su 10-4
www.theyarnstoreatnobhill.com

Ann Silva's Sewing Center Q M
4520 Alexander Blvd. NE, 87107
(505) 881-5253

Handi Quilter® Authorized Retailer
Designed by a Quilter, for Quilters.®

Ryan's Sewing and Vacuum Q M
5011 San Mateo Blvd., NE, 87109
(505) 237-8000

Stitchology Sewing Parlor and Fabric Boutique Q E
2400 Rio Grande Blvd. NW, Suite D, 87104
(505) 242-3288

The Stitcher's Garden Ⓒ
2801 Eubank NE, Suite I, 87112
(505) 881-6601

Artesia

Martha's Fabric Shop Ⓠ
316 W. Main Street, 88210
(575) 748-2231

Aztec

Quilt it! Ya Ya Ⓠ
201 S. Church Avenue, 87410
(505) 334-9566

Bosque Farms

Gathering Stitches Ⓠ
1900 Bosque Farms Blvd, Suite B, 87068
(505) 916-0458

Carlsbad

Jill's Fabric & Designs ⓆⒺⒸ
121 S. Canyon Street, 88220
(575) 885-1184

Chimayo

Los Vigiles Living Traditions ⓎⓌ
776 State Road 76, 87522
(505) 351-4522

Corrales

Quilts Olé Ⓠ
3923 Corrales Road, 87048
(505) 890-9416

Deming

Sew-n-Sew ⓆⒺ
609 E. Florida Street, 88030
(575) 546-8085

Edgewood

Busy Bee Quilts Ⓠ
150 State Road 344, Suite D, 87015
(505) 281-0195

Edgewood Yarns & Fibers ⓎⓌ
95 State Road 344, Suite 2, 87015
(505) 286-8900

Espanola

Espanola Valley Fiber Arts Center ⓆⒺⓎⓃⓌⓈⒸ
325 Paseo de Onate, 87532
(505) 747-3577

Quilters Corner* ⓆⒺ
2 County Road 544, 87532
(505) 747-6745 or (505) 929-7280

Gallup

Weaving In Beauty LLC ⓎⓌⓈ
233 W. Coal Avenue, 87301
(505) 297-6343

Gallup

Gallup Service Mart Vacuum and Sewing Center ⓆⓂ
104 W. Coal Avenue, 87301
(505) 722-9414

Hobbs

Got 2 Sew.com ⓆⓂ
209 W. Broadway Street, 88240
(575) 393-2739

The Quilting Gypsy* Ⓠ
3505 W. Alabama Street, 88242
(575) 390-8303

La Union

Mayaluna Yarns Ⓨ
3200 Highway 28, 88021
(915) 588-0983

Las Cruces

Be Sew Creative ⓆⓂ
1601 E. Lohman Avenue, 88001
(575) 523-2000 or (575) 523-2016

Las Vegas

ThreadBear Ⓠ Ⓔ Ⓨ
1813 Plaza Street, 87701
(505) 425-6263
MTuWFSa 9-5, Th 9-6:30; open Su 11-3 (June 1-Sept. 1)
http://www.threadbear-nm.com

Los Alamos

Atomic City Quilts Ⓠ Ⓔ Ⓒ
1247 Central Avenue, Suite C, 87544
(505) 662-1416

Los Ojos

Tierra Wools, LLC Ⓨ Ⓦ Ⓢ
91 Main Street, 87551
(575) 588-7231

Lovington

Country Store Quilt Shop Ⓠ
115 N. Main Street, 88260
(575) 396-4914

Mora

Mora Valley Spinning Mill* Ⓨ Ⓦ Ⓢ
298 State Highway 518, 87732
(575) 387-2247

Victory Ranch* Ⓨ Ⓦ Ⓢ
MM-1 Highway 434, 87732
(575) 387-2254

Raton

Patchwork Phoenix Ⓠ Ⓔ Ⓒ
228 S. 1st Street, 87740
(575) 445-8000

Rio Rancho

Enchanted Creations Ⓠ Ⓔ Ⓨ Ⓝ Ⓒ
1447 32nd Circle SE, 87124
(505) 892-8916

Roswell

Sew Easy Sewing Ⓠ Ⓔ Ⓜ
200 E. College Blvd., 88201
(575) 623-3774
Tu-F 10-5, Sa 10-3, SuM by appt.
www.seweasysewing.com

Calico Cow Quilt Shop Ⓠ
311 N. Main Street, 88201
(575) 623-8647

Ruidoso

A Quilting Stitchuation, LLC Ⓠ Ⓔ Ⓜ
1715 Sudderth Drive, 88345
(575) 315-0541 or (575) 973-2191

Books Etcetera Ⓔ Ⓨ
2340 Sudderth Drive, 88345
(575) 257-1594

Martha's Fabric Shop Ⓠ
101 Vision Drive, 88345
(575) 630-2231

Santa Fe

Looking Glass Yarn & Gifts Ⓨ Ⓦ Ⓢ
1802 2nd Street, Suite 2, 87505
(505) 995-9649

Ryan's Sewing and Vacuum Ⓠ Ⓔ Ⓜ
1607 St. Michaels Drive, 87505
(505) 820-1100

Santa Fe Quilting, Inc. Ⓠ Ⓔ
3018 Cielo Court, Suite A, 87507
(505) 473-3747

Santa Fe School of Weaving / Miriam's Well Ⓨ Ⓦ Ⓢ
614 Paseo De Peralta, 87501
(505) 982-6312

Yarn & Coffee Ⓔ Ⓨ Ⓝ Ⓦ
1836-B Cerrillos Road, 87505
(505) 780-5030

Silver City

Aunt Judy's Attic Ⓠ
1950 Highway 180 E, 88061
(575) 388-1620

Yada Yada Yarn Ⓨ Ⓦ Ⓢ
621 N. Bullard Street, 88061
(575) 388-3350

Taos

Mooncat Fiber Ⓨ Ⓢ
120 Bent Street, Suite B, 87571
(575) 758-9341

Taos Adobe Quilting Ⓠ Ⓔ Ⓒ
102 Teresina Lane, 87571
(575) 751-3219 or (575) 758-8195

Vortex Yarns Ⓨ Ⓢ
218A Paseo del Pueblo Norte, 87571
(575) 758-1241

Tucumcari

Desert Rose Center, LLC Ⓠ
208 E. Main Street, 88401
(575) 461-2342

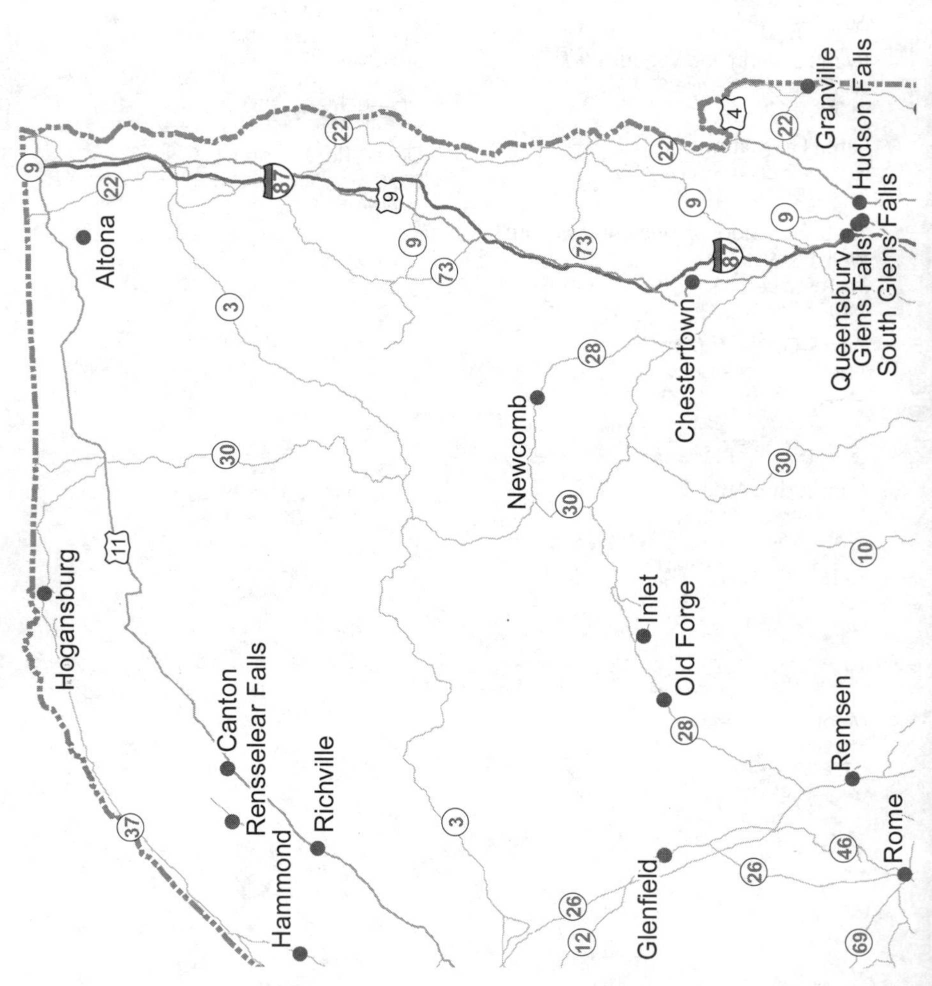
Altona
Hogansburg
Canton
Rensselear Falls
Richville
Hammond
Newcomb
Chestertown
Inlet
Old Forge
Remsen
Rome
Glenfield
Queensbury
Glens Falls
South Glens Falls
Hudson Falls
Granville
9
22
87
3
30
11
37
73
28
10
26
12
46
69
4

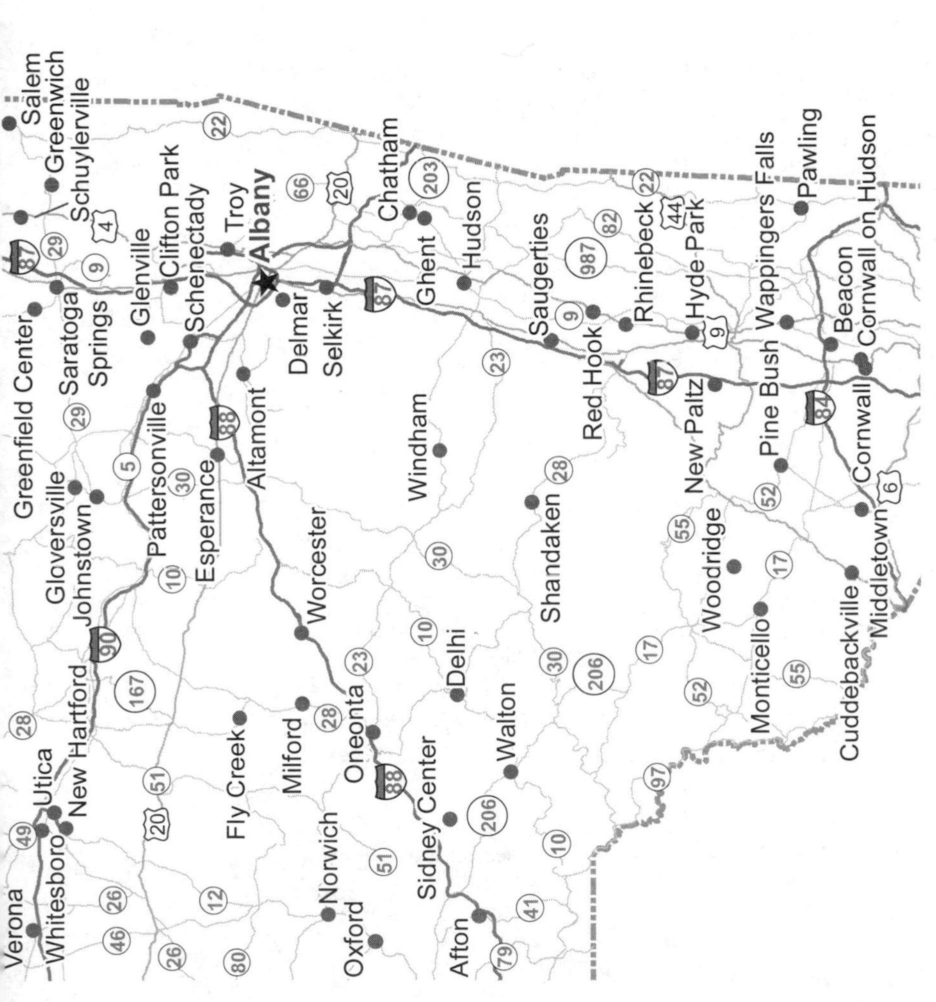
Salem
Greenwich
Schuylerville
Greenfield Center
Saratoga Springs
Glenville
Clifton Park
Schenectady
Troy
Albany
Chatham
Ghent
Hudson
Delmar
Selkirk
Altamont
Esperance
Pattersonville
Gloversville
Johnstown
Worcester
Windham
Saugerties
Rhinebeck
Hyde Park
Red Hook
Wappingers Falls
Pawling
Beacon
Cornwall on Hudson
New Paltz
Pine Bush
Cornwall
Shandaken
Woodridge
Middletown
Cuddebackville
Monticello
Delhi
Walton
Oneonta
Milford
Fly Creek
New Hartford
Utica
Verona
Whitesboro
Norwich
Oxford
Sidney Center
Afton

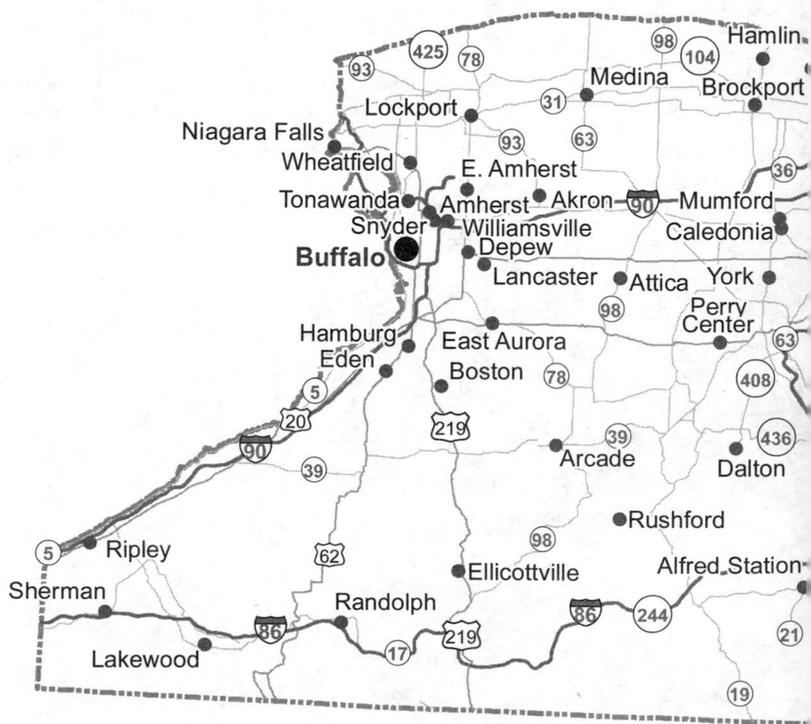
Hamlin
Medina
Brockport
Lockport
Niagara Falls
Wheatfield
E. Amherst
Tonawanda
Amherst
Akron
Mumford
Snyder
Williamsville
Caledonia
Buffalo
Depew
Lancaster
Attica
York
Perry Center
Hamburg
East Aurora
Eden
Boston
Arcade
Dalton
Rushford
Ripley
Ellicottville
Alfred Station
Sherman
Randolph
Lakewood

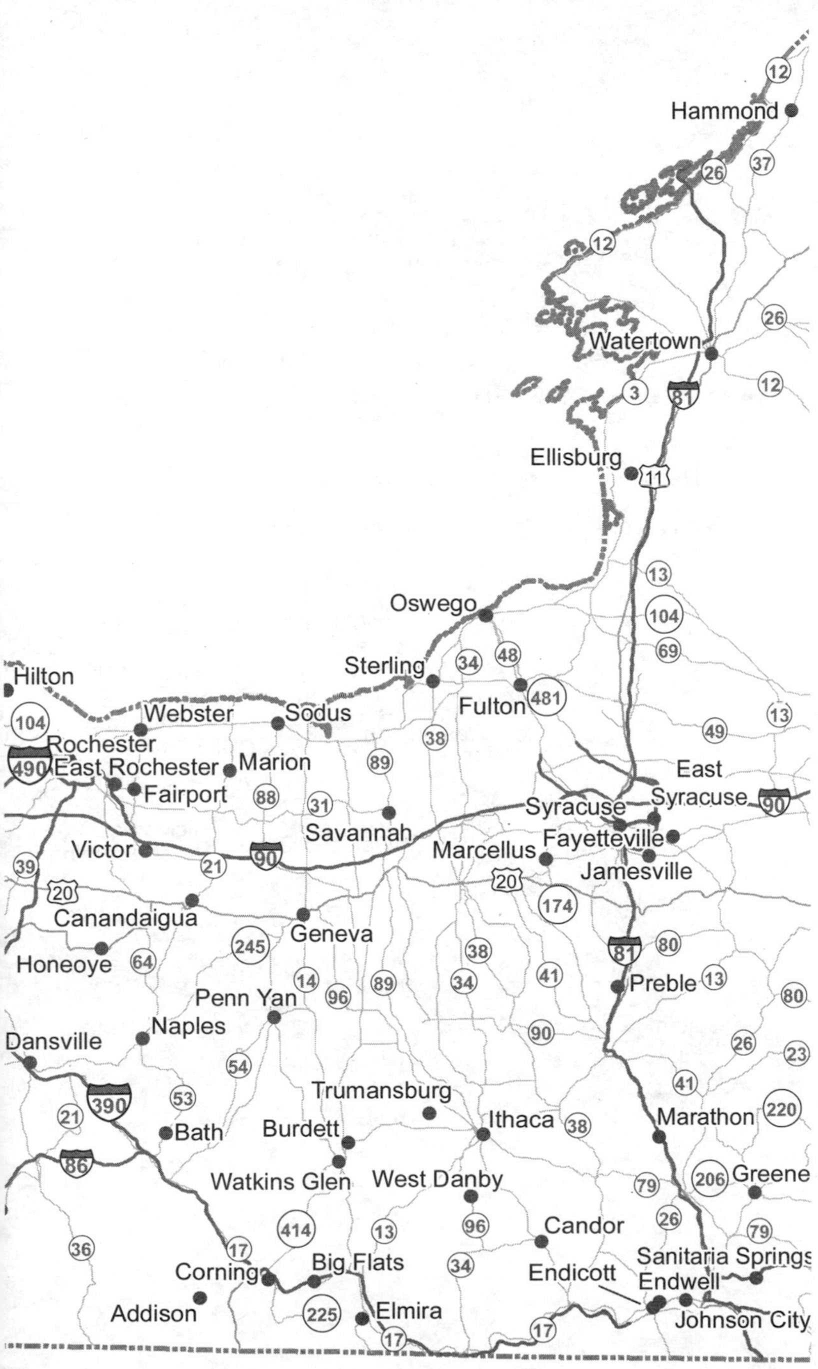
Hammond
Watertown
Ellisburg
Oswego
Sterling
Fulton
Hilton
Webster
Sodus
Rochester
East Rochester
Marion
Fairport
East
Syracuse
Syracuse
Savannah
Fayetteville
Marcellus
Jamesville
Victor
Canandaigua
Geneva
Honeoye
Preble
Penn Yan
Naples
Dansville
Trumansburg
Ithaca
Marathon
Bath
Burdett
Watkins Glen
West Danby
Greene
Candor
Sanitaria Springs
Corning
Big Flats
Endicott
Endwell
Addison
Elmira
Johnson City

Peekskill
Yorktown Heights
Warwick
Mt. Kisco
Nyack
Nanuet
Tarrytown
Pearl River
White Plains
Port Chester
Mamaroneck
Larchmont
East Northport
Huntington
Oyster Bay
S. Huntington
Port Washington
Sea Cliff
Roslyn
Hicksville
Oakland Gardens
Farmingdale
New York
Glendale
Brooklyn
Merrick
Oceanside
Staten Island

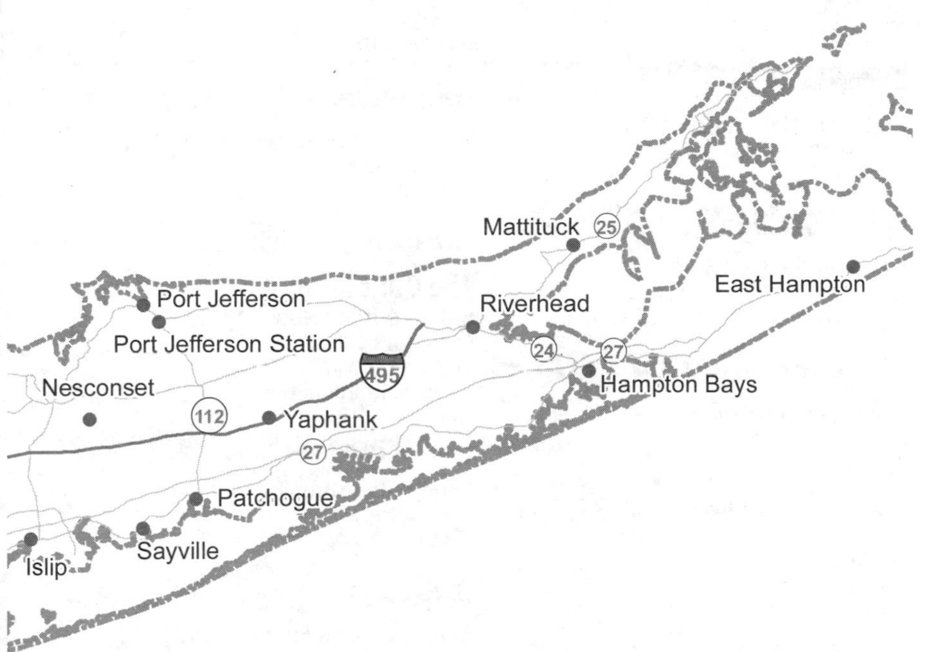

Mattituck
25
Port Jefferson
Riverhead
East Hampton
Port Jefferson Station
24
27
495
Hampton Bays
Nesconset
112
Yaphank
27
Patchogue
Sayville
Islip

New York

Addison

Sew What? Fabric Shoppe Q E M
7 W. Front Street, 14801
(607) 359-4308

Afton

Sew Clever Q E C M
195 State Route 41 S (corner of Co Rd 26), 13730
(607) 639-2460

Akron

Daft Dames Handcrafts* Y W S
13384 Main Road, Route 5, 14001
(716) 542-4235

Alfred Station

Alfred Knitting Studio* Y
569 Main Street, Route 244, 14803
(607) 587-8002

Altamont

Spinning Room Y W S
190 Main Street, 12009
(518) 861-0038

Amherst

Sew What? Q
6816 Main Street, 14221
(716) 632-8801

Arcade

Creekside Fabrics, Quilts & Yarn Q Y
237 Main Street, 14009
(585) 492-4226

Attica

Alpaca Play Pen E Y S
10869 Bowen Road, 14011
(585) 591-2520

Alpaca Play Pen E Y S
10869 Bowen Road, 14011
(585) 591-2520

Bath

Farm Fresh Fabrics Q
8825 State Route 53, 14810
(607) 329-1906

Beacon

Beetle and Fred Q E Y
171 Main Street, 12508
(845) 440-8867

Loopy Mango Y
500 Main Street, 12508
(845) 765-2476

Big Flats

The Witch's Stitches Q E Y N C M
18 Canal Street, 14814
(607) 358-4016

Boston

The Quilt Farm Q
5623 Feddick Road, 14025
(716) 941-3140
TuTh 11-7, WFSa 11-5
www.quiltfarm.net

Brockport

Country Treasures Q
61 Main Street, 14420
(585) 637-5148

Brooklyn

Ambiance Art & Framing Ltd. N
4906 13th Avenue, 11219
(718) 438-4664

Argyle Yarn Shop E Y W
288 Prospect Park W, 11215
(347) 227-7799

B & E Yarn E Y N C
784 Manhattan Avenue, 11222
(718) 383-8907

Brooklyn General Store Q E Y N S C M
128 Union Street, 11231
(718) 237-7753

Lana Fabrics Q E Y N
909 Kings Highway, 11223
(718) 339-8940

M & M Yarn Connection Ⓨ
1766 46th Street, 11204
(718) 436-5262

Sew Beary Special Ⓠ
1025 E. 28th Street, 11210
(718) 951-3973

Slip Stitch Needlecraft* Ⓨ Ⓝ
450 Nostrand Avenue, 11216
(347) 789-5371

SM Stitches Ⓝ
335 Avenue U, 11223
(917) 325-4435

String Thing Studio Ⓨ Ⓦ
54 7th Avenue, 11217
(929) 337-6130

The Book Mark Shoppe Ⓨ
8415 3rd Avenue, 11209
(718) 833-5115

Woolyn Ⓨ Ⓦ Ⓢ
105 Atlantic Avenue, 11201
(718) 522-5820

Burdett

Graceful Arts Fiber Studio Ⓔ Ⓨ Ⓦ Ⓢ
4760 State Route 414, 14818
(607) 546-8344

Caledonia

Chestnut Bay Quilting Ⓠ
262 North Street, 14423
(585) 538-4420

Canandaigua

Expressions In NeedleArt Ⓔ Ⓨ Ⓝ Ⓒ
110 S. Main Street, 14424
(585) 394-4870

Liberty Cottage Ⓠ Ⓔ Ⓨ
4390 Middle Cheshire Road, 14424
(585) 393-1070

Candor

Pucky Huddle Delight Ⓠ
71 Owego Road, 13743
(607) 659-7743

Canton

The Celtic Knot Textiles Ⓠ Ⓔ Ⓨ Ⓝ Ⓢ Ⓒ
17 Main Street, 13617
(315) 714-3206

The Fabric Corner Ⓠ
589 Pollock Road, 13617
(315) 386-3082

Chatham

The Warm Ewe Ⓠ Ⓔ Ⓨ
31 Main Street, 12037
(518) 392-2929

Chestertown

Country Girl Quilt Shop Ⓠ
6328 Route 9, 12817
(518) 494-2299

Clifton Park

Darn Good Yarn Ⓠ Ⓨ Ⓦ Ⓢ
11 a Solar Drive, 12065
(518) 831-1073 or (518) 377-1177

Corning

Wooly Minded Ⓨ
91 E. Market Street, Suite 102, 14830
(607) 973-2885

Cornwall

Cornwall Yarn Shop Ltd. Ⓨ
227 Main Street, 12518
(845) 534-0383

Cornwall on Hudson

Hudson Valley Quilt & Sew Ⓠ
1 Idlewild Avenue, #2, 12520
(845) 534-7300

Cuddebackville

Bonnie's Kozy Knit Ⓠ Ⓨ Ⓝ
300 State Route 211, 12729
(845) 754-0700

Dalton

Journey Quilt Company* Ⓠ
9630 Chidsey Road, 14836
(585) 476-2630

Dansville

Material Rewards Ⓠ
10160 Sandy Hill Road, 14437
(585) 335-2050

Delhi

The Yarn Shop* ⓎⓌⓈ
3428 Peakes Brook Road, 13753
(607) 746-3316

Delmar

Amelia's Garden Ⓠ
340 Delaware Avenue, 12054
(518) 439-4614

Depew

Sew On-Sew Forth ⓆⒺⓂ
6152 Transit Road, 14043
(716) 684-4880

East Amherst

Patchwork Garden ⓆⒺ
6281 Transit Road, 14051
(716) 810-9088

East Aurora

Aurora Sewing Center ⓆⒺⓂ
659 Main Street, 14052
(716) 652-2811
M-F 10-5:30, Sa 10-4, Su 12-4
www.aurorasewingcenter.com

The Carriage Quilt Shoppe Ⓠ
586 Main Street, 14052
(716) 655-4561

Vidler's 5 & 10 ⓆⒺⓎⒸ
676-694 Main Street, 14052
(716) 652-0481

East Hampton

Black Sheep Knitworks Ⓨ
47 Newton Lane, 11937
(631) 527-5800

East Northport

Pieceful Quilting* Q E M
3027 Jericho Turnpike, 11731
(631) 670-6254

East Rochester

Golden Thread Needlearts E N C
349 W. Commercial Street, Suite 1250, 14445
(585) 248-3869

The Village Yarn & Fiber Shop Y S
350 W. Commercial Street, 14445
(585) 586-5470

East Syracuse

Pick Your Stitch, LLC Q M
6701 Manlius Center Road, 13057
(315) 437-0962

Eden

Marie's Sewing Center Q E M
➡ SEE AD AT LEFT
8386 N. Main Street, 14057
(716) 992-4364
Tu-F 10-5, Sa 10-3
www.mariessewingcenter.com

Ellicottville

The Ellicottville Quilt Shop Q
19 Jefferson Street, 14731
(716) 699-2065

Ellisburg

The Old Creamery Fabrics & Quilting Q M
12022 State Route 193, 13636
(315) 846-5393

Elmira

Stephanie's Yarns Y
729 Kinyon Street, 14904
(607) 426-1980

Endicott

Patchwork Angels Quilt Shop Q M
➡ SEE AD BELOW
307 W. Main Street, 13760
(607) 748-0682
MThF 11-8, TuW 11-5, Sa 9:30-4
www.patchworkangels.com

Stitchery Row E N C
55 Washington Avenue, 13760
(607) 786-7768
WF 10-4, Th 10-6, Sa 10-3
www.stitcheryrow.com

Endwell

Yarns N' More* E Y W S
2605 E. Main Street, 13760
(607) 786-9276

Esperance

CeCe's Wool Y S
169 Main Street, 12066
(518) 779-9985

Fairport

Yarn Culture Y
1387 Fairport Road, #885, 14450
(585) 678-4894
Winter: W-F 11-5, Sa 10-4, Su please call ahead; Summer: W-F 11-5, Sa 10-4
www.yarnculture.com

Sew Creative Q M
650 Whitney, Suite B, 14450
(585) 388-0230

Farmingdale

Infinite Yarns, Inc. Ⓨ
34 Hempstead Turnpike, 11735
(516) 293-0010

Fayetteville

A Stitcher's Garden ⒺⒸ
7070 Cedar Bay Road, 13066
(315) 449-2181

Fly Creek

Heartworks Quilts And Fabrics ⓆⓂ
6237 State Highway 28, 13337
(607) 547-2501

Fulton

The Robin's Nest Quilt Shop & More Ⓠ
111 W. Broadway, 13069
(315) 598-1170 or (315) 529-5354

Geneva

Quilty Pleasures Ⓠ
492 Exchange Street, 14456
(315) 325-4248

Ghent

Turose ⒺⓎⒸ
330-B County Route 21C, 12075
(518) 672-0052

Glendale

Cooks Arts & Crafts Shoppe ⒺⓎⓃⓌⒸ
80-09 Myrtle Avenue, 11385
(718) 366-6085

Glenfield

Sew Crazy Fabric Shop Ⓠ
5146 State Route 12, 13343
(315) 376-7630
MTh 9-5, TuWF 1-6, Sa 10-3
www.sewcrazyfabrics.com

Glens Falls

Patti's Sewing Machines & More ⓆⓂ
485 Glen Street (Route 9), 12801
(518) 409-4533

Glenville

The Joyful Quilter ⓆⓂ
19 Glenridge Road, Unit A, 12302
(518) 399-0128

Gloversville

Gloversville Sewing Center ⓆⒺⓂ
➡ SEE AD AT RIGHT
385 S. Main Street, 12078
(518) 725-4919
M-F 9-5:30, Sa 9-5; Sa 9-4 (Memorial Day-Labor Day)
www.gloversvillesewingcenter.com

Granville

Village Yarn Shop Ⓨ
4 E. Main Street, 12832
(518) 796-3188

Greene

Creative Threads ⓆⒺ
604 Jackson Hill Road, 13778
(607) 656-8883

Greenfield Center

General Bailey Homestead Farm* ⓎⓌⓈ
340 Spier Falls Road, 12833
(518) 893-2015

Greenwich

Battenkill Fibers Carding & Spinning Mill ⓎⓈ
2532 State Route 40, 12834
(518) 692-2700

Hamburg

Embraceable Ewe Knitter Retreat Ⓨ
213 Main Street, 14075
(716) 646-6674

Hamlin

The Fiber Factory ⒺⓎ
408 Drake Road, 14464
(585) 709-5099

Hammond

Phoenix Fabric * Q
1251 County Road 6, 13646
(315) 324-5462

Hampton Bays

Rainbow Yarns & Needlecraft Shoppe E Y N C
13 Ponquogue Avenue, 11946
(631) 728-3085

Hicksville

Gone Sewin Q
161-D Levittown Parkway, 11801
(516) 342-1127

Hilton

Amelia's Fabric & Yarn Shoppe Q Y
7 Upton Street, 14468
(585) 392-1192

Hogansburg

Dreamcrafters Quilt Shop Q
1422 State Route 37, 13655
(518) 358-4285

Honeoye

Honeoye Craft Lab* Y S
6 Honeoye Commons, 14471
(802) 342-6342

Hudson

Countrywool Q Y W S
59 Spring Road, 12534
(518) 828-4554

Hudson Falls

Serenity Stitches Y
315 Main Street, 12839
(518) 741-6561

Huntington

Rumpelstiltskin Yarns Ⓨ Ⓦ Ⓢ
269 Main Street, 11743
(631) 824-6688

The Knitting Garden Ⓨ
49 Green Street, 11743
(631) 923-3222

Hyde Park

Deer Hill Farm Cross Stitching Ⓒ
➡ SEE AD BELOW
1225 Route 9G, Suite D
Country Plaza, 12538
(845) 229-0246
TuWF 10-5, Th 10-7, Sa 10-4
www.facebook.com/
DeerHillFarmCrossStitching/

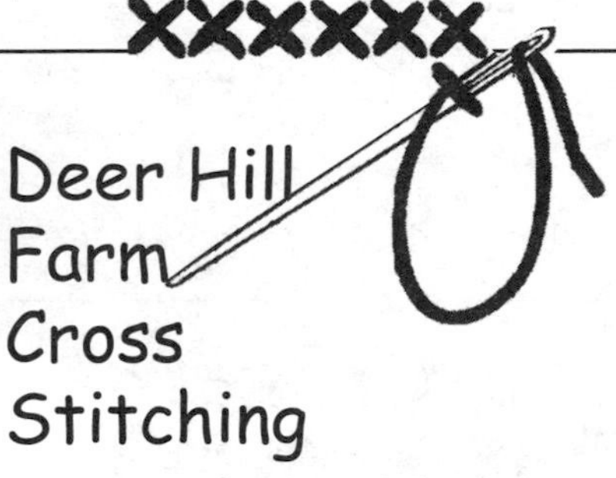

Inlet

Crazy Moose Quilt Shop Ⓠ
115 Route 28, 13360
(315) 357-5092

Islip

Sew What's New and Yarn Too! Ⓠ Ⓨ Ⓜ
400 Main Street, 11751
(631) 277-4215
Handi Quilter® Authorized Retailer
Designed by a Quilter, for Quilters.®

Ithaca

Quilters Corner Ⓠ Ⓜ
518 W. State / MLK Jr. Street, 14850
(607) 266-0850

Jamesville

Yarn Cupboard Ⓨ Ⓦ Ⓢ
6487 E. Seneca Turnpike, 13078
(315) 399-5148

Jamesville (Syracuse)

Yarn Cupboard Ⓨ Ⓦ Ⓢ
6487 E. Seneca Turnpike, 13078
(315) 399-5148

Johnson City

Southern Tier Sewing Center Ⓠ Ⓜ
800 Valley Plaza Drive, 13790
(607) 797-7022

Johnstown

At Home Quilting (Quilters Stash Store) Ⓠ Ⓜ
22 S. Perry Street, 12095
(518) 774-0475

Lakewood

Quilters' Haven Ⓠ Ⓔ Ⓨ
167 W. Fairmount Avenue, 14750
(716) 763-0342

Lancaster

From the Attic* Ⓨ
39 Central Avenue, 14086
(716) 395-3297

Simple Pleasures & Homespun Treasures Ⓠ
5300 William Street, 14086
(716) 359-5038

Larchmont

Stitch By Stitch Ⓝ
1971 Palmer Avenue, 10538
(914) 834-1886

Lockport

Marie's Sewing Center ⓆⒺⓂ
➡ SEE AD PAGE 390
6310 Robinson Road, 14094
(716) 434-2583
M-F 10-5, Sa 10-3, and Labor Day-Memorial Day, Th evenings by appt.
www.mariessewingcenter.com

Niagara Alpaca Shop* Ⓨ
7403 Tonawanda Creek Road, 14094
(716) 439-4551

Mamaroneck

Knit Shoppe Ⓨ
501 E. Boston Post Road, 10543
(914) 630-7647

Marathon

The Fabric Patch Quilt Shop* Ⓠ
5 W. Main Street, 13803
(607) 849-3611

Marcellus

Patchwork Plus ⓆⓂ
2532 Cherry Valley Turnpike, US Route 20, 13108
(315) 673-2208

Marion

Bead & Fiber Fantasy* ⓎⓈ
4849 Cory Corners Road, 14505
(315) 926-5765

Mattituck

Altman's NeedleArts ⒺⓎⓃⒸ
195 Love Lane, 11952
(631) 298-7181
MTuW 10-6, Th 10-8, FSa 10-5
www.altmansneedlearts.com

Medina

A Knitters Corner Ⓨ
111 W. Center Street, 14103
(585) 798-5648

Merrick

The Needlepaint Nook* Ⓝ
2110 Merrick Mall, 11566
(516) 623-0250

Middletown

Ekker Vac & Sew ⓆⒺ
150 Carpenter Avenue, 10940
(845) 343-0925

Milford

Sybil's Yarn Shop ⓎⓈ
65 South Main, 13807
(607) 286-4061

Monticello

Knit One Needlepoint Too ⒺⓎⓃⒸ
366 E. Broadway, 12701
(800) 791-5650 or (845) 791-5648

Mt. Kisco

Pick Up Every Stitch* Ⓨ
200 E. Main Street, 10514
(914) 864-2828

Pins and Needles ⓆⓂ
159 Lexington Avenue, 10549
(914) 666-0824

Mumford

Woolen Stitches At The Genesee Country Inn Ⓨ
948 George Street, 14511
(585) 538-2500
W-Sa 11-5
http://www.geneseecountryinn.com

Nanuet

Above and Beyond Creative Sewing ⓆⓂ
38 N. Middletown Road, 10954
(845) 623-4313

Naples

Carriage House Quilts* Ⓠ
201 N. Main Street, 14512
(585) 374-9580

Nesconset

Keep Me In Needlepoint Ⓝ
127-14 Smithtown Blvd., 11767
(631) 724-1440

New Paltz

White Barn Farm Sheep & Wool* ⓎⓌⓈ
815 Albany Post Road, 12561
(914) 456-6040

New York

Lion Brand Yarn Studio ⓎⓌⓈ
➡ SEE AD PAGE 328
34 W. 15th Street, 10011
(212) 243-9070
MTuW 11:30-7, Th 11:30-8, F 10-4, Su 11:30-5
www.lionbrandyarnstudio.com

Annie & Company Needlepoint & Knitting ⓎⓃⒸ
1763 2nd Avenue, 10128
(212) 360-7266 or (212) 289-2944

B & J Fabrics Ⓠ
525 7th Avenue, 2nd Floor, 10018
(212) 354-8150

Downtown Yarns ⒺⓎⓈ
45 Avenue A, 10009
(212) 995-5991

Gotham Quilts* ⓆⒺⓂ
40-B W 37th Street, 10018
(212) 220-3958

Knitting 321* Ⓨ
321 E. 75th Street, 10021
(212) 772-2020

Knitty City ⓎⓈ
208 W. 79th Street, 10024
(212) 787-5896

Loop Of The Loom ⓎⓌⓈ
227 E. 87th Street, Suite E, 10128
(212) 722-2686

Purl Soho ⓆⒺⓎⓃⓌⓈⒸ
459 Broome Street, 10013
(212) 420-8796

Rita's Needlepoint Ⓝ
150 E. 79th Street, 10075
(212) 737-8613

School Products Yarn Shop ⓎⓌ
13 E. 37th Street, 10016
(212) 679-3516

Seaport Yarn Ⓨ
181 Broadway, 4th Floor, 10007
(212) 220-5230

String Yarns Ⓨ
144 E. 74th Street, 2nd Floor, 10021
(212) 288-9276

Vardhman, Inc. ⒺⓎⓃⓈⒸ
269 W. 39th Street, 10018
(212) 840-6950

Victoria Findlay Wolfe Quilts Ⓠ
325 W. 38th Street, Suite 803, 10018
(718) 877-6710

Newcomb

Aunt Polly's Material Girls ⓆⒺⓎⓃⒸ
3 Hudson River Road, 12852
(518) 582-2260
M-Sa 9-5, Su by appt.
www.auntpollysmaterialgirls.com

Niagara Falls

Quiltmakers & Friends Q
6404 Packard Road, 14304
(716) 297-4067
Tu 10-2:30, WF 10-8:30, Th 10-4:30, Sa 10-3
www.facebook.com/quiltmakersandfriends/

Auntie's Attic Quilt Shop Q
1995 Military Road, 14304
(716) 297-3636

Norwich

Sew Nice Q
6142 State Highway 12, 13815
(607) 334-2477

Nyack

Knitting Nation* Y S
30 N. Broadway, 10960
(845) 348-0100

The Quilt Tree Q M
9 S. Broadway, 10960
(845) 353-1501

Oakland Gardens

Sew Right Sewing Machines Q E M
223-20 Union Turnpike, 11364
(718) 468-5858

Sewtime Sewing Centers Q M
7835 Springfield Blvd., 11364
(718) 776-1900

Oceanside

The Knitting Store LLC Y
2 Poole Street, 11572
(516) 442-0722

Old Forge

Old Forge Hardware Y
104 Fulton Street, 13420
(315) 369-6100

Oneonta

Country Fabrics and Quilts Q
6187 State Highway 23, 13820
(607) 432-9726

Oswego

Quilt With Passion Q M
142 W. 2nd Street, 13126
(315) 207-0008

Oxford

Shadyside Fibers LLC Y S
109 Brown Road, 13830
(607) 843-8243 or (877) 320-8243

Oyster Bay

The Knitted Purl Y
80 South Street, 11771
(516) 558-7800

Patchogue

112 Sewing Supplies, Inc. Q M
142 Route 112, 11772
(631) 475-8282

Pattersonville

A Touch Of Twist Y W S
1286 Weast Road, 12137
(518) 864-5885

Pawling

Yarn & Craft Box E Y N C
24 Charles Colman Blvd., 12564
(845) 855-1632
MTuWF 10-5:30, Th 10-7:30, Sa 10-4:30
www.yarnandcraftbox.com

Pearl River

The Stitchery Y N
49 E. Central Avenue, 10965
(845) 735-4534
MTuThF 10-6, Sa 10-5
www.thestitcheryny.com

Peekskill

Cozy Corner Yarn Shop Y N
116 Washington Street, 10566
(914) 737-0179

Penn Yan

Golden Lane Fabrics Ⓠ Ⓔ Ⓒ
3732 State Route 14A, 14527
(315) 536-8342
M-F 8-5, Sa 8-4

Country Quest Ⓠ
2358 Bellona Station Road, 14527
(315) 536-4878

Edgewood Country Store Ⓠ Ⓔ
1427 Voak Road, 14527
(315) 536-7562

Perry Center

The Quilter's Daughter Ⓠ
2817 State Route 246, 14530
(585) 770-4926

Pine Bush

Quilter's Attic Sewing Center Ⓠ Ⓜ
118 Maple Avenue (Route 302), 12566
(845) 744-5888

Port Chester

The Nimble Thimble, Inc. Ⓠ Ⓨ Ⓜ
21 Putnam Avenue, 10573
(914) 934-2934

Port Jefferson

Knitting Cove & Yarn Shop* Ⓨ
116 E. Main Street, 11777
(631) 473-2121

Port Jefferson Station

Beyond The Thimble Quilting Center Ⓠ Ⓜ
Call for new address, 11776
(631) 737-3944

Port Washington

The Knitting Place Ⓨ
191 Main Street, 11050
(516) 944-9276

Preble

A Kaleidoscope Of Quilts* Ⓠ
6720 Little York Lake Road, 13141
(607) 749-2628

Queensbury

Heirloom Sewing Center & Quilt Shop* Ⓠ
820 State Route 9, Suite 2A, 12804
(518) 761-6619

Wynter Haven Quilt Studio Ⓠ Ⓜ
4 S. Western Avenue, 12804
(518) 792-2077

Randolph

Yarn For Ewe* Ⓨ
129 Main Street, 14772
(716) 267-2070

Red Hook

Hudson Valley Sheep & Wool Company Ⓨ Ⓦ Ⓢ
190 Yantz Road, 12571
(845) 758-3130

The Village Fabric Shoppe Ⓠ Ⓔ
7578 N. Broadway, Suite 4, 12571
(845) 758-8541

Remsen

WoolHaven Yarn & Fiber Shop* Ⓨ Ⓢ
10071 Bardwell Mills Road, 13438
(315) 794-3769

Rensselear Falls

Susan's Stitches Ⓠ Ⓨ
216B Rensselear Street, 13680
(315) 344-5043

Rhinebeck

The Knitting Garage At Stickles Ⓔ Ⓨ
13 E. Market Street, 12572
(845) 876-3206

Richville

Hart Country Fabrics* Ⓠ
115 County Route 20, 13681
(315) 287-3250

Ripley

Concord Quilting Studio Ⓠ
9009 Old Route 20, 14775
(716) 753-6996

Riverhead

Riverhead Vacuum and Sewing Center Q M
31 E. Main Street, 11901
(631) 727-1550

Rochester

Discount Sewing Center & Jackie Lynn's Fabric Center Q M
475 E. Ridge Road, 14621
(585) 544-4110 or (585) 336-9280

The Black Purl Y S
274 N. Goodman Street, 14607
(585) 309-7871

Rome

Carol's Crafts E Y N C
1245 Erie Blvd. W, 13440
(315) 336-3785

Stash Away Quilt Shoppe LLC Q
1249 Erie Blvd. W, 13440
(315) 533-7611

Roslyn

KNIT Y
1353 Old Northern Blvd., 11576
(516) 625-5648

Rushford

The Barefoot Quilter Q
9005 Main Street, 14777
(585) 437-2241

S. Huntington

Knitting On The Lamb Y N W
456 E. Jericho Turnpike, 11746
(631) 271-9276

Salem

Fiber Kingdom Y W S
137 E. Broadway, 12865
(518) 854-7225

Simple Pleasures Farm Y W S
588 Chamberlain Mill Road, 12865
(518) 744-8586

The Quilting Beaver Q E Y
217 Main Street, 12865
(518) 605-2445

Sanitaria Springs

Quilted Crow Fabric & Quilt Shop Q
54 Cafferty Road, 13787
(607) 648-8956

Saratoga Springs

Gloversville Sewing Center Q E M
➡ SEE AD PAGE 393
426 Maple Avenue, 12866
(518) 584-2695
M-F 9:30-5:30, Sa 9:30-5, Sa 9:30-4 (Memorial Day-Labor Day)
www.gloversvillesewingcenter.com

Common Thread Saratoga Y W S
512 Broadway, 12866
(518) 583-2583

KC Framing and Fabrics Q E M
67 Davidson Drive, 12866
(518) 580-9055

Stitches & Time Q
945 Route 29 E, 12866
(518) 695-5643

Saugerties

Pinewoods Farm - Wool Shop Y W S C
71 Phillips Road, 12477
(845) 246-2203

The Perfect Blend Yarn And Tea Shop Y
50 Market Street, 12477
(845) 246-2876

Savannah

Spring Lake Fabrics Q E Y N C
4250 Wolcott Spring Lake Road, 13146
(315) 594-8485

Sayville

Patchworks Q
299 Raft Avenue J5, 11782
(631) 589-4187

Rumpelstiltskin Yarns Y W S
22 Main Street, 11782
(631) 750-1790

Schenectady

Quiltbug.com Ⓠ
3637 Carman Road, 12303
(518) 280-2586

Schuylerville

The Yarn Shop at Foster Sheep Farm ⓎⓈ
460 W. River Road, 12871
(518) 338-6679

Sea Cliff

Sea Cliff Stitchery* Ⓝ
70 8th Avenue, 11579
(516) 320-1789

Selkirk

Log Cabin Fabrics ⓆⒺ
1145 Route 9W, 12158
(518) 767-2040
MWF 10-6, TuTh 10-8, Sa 10-4, Su 12-4
www.logcabinfabrics.com

Shandaken

Mountain Yarns ⓎⓌⓈ
560 Rt 42, 12480
(845) 750-9295

Sherman

Fabric Outlet Barn / Needle in a Haystack Retreat ⓆⓂ
3141 North Road, 14781
(716) 769-7878
Winter: M-Sa 10-3; Summer: M-Sa 10-4
www.fabricoutletbarn.com

Sidney Center

The Fieldstone House* Ⓠ
1884 Wheat Hill Road, 13839
(607) 369-9177

Snyder

Have Ewe Any Wool? Ⓨ
4551 Main Street, 14226
(716) 839-7800

Sodus

The Quilting Bee Ⓠ
10 Maple Avenue, 14551
(315) 553-2383

South Glens Falls

Adirondack Quilts LLC ⓆⒺⓂ
22 5th Street, 12803
(518) 615-0134

Staten Island

Crafting on the Plaza with M&M ⓆⓃ
40 Hillview Place, 10304
(718) 501-7402

The Naked Sheep ⓎⓌⓈ
4038 Victory Blvd., 10314
(718) 477-9276

Sterling

Maplegrove Wool Boutique ⓎⓈ
1275 State Route 104A, 13156
(315) 947-5408

Syracuse

Calico Gals ⓆⒺⓂ
3906 New Court Avenue, 13206
(315) 445-0617

Knitty Gritty Yarns Ⓨ
1153 W. Fayette Street, 13204
(315) 472-9276

Seams Possible Quilt Shoppe & Sew Much More Ⓠ
506 Vine Street, 13203
(315) 314-7829

The 12th Stitch Quilts ⓆⓂ
5996 E. Molloy Road, 13211
(315) 433-2387

Tarrytown

Flying Fingers Ⓨ
15 Main Street, 10591
(877) 359-4648 or (914) 631-4113

Troy

Kathleen's Fiber Arts Y W S
212 River Street, 12180
(518) 326-0919.

Pookie's Fabrics Q
615 Pawling Avenue, 12180
(518) 272-6479

Trumansburg

Homespun Boutique Q Y W
51 E. Main Street, 14886
(607) 387-7786

Utica

Tiger Lily Quilt Co. Q
809 Court Street, 13502
(315) 735-5328

Handi Quilter® Authorized Retailer
Designed by a Quilter, for Quilters.®

Verona

Liberty Ridge Yarns Y W S
6175 Greenway Lowell Road, 13478
(315) 337-7217

Victor

Ivy Thimble Quilt & Gift Shop Q
11 Framark Drive, 14564
(585) 742-2680

Walton

Yarn Over Crafts and Hobbies Q Y
22 North Street, 13856
(607) 287-0083

Wappingers Falls

Quilt Basket Q M
942 Route 376, 12590
(845) 227-7606

Handi Quilter® Authorized Retailer
Designed by a Quilter, for Quilters.®

Warwick

Sew-cology, Inc. Q M
28 Ronald Reagan Blvd., 10990
(845) 987-8435

Watertown

Gunns Country Corner* Q
29606 State Route 12, 13601
(315) 658-2828

Just Threads Q
22440 Swan Road, 13601
(315) 782-1674

Watkins Glen

FiberArts in the Glen Y W S
315 N. Franklin Street, 14891
(607) 535-9710

Webster

Cafe Sewciety Quilts* Q
2126 Empire Blvd., 14580
(585) 347-4852

West Danby

Susan's Spinning Bunny Y W S
311B Tupper Road, 14883
(607) 227-1216

Wheatfield

Raveloe Fibers Y W S
7296 Schultz Road at Niagara Falls Blvd., 14120
(716) 692-0052 or (716) 830-8562

White Plains

Sewing Machines Q E Y N W C M
200 Hamilton Avenue, 10601
(914) 682-0595

Whitesboro

Love and Stitches Y
214 Oriskany Blvd., 13492
(315) 570-3316

Williamsville

Aurora Sewing Center Ⓠ Ⓔ Ⓜ
8575 Main Street, 14221
(716) 204-8350
M-F 10-5:30, Sa 10-4, Su 12-4
http://www.aurorasewingcenter.com

Windham

The Patchwork Co. Ⓠ
5326 State Route 23, 12496
(518) 734-6838

Woodridge

Needlepoint Gallery & More Ⓔ Ⓝ Ⓒ
51 Broadway, 12789
(845) 434-1834

Worcester

The Quilt Zoo Ⓠ
88 Main Street, 12197
(607) 397-9047

Yaphank

Long Island Yarn & Farm Ⓨ Ⓢ
125 Gerard Road, 11980
(631) 924-8110 or (631) 680-6721
By appt. only
www.liyarnandfarm.com

York

Mt. Pleasant Quilting Company Ⓠ
2877 Mt. Pleasant Road, 14592
(585) 243-0767

Yorktown Heights

Fabric Mart - NY Ⓠ Ⓜ
2019 Crompond Road, 10598
(914) 962-3328

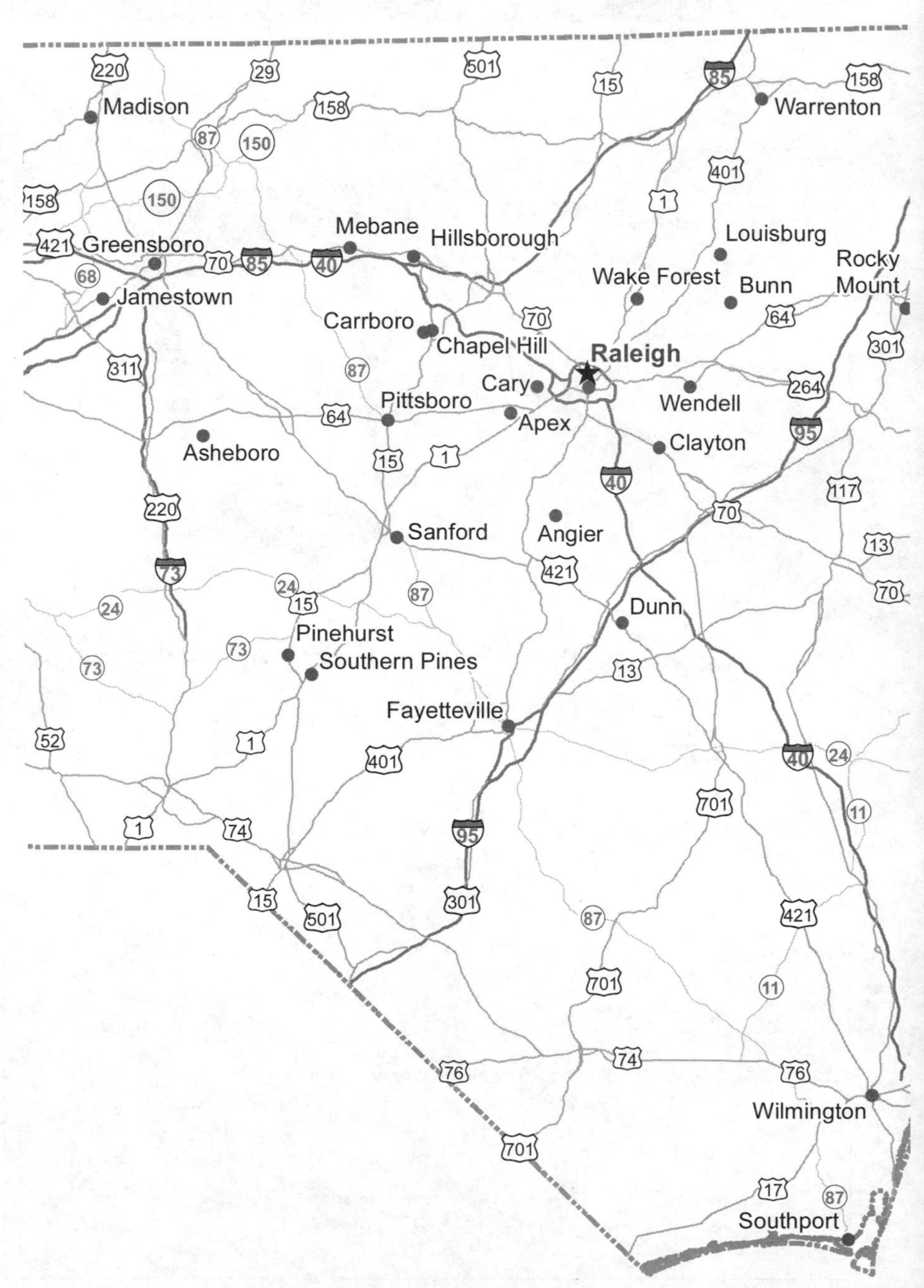
Madison
Warrenton
Mebane
Hillsborough
Louisburg
Greensboro
Rocky Mount
Wake Forest
Bunn
Jamestown
Carrboro
Chapel Hill
Raleigh
Cary
Pittsboro
Wendell
Apex
Asheboro
Clayton
Sanford
Angier
Dunn
Pinehurst
Southern Pines
Fayetteville
Wilmington
Southport

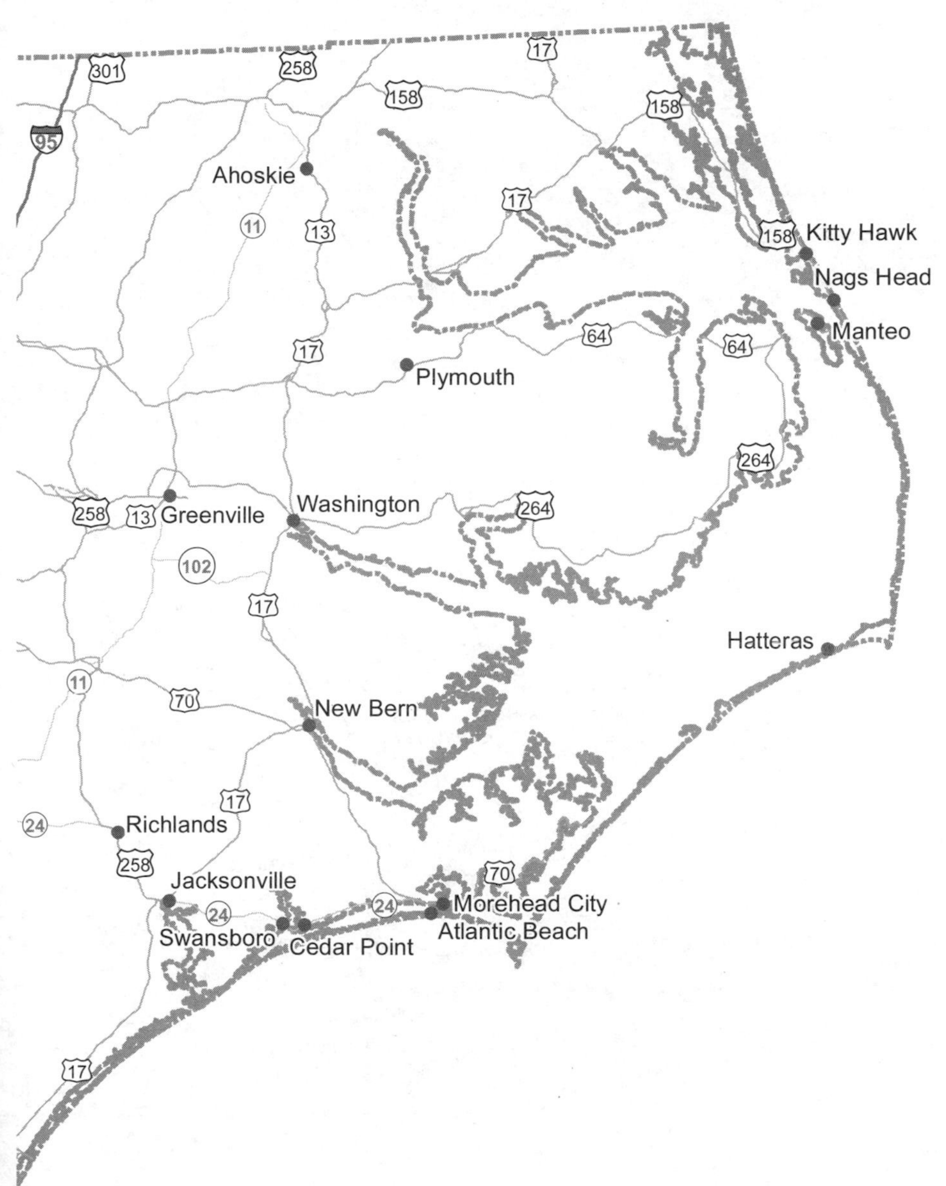
301
258
17
158
158
95
Ahoskie
11
13
17
Kitty Hawk
Nags Head
Manteo
64
64
17
Plymouth
264
258
13
Greenville
Washington
264
102
17
Hatteras
11
70
New Bern
17
24
Richlands
258
Jacksonville
70
24
24
Morehead City
Swansboro
Cedar Point
Atlantic Beach
17

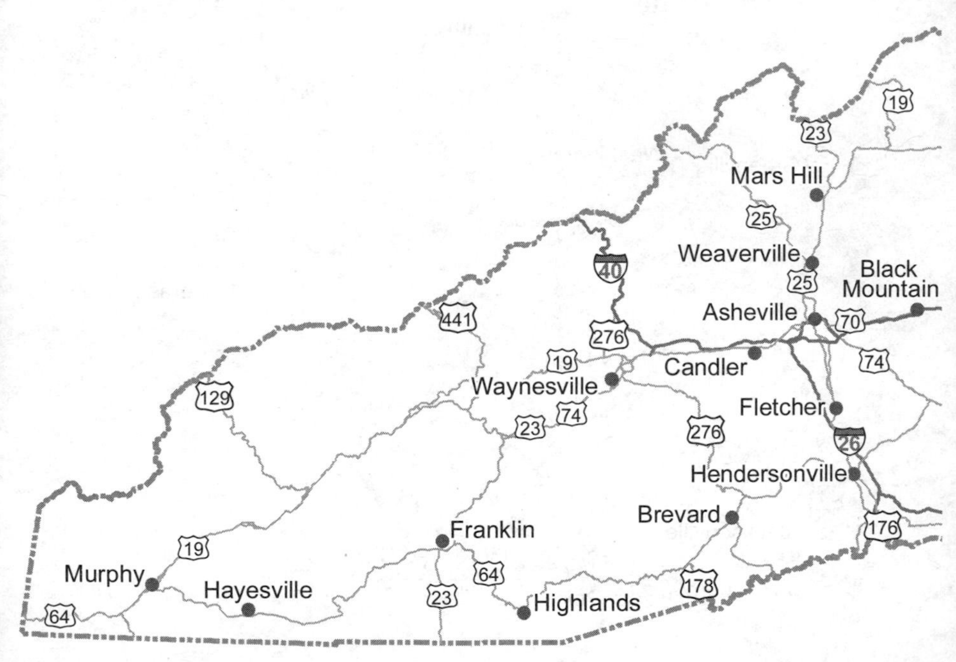
19
23
Mars Hill
25
Weaverville
40
Black
Mountain
25
Asheville
70
441
276
Candler
19
74
Waynesville
129
74
Fletcher
23
276
26
Hendersonville
Brevard
176
Franklin
19
64
Murphy
Hayesville
178
23
Highlands
64

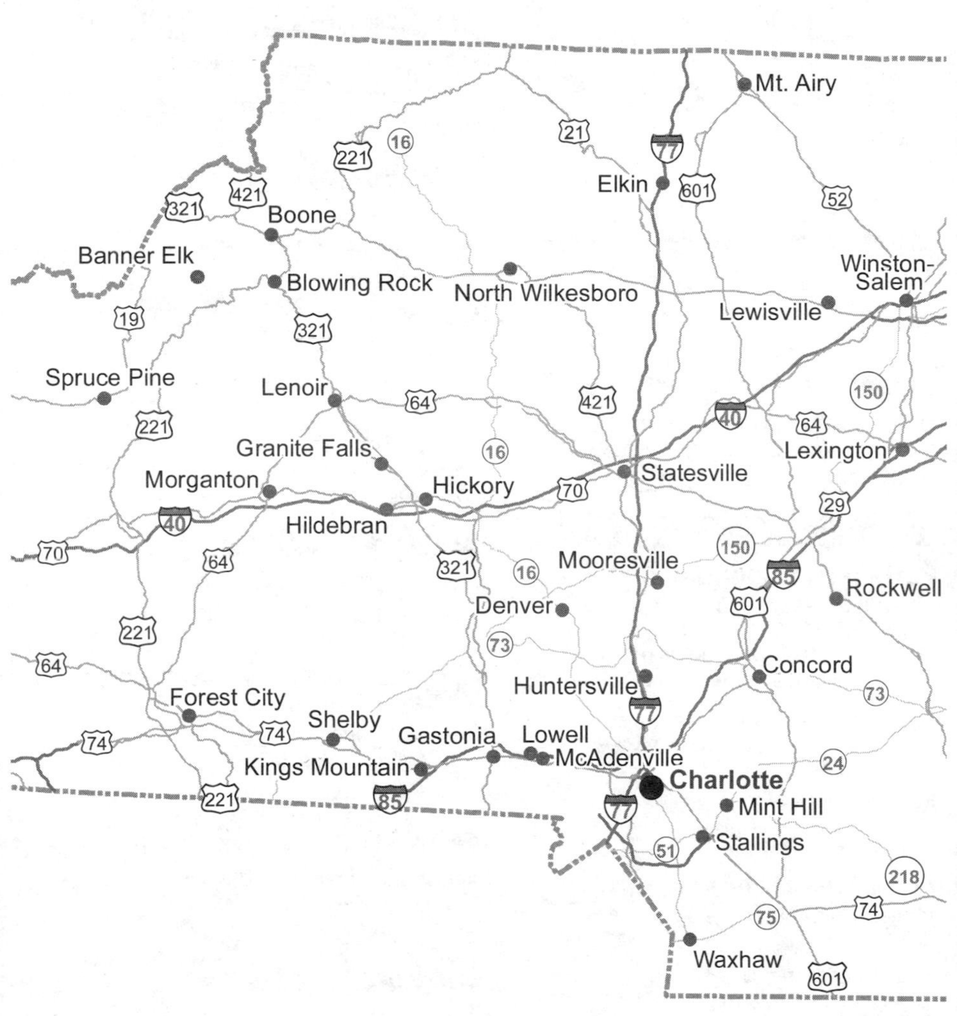
Mt. Airy
Elkin
Boone
Banner Elk
Blowing Rock
North Wilkesboro
Winston-Salem
Lewisville
Spruce Pine
Lenoir
Granite Falls
Lexington
Statesville
Morganton
Hickory
Hildebran
Mooresville
Rockwell
Denver
Concord
Huntersville
Forest City
Shelby
Gastonia
Lowell
McAdenville
Kings Mountain
Charlotte
Mint Hill
Stallings
Waxhaw

North Carolina

Ahoskie

Southern Purls Ⓨ
606 NC 561 E, 27910
(252) 287-8469

Angier

Sew There! ⓆⒺⓂ
27 E. Depot Street, 27501
(919) 331-2499

Apex

Downtown Knits -Yarns & Fabric ⓆⓎⓌⓈ
122 N. Salem Street, 27502
(919) 249-5638

Asheboro

The Quilting Coop Ⓠ
312 Sunset Avenue, Suite C, 27203
(919) 628-5210

Asheville

Purl's Yarn Emporium Ⓨ
10 Wall Street, 28801
(828) 253-2750
MTuWFSa 10-6, Th 10-8, Su 1-5
www.purlsyarnemporium.com

Asheville Cotton Co. Ⓠ
1378 Hendersonville Road, Suite B, 28803
(828) 277-4100

Asheville Custom Framing Ⓝ
856 Merrimon Avenue, 28804
(828) 252-8001

Asheville Homecrafts ⓎⓈ
1 Page Avenue, 28801
(828) 350-7556

Earth Guild ⒺⓎⓌⓈ
33 Haywood Street, 28801
(828) 255-7818 or (800) 327-8448

Atlanic Beach

Coastal Crafts Plus Ⓨ
1010 W. Fort Macon Road, 28512
(252) 247-7210

Banner Elk

Apple Hill Farm Store Ⓨ
400 Apple Hill Road, 28604
(828) 963-1662

Black Mountain

Black Mountain Yarn Shop ⓎⓌⓈ
203-A W. State Street, 28711
(828) 669-7570

Blowing Rock

Unwound Ⓨ
1132 Main Street, Suite 105, 28605
(828) 295-5051

Boone

Sew Original ⓆⓂ
1542 US Highway 421S, Suite G, 28607
(828) 264-1049

The Quilt Shop Ⓠ
2348 Highway 105, 28607
(828) 263-8691

Brevard

Sun Dragon Art & Fiber, LLC Ⓨ
43 S. Broad Street, Suite 102, 28712
(828) 877-3550

Bunn

The Broken Needle ⓆⓎⓂ
219 NC Highway 98E, 27508
(919) 497-0828

Candler

Friends and Fiberworks ⓎⓌⓈ
19 Westridge Marketplace, 28715
(828) 633-2500

Carrboro

Mulberry Silks and Fine Fabrics Ⓠ
200 N. Greensboro Street, B6, 27510
(919) 942-7455

Cary

Cary Quilting Company Ⓠ
935 N. Harrison Avenue, 27513
(919) 238-9739

Elegant Stitches Q M
316 Colonades Way, Suite 210, 27518
(919) 852-4445

Warm 'n Fuzzy Y W
200 S. Academy Street, Suite 140, 27511
(919) 380-0008

Cedar Point

A Frayed Knot Y
101 VFW Road, Suite 2c, 28584
(210) 419-2273

Chapel Hill

Chapel Hill Needlepoint N
762-B Martin Luther King Blvd., 27514
(919) 929-3999

Yarns Etc. Y W S
1322 Fordham Blvd., Suite 4, 27514
(919) 928-8810

Charlotte

Po's Point N
6700 Fairview Road, Suite 106, 28210
(704) 553-8777
M-Sa 10-4, please call ahead
www.posneedlepoint.com

Baskets Of Yarn Y
1318 Central Avenue, Suite E3, 28205
(704) 733-9053

Charlotte Yarn Y
1235 East Blvd., Suite D, 28203
(704) 373-7442

Lee's Creative Sewing and Vacuums Q M
7868-D Rea Road, 28277
(704) 542-8760

The Fibre Studio at Yarns To Dye For Y W S
658 Griffith Road, Suite 107, 28217
(980) 475-4705

Charlotte (Mint Hill)

Cottage Yarn Y
7717 Matthews-Mint Hill Road, 28227
(704) 545-8440

Clayton

Sew Happy Fabrics Q E
100 Pecan Lane, 27527
(919) 359-8500

Concord

We're Sew Creative Q E M
8637 Concord Mills Blvd., 28027
(704) 971-0351
M-F 10-6, Sa 9-4
www.weresewcreative.com

Creative Home and Floral* Q Y
1388 Warren C. Coleman Blvd., 28025
(704) 788-7921

Denver

A Tangled Yarn Shop Y W
3692 N. Highway 16, 28037
(704) 966-1300
M 10-7:30, TuWF 10-5, Th 10-8, Sa 10-4
www.atangledyarnshop.com

Dunn

Memories In Stitches Q M
214 E. Broad Street, 28334
(910) 292-2391

Elkin

Yadkin Valley Quilts Q
109 W. Main Street, 28621
(336) 258-8383

Fayetteville

Loving Stitches Q E M
7076 Ramsey Street, Highway 401, 28311
(910) 630-3912
M-Sa 9-5
www.lovingstitches.net

Crafts Frames & Things Q E Y N C
108 Owen Drive, 28304
(910) 485-4833

Fletcher

Foam & Fabric Outlet Q E C
3049 Hendersonville Highway, 28732
(828) 684-0801

Forest City

Schoolhouse Quilts Q
399 Sunset Memorial Road, 28043
(828) 245-9774

Franklin

A Stitch In Time* Q M
23 Macon Center Drive, 28734
(828) 524-3300

Handi Quilter® Authorized Retailer
Designed by a Quilter, for Quilters.®

Maxie Makes Q
25 Macon Center Drive, 28734
(828) 349-1199

Sassy Stitches Q E M
106 W. Palmer Street, 28734
(828) 349-8912

Sew Creative Q E Y N C
91 Highlands Road, 28734
(828) 524-5221

Silver Threads & Golden Needles E Y W S
41 E. Main Street, 28734
(828) 349-0515

Gastonia

Mary Jo's Cloth Store, Inc. Q E
401 Cox Road, 28054
(704) 861-9100 or (800) 627-9567
M-Sa 9-6, Su 12-6
www.maryjos.com

Granite Falls

The Cotton Quilt Q E
4900 Troy Road, 28630
(828) 726-6786 or (828) 244-7797

Greensboro

Calla Lily Quilts Q E M
2921 Battleground Avenue, Suite E, 27408
(336) 763-0528
M-F 10-6, Sa 10-5
www.callalilyquilts.com

Stitch Point E Y N C
1614-C W. Friendly Avenue, 27403
(336) 272-2032
M-F 10-6, Sa 10-4
www.stitchpointonfriendly.com

Gate City Yarns Y W S
231 S. Elm Street, 27401
(336) 370-1233

Studio Stitch Q
3215-B Battleground Avenue, 27408
(336) 288-9200

Ye Olde Forest Quilters Q E
107 Creek Ridge Rd., Unit H, 27406
(336) 339-5190

Greenville

Sewing Creations Q
2508 S. Charles Blvd., 27858
(252) 321-0829

Hatteras

Blue Pelican Gallery Gifts and Yarn Y
57762 NC Highway 12, 27943
(252) 986-2244

Hayesville

Just Stitchin' Quilt Shop Q M
321 Highway 64 W, 28904
(828) 644-3368

Handi Quilter® Authorized Retailer
Designed by a Quilter, for Quilters.®

Hendersonville

Beginnings Quilt Shop Q
1038-C Greenville Highway, 28792
(828) 693-6622

Sandy's X Stitch On The Go N C
918 Kanuga Road, 28739
(828) 693-4499

Sheridan Kay Quilting Ⓠ Ⓜ
1680 Spartanburg Highway, Suite F, 28792
(828) 595-2296 or (828) 808-0065

Hickory

Lee's Sewing Center Ⓠ Ⓜ
2361 US Highway 70 SE, 28602
(828) 327-6888

Wildskeins Yarn Company Ⓨ Ⓦ Ⓢ
123 2nd Avenue NE, 28601
(828) 855-9245

Highlands

Needlepoint of Highlands Ⓔ Ⓝ Ⓒ
210 N. 5th Street, 28741
(828) 526-3901 or (800) 526-3902

Hildebran

Bill's Sewing Machine Co. Ⓠ Ⓜ
301 Main Avenue E, Exit 119 I-40, 28637
(828) 397-6941

Hillsborough

The Hillsborough Yarn Shop Ⓨ Ⓦ
114 S. Churton Street, 27278
(919) 732-2128
Tu-F 11-5:30, Sa 10-5, Su 1-5
www.hillsboroughyarn.com

Huntersville

Cheers To Ewe! Ⓨ
9856 Gilead Road, Suite E-105, 28078
(704) 706-9425

Knit One, Stitch Too Ⓔ Ⓨ Ⓝ
9709-C Sam Furr Road, 28078
(704) 655-9558

Jacksonville

All About Quilting Ⓠ Ⓜ
3736 Henderson Drive, 28546
(910) 577-9200

Quilt Lizzy Ⓠ Ⓜ
126 Henderson Drive, 28540
(910) 219-3300

Jamestown

Out of Hand Ⓨ Ⓝ
116-C E. Main Street, 27282
(336) 337-2798

Kings Mountain

Carolina Cotton Company Ⓠ
227 S. Battleground Avenue, 28086
(704) 750-4164

Kitty Hawk

Knitting Addiction Ⓨ Ⓢ
3708 N. Croatan Highway, Suite 2, 27949
(252) 255-5648
Winter: Tu-F 10:30-5:30, Sa 10-4; Summer (Memorial Day thru Labor Day) M-F 10:30-5:30, Sa 10-4
www.knittingaddiction.com

Lenoir

Chix With Stix Ⓨ
230 Morganton Blvd., SW, Suite B, 28645
(828) 758-0081
TuWF 11-5, Th 11-8, Sa 10-3
www.chixwithstixknit.com

The Last Stitch* Ⓠ Ⓔ Ⓝ Ⓒ
2018 Connelly Springs Road, 28645
(828) 244-2537

Lewisville

Sewingly Yours Ⓠ Ⓜ
1329 Lewisville Clemmons Road, 27023
(336) 766-8271

Lexington

The Stitchin' Magician Ⓠ Ⓜ
110-G Cotton Grove Road, 27292
(336) 247-1206

Louisburg

Alpaca Dreams, LLC Ⓨ Ⓢ
2714 Schloss Road, 27549
(919) 340-0070
By appt., please call ahead
http://www.alpacadreamsnc.com

Lowell

Sew Much Fun! Q M
831 S. Church Street, 28098
(704) 824-1961

Madison

Stitch Party Studio Q
124 W. Murphy Street, 27025
(336) 427-7144 or (336) 706-9888

Manteo

Outer Banks Quilts & Antiques Q
108 Sir Walter Raleigh Street, 27954
(252) 473-4183

Shoreline Handwerks Q M
4250 Maritime Woods Drive, 27954
(252) 473-2271

Mars Hill

Bovidae Sheep Farm Yarn Shop Y W S
1608 Jarvis Branch Road, 28754
(828) 689-9931

McAdenville

Quilted Thimble Cottage Q
317 Wesleyan Drive, 28056
(704) 266-6445

Mebane

The Twisted Knitter Y
109 N. Third Street, 27302
(919) 563-2468

Mooresville

Quilters Loft Company Q E M
109 Professional Park Drive, Suite 103, 28117
(704) 662-8660

Morehead City

Knit Knook Y
807 Arendell Street, 28557
(252) 646-6704
Tu-F 11-5, Sa 10-2
www.myknitknook.com

The Quilted Butterfly Q
110 Little Nine Road, 28557
(252) 222-0787

Morganton

Morganton Sewing Center Q E M
128 N. Sterling Street, 28655
(828) 439-8050

OSuzannah's Yarn on Union E Y W
130 W. Union Street, 28655
(828) 430-3300

Mt. Airy

Creative Sewing Machines Q M
247 N. Main Street, 27030
(336) 786-7074

Oopsy Daisy Fabric Boutique Q
411 N. Main Street, 27030
(336) 648-8161

Treasure Chest* Q E Y C
1632 Red Brush Road, 27030
(336) 320-2110

Murphy

Bless My Stitches Quilt Shop Q E C M
498 Hill Street, 28906
(828) 835-4900

Nags Head

Yarn and More, Inc. E Y N C
4104 S. Virginia Dare Trail, 27959
(252) 715-2244
Winter: Mon 9-5, Tues 9-6, Wed-Sat 9-5, Su 12-4; Summer: M-F 9-6, Sa 9-5, Su 12-4
http://www.yarnandmoreinc.com

New Bern

Mill Outlet Village Q
3915 M.L. King Jr. Blvd., 28562
(252) 633-5675

New Bern Fabric Center Q E M
1218 S. Glenburnie Road, 28562
(252) 633-4780

Sewing On The River Shop Q M
127 Market Street, 28560
(252) 671-0611

Sewing Solutions Q M
1505 S. Glenburnie Road, Suite G, 28562
(252) 633-1799

North Wilkesboro

Gloria Sews Q
303 10th Street, 28659
(336) 818-0940

Sew Blessed Quiltworks* Q
201 Sparta Road, Suite A, 28659
(336) 818-0852

Pinehurst

Moore than Needlepoint E N C
850 Linden Road, 28374
(910) 295-3727

Pittsboro

French Connections Q
178 Hillsboro Street, 27312
(919) 545-9296

Plymouth

Yearning For Yarn Y
109 W. Water Street, 27962
(252) 793-2500

Raleigh

My Sewing Shoppe Q E M
5910 Duraleigh Road, Suite 139, 27612
(919) 784-9300
MTWThF 10-5, Sa 10-3
http://www.mysewingshoppe.com

Needlepoint.Com N
3811 Hillsborough Street, 27607
(919) 828-5538 or (888) 769-7446
Tu-F 9:30-4:30, Sa 10-4
www.needlepoint.com

Bernina World of Sewing Q M
6013 Glenwood Avenue, 27612
(919) 782-2945

Carolina Sew-N-Vac Q M
1249 Buck Jones Road, 27606
(919) 469-4730

Carolina Sew-N-Vac Q M
6320-125 Capital Blvd., 27616
(919) 873-1981

Great Yarns Y
1208 Ridge Road, 27607
(919) 832-3599

Mill Outlet Village Q
4601 Paragon Park Road, 27616
(919) 876-0292

Thread Waggle Quilting APQS Raleigh Q M
8330 Banford Way
Ste 005, 27615
(919) 576-9897

Wish Upon A Quilt Q E M
8817 Westgate Park Drive, Suite 104, 27617
(919) 782-6363

Richlands

The Tail Spinner Y W S
109 N. Wilmington Street, 28574
(910) 324-6166

Rockwell

Anderson's Sew & So LLC Q E M
10104 Old Beatty Ford Road, 28138
(704) 279-3647

Rocky Mount

Yarn Parlor Y
840 S. Wesleyan Blvd., 27803
(252) 443-4021

Sanford

Find X Designs Sewing Center Q E M
719 Carthage Street, 27330
(919) 774-4700

Shelby

Lee's Sewing Center Q M
114 W. Graham Street, 28150
(704) 487-5224

Southern Pines

Bella Filati Luxury Yarns Y
277 NE Broad Street, 28387
(910) 692-3528

Memories in Stitches* Q M
1150 Old US Highway 1 S, 28387
(910) 987-2121

Southport

Angelwing Needle Arts Q E Y N W C
507 N. Howe Street, 28461
(910) 454-9163

Spruce Pine

Fabrics In The Fray Q E
2601 Highway 19 E, Suite 2, 28777
(828) 467-3991

Stallings

Quilt Patch Fabrics, Ltd. Q
➡ SEE AD BELOW
1017 Stallings Road, 28104
(704) 821-7554
M-Th 10-4:30, FSa 10-4
www.quiltpatchfabrics.com

Statesville

JS Quilt Shop Q M
1250 Northside Drive, 28625
(704) 871-1939

JS Quilt Shop Q M
1250 Northside Drive, 28625
(704) 871-1939

Needle and Thread Q
101 S. Center Street, 28677
(704) 838-1100

Swansboro

The Salty Sheep Yarn Shop Y
774 W. Corbett Avenue, 28584
(910) 325-0018

Wake Forest

Creative Threads Q Y S M
992 Durham Road, Suite B, 27587
(984) 235-1208

Quilt Lizzy Q M
12223 Hampton Way, Suite 100, 27587
(919) 570-0777

Quilts Like Crazy Q M
1241 S. Main Street, Suite 8, 27587
(984) 237-0071

Whatever's Quilted Q M
936 Gateway Commons Circle, 27587
(888) 546-0665

Warrenton

Friends Two Y
126 S. Main Street, 27589
(252) 257-1604

Quilt Lizzy Q M
132 S. Main Street, 27589
(252) 257-4800

Quilt Lizzy Q M
115 E. Market Street, 27589
(252) 257-3800

Quilt Lizzy Q M
110 E. Macon Street, 27589
(252) 257-7117

Washington

Cotton Fields Quilt Shop Q
3751 Wharton Station Road, 27889
(252) 948-0372

Waxhaw

Tangles Knitting on Main Y
200 W. North Main Street, 28173
(704) 243-7150

Waynesville

J Creek Fabrics Q
3391 Dellwood Road, 28786
(828) 400-0276

Quilters Quarters Q E M
1510 Dellwood Road, 28786
(828) 926-0803

Weaverville

5 Little Monkeys Quilt & Sew Q M
32 N. Main Street, 28787
(828) 484-7200

Echoview Fiber Mill Y S
76 Jupiter Road, 28787
(855) 693-4237

Sassy Jacks Stitchery E N C
30 N. Main Street, 28787
(828) 785-4405

Wendell

Ladybug's Cottage, Inc. Q
5 N. Main Street, 27591
(919) 365-3636

Wilmington

Fran's Sewing Circle Q E M
5751 Oleander Drive, Suite 5, 28403
(910) 397-9399
M-F 10-5, Sa 10-4
www.franssewingcircle.com

The Noble Thread E Y W S
119 S. Water Street, 28401
(910) 742-5079
Every Day 10-6
www.thenoblethread.com

Mill Outlet Village Q
2515 S. College Road, 28412
(910) 392-0287

Quilting-N-Crafts-N-Things Q M
1616 Shipyard Blvd., Suite 16, 28412
(910) 444-4503

Yarns of Wilmington E Y N W S
3410 Wrightsville Avenue, 28403
(910) 791-2157

Winston-Salem

Knit One Smock Too, Inc. Q E Y
4003 Country Club Road, Suite A, 27104
(336) 765-9099

Sew Original Q M
3358 Robinhood Road, 27106
(336) 760-1121

Village Fabric Shop Q
114-R Reynolda Village, 27106
(336) 779-6155

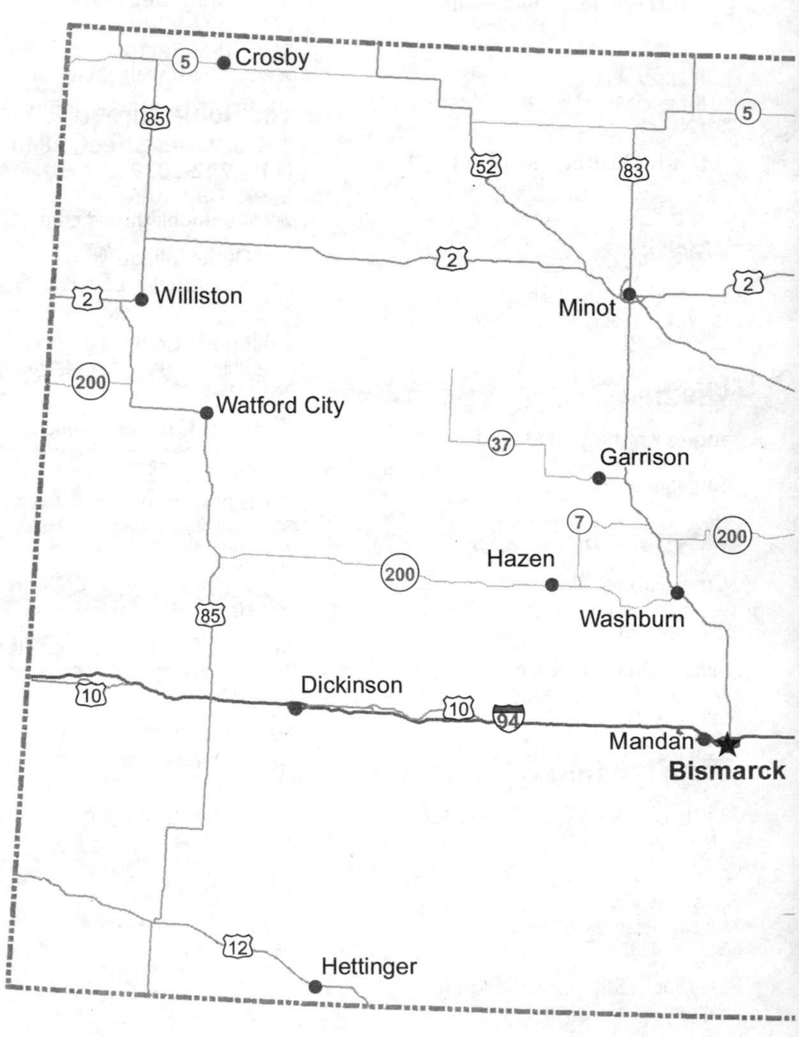

Crosby
5
85
52
83
5
2
2
Williston
2
Minot
200
Watford City
37
Garrison
7
200
Hazen
200
Washburn
85
10
Dickinson
10
94
Mandan
Bismarck
12
Hettinger

Langdon
5
81
St. Thomas
Grafton
2
18
Devils Lake
281
52
3
18
Mayville
Carrington
200
7
Hunter
29
18
Jamestown
Valley City
94
Fargo
83
3
46
46
13
Wishek
13
13
Oakes
281
18
3

North Dakota

Bismarck

Bismarck Sewing & Quilting Q E M
1300 Skyline Blvd., Suite 106, 58503
(701) 258-5139

J & R Vacuum & Sewing Center Q E M
223 E. Main Avenue, 58501
(701) 258-5619 or (800) 371-5515

Carrington

Designer Fabrics Q E
6711 Highway 200, 58421
(701) 652-3535

Crosby

Pleasant Pheasant Fabrics Q
21 N. Main Street, 58730
(701) 965-5000

Devils Lake

Quilt Essential Q E C
206 5th Street NE, 58301
(701) 662-3634

Dickinson

Dakota Sew And So Q E Y N C M
2797 3rd Avenue W, 58601
(701) 225-1408

Fargo

Rae-Bon Sew & Quilt Shop Q E M
3060 25th Street S, 58103
(701) 433-7203
M-F 10-5:30, Sa 10-4
www.rae-bon.com

Garrison

The Merry Moose Quilt Shoppe Q
11 N. Main Street, 58540
(701) 463-2199

This That 'N More Q E Y N C
62 N. Main Street, 58540
(701) 463-2671

Grafton

Embroidery Plus Quilt Shop Q
720 Hill Avenue, 58237
(701) 352-9553

Hazen

Quilts From The Heart and More Q E
213 1st Avenue NW, 58545
(701) 748-3999

Hettinger

Buffalo Creek Quilt Shop, Inc. Q
218 S. Main Street, 58639
(701) 567-2277

Hunter

JDR Brazilian Elegance E Y
320 E. 2nd Street, 58048
(701) 874-2430

Jamestown

Comforts of Home Q M
112 17th Street SE, 58401
(701) 252-5691

Langdon

Sew On & Sew North Q M
706 3rd Street, 58249
(701) 256-2526

Mandan

Sewing Machines Plus Q M
322 W. Main Street, 58554
(701) 663-9025

Mayville

SewBatik Q
879 W. Main Street, 58257
(877) 235-5025 or (701) 788-5556
M-Sa 9-5
www.sewbatik.com

Minot

Bernina Plus Q E M
104 Main Street S, 58701
(701) 837-5638

Fiber Basket Y
1407 S. Broadway, Suite E, 58701
(701) 852-9292

Good Vibrations Quilt Shop Q
213 7th Street SE, 58701
(701) 839-5645

Prairie Rose Q
1500 53rd Avenue SW, 58701
(701) 852-2835

The Yarn Stash Y W S
3305 4th Street SW, #7, 58701
(701) 839-4099

Oakes

Quilt-N-Sew, LLC Q E C
514 Main Avenue, 58474
(701) 742-2642
M-F 9:30-5:30, Sa 9:30-1:30
www.quilt-n-sew.net

St. Thomas

3 Red Hens Q Y
14779 80th Street NE, 58276
(701) 257-6888
Tu-F 10-5, Sa 10-4, SuM by appt.
www.3redhens.com

Valley City

Quilted Ceiling Q E Y C
316 Central Avenue N, Suite 1, 58072
(701) 845-4926

Washburn

Quilting for You Q M
210 7th Street, 58577
(701) 315-0053

Watford City

Barrett Pharmacy and Variety Q E Y N C
145 N. Main Street, 58854
(701) 842-3311

Williston

Cedar Chest E C
201 Main Street, 58801
(701) 572-5977

Wishek

J's Gift Shop Q E Y N W C
114 N. Centennial Street, 58495
(701) 452-2395

Rumpelquiltskin Q
18 N. 5th Street, 58495
(701) 452-6100

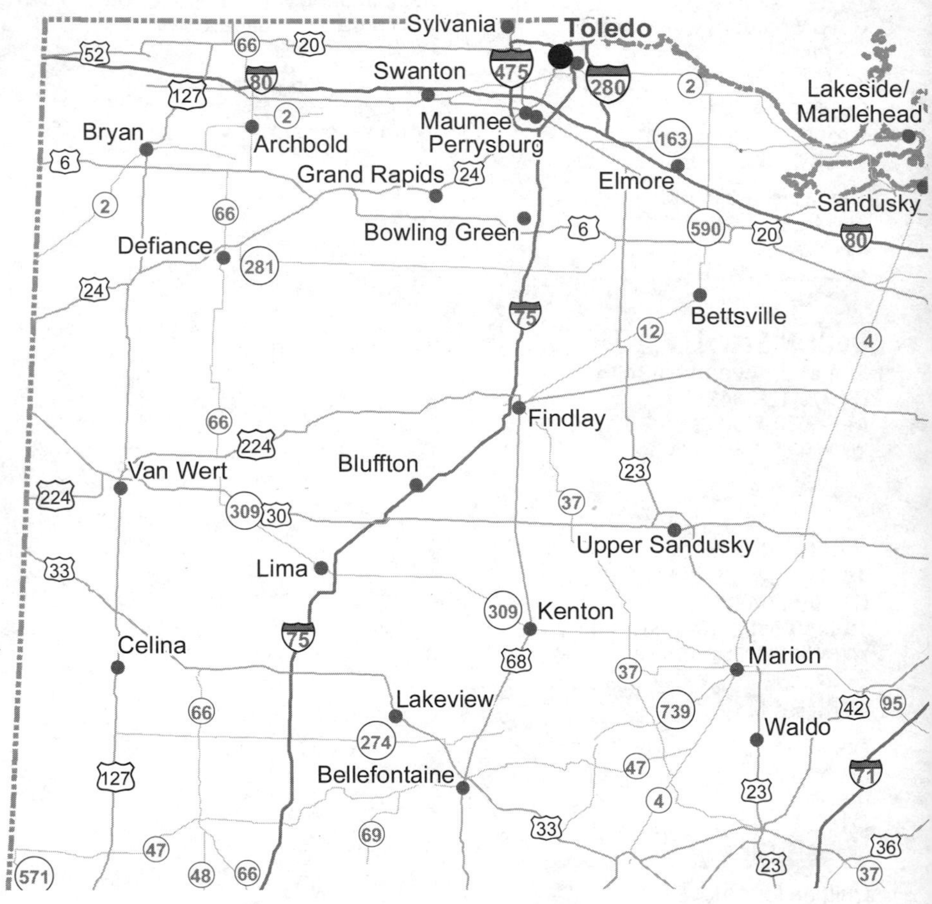

Sylvania
Toledo
Swanton
Lakeside/
Marblehead
Maumee
Perrysburg
Bryan
Archbold
Grand Rapids
Elmore
Sandusky
Bowling Green
Defiance
Bettsville
Findlay
Van Wert
Bluffton
Upper Sandusky
Lima
Kenton
Celina
Marion
Lakeview
Waldo
Bellefontaine

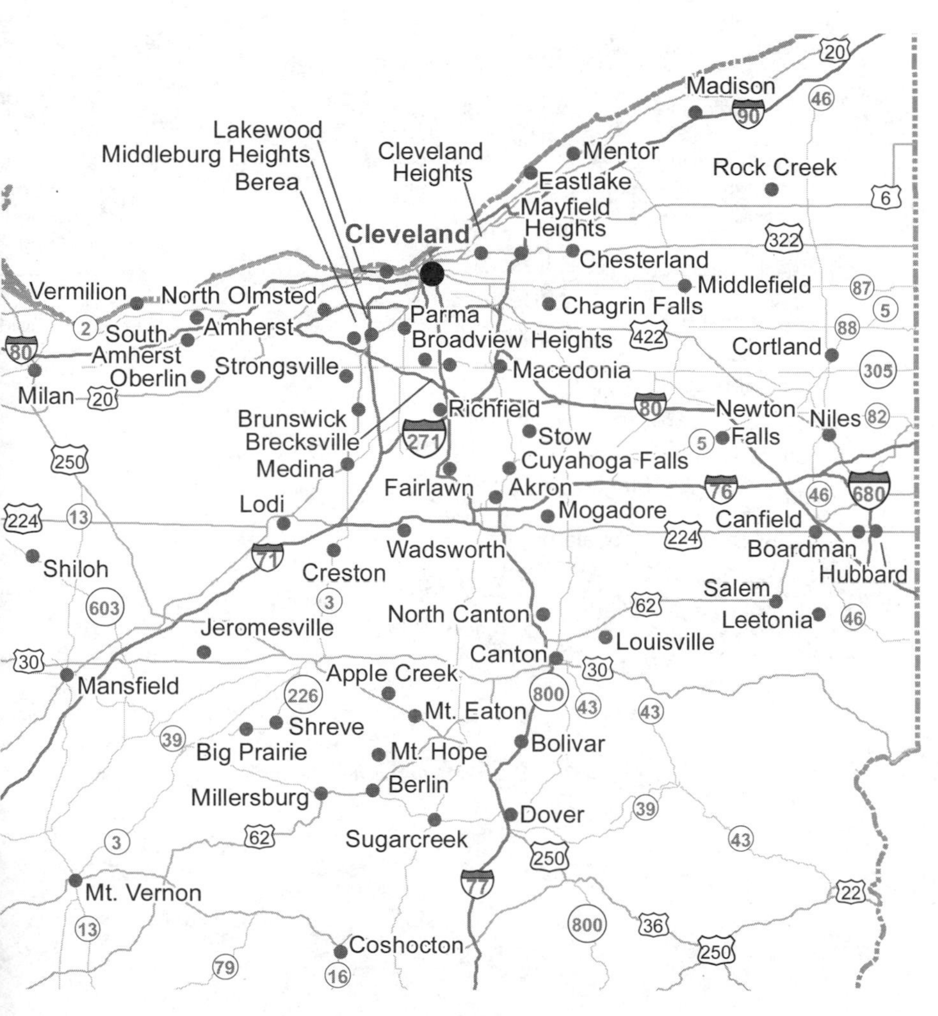

Madison
Lakewood
Middleburg Heights
Berea
Cleveland Heights
Mentor
Eastlake
Rock Creek
Mayfield Heights
Cleveland
Chesterland
Middlefield
Vermilion
North Olmsted
Chagrin Falls
Parma
South Amherst
Amherst
Broadview Heights
Cortland
Oberlin
Strongsville
Macedonia
Milan
Richfield
Newton Falls
Niles
Brunswick
Brecksville
Stow
Medina
Cuyahoga Falls
Fairlawn
Akron
Lodi
Mogadore
Canfield
Wadsworth
Boardman
Shiloh
Creston
Hubbard
Salem
North Canton
Leetonia
Jeromesville
Louisville
Canton
Apple Creek
Mansfield
Mt. Eaton
Shreve
Bolivar
Big Prairie
Mt. Hope
Berlin
Millersburg
Dover
Sugarcreek
Mt. Vernon
Coshocton

Piqua
Troy
Ludlow Falls
Tipp City
West Milton
Springfield
Englewood
Vandalia
Huber Heights
Dayton
Beavercreek
Miamisburg
Bellbrook
Centerville
Somerville
Springboro
Waynesville
Trenton
Hamilton
Wilmington
Mason
Fairfield
Sharonville
Loveland
Goshen
Madeira
Milford
Cincinnati
Hillsboro
Sardinia
Georgetown
Powell
Dublin
Worthington
Columbus
Grandview Heights
London
Canal Winchester
South Bloomfield
Chillicothe
Lucasville

St. Clairsville
Newark
Pataskala
Zanesville
Quaker City
Lancaster
Beverly
Whipple
Nelsonville
Marietta
McArthur
Albany
Belpre
Pomeroy
South Point

Ohio

Akron

Blueberry Hill Stitchery Ⓔ Ⓒ
880 Mull Avenue, Suite 101, 44313
(330) 864-9688 or (866) 366-9688
MTuThF 11-5
https://www.facebook.com/blueberryhillstitchery/

Liberty Green Quilt Shop Ⓠ
3430 S. Arlington Road, 44312
(234) 571-2582
TuThF 10-6, Sa 10-4
www.libertygreenquiltshop.com

Ohio Star Quilts Ⓠ
2383 S. Main Street, Suite C101, 44319
(330) 644-6100
TuThFSa 10-5, W 10-6:30, Su 12-4
www.ohiostarquilts.com

Albany

Fiber FUN Studio Ⓔ Ⓨ Ⓝ Ⓦ Ⓢ Ⓒ
28743 Gaston Road, 45710
(740) 698-0101

Amherst

Mom's Sewing Basket Ⓠ Ⓜ
1907 Cooper Foster Park Road, 44001
(440) 984-1444

Apple Creek

Homespun Flowers & Fabrics Ⓠ
6397 Kidron Road, 44606
(330) 857-0317

Archbold

Threads of Tradition Ⓠ Ⓔ
22611 State Route 2, 43502
(419) 445-9610 or (800) 590-9755

Beavercreek

Busy Beaver Arts and Crafts Ⓔ Ⓨ Ⓝ Ⓒ
3445 Dayton Xenia Road, 45432
(937) 429-3920
M-F 10-6, Sa 10-5
www.busybeaverarts.com

Bellbrook

Crafters Lodge Ⓠ Ⓔ Ⓨ Ⓦ Ⓢ Ⓒ Ⓜ
4417 W. Franklin Street, 45305
(937) 310-1296

Bellefontaine

Coblentz Crafts and Fabrics Ⓠ
5451 County Road 25 N, 43311
(937) 468-2081

The Sewing & Yarn Shop Ⓨ
118 N. Main Street, 43311
(937) 592-1885

Belpre

Neff's Country Loft Ⓠ Ⓔ
2514 Washington Blvd., 45714
(740) 423-1965
M-F 10-5:30, Sa 10-5
www.facebook.com/pages/Neffs-Country-Loft/230960890260076

Sew Happy Quilting Traditions Ⓠ
407 Washington Blvd., 45714
(740) 401-0031

Berea

Abigayle's Quiltery Ⓠ Ⓔ Ⓜ
591 W. Bagley Road, 44017
(440) 239-9000

Berlin

Helping Hands Quilt Shop Ⓠ Ⓔ
4818 State Route 39 (W. Main Street), 44610
(330) 893-2233
M-Sa 9-5; Jan. and Feb. M-Th 10-4, FSa 10-5
www.helpinghandsquilts.com

Berlin Fabrics and Clothing LLC Q E Y
4900 Oak Street, 44610
(330) 893-3898

Berlin (Millersburg)

Zinck's Fabric Outlet Q
4568 State Route 39, 44654
(330) 893-7225
M-Sa 8-5
www.zincksfabric.com

Bettsville

The Door Mouse Q
5047 W. State Route 12, 44815
(419) 986-5667

Beverly

Jacobs Ladder Quilting Shop LLC Q
131 5th Street, 45715
(740) 410-1175

Big Prairie

Yarn And Bead Shop Y
9049 Township Road 1043, 44611
(330) 496-3574
Please call ahead
www.yarnandbeadshop.com

Bluffton

Forever In Stitches, LLC Q M
120 N. Main Street, Suite B, 45817
(419) 358-0656

Boardman

With Needle in Hand E N C
➡ SEE AD BELOW
224A Boardman-Canfield Road, 44512
(330) 758-8122
MWTh 10-5, F 10-6, Sa 12-6
www.withneedleinhand.com

Bernina Store and Sew Much More Q E M
7081 West Blvd., 44512
(330) 726-9396

Handi Quilter® Authorized Retailer
Designed by a Quilter, for Quilters.®

The Flaming Ice Cube Knit Shop Y W
1449 Boardman-Canfield Road, 44512
(330) 726-4766

Three Sheep Gallery & Workshop Y W S
6010 Market Street, 44512
(330) 953-3600

Bolivar

The Shop on Canal Street (aka Material Girl) Q Y M
127 Canal Street, 44612
(330) 874-6013

Bowling Green

The Busy Thimble Q E Y C
148 S. Main Street, 43402
(419) 806-4022 or (800) 439-7719

Brecksville

Crochet Innovations Y
7660 Chippewa Road (Route 82), 44141
(440) 838-4455

Broadview Heights

Crafty Ewe, Inc. E N C
➡ SEE AD BELOW
8035 Broadview Road, 44147
(440) 838-1600
MTuWFSa 10-5:30, Th 10-8
www.thecraftyewe.net

Brunswick

Carol's Fabric Shop Q E
1325 N. Carpenter Road, 44212
(330) 225-4436 or (888) 966-6680

Bryan

Jack's Sew & Vac etc. Q E M
124 N. Main Street, 43506
(419) 636-4914

Canal Winchester

The Laughing Ewe Q E
360 W. Waterloo Street, Unit A, 43110
(614) 829-7450

Canfield

Village Quilts Q
17 W. Main Street, 44406
(330) 533-0545

Canton

Angelics... A Quilters Haven Q E M
3095 Cleveland Avenue SW, 44707
(330) 484-5480
TuWF 9:30-5:30, Th 9:30-7, Sa 9:30-3
(Memorial Day - Labor Day Th 9:30-6)
www.angelics.net

Celina

Linda's Sew 'n So Q E
216 W. Fayette Street, 45822
(419) 586-2324

The Quilterie Q
126 S. Main Street, 45822
(419) 586-0910

Centerville

Sew-A-Lot Q M
232 N. Main Street, 45459
(937) 433-7474

Chagrin Falls

The Artful Yarn Y
100 N. Main Street, Suite 230, 44022
(440) 321-9754
M 12-5, Tu-Sa 10-5, Su 12-4
www.TheArtfulYarn.com

Chesterland

The Quilted Thimble Q E
12628 Chillicothe Road, 44026
(440) 729-2259
M 10-6, Tu-F 10-5, Sa 10-4
www.facebook.com/TheQuiltedThimble

Chillicothe

Creations Sew Clever Q M
192 S. Paint Street, 45601
(740) 775-1957
M-F 10-5, Sa 10-3
www.creationssewclever.com

Chillicothe Sewing Center* M
20 W. Water Street, 45601
(740) 775-3553

Old Town Fabric Shop Q E
56 W. Water Street, 45601
(740) 779-9898

Cincinnati

Silk Road Textiles Q E Y W
6106 Hamilton Avenue, 45224
(513) 541-3700
TuW 10-6, Th 10-8, FSa 10-5, Su 12-5
www.silkroadcincinnati.com

Absolutely Needlepoint N
7117 Miami Avenue, 45243
(513) 561-7999

Cincinnati Needlepoint N
7006 Center Street, 45243
(513) 271-0271

Fiberge: Knits + Bolts Q Y
6200 Montgomery Road, 45213
(513) 351-1251

Hank... a yarn boutique Y
2651 Observatory Avenue, Suite 101, 45208
(513) 386-9869

HomeGrown HomeSewn Q E
5761 Springdale Road, Suite L, 45247
(513) 401-9747

Skein Shop Y W S
800 Compton Road, Suite 30, 45231
(513) 463-3274

Stitches N Such Q M
16 Village Square, 45246
(513) 733-3999

The Hoop & Needle* E C
4019 Hamilton Avenue, 45223
(330) 715-6064

Cincinnati (Maderia)

Fiberlicious Y W S
8157 Camargo Road, 45243
(513) 561-8808

Cleveland

Fine Points Ⓨ
12620 Larchmere Blvd., 44120
(216) 229-6644

Cleveland Heights

Wool & Willow Needlepoint Ⓝ
➡ **SEE AD BELOW**
3475 Fairmount Blvd., 44118
(216) 791-7952
Tu-F 11-5, Sa 11-4
www.woolandwillow.com

Susan Yarns Ⓨ Ⓢ
2166 S. Taylor Road, 44118
(216) 321-2687

Columbus

The Yarn Shop Ⓨ Ⓝ Ⓢ
➡ **SEE AD BELOW**
1125 Kenny Centre Mall, 43220
(614) 457-7836 or (800) 859-9276
MThFSa 10-6, TuW 10-8
www.yarnshoponline.com

Columbus, Continued

614 Knit Studio Ⓨ Ⓦ Ⓢ
4400 Indianola Avenue, 43214
(614) 670-5629
M-W 12-6, Th 10-8, F 1-8, Sa 10-4; Open Stitch hours- Tu 12-2, Th 10-8, F 1-8
http://www.614knitstudio.com

Cross My Heart, Ltd Ⓒ
1141 Kenny Centre, 43220
(614) 442-0820

Dabble & Stitch Ⓠ Ⓨ Ⓜ
211 Arcadia Avenue, 43202
(614) 407-4987

Conneaut

Sweet Heart Suri Alpacas Ⓨ
4813 Church Street, 44030
(440) 224-1868

Cortland

Olive Grace Studios Ⓠ Ⓔ Ⓒ
2627 Youngstown-Kingsville Road, 44410
(330) 637-0800

Quilter's Fancy Ⓠ Ⓔ
225 S. High Street, 44410
(330) 637-3106 or (866) 953-0722

Coshocton

Mercantile on Main, LLC Ⓠ
313 Main Street, 43812
(740) 622-5956

Creston

Moonstruck Farm & Fiber* Ⓨ Ⓢ
9874 Cleveland Road, 44217
(330) 435-6669

Cuyahoga Falls

Harps & Thistles Yarn Emporium Ⓨ Ⓢ
129 Portage Trail, 44221
(234) 208-9482

Dayton

Park Avenue Needlepoint Ⓝ
41 Park Avenue, 45419
(937) 298-5776

Strings Attached Yarns Ⓨ
225 N. Main Street, 45402
(937) 221-9585

Dayton (Beavercreek)

Fiberworks Ⓨ Ⓢ
1350 N. Fairfield Road, 45432
(937) 429-9276

Stitching Cottage Ⓔ Ⓒ
1263 N. Fairfield Road, 45432
(937) 320-9055

Defiance

Fifth Stitch - not just your grandma's yarn shop Ⓨ
300 Clinton Street, 43512
(419) 782-0991

Dover

Anything Sews Fine Fabrics and Gallery Ⓠ
209A E. Ohio Avenue, 44622
(330) 365-9707

Dublin

Knitting Temptations Ⓨ
35 S. High Street, 43017
(614) 734-0618

Quilt Beginnings North Ⓠ Ⓜ
6591 Sawmill Road, 43017
(614) 799-2688

Red Rooster Quilts Ⓠ Ⓜ
48 Corbins Mill Drive, 43017
(614) 734-9007

Handi Quilter® Authorized Retailer
Designed by a Quilter, for Quilters.®

What's The Point? Ⓨ Ⓝ
126 S. High Street, 43017
(614) 717-9008

Eastlake

Mara's Fabric & Quilts Ⓠ
35003 Vine Street, 44095
(440) 942-7849

Elmore

Crafty Needle Yarns and Threads Ⓨ
366 Rice Street, 43416
(419) 862-0333
TuW 10-5, Th 10-8,F 10-4 Sa 10-3
http://www.craftyneedleyarns.com

Perfectly Pink Fabric & More Ⓠ
336 Rice Street, 43416
(419) 309-4949

Englewood

The Rabbit Hutch Ⓨ
5 N. Walnut Street, 45322
(937) 540-9292

Fairfield

Seams Sew Easy ⓆⓂ
➡ SEE AD BELOW
2326 Mack Road, 45014
(513) 860-1373
MTuWF 10-5, Th 10-7, Sa 10-3, Su 11-3
www.seams-sew-easy.com

Fairlawn

I Of The Needle Ⓝ
55 Shiawassee Avenue, Suite 8, 44333
(330) 867-0005

The Designing Woman ⓆⓎ
137 Ghent Road, 44333
(330) 835-9400

Findlay

Craft Gallery, Ltd. Ⓒ
406 Walnut Street, 45840
(419) 422-7980
TuWThF 10-5, Sa 10-4, 3rd Th of month 10-8
http://www.craftgalleryohio.com

Findlay Sewing Center ⓆⓂ
1207 Tiffin Avenue, 45840
(419) 422-5812

Yarn Farm* ⓎⓈ
11610 Township Road 180, 45840
(419) 423-4252

Georgetown

Schoolhouse Quilts Ⓠ
118 N. Main Street, 45121
(937) 378-4828

Goshen

The Quilt Cabin, LLC Ⓠ
1703 State Route 28, 45122
(513) 722-7332

Grand Rapids

Natural Fiber & Yarn Company ⓎⓌⓈ
24122 Front Street, 43522
(419) 832-5648

Grandview Heights

Yarn It & Haberdashery ⓎⓌⓈ
1093 W. 1st Avenue, 43212
(614) 736-6464
M-W 11-7, Thurday 12:30-7, Friday 11-6, Sa 10-4, Su 12-4
http://www.yarnitanddash.com

Hamilton

Lambikin's Hideaway Yarn & Stitchery Ⓨ
217 S. B Street, 45013
(513) 895-5648
M 11-7, TuThF 11-5, Sa 10-5, Su 12-5
www.lambikinshideaway.com

Hillsboro

Margaret's Memories E Y C
220 W. Beech Street, 45133
(937) 763-1831

Hubbard

Gwen Erin Natural Fibers Y S
44 N. Main Street, 44425
(330) 269-9511

Huber Heights

Sulphur Grove Quilt Shop Q
7340 Taylorsville Road, 45424
(937) 233-7021
Handi Quilter® Authorized Retailer
Designed by a Quilter, for Quilters.®

Jeromesville

Country Charm Fabrics Q
14 E. South Street, 44840
(419) 368-6403

Kenton

Country Stitches Fabrics Q
18031 State Route 309, 43326
(419) 675-3337

Lakeside / Marblehead

Christi's Just for Ewe Gift and Yarn Shop Y W S
9523 E. Harbor Road (Route 163), 43440
(419) 798-5499

Lakeview

Sew N Love Fabrics* Q
422 State Route 385, 43331
(937) 935-4770

Lakewood

River Colors Studio Y
1387 Sloane Avenue, 44107
(216) 228-9276

Lancaster

Farmers Country Store Q
540 N. High Street, 43130
(740) 654-4853

Lunn Fabrics Ltd. Q
317 E. Main Street, 43130
(740) 654-2202

Pleasant Mountain Stitchery Q E M
743 N. Pierce Avenue, 43130
(740) 652-9688
Handi Quilter® Authorized Retailer
Designed by a Quilter, for Quilters.®

Leetonia

Amish Quilts & Craft Shop* Q
41658 Kelly Park Road, 44431
(330) 482-3230

Lima

Heavenly Stitches Q Y M
2696 Greely Chapel Road, 45804
(419) 979-0218
MWF 9-5, TuTh 9-6, Sa 8-1
http://www.heavenlystitchesquilts.com

For the Love of Quilts Q
115 N. Elizabeth Street, 45801
(419) 228-9801

Lodi

Black Locust Farm* Y W S
110 Bank Street, 44254
(330) 948-9276

London

Yesterday's Ewes Y S
66 S. Main Street, 43140
(740) 845-8840 or (614) 801-9384

Louisville

AnnaLouisa's Quilt Shop Q E
1408 N. Chapel Street, 44641
(330) 875-5300

Loveland

The Quilter's Studio of Loveland & QSL Workshop Q
535 W. Loveland Avenue, 45140
(513) 683-3666 or (513) 683-1666

Lucasville

Stippling Stitches Quilt Shop Q
1179 Owensville Road, 45648
(740) 935-7482

Ludlow Falls

Fabric Crafts By Rosalie Q
2810 State Route 48, 45339
(937) 698-4066

Macedonia

Long Tail Knits Y W S
9838 Valley View Road, 44056
(234) 808-4383
M-F 10-8, Sa 10-4
http://www.longtailknits.com

Madison

Bracken Moss Farm Fine and Rare Fibers Y W S
50 W. Main Street, 44057
(440) 983-4538

Mansfield

Alpaca Meadows* Y S
1200 Rock Road, 44903
(419) 529-8152

Alpacatales Yarn & Gifts at Storybook Alpacas Y S
1051 Reed Road, 44903
(419) 589-3745

Marietta

Quilter's Corner Q
400 Tennis Center Drive, 45750
(740) 373-6150

Marion

Spin A Yarn Fiber Garden* Y W S
868 Woodlawn Drive, 43302
(740) 382-6969

Mason

A Stitch Above E N C
7577 Central Parke Blvd., Suite 326, 45040
(513) 271-2712
M-Sa 11-4; W stitching group until 6
http://www.astitch-above.com

Main Street Yarns Y
126 W. Main Street, 45040
(513) 204-0078

Martha's Heirlooms E C
315 W. Main Street, 45040
(513) 229-7340 or (888) 277-6432

Maumee

The Quilt Foundry Q M
234 W. Wayne Street, 43537
(419) 893-5703

Mayfield Heights

Pins & Needles Sewing Shoppes Q E M
➡ SEE AD AT RIGHT
5937 Mayfield Road, 44124
(440) 446-1484
MTuWF 10-5:30, Th 10-8, Sa 10-4
www.pinsandneedles.com

McArthur

McArthur Quilt Shop Q M
118 W. Main Street, 45651
(740) 596-2345

Medina

Little Red Quilt House Q
3616 Ridge Road, 44256
(234) 248-4492
MTuThF 10-5, W 10-7, Sa 9-4
www.littleredquilthouse.com

Mentor

Quilts and Sew Forth Q
7406 Center Street, 44060
(440) 266-1601
MWThF 9-5, Tu 9-7, Sa 10-3
www.quiltsandsewforth.com

Sweet Dreams Quilts Q
7292 Lakeshore Blvd., 44060
(440) 571-4033
MTuWF 10-5, Sat10-3
http://www.sweetdreamsquiltshoppe.com

Alko Sewing Center M
7511 Mentor Avenue, 44060
(440) 951-3435

Handi Quilter® Authorized Retailer
Designed by a Quilter, for Quilters.®

Miamisburg

The Little Shop of Stitches Q E
79 S. Main Street, 45342
(937) 384-0804

Middleburg Heights

Pins & Needles Sewing Shoppes Q E M
➨ SEE AD PAGE 433
7300 Pearl Road, 44130
(440) 243-6400
MTuWF 10-5:30, Th 10-8, Sa 10-4
www.pinsandneedles.com

Middlefield

The Craft Cupboard Q E Y
14275 Old State Road, 44062
(440) 632-5787

Tiny Stitches Quilt Shop LLC Q
14277 Old State Road, 44062
(440) 632-9410

Milan

The Sewing Connection Q M
11001 US Highway 250, B-2, 44846
(419) 499-9393
Tu-F 10-5:30, W evenings by appt., Sa 10-3
http://www.sewing-connection.com

Milford

Fiber Optic Yarns Y W S
726 Mohawk Trail, 45150
(513) 248-0752

Millersburg

Lone Star Quilt Shop Q M
7700 CR 77, 44654
(330) 674-3858

Miller's Dry Goods Q E C
4500 State Route 557, 44654
(330) 893-9899 or (330) 893-1117

Somewhere Sewing Q M
11004 County Road 320, 44654
(330) 674-1677 or (866) 558-9739

Millersburg (East of Berlin)

Plaid Sheep Company Q E
4375 State Route Highway 39, 44654
(330) 893-3163

Mogadore

The Spider's Web Fabric & Quilt Shop Q
2123 Martin Road, 44260
(330) 594-7119

Mt. Eaton

Spector's Store Q E Y C
1 W. Main Street, 44659
(330) 359-5467

Mt. Hope

Mt. Hope Fabrics and Gift Shop Q
8114 State Route 241, 44660
(330) 674-5292

Mt. Vernon

The Makery Q E Y N W C
1 N. Main Street, 43050
(740) 324-5124
M-Sa 10-6
www.themakeryonmain.com

Paw Patch Quilt Shop Q E M
444 Columbus Road, Suite E, 43050
(740) 397-9450

Sharon's Quilts & Embroidery Q M
555 Harcourt Road, 43050
(740) 393-2347

Nelsonville

Nelsonville Quilt Co. Q M
52 W. Washington Street, 45764
(740) 753-3343

Newark

Bunny's Sew Fine Fabrics Q
28 Price Road, 43055
(740) 366-1433

Lola's Alpaca Shop Y S
2653 Swans Road, 43055
(740) 345-2199

Newton Falls

Elsie's Custom Creations LYNS Y C
139 1/2 Windham Road, 44444
(330) 609-9376

Niles

Yarn Works Y
815 Youngstown Warren Road, Suite 12, 44446
(330) 989-8095

North Canton

Artists' Gallery Yarn Y
1142 S. Main Street, 44720
(330) 494-8838

North Olmsted

Pins & Needles Sewing Shoppes Q E M
➡ SEE AD PAGE 433
24201 Lorain Avenue, 44070
(440) 734-8330
MTuWF 10-6, Th 10-8, Sa 10-4
www.pinsandneedles.com

Anna's Sewing Center Q M
23134 Lorain Road, 44070
(440) 716-8884

Small Studio Y
24549 Lorain Road, 44070
(440) 808-8599

Oberlin

Ginko Gallery & Studio Y
19 S. Main Street, 44074
(440) 774-3117

Parma

Quilter's Source Q
6683 State Road, 44134
(440) 843-2464

Pataskala

Calico Cupboard Quilt Shop Q M
➡ SEE AD BELOW
74 Oak Meadow Drive, 43062
(740) 927-2636
MTuWFSa 10-5, Th 10-7
www.calico-cupboard.com

Quilt Store On Main Q Y
365 S. Main Street, 43062
(614) 382-8008

Perrysburg

Yarn Cravin', LLC Y
146 E. 2nd Street, 43551
(419) 872-9276

Piqua

The Tapestry Angel E N C
516 Spring Street, 45356
(937) 773-6352

Pomeroy

The Fabric Shop, LLC Q
110 W. Main Street, 45769
(740) 992-2284

Powell

Louise's Needlework Ⓝ
244 W. Olentangy Street, 43065
(614) 436-3905

Quaker City

The Old Bank Mercantile Ⓠ
180 Broadway Street, 43773
(740) 679-3342

Richfield

The Polka Dot Pincushion Ⓠ Ⓔ
3807 Brecksville Road, Suite 8, 44286
(330) 659-0233

Rock Creek

The Quilting Block Ⓠ Ⓔ
4150 State Route 45, 44084
(440) 563-9386

Salem

Knit Wit Knits Ⓨ
645 E. State Street, 44460
(330) 337-5648

Sandusky

M&E Quilt Shoppe Ⓠ
279 E. Market Street, 44870
(419) 502-9123
TuWF 10-5, Th 12-7, Sa 9-2
www.mequiltshoppe.com

Sardinia

Ohio Valley Natural Fibers Ⓠ Ⓨ Ⓦ Ⓢ
8541 Louderback Road, 45171
(937) 446-3045 or (513) 646-5503
M-F 9-4
www.ovnf.com

Sharonville

Keepsakes Ⓒ
11423 Lebanon Road, 45241
(513) 563-6845

Sew-Ezy Sewing Studio Ⓠ Ⓜ
11427 Lebanon Road, 45241
(513) 563-7474

Shiloh

Country Fabrics Ⓠ
6142 Ganges Five Points Road, 44878
(419) 896-3785
MTuWF 9-5, Th 9-7, Sa 9-3
www.shopcountryfabrics.com

Shreve

Noah's Landing Ⓨ Ⓢ
7575 Brown Road, 44676
(330) 465-1820

Somerville

The Yarn Barn @ Blessed Criations Ⓨ Ⓢ
3381 Northern Road, 45064
(937) 705-0068

South Amherst

Quilts & Kreations Ⓠ Ⓜ
101 E. Main Street, 44001
(440) 986-4132

South Bloomfield

VonStrohm Woolen Mill* Ⓨ Ⓦ Ⓢ
5010 N. Walnut Street, 43146
(740) 983-2042

South Point

Quilts and Things* Ⓠ
201A Solida Road, 45680
(740) 377-4551

Springboro

Wooly Bully Yarn Company Ⓨ
135 S. Main Street, 45066
(937) 748-1002

Springfield

Creative Fires LLC* Ⓠ Ⓜ
1525 Progress Drive, 45505
(937) 327-9420

St. Clairsville

From Past To Present Quilt & Embroidery Shop Ⓠ
139 W. Main Street, 43950
(740) 526-9371

Stow

Sew Deja Vu Ⓠ
1608 Norton Road, 44224
(330) 653-5598
M-F 10-5, Sa 10-4
www.sewdejavu.com

Strongsville

Just Stitching Ⓒ
13211 Prospect Road, 44149
(440) 572-9777
TuWFSa 10-5, Th 12-8
www.facebook.com/juststitching/

Sugarcreek

Carlisle Fabric & Quilts ⓆⒺⒸⓂ
108 E. Main Street, 44681
(330) 852-2264

Swanton

Sew Purrfect Notions ⓆⒺⓎⓃⒸ
236 S. Munson Road, 43558
(419) 973-6273

Sylvania

Yarn Company Ⓨ
5704 W. Alexis Road, 43560
(419) 474-6744

Tipp City

Tippecanoe Weaver and Fibers Too ⓎⓌⓈ
17 N. 2nd Street, 45371
(937) 667-5358
Tu-Sa 1-6
www.tippweaveyarn.com

Toledo

Stitch* Ⓠ
3435 N. Holland Sylvania Road, 43623
(419) 517-7092

Trenton

Valley Quilts ⓆⓂ
104 E. State Street, 45067
(513) 988-2560

Troy

Lion & Lamb Yarn Boutique* Ⓨ
121 Public Square NE, 45373
(937) 703-9323

Upper Sandusky

Sew Nice ⓆⓂ
200 W. Wyandot Avenue, 43351
(419) 294-2200

Van Wert

Leesburg Looms Inc. Ⓦ
201 N. Cherry Street, 45891
(419) 238-2738 or (800) 329-9254

Vandalia

Fiber and Fusion Studio Ⓨ
11180 N. Dixie Drive, 45377
(937) 602-3248
W-F 1-6, Sa 11-4
www.fiberandfusion.com

Vermilion

Cast On Yarn Studio, LLC Ⓨ
5532 Liberty Avenue, 44089
(440) 984-6063

Clare's Stitching Post LLC Ⓒ
682 Main Street, 44089
(440) 967-0826

Wadsworth

The Fabric Peddler ⓆⒺⒸ
139 College Street, 44281
(330) 336-1101

Waldo

Serendipitee Quilt Shop Ⓠ
7143 Waldo Delaware Road, 43356
(740) 726-2900
Tu-Sa 10:30-5
www.facebook.com/Serendipitee-155664834473427/

Waynesville

Fabric Shack Quilt Shop Ⓠ
99 S. Marvin Lane, 45068
(513) 897-0092 or (877) 666-4245

Katherine's Web* ⓎⓌⓈ
174 S. Main Street, 45068
(937) 728-0126

West Milton

Wertz Variety Store ⓆⒺⓎⓃⓈⒸ
6 N. Miami Street, 45383
(937) 698-5212

Whipple

The Quilted Work Ⓠ
320 Stanleyville Narrows Road, 45788
(740) 373-0579

Wilmington

Cotton Junky Quilt Shop Ⓠ
110 W. Main Street, 45177
(937) 366-6302

Worthington

Sew To Speak ⓆⒺⓎⓌⓈⒸⓂ
752 High Street, 43085
(614) 549-4428

Zanesville

A Touch Of Thread Quilting Gallery Ⓠ
2885 E. Pike, US Route 40, 43701
(740) 454-8372 or (800) 760-7701

Nonna's Quilting Nook ⓆⒺⓂ
1004 Beverly Avenue, 43701
(740) 450-2626

The Alpacas Of Spring Acres Farm Store ⓎⓌⓈ
3370 Big B Road, 43701
(740) 796-2195

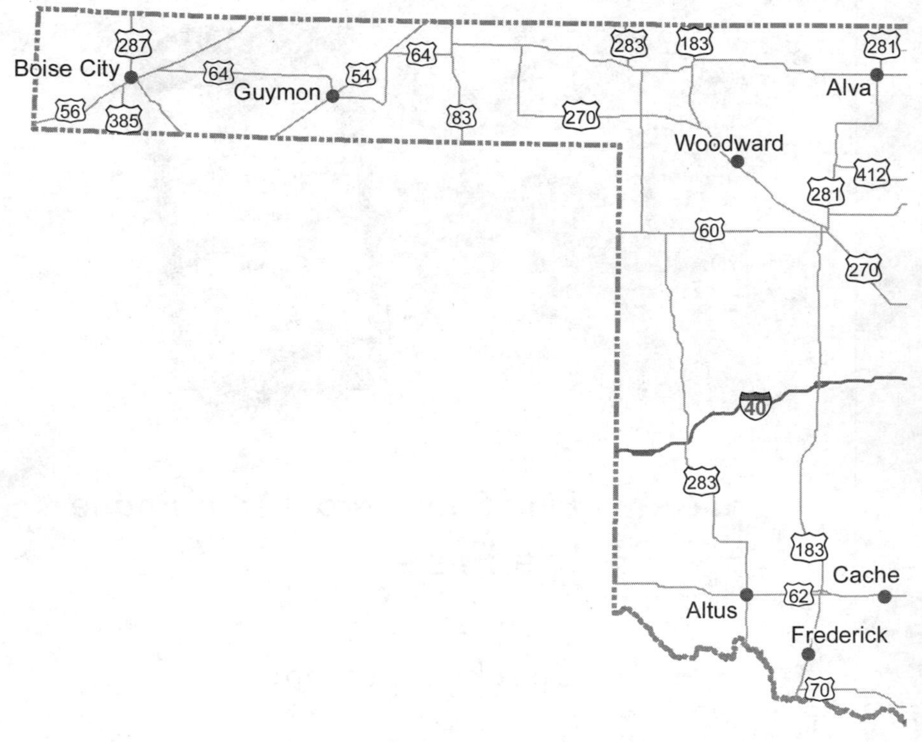
287
Boise City
64
Guymon
54
64
56
385
83
270
283
183
281
Alva
Woodward
412
281
60
270
40
283
183
Cache
62
Altus
Frederick
70

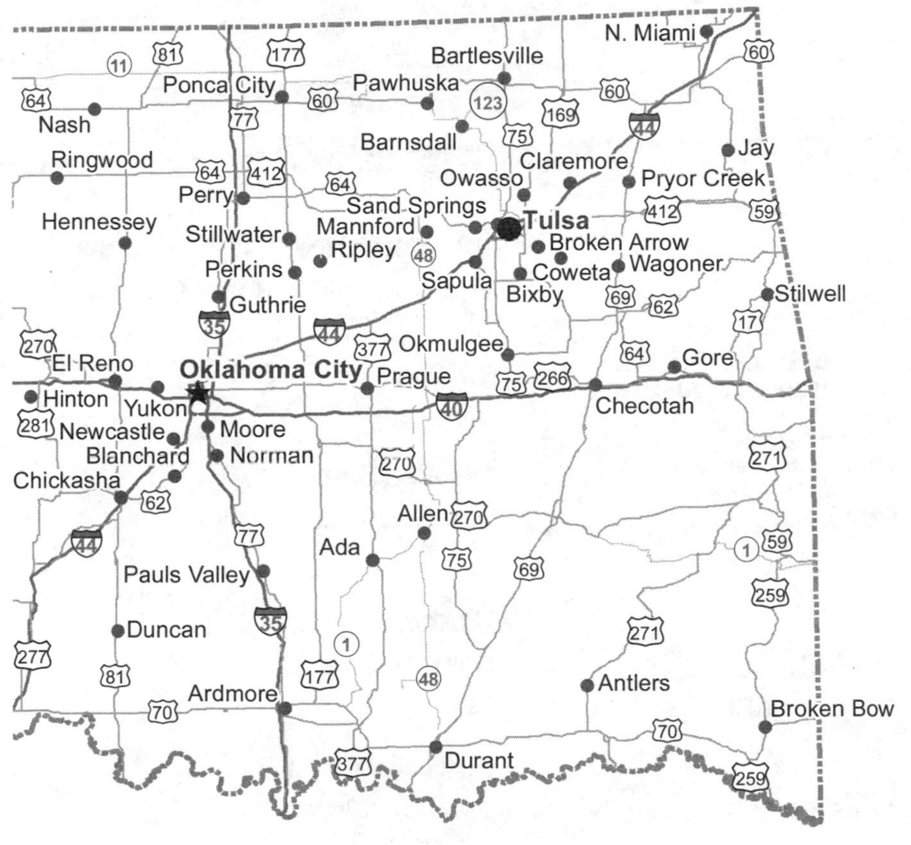
N. Miami
Bartlesville
Ponca City
Pawhuska
Nash
Barnsdall
Jay
Ringwood
Claremore
Owasso
Pryor Creek
Perry
Sand Springs
Hennessey
Tulsa
Stillwater
Mannford
Ripley
Broken Arrow
Perkins
Wagoner
Coweta
Sapula
Bixby
Stilwell
Guthrie
Okmulgee
El Reno
Oklahoma City
Gore
Prague
Hinton
Yukon
Checotah
Newcastle
Moore
Blanchard
Norman
Chickasha
Allen
Ada
Pauls Valley
Duncan
Antlers
Ardmore
Broken Bow
Durant

Oklahoma

Allen

Prairie Notions Q E
701 E. Gilmore Street, 74825
(580) 857-2831

Altus

Johnson's Vacuum Shop & Sewing Basket Q E C M
105 W. Commerce Street, 73521
(580) 477-1398

Alva

Fabrics & More Etc. Q E
413 Barnes Avenue, 73717
(580) 327-0240

Antlers

Betsy's Quilts, LLC Q E Y C
419580 E.1930 Road, 74523
(580) 298-5821
M-F 9-5, Sa 9-3
http://www.betsysquilts.com

Ardmore

Key Grocery and Quilts Q E M
116 E. Broadway Stret, 73401
(580) 223-8821

Barnsdall

Red Barn Quilting Q Y
99 CR 2285, 74002
(918) 847-2544

Bartlesville

Quilter's Hideaway Q
3910 Tuxedo Blvd., 74006
(918) 214-8714

Sew Uptown Q
316 SE Dewey, 74003
(918) 332-8956

Bixby

The Log Cabin Quilt Shop* Q
14803 E. 171st Street S, 74008
(918) 366-6902

Blanchard

Beth's Quilting Quarters and Fabric Shoppe* Q
114 N. Main Street, 73010
(405) 485-3880

Boise City

Pam's Variety Fabric Q E
23 E. Main Street, 73933
(580) 544-2989

Broken Arrow

Gypsy Moon Studios* Q E Y N C
2101 N. Beech Avenue, 74012
(918) 251-7188

Sew Much More Fabrics Q
1750-B S. Aspen, 74012
(918) 893-5813

Broken Bow

Quilt Shoppe Boutique* Q E N C
200 N. Main Street, 74728
(580) 584-7858

Cache

Quilt N Bee Q E M
506 C Avenue, 73527
(580) 429-2400

Checotah

Sew Many Quilts Q E
427332 E 1050 Road, 74426
(918) 473-4318

Chickasha

Bush Family Affair / Quilts By Gail Ⓠ
401 W. Chickasha Avenue, Suite 202, 73018
(405) 224-2280
M-F 8-5, Sa 8-4
www.bushfamilyaffair.com

Steelman's Ⓠ
410 Chickasha Avenue, 73018
(405) 224-2036

Claremore

Shepherd's Cross Ⓨ Ⓦ Ⓢ
16792 E 450 Road, 74017
(918) 342-5911

The Cotton Cottage Ⓠ
23000 S Highway 88, Unit 101, 74017
(918) 607-0831

Coweta

Aunt Mary's Sewing Room Ⓠ
123 E. Chestnut Street, 74429
(918) 486-6400

Duncan

Deb's Quilt Shop Ⓠ
427 S. Highway 81, 73533
(580) 255-2843

Durant

Lulu and Hazel Ⓠ Ⓔ Ⓝ Ⓒ Ⓜ
502 Bryan Drive, 74701
(580) 931-9112

El Reno

K's Quilting Studio, LLC* Ⓠ
107 S. Bickford Avenue, 73036
(405) 422-2707

Frederick

Thayer Rags Fabric Center Ⓠ Ⓔ Ⓨ Ⓒ
108 W. Grand Avenue, 73542
(580) 335-3380

Gore

Fabric Patch Quilt Shop* Ⓠ
305 S. Main Street, 74435
(918) 489-5163

Guthrie

Sealed With A Kiss Ⓨ
109 E. Oklahoma Avenue, 73044
(405) 282-8649

Sooner Quilts Ⓠ Ⓜ
7821 S. Sooner Road, 73044
(405) 282-2070

Weavery at Indian Meridian Ⓨ Ⓦ Ⓢ
624 S. Henney Road, 73044
(405) 822-8927

Guymon

Cheryl's Quilt Corner Ⓠ
1608 N. Ellison, 73942
(580) 338-3677

Hennessey

Prairie Quilt Ⓠ Ⓔ Ⓜ
➡ SEE AD AT LEFT
101 S. Main Street, 73742
(405) 853-6801
M-F 10-5, Sa 10-4, Su 1-4 PM
www.quiltnow.com

Hinton

Main Street Fabrics Etc.* Ⓠ Ⓜ
115 W. Main, 73047
(405) 542-6545

Jay

Keepin U - N Stitches Ⓠ Ⓔ
705 N. 4th Street, 74346
(918) 253-2455

Zena Suri Alpacas Ⓨ Ⓦ Ⓢ
35401 S. 580 Road, 74346
(804) 389-2579 or (918) 253-7317

Mannford

Reddiks Country Living Store Ⓠ Ⓔ
140 Evans Avenue, 74044
(918) 865-2470

Moore

The Stitching Post Inc. Ⓠ Ⓜ
316 N. Broadway Street, 73160
(405) 794-0026
MSa 10-5, TuWF 10-5:30, Th 10-8
www.sewbargain.com

N. Miami

Cotton Pickin' Quilts Ⓠ Ⓔ
612 Nebraska Road, 74358
(918) 542-2836

Nash

Stash to Stitches* Ⓠ
14077 Highway 132, 73761
(580) 839-2555

Newcastle

The Quilted Hart Ⓠ
3595 NW 32nd Street, 73065
(405) 387-4342

Norman

L & B Yarn Co. Ⓨ
425 W. Gray Street, 73069
(405) 310-3636

Oklahoma City

The Savage Quilter Ⓠ Ⓔ Ⓒ Ⓜ
➡ SEE AD NEXT PAGE
6903 N. May Avenue, 73116
(405) 840-1466
M-F 10-5, Sa 10-4
www.savagequilter.com

The Stitching Post Inc. Ⓠ Ⓔ Ⓜ
5928 NW 16th Street, 73127
(405) 495-4699
M-Sa 10-5
http://www.sewbargain.com

Handi Quilter® Authorized Retailer
Designed by a Quilter, for Quilters.®

Oklahoma Quiltworks Ⓠ Ⓔ
9323 N. Pennsylvania Avenue, 73120
(405) 842-4778

Sew & Sews, Inc. Ⓠ Ⓜ
5125 N. Portland, 73112
(405) 942-2700

The Gourmet Yarn Company* Ⓨ Ⓦ Ⓢ
2915 W. Britton Road, 73120
(405) 286-3737

Yarnatopia Ⓨ Ⓦ Ⓢ
8407 S. Western, 73139
(405) 601-9995

Okmulgee

Thread Lightly Studio* Ⓠ Ⓔ Ⓒ Ⓜ
1600 S. Wood Drive (Highway 75), 74447
(918) 777-2580

Owasso

The Knitting Nook Ⓨ
12500 E. 86th Street N, Suite 106, 74055
(918) 272-6665

Pauls Valley

The Quilt Shoppe* Ⓠ
32694 E. County Road 1598, 73075
(405) 238-4098

Pawhuska

The Tangled Thread Q
230 E. 6th Street, 74056
(918) 287-4826

Perkins

The Quilt Box* Q
118 1/2 NW 1st Street, 74059
(405) 747-5704

Perry

Noble County Yarns Y W
639 Delaware Street, 73077
(580) 307-2096

Ponca City

Completely Quilted* Q M
315 E. Grand Avenue, 74601
(580) 718-9300

Prague

Gwen's Unwind & Sew Shop* Q
1712 Sherry Lane, 74864
(405) 831-3514

Pryor Creek

Capstone Creations Q E Y C M
504 S. Mill (Highway 69), 74361
(918) 824-1990

Ringwood

Quilter's Depot* Q E
116 E. 3rd Street, 73768
(580) 883-4999

Ripley

Nancy's Trunk* Q E M
9211 W. Main Street (Highway 33), 74062
(405) 413-5037

Sand Springs

Quilt Nuts Q
216 N. Main Street, 74063
(918) 613-9341

Sweet Pea's Quilt Company* Q
1415 Water Tower Road, 74063
(918) 230-4910

The Little Quilt Shop Q
1 W. 41st Street, Suite H, 74063
(918) 245-1339

Sapula

Quilt Styles Q E
18 S. Water Street, 74066
(918) 224-6299

Stillwater

Quilting Post Q E
717 S. Main Street, 74074
(405) 624-0303

Sew & Sews, Inc. Q M
211 N. Perkins Road, Suite 7, 74075
(405) 707-0700

Stilwell

Front Porch Fabrics Q
10 W. Chestnut Street, 74960
(918) 797-2206

Tulsa

The Silver Needle Ⓔ Ⓒ
➡ SEE AD BELOW
6068 S. Sheridan Road, 74145
(918) 493-1136 or (888) 543-7004
M-Sa 10-6
www.thesilverneedle.com

Get Stitchin' LLC* Ⓔ Ⓨ Ⓝ Ⓢ Ⓒ
6562 E. 51st Street, 74145
(918) 481-1055

Loops Ⓨ
6034 S. Yale Avenue, 74135
(918) 742-9276 or (877) 566-7765

Lori Hall* Ⓨ Ⓦ Ⓢ Ⓒ
6562 East 51st Street, 74145

Owl & Drum Ⓠ Ⓔ
1216 S. Harvard Avenue, 74112
(918) 742-1404

Stitches of Tulsa Ⓝ
5217 S. Sheridan Road, 74145
(918) 747-8838

Wagoner

A Bolt Load of Fabric Ⓠ
101 S. Polk Avenue, 74467
(918) 351-4857

Woodward

Quiltworks* Ⓠ
917 Main Street, 73801
(580) 254-0464

Yukon

Threads of Tradition Ⓠ Ⓔ
928 W. Main Street, 73099
(405) 693-2500
M-F 10-5:30, Sa 10-4
http://www.threads-of-tradition.com

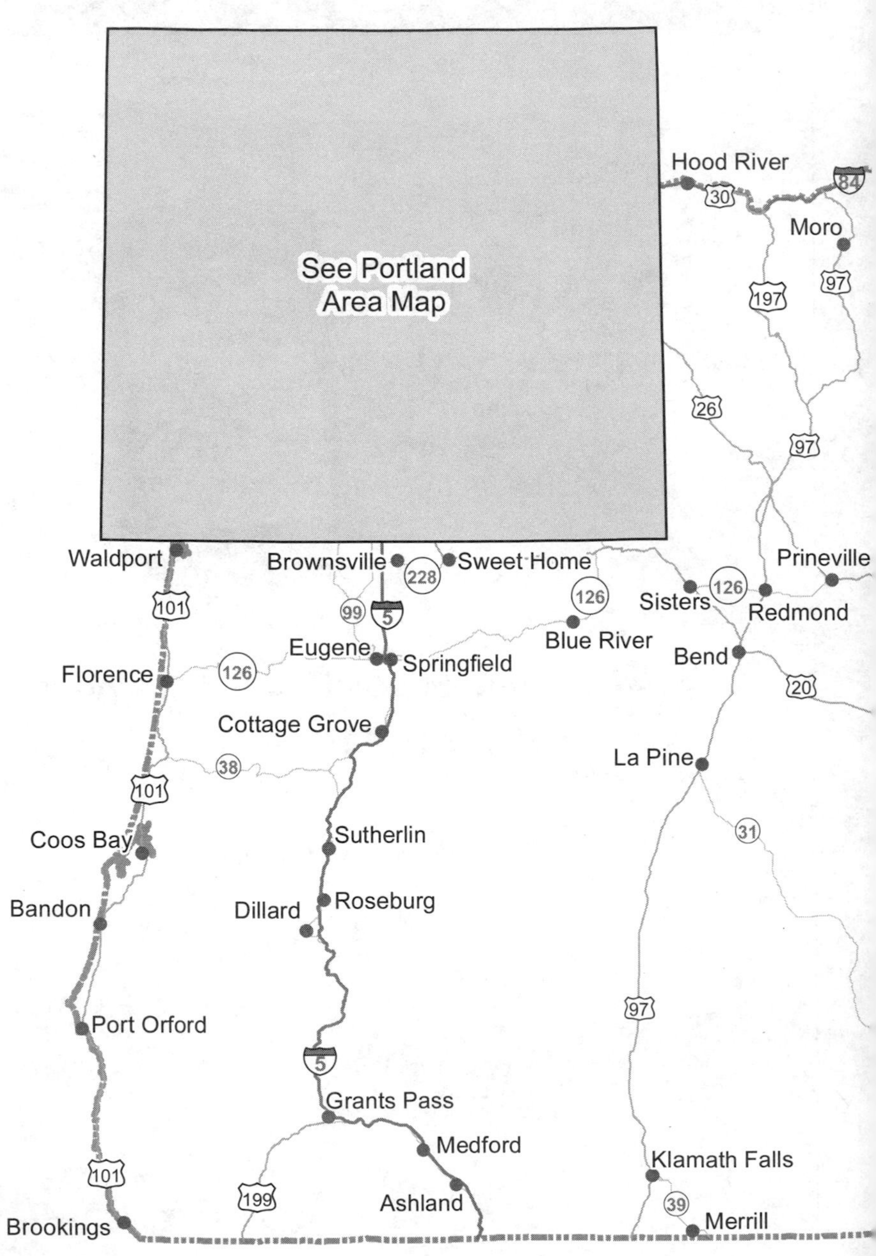
See Portland
Area Map
Hood River
30
84
Moro
97
197
26
97
Prineville
Waldport
Brownsville
Sweet Home
228
101
99
5
126
Sisters
126
Redmond
Blue River
Eugene
Springfield
Bend
Florence
126
20
Cottage Grove
La Pine
38
101
31
Coos Bay
Sutherlin
Bandon
Dillard
Roseburg
97
Port Orford
5
Grants Pass
Medford
Klamath Falls
101
199
Ashland
39
Merrill
Brookings

730
82
84
Milton-Freewater
Athena
11
30
Pendleton
82
Joseph
Heppner
La Grande
Union
395
Fossil
30
86
Baker City
84
Mt. Vernon
Prairie City
30
26
Ontario
Nyssa
395
20
Christmas Valley
395
Paisley
31
95
Lakeview

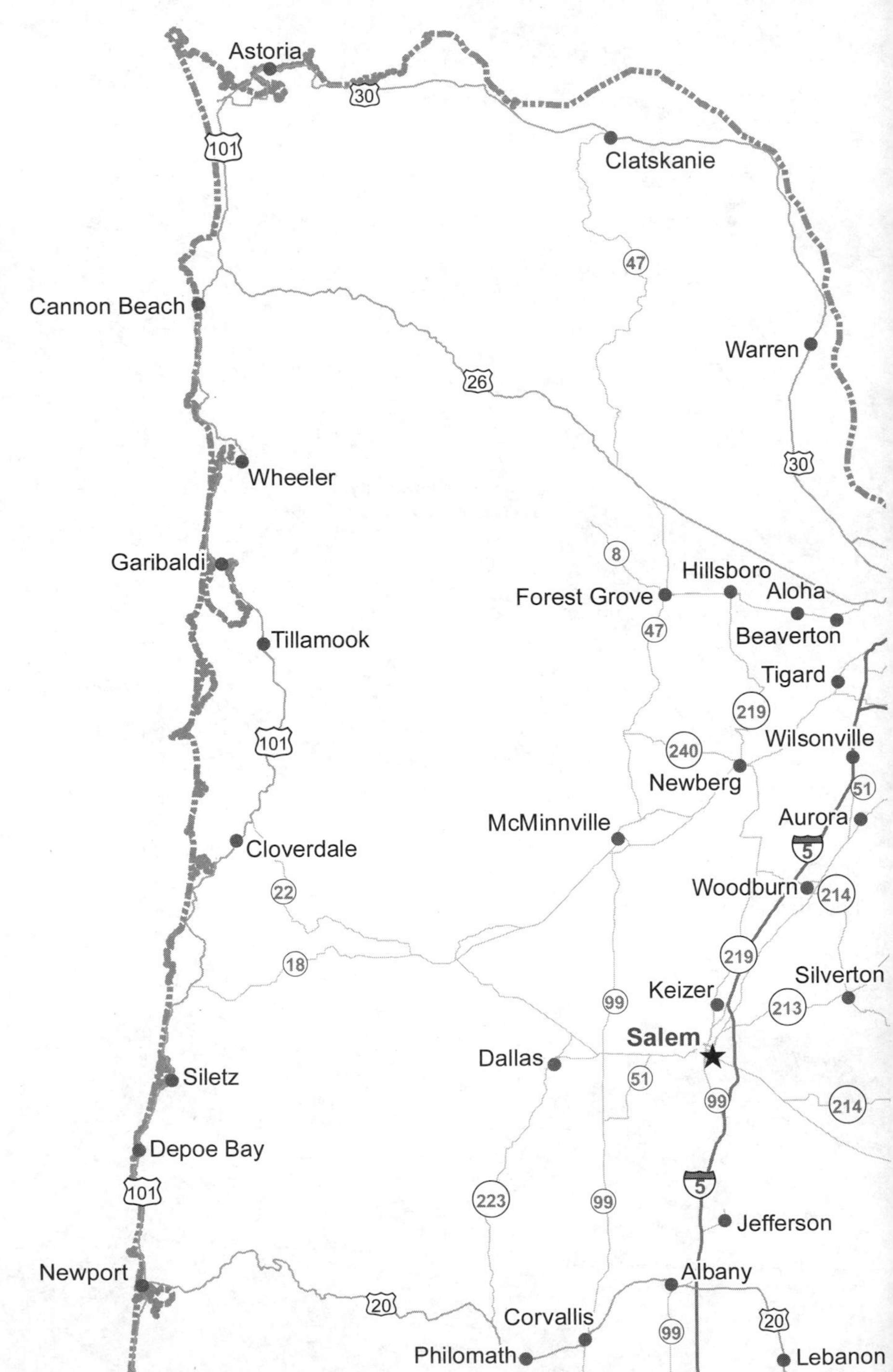
Astoria
30
101
Clatskanie
47
Cannon Beach
Warren
26
30
Wheeler
8
Garibaldi
Hillsboro
Forest Grove
Aloha
47
Beaverton
Tillamook
Tigard
219
101
Wilsonville
240
Newberg
51
Aurora
McMinnville
5
Cloverdale
Woodburn
214
22
219
18
Silverton
Keizer
99
213
Salem
Dallas
51
Siletz
99
214
Depoe Bay
101
5
223
99
Jefferson
Newport
Albany
20
Corvallis
20
99
Philomath
Lebanon

Hood River
84
30
99
Portland
30
205
Troutdale
Gresham
Milwaukie
Happy Valley
Sandy
Oregon City
99
213
26
214
22

Oregon

Albany

Bolts to Blocks Q E
950 SE Geary Street, Suite B, 97322
(541) 704-0386

The Quilt Loft Q
405 1st Avenue W, 97321
(541) 928-7242

Aloha

Aloha Sewing & Vacuum Q M
18335 SW Tualatin Valley Highway, 97006
(503) 649-6050

Ashland

Sew Creative Ashland Q E
115 E. Main Street, 97520
(541) 482-1665

The Websters, Inc. Y W S
11 N. Main Street, 97520
(541) 482-9801

Astoria

Astoria Fiber Arts Studio* Y W S
1296 Duane Street, 97103
(503) 325-5598

Homespun Quilts & Yarn Q Y M
108 10th Street, 97103
(503) 325-3300

Athena

Highland Quilts Q
312 E. Main Street, 97813
(541) 969-6178

Aurora

Speckled Hen Quilts Q E C
25455 NE Boones Ferry Road, 97002
(503) 678-3368

Baker City

Treasure Every Stitch Q E
2101 Main Street, Suite 108, 97814
(541) 523-9499

Bandon

The Wool Company Q Y W S
990 2nd Street SE (Highway101), 97411
(541) 347-3912 or (888) 456-2430
M-Sa 10-5,
www.woolcompany.com

Forget-Me-Knots Q E C
640 2nd Street SE, 97411
(800) 347-9021

Beaverton

For Yarn's Sake Y
11767 SW Beaverton-Hillsdale Highway, 97005
(503) 469-9500

Mill End Store Q E N C
4955 SW Western Avenue, 97005
(503) 646-3000

Nitro Knitters Yarn Shop & Knitting School Y
10047 SW Nimbus Avenue, 97008
(503) 372-9318

Bend

BJ's Quilt Basket Q E
20225 Badger Road, 97702
(541) 383-4310

Cynthia's of Bend Sewing Machine & Learning Center* M
1245 SE 3rd Street, Suite B-1, 97702
(541) 383-1999

Handi Quilter® Authorized Retailer
Designed by a Quilter, for Quilters.®

Fancywork Yarn Shop Y C
200 NE Greenwood Avenue, 97701
(541) 323-8686

QuiltWorks Q M
926 NE Greenwood Avenue, Suite B, 97701
(541) 728-0527

Sew Many Quilts & Bernina Q E M
2550 NE Highway 20, Suite 140, 97701
(541) 385-7166

Blue River

Rustic Quilt Shop* Q
54771 McKenzie Highway, 97413
(541) 822-6236

Brookings

By My Hand Ⓠ Ⓔ Ⓨ Ⓝ Ⓦ Ⓢ Ⓒ
➡ SEE AD BELOW
1109 Chetco Avenue, 97415
(541) 412-0917
M-F 10-5, Sa 10-4
www.facebook.com/pages/By-My-Hand/396788073678484

By My Hand
A Yarn & Fabric Store
541-412-0917
1109 Chetco Ave.
Brookings, OR 97415

ABC Creations Ⓠ
519 Chetco Avenue, Unit 8, 97415
(541) 661-7930

Brownsville

Brownsville Stitching Parlor* Ⓨ Ⓢ
104 Spaulding Avenue, 97327
(541) 466-3660

Yankee Dutch Quilting & Dry Goods Ⓠ Ⓔ
140 Spaulding Avenue, 97327
(541) 466-3662

Cannon Beach

Center Diamond Ⓠ Ⓔ
1065 S. Hemlock Street, 97110
(888) 305-0854 or (503) 436-0833

Coastal Yarns Ⓨ Ⓢ Ⓒ
255 N. Hemlock Street, 97110
(503) 436-1128

Christmas Valley

The Willows Antiques & Gifts Ⓨ
86426 Christmas Valley Highway, 97641
(541) 576-2199

Clatskanie

Nancy Williamson Framing & Fibers Ⓨ
160 N. Nehalem, 97016
(503) 728-3793

The Bag Ladies Yarn Shop Ⓔ Ⓨ Ⓒ
265 W. Columbia River Highway, 97016
(503) 728-3666

Cloverdale

BJ's Fabrics & Quilts Ⓠ
34365-B Highway 101S, 97112
(503) 392-6195 or (877) 690-5267

Coos Bay

Kruusn Quilt Designs Ⓠ
92772 Cape Arago Highway, 97420
(541) 808-2761

My Yarn Shop LLC* Ⓨ
264 S. Broadway, 97420
(541) 266-8230 or (888) 664-9276

Threads That Bind Ⓠ
120 Central Avenue, 97420
(541) 267-0749

Corvallis

Stash Ⓨ Ⓢ
110 SW 3rd Street, 97333
(541) 753-9276

The Starlight Stitchery Ⓔ Ⓒ
211 SW 2nd Street, 97333
(541) 758-4152

Cottage Grove

Mountain Shadow Ranch Ⓨ Ⓦ Ⓢ
31354 Veatch Road, 97424
(530) 409-2018

Pandora's Box Ⓠ
602 E. Main Street, 97424
(541) 942-5194

Dallas

Grandma's Attic Sewing Emporium, Inc. Ⓠ Ⓔ
167 SW Court Street, 97338
(503) 623-0451

Depoe Bay

Elsie's Discount Roving and Dyes (S)
4210 N. Highway 101, 97341
(541) 764-3997

Dillard

Sew Cute Quilting & Fabric Boutique (Q)
11707 Old Highway 99 S, 97457
(541) 580-7700

Eugene

Eugene Textile Center (Y)(W)(S)
1510 Jacobs Drive, 97402
(541) 688-1565
M-Sa 10-5:30
www.eugenetextilecenter.com

Piece by Piece Fabrics (Q)(M)
62 W. 13th Avenue, 97401
(541) 743-0266
M-Sa 10-5:30, Su 12-4
www.piecebypiecefabrics.com

Handi Quilter® Authorized Retailer
Designed by a Quilter, for Quilters.®

Cozy (Y)(W)
285 E. 5th Avenue, 97401
(541) 485-9204

Glimakra USA (Y)(W)
1471 Railroad Blvd. #5, 97402
(541) 246-8679

Mindy's Needlepoint Factory (Q)(E)(N)(C)
296 E. 5th Avenue, Suite 227, 97401
(541) 344-7132

Paramount Sewing & Vacuum (Q)(M)
1056 Green Acres Road, Suite 104, 97408
(541) 345-2100

Soft Horizons Fibre (Y)(W)(S)
412 E. 13th Avenue, 97401
(541) 343-0651

Florence

Happy Kampers Yarn Barn (Y)
88878 Highway 101 N, 97439
(541) 997-9414

Wenz-daze Quilter's Emporium (Q)(E)
1745 W. 15th Street (Airport Road), 97439
(541) 997-3293

Handi Quilter® Authorized Retailer
Designed by a Quilter, for Quilters.®

Forest Grove

Knotty Lamb (Y)(S)
2003 19th Avenue, 97116
(503) 992-0606

Needles in the Grove (Q)(E)(N)(C)
2735 20th Place, Suite A, 97116
(503) 820-9361

Fossil

Fossil General Mercantile (Q)
555 Main Street, 97830
(541) 763-4617

Garibaldi

Swift Stitches (Q)
102 11th Street, 97118
(971) 265-1090

Grants Pass

Unique Lee Yours Cross-Stitch and Needlework Ⓔ Ⓝ Ⓒ

➡ SEE AD BELOW

3921 Highland Avenue, 97526
(541) 476-6229
Open Tu-F 11-5, Sa 10-3
www.facebook.com/Unique-Lee-Yours-Cross-Stitch-Needlework-1450300422195042/

Bead Merchant & Yarn Supply Ⓨ
115 SW H Street, 97526
(541) 471-0645

Jordan Fabrics Quilt Shop Ⓠ
1595 NE 7th Street, 97526
(541) 476-0214

Plaza Quilting and Sewing Center Ⓠ
311 SE 6th Street, 97526
(541) 479-5757

Gresham

Feather Your Nest Ⓠ
126 N. Main Avenue, 97030
(971) 220-0936

Happy Valley

Quilting Delights Ⓠ Ⓔ Ⓜ
12117 SE Stevens Court, 97086
(503) 658-1600

Heppner

Artisan Village* Ⓠ
193 N. Main Street, 97836
(541) 676-8282

Hillsboro

Aloha Sewing & Vacuum Ⓠ Ⓜ
7550 E. Main Street, 97124

BlackSheep Fiber Emporium Ⓔ Ⓨ Ⓦ Ⓢ
173 NE 3rd Street, Suite 103, 97124
(971) 732-5391

Casa Crafty* Ⓠ Ⓜ
173 NE 3rd Avenue, 97123
(541) 788-9370

Sharon's Attic Quilt Shop Ⓠ Ⓔ
2950 SW Cornelius Pass Road, Suite 100, 97123
(503) 259-3475

Hood River

Knot Another Hat Ⓨ Ⓦ Ⓢ
11 3rd Street, Suite 103, 97031
(541) 308-0002

LavenderSheep's Fiber Garden Ⓨ Ⓦ Ⓢ
1844 Rebecca Avenue (Shop is Moving in March. Call for address), 97031
(541) 392-1828

Jefferson

The Purple Frog Quilt Shop Ⓠ Ⓔ Ⓒ
890 N. 2nd Street, 97352
(541) 327-3764

Joseph

The Sheep Shed Ⓨ Ⓦ Ⓢ
3 S. Main Street, 97846
(541) 432-7000

Keizer

Bernina/Stretch & Sew Fabrics Q M
5089 River Road N, 97303
(503) 393-0132

The Cotton Patch Q
4475 River Road N, 97303
(503) 463-1880

Klamath Falls

Cagey Quilter Q M
5718 S. 6th Street, 97603
(541) 884-1533

My Little Quilt Shop Q M
4230 Winter Avenue, 97603
(541) 891-9873

Yarnz 4 Ewe Y
2617 Pershing Way, 97603
(541) 851-9051

La Grande

Claudson's Sew & Soak Q E M
1401 Adams Avenue, 97850
(541) 963-6402
M-F 9:30-5:30, Sa 10-3
www.claudsons.com

La Grande Quilt Shop Q
1107 Washington Avenue, 97850
(541) 663-1817

La Pine

Homestead Quilts and Gallery Q E Y C M
51425 Highway 97, 97739
(541) 536-2360

Lakeview

Goose Tracks Quilting & Fabric Arts* Q
728 N. 2nd Street, 97630
(541) 947-0299

Lebanon

Knitty Gritty Y S
824 S. Main Street, 97355
(541) 936-4677
TuThFSa 11-6, W 11-8
http://www.knittygrittyoregon.com

Finally Together Quilt Shop Q
54 W. Ash Street, 97355
(541) 258-6006

McMinnville

Boersma's Sewing Center Q E N
203 NE 3rd Street, 97128
(503) 472-4611

Medford

Cottage Quilts * Sew Creative Studio Q E M
1310 Center Drive, Unit A, 97501
(541) 500-8071

Fasturn LLC Q E
3859 S. Stage Road, 97501
(541) 772-8430 or (800) 729-0280

Handi Quilter® Authorized Retailer
Designed by a Quilter, for Quilters.®

SethanyKnits Y S
825 E. Main Street, Unit B, 97504
(541) 499-6295

Top Stitch Q
1596 Biddle Road, 97504
(541) 608-7722

Merrill

Tater Patch Quilts Q E
109 E. Front Street, 97633
(541) 798-5955

The Sewing Works* M
109 E. Front Street, 97633
(541) 798-1100

Handi Quilter® Authorized Retailer
Designed by a Quilter, for Quilters.®

Milton-Freewater

Oregon Trail Yarn Y W S
1112 S. Main Street, 97862
(541) 310-1857 or (541) 938-4451

Milwaukie

Mill End Store Q E Y N W C
9701 SE McLoughlin Blvd., 97222
(503) 786-1234

Moro

Sage Mountain Primitives Y W S
408 1/2 Main Street
P.O. Box 101, 97039
(541) 705-0232
Call for Hours
http://www.sagemountainprimitives.com

Mt. Vernon

Shiny Thimble Quilt Studio Q E
100 E. Main Street, 97865
(541) 932-4111

Newberg

Ace Sewing & Vacuum Q E M
2414 Portland Rd, Suite 1, 97132
(503) 538-1122

Pacific Wool And Fiber Y W S
2505 Portland Road, Suite 104, 97132
(503) 538-4741

Newport

Quilter's Cove Q
27 N. Coast Highway, 97365
(541) 265-2591

Nyssa

Marilynn's Pickets & Patchwork Q E
118 Main Street, 97913
(541) 372-5336

Ontario

Charmed Needles LLC Q E C
222 S. Oregon Street, 97914
(541) 889-6215

Oregon City

Knit-A-Bit Y
16925 S. Beckman Road, 97045
(503) 631-4596

Save Stores M
1900 McLoughlin Blvd., Suite #80, 97045

Authorized Retailer

Paisley

Paisley Fabric and Quilt Q
515 Mill Street, 97636
(541) 219-6700

Pendleton

Thimbles Fabric-N-More Q E Y N C
1849 Westgate Place, 97801
(541) 278-7910

Philomath

JanniLou Creations Q E
1243 Main Street, 97370
(541) 929-3795

Port Orford

Quilter's Corner Q E
335 7th Street, 97465
(541) 332 0502

Portland

Fiber Rhythm Craft & Design Ⓨ Ⓦ Ⓢ

➡ SEE AD BELOW

At Southeast Division Street at 10th (In Ford Bldg), 97202
(503) 236-7318
May - Sept: SuM 12-6, Th 11-8, FSa 11-6; Check website for fall and winter hours
www.fiberrhythm.com

In Stitches Ⓝ

2361 NW Westover Road, 97210
(503) 226-0814
M-F 10-5, Sa 10-4:30
www.institchespdx.com

McKenna Ryan Quilt & Fabric Shop Ⓠ

1925 SE Jefferson Street, 97222
(800) 728-2278 or (503) 374-1930
Check our website or Facebook, or call to confirm hours.
www.pineneedles.com

Pendleton Woolen Mill Store Ⓠ Ⓨ Ⓦ Ⓢ

8500 SE McLoughlin Blvd., 97222
(866) 865-9285 or (503) 535-5786
M-Sa 10-5:30, Su 11-4
https://woolenmill.store/

Pioneer Quilts Ⓠ Ⓔ

3101 SE Courtney, 97222
(503) 654-1555
M-Sa 10-5, Su 11-4
www.pioneerquiltshop.com

Acorns & Threads Ⓔ Ⓒ
4475 SW Scholls Ferry Road, Suite 158, 97225
(503) 292-4457

Bolt Neighborhood Fabric Boutique Ⓠ Ⓔ
4636 NE 42nd Avenue, Suite C, 97218
(503) 287-2658

Close Knit Ⓨ
2140 NE Alberta Street, 97211
(503) 288-4568

Cool Cottons Ⓠ
2417 SE Hawthorne Blvd., 97214
(503) 232-0417

Knitting Bee Ⓨ
10934 SW Barnes Road, 97225
(503) 439-3316

Modern Domestic Ⓠ Ⓔ Ⓜ
422 NE Alberta Street, 97211
(503) 808-9910

Northwest Wools Ⓨ Ⓦ Ⓢ
3524 SW Troy Street, 97219
(503) 244-5024

Pearl Fiber Arts Ⓨ Ⓢ
428 NW 11th Avenue, 97209
(503) 227-7746

Save Stores Ⓜ
6701 SE Foster Road, 97206
(844) 276-3286 or (503) 775-7283

Authorized Retailer

Starlight Knitting Society LLC Ⓨ
7028 SE 52nd Avenue, 97206
(503) 777-1715 or (503) 975-3720

The NeedleArt Closet Ⓝ Ⓒ
4231 NE Broadway Street, 97213
(503) 288-3992

Twisted Ⓨ Ⓦ Ⓢ
2310 NE Broadway Street, 97232
(503) 922-1150

Prairie City

Quilts and Beyond* Ⓠ Ⓔ
209 N. McHaley Avenue, 97869
(541) 820-4777

Prineville

The Quilt Shack Ⓠ Ⓔ
1211 NW Madras Highway 26, 97754
(541) 447-1338

Redmond

High Mountain Fabric Quilt Shop Ⓠ
1542 S. Highway 97, 97756
(541) 548-6909

Material Girl Fabrics Ⓠ
307 NW 7th Street, 97756
(541) 923-1600

Roseburg

Knotty Lady Yarns Ⓨ Ⓦ Ⓢ
632 SE Jackson Street, 97470
(541) 673-2199
Tu-F 10-5, Sa 10-4
www.knottyladyyarns.com

Country Lady Quilt Shop Ⓠ
611 SE Jackson Street, 97470
(541) 673-1007

Everything Sew Nice* Ⓠ Ⓜ
250 NE Garden Valley Blvd., Suite 16, 97470
(541) 236-7139

Lydia's Quilt & Crafts Studio* Ⓠ
960 W. Harvard Avenue, 97471
(541) 391-6661

Salem

Discover Quilting Ⓠ
910 Commercial Street SE, 97302
(971) 304-7349

Paramount Sewing & Vacuum Ⓠ Ⓜ
3960 Rickey Street SE, 97317
(503) 990-8186

Tangled Purls Ⓨ Ⓢ
2290 Commercial Street SE, Suite 140, 97302
(503) 339-7556

Teaselwick Wools Ⓨ
1313 Mill Street SE, 97301
(971) 304-7050

Whitlocks Vacuum and Sewing Supercenter Ⓜ
455 Court Street NE, 97301
(888) 224-9912 or (503) 585-7771

Handi Quilter® Authorized Retailer
Designed by a Quilter, for Quilters.®

Sandy

Designer Yarn Ⓨ Ⓢ
38871 Proctor Blvd., 97055
(503) 826-0123

Paradise Quilts & Fabrics Ⓠ
39400 Pioneer Blvd., Suite 7, 97055
(503) 668-3106

Siletz

Sew Hound Ⓠ
109 N. Gaither Street, 97380
(541) 444-1251

Silverton

Apples to Oranges Ⓨ Ⓢ
204 E. Main Street, 97381
(503) 874-4901

Sisters

The Stitchin' Post Ⓠ Ⓔ Ⓨ Ⓜ
311 W. Cascade Street, 97759
(541) 549-6061

Springfield

Ben Franklin Crafts* Ⓔ Ⓨ Ⓝ Ⓒ
1028 Harlow Road, 97477
(541) 726-2641

Jean Marie's Fabrics Ⓠ
110 Main Street, 97477
(541) 746-0433

Something to Crow About* Ⓠ Ⓔ
4227C Main Street, 97478
(541) 746-3256

Sutherlin

Chicks and a Rooster Ⓠ Ⓔ
460 S. Comstock Street, 97479
(541) 860-8140

Sweet Home

Seamingly Creative* Ⓠ Ⓔ Ⓒ
1245 Main Street, 97386
(541) 367-8934

Tigard

Ace Sewing & Vacuum Ⓠ Ⓔ Ⓜ
12195 SW Main St, 97223
(503) 598-0122

Tillamook

Jane's Fabric Patch Ⓠ Ⓔ Ⓨ Ⓒ Ⓜ
➡ SEE AD BELOW
1110 Main Avenue, 97141
(503) 842-9392
Winter: M-F 9-5, Sa 10-4; Summer (Memorial Day thru Labor Day): M-F 9-5, Sa 10-4, Su 11-3
www.janesfabricpatch.com

Friends of Latimer Quilt & Textile Center Ⓠ Ⓨ Ⓦ Ⓢ
2105 Wilson River Loop, 97141
(503) 842-8622

Tangled Yarns Ⓨ
207 Main Street, 97141
(541) 418-2329

Troutdale

My Quilting Loft Ⓠ Ⓜ
➡ SEE AD BELOW
253 E. Historic Columbia River, 97060
(503) 419-7154
Tu-Sa 10-5

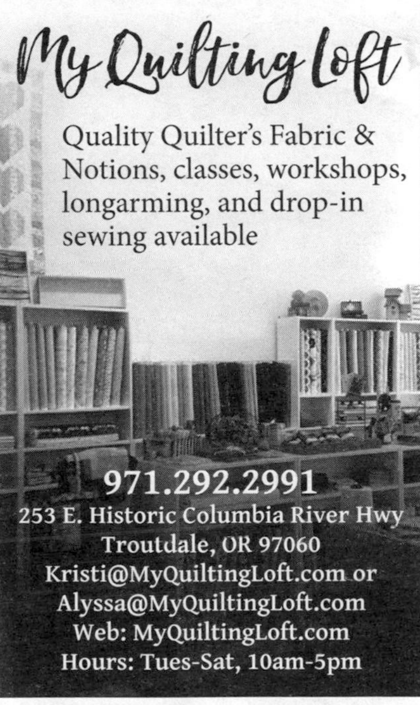

My Quilting Loft
Quality Quilter's Fabric & Notions, classes, workshops, longarming, and drop-in sewing available
971.292.2991
253 E. Historic Columbia River Hwy
Troutdale, OR 97060
Kristi@MyQuiltingLoft.com or
Alyssa@MyQuiltingLoft.com
Web: MyQuiltingLoft.com
Hours: Tues-Sat, 10am-5pm

Union

Knitkabob* Ⓨ Ⓢ
156 S. Main Street, 97883
(541) 562-2276

Waldport

Family Fabrics Ⓠ Ⓔ Ⓨ Ⓝ Ⓒ Ⓜ
650 NW Hemlock Street, Suite B, 97394
(541) 563-3064

Warren

Fibers & Stitches Fabric and Quilting Supplies Ⓠ
58093 Columbia River Highway, 97053
(503) 397-5536

Wheeler

Creative Fabrics* Ⓠ Ⓔ Ⓒ
475 Highway 101, 97147
(503) 368-5900

Wilsonville

Hollyhill Quilt Shoppe & Mercantile* Ⓠ Ⓔ Ⓒ
31840 SW Charbonneau Drive, Suite F, 97070
(503) 694-8052

Sewn Loverly* Ⓠ
8502 SW Main Street, Suite 100, 97070
(971) 224-5712

Woodburn

Woodburn Sew & Vac Center Ⓠ
1585 N. Pacific Highway, Suite D, 97071
(503) 981-6921

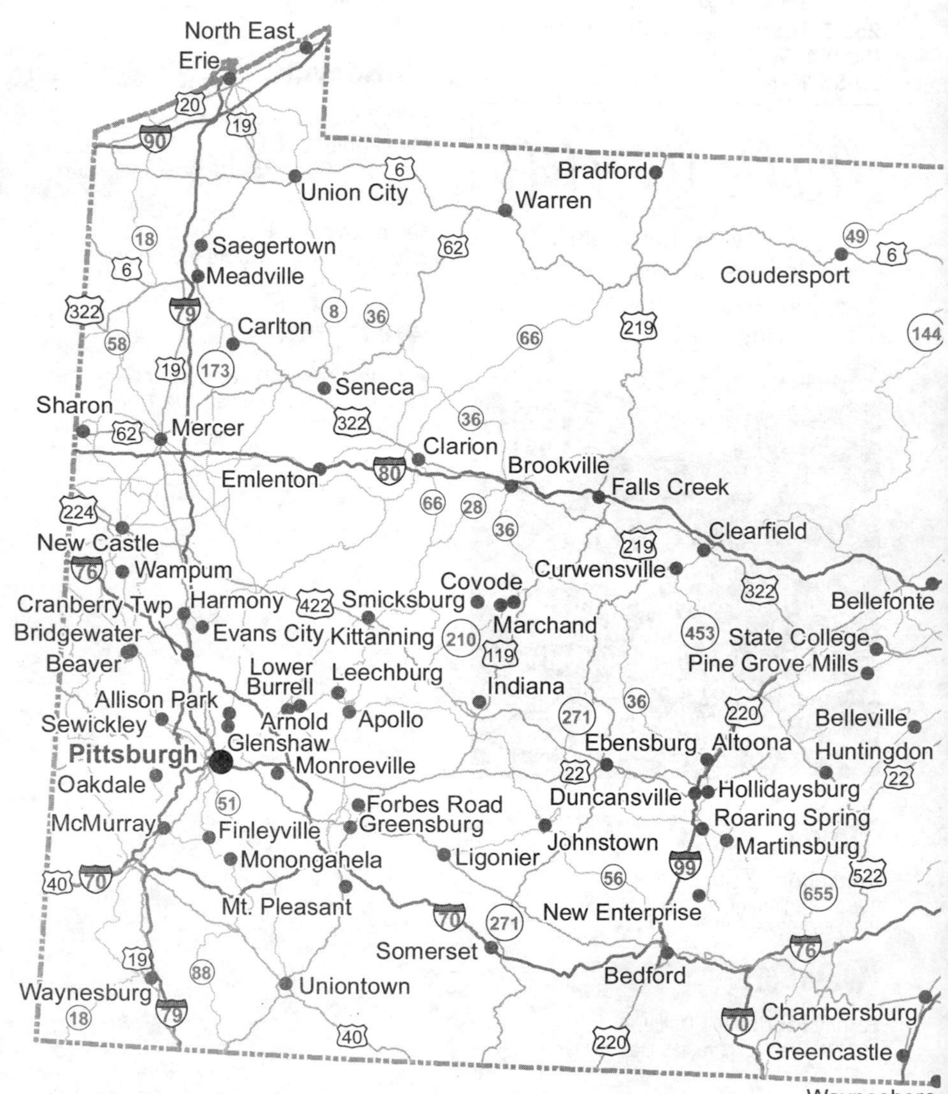
North East
Erie
Union City
Bradford
Warren
Saegertown
Meadville
Coudersport
Carlton
Seneca
Sharon
Mercer
Clarion
Emlenton
Brookville
Falls Creek
New Castle
Clearfield
Wampum
Curwensville
Covode
Cranberry Twp
Harmony
Smicksburg
Bellefonte
Evans City
Marchand
Bridgewater
Kittanning
State College
Beaver
Lower Burrell
Leechburg
Pine Grove Mills
Indiana
Allison Park
Arnold
Apollo
Belleville
Sewickley
Glenshaw
Ebensburg
Altoona
Huntingdon
Pittsburgh
Monroeville
Oakdale
Duncansville
Hollidaysburg
Forbes Road
McMurray
Finleyville
Greensburg
Roaring Spring
Johnstown
Martinsburg
Monongahela
Ligonier
Mt. Pleasant
New Enterprise
Somerset
Bedford
Waynesburg
Uniontown
Chambersburg
Greencastle
Waynesboro

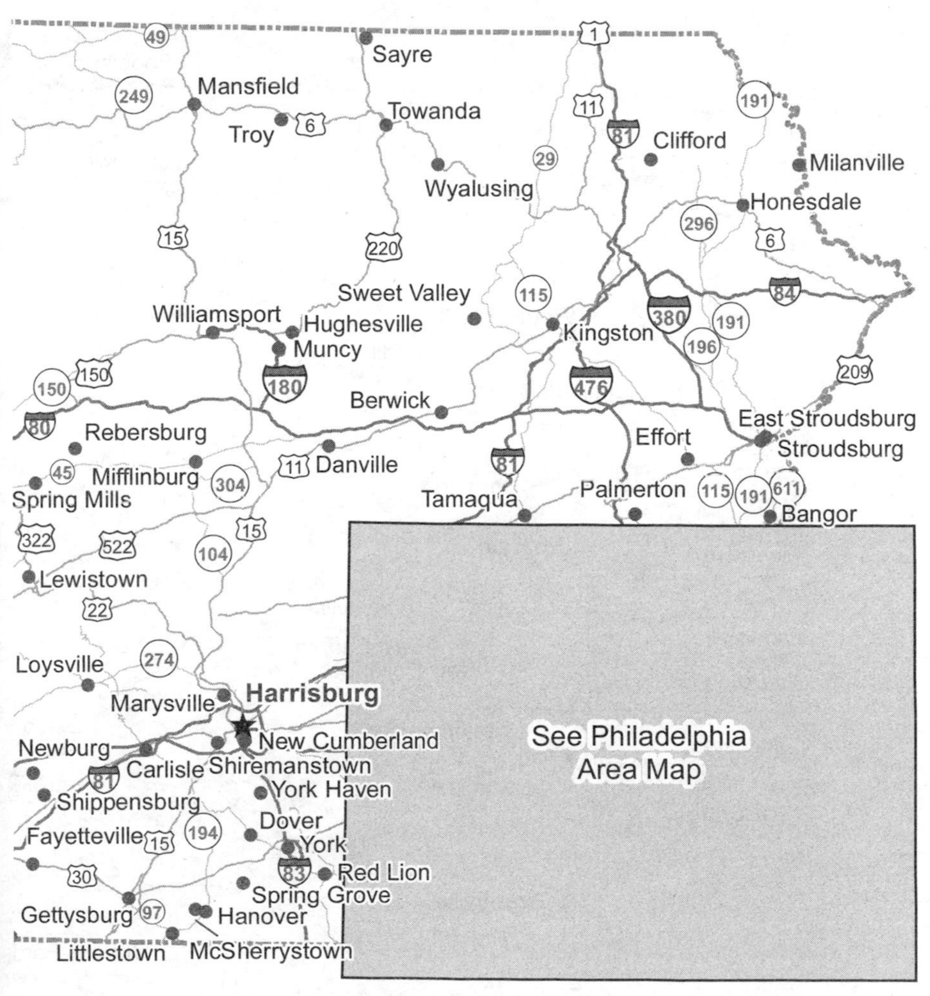

Sayre
Mansfield
Troy
Towanda
Wyalusing
Clifford
Milanville
Honesdale
Sweet Valley
Williamsport
Hughesville
Muncy
Kingston
Berwick
East Stroudsburg
Stroudsburg
Rebersburg
Effort
Danville
Mifflinburg
Spring Mills
Tamaqua
Palmerton
Bangor
Lewistown
Loysville
Harrisburg
Marysville
New Cumberland
Newburg
Carlisle
Shiremanstown
York Haven
Shippensburg
Dover
Fayetteville
York
Red Lion
Spring Grove
Gettysburg
Hanover
Littlestown
McSherrystown
See Philadelphia Area Map

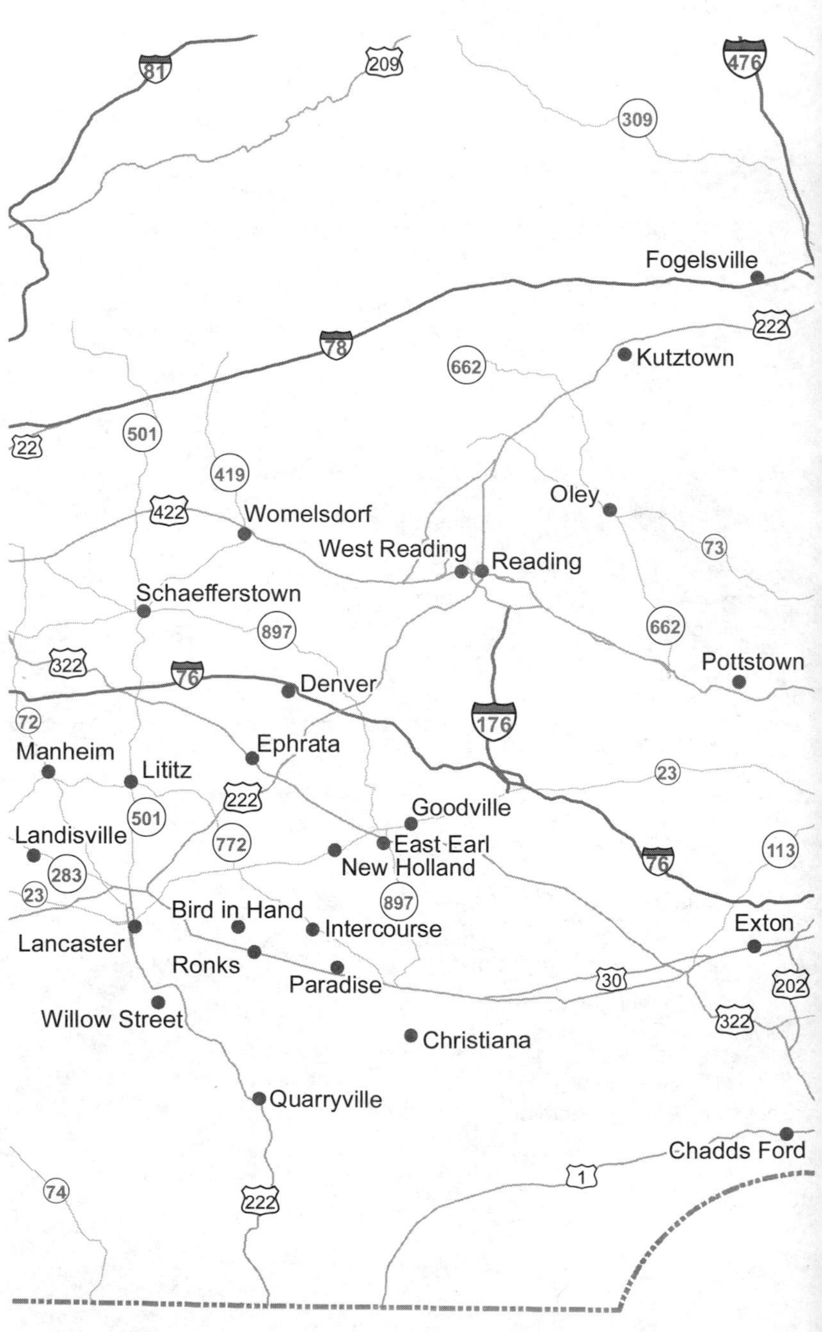
81
209
476
309
Fogelsville
78
222
Kutztown
662
22
501
419
Oley
422
Womelsdorf
West Reading
Reading
73
Schaefferstown
897
662
Pottstown
322
76
Denver
176
72
Manheim
Ephrata
Lititz
23
222
Goodville
501
Landisville
772
East Earl
New Holland
76
113
283
23
897
Bird in Hand
Intercourse
Exton
Lancaster
Ronks
Paradise
30
202
Willow Street
322
Christiana
Quarryville
Chadds Ford
1
74
222

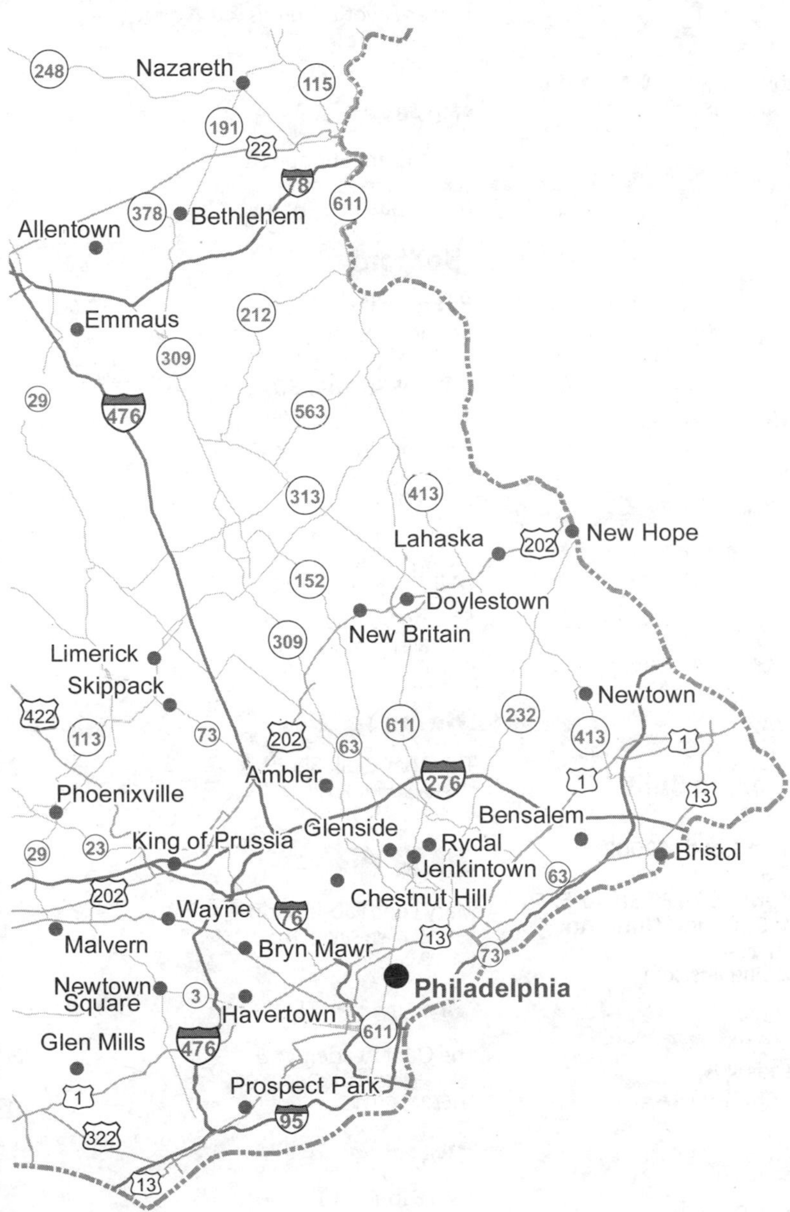
Nazareth
Bethlehem
Allentown
Emmaus
Lahaska
New Hope
Doylestown
New Britain
Limerick
Skippack
Newtown
Ambler
Phoenixville
Bensalem
Glenside
Rydal
King of Prussia
Bristol
Jenkintown
Chestnut Hill
Wayne
Malvern
Bryn Mawr
Philadelphia
Newtown Square
Havertown
Glen Mills
Prospect Park

Pennsylvania

Allentown

Tucker Yarn Company, Inc. Ⓠ Ⓔ Ⓨ Ⓝ Ⓦ Ⓒ
950 W. Hamilton Street, 18101
(610) 434-1846 or (610) 439-8811

Allison Park

HipStrings* Ⓨ Ⓦ Ⓢ
3812 William Flinn Highway, Bldg. 4, 2nd Floor, 15101
(814) 777-5301

The Quilt Company Ⓠ Ⓜ
3940 Middle Road, 15101
(412) 487-9532

Altoona

Frye's Sweeper & Sewing Center* Ⓠ Ⓜ
1400 Valley View Blvd., 16602
(814) 943-5001

Moore Stitches Ⓨ Ⓒ
1635 E. Pleasant Valley Blvd., 16602
(814) 943-2977

Ambler

The Round Bobbin Quilt Shop Ⓠ Ⓔ
1126B Horsham Road, 19002
(215) 367-5596
Winter: (Sept.-May) TuWFSa 10-5, Th 10-7, Su 12-4; Summer: (June-Aug) Tu-Sa 10-5, Su 12-4
www.roundbobbinquilts.com

Apollo

Common Threads Ⓠ Ⓜ
322 N. Second Street, 15613
(724) 236-0196

Arnold

Country Counter Ⓒ
1807 5th Avenue, 15068
(724) 339-0550

Bangor

Hope's Favorite Things Ⓔ Ⓨ Ⓦ Ⓢ
8480 Delaware Drive, 18013
(610) 599-1615

Beaver

Beaver Yarn Shoppe* Ⓨ
568 Third Street, 2nd Floor, 15009
(724) 709-0272

Bedford

Yarn Knitch Ⓨ
109 W. Pitt Street, 15522
(814) 310-2156
MWThFSa 10-5:30
www.yarnknitch.com

Firesong Studio Ⓨ Ⓦ Ⓢ
201 W. Penn Street, 15522
(814) 623-0776

Mary's Quilt Shop Ⓠ
113 W. Pitt Street, 15522
(814) 310-2278

Sewing Solutions Ⓠ Ⓜ
6068 Business 220, 15522
(814) 623-2413

Bellefonte

Third Bay Quilt Shop* Ⓠ
105 Rabbit Hill Road, 16823
(814) 355-7108

Belleville

Mary Lee's Fabric Shop Ⓠ Ⓔ Ⓒ
3510 W. Main Street, 17004
(717) 935-2691

Bensalem

The Quilt Academy* Ⓠ
3671 Hulmeville Road, 19020
(215) 245-2011

Berwick

J & B Fabrics Ⓠ Ⓔ
2617 W. Front Street, 18603
(570) 752-2627

Bethlehem

The Knitter's Edge Ⓨ Ⓦ
1601 W. Broad Street, 18018
(610) 419-9276

Bird in Hand

Labadie Looms* Ⓨ Ⓦ Ⓢ
2572 Old Philadelphia Pike, 17505
(717) 291-8911

Log Cabin Quilt Shop Ⓠ
2679 Old Philadelphia Pike, 17505
(717) 393-1702

The Quilt and Fabric Shack* Ⓠ
3137 Old Philadelphia Pike, 17505
(717) 768-0338

Bradford

Knit Kits to Go Ⓨ
45 Main Street, 16701
(814) 598-0330

Little Fabric Garden* Ⓠ
25 Main Street, 16701
(814) 362-6070 or (814) 362-1606

Bridgewater

Covered Bridge Needle Art Ⓒ
300 Bridge Street, 15009
(724) 775-4440

Bristol

Ye Olde Cross Stitchery Ⓔ Ⓝ Ⓒ
119 Pond Street, 19007
(215) 785-0870 or (877) 785-0870
Tu 10:30-5, ThF 12:30-6, Sa 10:30-3
www.yeoldecs.com

Brookville

Heirloom Quilting Ⓠ Ⓔ Ⓒ Ⓜ
1225 Route 36 N, 15825
(814) 849-8739

Spin-A-Yarn Ⓨ
360 Main Street, 15825
(814) 849-2512

Bryn Mawr

Creative Way Needlepoint Ⓝ
849 W. Lancaster Avenue, 19010
(610) 525-2366
Tu-Sa 10-5
http://www.facebook.com/pg/CreativeWayNeedlepoint

Carlisle

The Fabric Center* Ⓠ
41 W. Pomfret Street, 17013
(717) 243-5076

Carlton

Homespun Treasures Quilt Shop Ⓠ
509 U.S. Highway 322
(GPS: 28th Division Highway), 16311
(814) 425-2889

Chadds Ford

A Garden of Yarn Ⓨ
34 Olde Ridge Village, 19317
(610) 459-5599

Chambersburg

The Yarn Basket Ⓨ
150 Falling Spring Road, 17202
(717) 263-3236 or (888) 976-2758

Chestnut Hill

The Knit With Ⓨ
8226 Germantown Avenue, 19118
(215) 247-9276

Christiana

The Quilt Ledger Ⓠ
326 N. Bridge Street, 17509
(610) 593-7300

Clarion

Cotton Creations* Ⓠ
10688A Route 66, 16214
(814) 764-6080

Clearfield

Quilter's Stash Plus Q
500 Turnpike Avenue, 16830
(814) 765-2162
Tu-F 10-5, Sa 10-3
www.quiltersstashplus.com

Clifford

Alpacabilities Y W S
Please call for directions, 18413
(570) 280-2272

Coudersport

Yarn at Olga's Y
10 E. 2nd Street
(Route 6 East), 16915
(814) 260-9966

Covode

Autumn House Farm & Heritage Artworks Y W S
1001 Locust Road, 15771
(724) 286-9596

Cranberry Township

Amy Baughman Sew and Quilt Q M
20215 Route 19, Suite 106, 16066
(724) 779-1390

Curwensville

Lisa's Sew Crafty Q E Y S
315 Filbert Street, 16833
(814) 577-0819

Danville

Swisher's Yarn Basket Y
487 Ferry Street, 17821
(570) 275-9276

Denver

Burkholder's Fabric Store Q E
2155 W. Route 897, 17517
(717) 336-6692

Weaver's Store, Inc.* Q E Y N C
1011 Dry Tavern Road, 17517
(717) 445-6791

Dover

The Finishing Stitch* Q
4103 Carlisle Road, 17315
(717) 467-8274

Doylestown

Forever Yarn* Y
15 W. Oakland Avenue, 18901
(215) 348-5648

The Sewing Room Q E N C M
130 S. Clinton Street, 18901
(267) 406-0486

Duncansville

Connie's Collectibles & Quilt Shop* Q
469 Foot of Ten Road, 16635
(814) 695-2786

Handi Quilter® Authorized Retailer
Designed by a Quilter, for Quilters.®

East Earl

Zinck's Fabric Outlet Q
1564 Main Street, Suite 500, 17519
(717) 445-6123
M-Sa 8-5
www.zincksfabric.com

Family Farm Fabrics Q
1121 Main Street, 17519
(717) 354-2086

Good's Store* Q E Y C
1338 Main Street, 17519
(717) 354-4026

East Stroudsburg

Mountain Knits & Pearls Y
114 Washington Street, Suite 100, 18301
(570) 424-7770

Ebensburg

Creative Fabrics & Quilt Shop* Q
3135 New Germany Road, Suite 25, 15931
(814) 419-8227

Effort

The Country Quilterie Q M
2783 Route 115, 18330
(570) 620-9707

Emlenton

Amazing Stitches Q E M
611 Main Street, 16373
(724) 867-0880

Emmaus

Conversational Threads Fiber Arts Studio Y W S
6 S. 4th Street, 18049
(610) 421-8889

Ephrata

Good's Store* Q
1686 W. Main Street, 17522
(717) 733-7356

Piece by Piece Quilt Shop Q
55 New Street, 17522
(717) 738-6983

West Earl Woolen Mill Y S
126 Cocalico Creek Road, 17522
(717) 859-2241

Erie

Millcreek Sewing & Fabric Q E M
6044 Peach Street, 16509
(814) 866-8227
M-Sa 10-5
www.millcreeksew.com

Cultured Purl* Y W
3141 W. 26th Street, 16506
(814) 836-7875

Kelly's Sewing Corner Q
3330 W. 26th Street, Suite 15, 16506
(814) 838-7158

Rustic and Refined Y
2598 W. 8th Street, 16505
(814) 838-1710

Evans City

Little Foot Quilt Shoppe* Q
115 W. Main Street, 16033
(724) 482-6334 or (800) 597-7075

Exton

The Quilt Block Inc. Q
95 E. Welsh Pool Road, 19341
(610) 363-0404

Falls Creek

Amy's Yarn Boutique Y W
394 Slab Run Road, 15840
(814) 371-4300

Fayetteville

The Sew'n Place Q
6195 Chambersburg Road, 17222
(717) 352-3050

Finleyville

Quilters Corner Q
6101 State Route 88, 15332
(724) 348-8010

Fogelsville

Althouse's Sewing Machine Y W S M
2371 Packhouse Road, 18051
(610) 285-6597

Forbes Road

Raggz Fiber Art Y S
118A General Street, 15633
(724) 600-5550

Gettysburg

Needle & Thread Q E
2215 Fairfield Road, 17325
(717) 334-4011

Glen Mills

The Strawberry Sampler C
364 Wilmington Pike, A-2, 19342
(610) 459-8580 or (800) 634-6106
Tu-Sa 10-3
www.strawberrysampler.com

Glenshaw

The Quilting Needle* Q
3394 Saxonburg Blvd., Suite 550, 15116
(412) 767-5500

Glenside

Stitchers' Dream Q E Y M
221 S. Easton Road, 19038
(215) 885-3780

Goodville

H. W. Oberholzer & Son (Obie's Country Store) Q
1585 Main Street (Route 23), 17528
(717) 445-4616

Greencastle

Stitch-N-Time Q M
14472 Molly Pitcher Highway, 17225
(717) 597-0051
MTuF 9-5, WSa 9-3, Th 9-7
www.greencastlesewing.com

Handi Quilter® Authorized Retailer
Designed by a Quilter, for Quilters.®

Shady Grove Fabrics* Q E
2900 Buchanan Trail E, 17225
(717) 593-9900

Greensburg

The Stitch in Time Shoppe* Q M
801 N. Greengate Road, Suite 370, 15601
(724) 836-0611

Hanover

Danner's Bernina Shoppe* Q M
551 Beck Mill Road, 17331
(717) 637-4685

Harmony

Darn Yarn Needles and Thread Y W S
➡ SEE AD BELOW
253 Mercer Street, Unit D, 16037
(724) 473-0983
TuWFSa 10-4, Th 10-7
www.darnyarnneedlesandthread.com

Harrisburg

Knitters Dream* Y W S
605 LeSentier Lane, 17112
(717) 599-7665 or (800) 458-4177

Little Owl's Knit Shop* Y
2209 Paxton Church Road, 17110
(717) 412-0900

Havertown

Needle Me N
12 E. Eagle Road, 19083
(610) 446-4004

Hollidaysburg

Delightful Ewe Y
206 Bedford Street-Rear, 16648
(814) 696-0331

Honesdale

The Mountain Quiltworks Q
20 Grandma's Lane, 18431
(570) 253-9510
Tu-Sa 10-5
http://www.themountainquiltworks.com

Hughesville

Lazy Meadows Alpacas and Fiber Mill* Ⓨ Ⓦ Ⓢ
486 Lime Bluff Road, 17737
(570) 546-2291

Huntingdon

Hindman's Fabrics Ⓠ Ⓜ
11569 Hartslog Valley Road, 16652
(814) 627-4195

Indiana

Yarns Ⓨ
1136 Philadephia Street, 15701
(724) 349-3240

Intercourse

Zook's Fabric Ⓠ
➡ SEE AD BELOW
3535 Old Philadelphia Pike, 17534
(717) 768-8153
M-Sa 8-5
www.saudersfabric.com

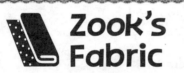

Lancaster Yarn Shop Ⓨ Ⓢ
3519 Old Philadelphia Pike, 17534
(717) 768-8007

Nancy's Corner Ⓠ
3503 Old Philadelphia Pike, 17534
(717) 768-8790

The Old Country Store Ⓠ
3510 Old Philadelphia Pike, 17534
(717) 768-7101 or (800) 828-8218

Jenkintown

Luv2Knit & More* Ⓔ Ⓨ Ⓦ Ⓒ
610 Old York Road, Suite 121, 19046
(267) 886-2000 or (215) 783-3783

Johnstown

Schraders Fabrics by Barb* Ⓠ
2078 Bedford Street, 15904
(814) 266-3113

The Quilt Peddler Ⓠ Ⓜ
620 Lamberd Avenue, 15904
(814) 262-9656

King of Prussia

Steve's Sewing, Vacuum & Quilting Ⓠ Ⓜ
314 S. Henderson Road, 19406
(610) 768-9453 or (800) 585-9453

Kingston

Gosh Yarn It!* Ⓨ
303 Market Street, 18704
(570) 287-9999

Kittanning

Claypoole's Fabrics* Ⓠ
592 Claypoole Road, 16201
(724) 297-3860

Kutztown

Wooden Bridge Drygoods Ⓠ Ⓔ Ⓨ Ⓒ
195 Deysher Road, 19530
(610) 683-7159

Lahaska

Twist Knitting & Spinning Ⓨ Ⓦ Ⓢ
5743 Lower York Road, 18931
(215) 794-3020

Lancaster

Stitches Unlimited Ⓝ Ⓒ
➡ **SEE AD BELOW**
The Village of Olde Hickory
721 Olde Hickory Road, 17601
(717) 560-9416
Tu-F 10-5, Sa 9-2
www.facebook.com/pages/Stitches-Unlimited-at-Olde-Hickory-Shops/332545533485481

The Speckled Sheep Ⓨ Ⓦ Ⓢ
➡ **SEE AD BELOW**
705 Olde Hickory Road, 17601
(717) 435-8359
MWFSa 9-4, TuTh 9-7; Call for summer hours
www.thespeckledsheep.com

AAA Vacuum & Sewing Center* Ⓜ
1357 Fruitville Pike, 17601
(717) 397-5776

Authorized Retailer

Oh Susanna Ⓨ
2204 Marietta Avenue, 17603
(717) 393-5146

Landisville

Flying Fibers Ⓨ Ⓦ Ⓢ
329 Main Street, 17538
(717) 898-8020

Leechburg

Farmhouse Fabrics at Old Springhouse Antiques Ⓠ Ⓔ
786 Schenley Road, 15656
(724) 845-2745

Lewistown

Marty's Quilt Shop* Ⓠ Ⓨ Ⓢ Ⓒ
135 Nolan Drive, 17044
(717) 953-9947

Ligonier

Bo Peep Fine Yarns* Ⓨ Ⓢ
221 W. Main Street, 15658
(724) 238-4040

Kathy's Kreations Ⓨ
141 E. Main Street, 15658
(724) 238-9320

Limerick

Just Cross Stitch Ⓒ
308 W. Ridge Pike, 19468
(610) 409-9373
W-Sa 11-4, 1st Su 11-2
www.facebook.com/pages/Just-Cross-Stitch-PA/1379508228949553

Lititz

Ewebiquitous* Ⓨ Ⓦ Ⓢ
15 S. Broad Street, 17543
(717) 568-8890

Weavers Dry Goods Ⓠ Ⓔ
108 W. Brubaker Valley Road, 17543
(717) 627-1724

Littlestown

Simply Stashing Fabric & Quilts Ⓠ
1897 Hanover Pike, 17340
(717) 359-4121

Lower Burrell

The Sewing Store* Q M
103 Macbeth Drive, 15068
(724) 334-1985

Loysville

Wise Dry Goods* Q E Y C
5683 Sherman Valley Road, 17047
(717) 789-4308

Malvern

Fireside Stitchery N
179 Lancaster Ave, Suite 3, 19355
(610) 889-9835 or (800) 531-2607

Manheim

Stitch & Craft Q M
2957 Lebanon Road, 17545
(717) 664-4230

Mansfield

Yorkshire Meadows Knitting & Spinning Shop Y S
9646 N. Elk Run Road, 16933
(570) 549-2553

Marchand

Silverbrook Fiber Arts & Sheepskins* Y W S
16040 Route 119 Highway N, 15758
(724) 286-3317

Martinsburg

Traditions Q E C
2327 Curryville Road, 16662
(814) 793-3980

Marysville

Smile Spinners Q M
1975 Valley Road, 17053
(717) 957-4225

McMurray

Sew Much Fun* Q M
242 E. McMurray, 15317
(724) 942-9425

McSherrystown

Creative Ewe Yarn Shop Y W S
11 N. 5th Street, 17344
(717) 634-2416

Meadville

Fox's Sew & Vac Q M
900 Water Street, Suite 22, 16335
(814) 333-1400

Yarn Vault Y
900 Water Street
Downtown Mall, 16335
(814) 758-8837

Mercer

The Gallery of Fabric Q E M
116 N. Pitt Street, 16137
(724) 662-0464

Mifflinburg

Hoover's Bernina Sew, LLC Q E M
2282 Beaver Road, 17844
(570) 966-3822

Verna's Fabric Q E
1430 Redbank Road, 17844
(570) 966-2350

Milanville

Skirted Fleece Mill* Y S
657 Calkins Road, 18443
(570) 729-8162

Monongahela

The Memory Tree and Yarn Branch Y C
1015 Chess Street, 15063
(724) 258-6758

Monroeville

Thornton Company M
5046 William Penn Highway, 15146
(724) 733-8440

Mt. Pleasant

Quilt Patch, Etc. Q E N C
806 W. Main Street, 15666
(724) 887-4160

Muncy

Ben Franklin Store and Pharmacy* Q E Y N W S C
2195 State Route 442, 17756
(570) 546-8272

Nazareth

Kraemer Yarn Shop* Y S
240 S. Main Street, 18064
(610) 759-1294

New Britain/Doylestown

Byrne Sewing Connection Q E M
422 E. Butler Avenue, 18901
(215) 230-9411 or (888) 302-9411

New Castle

Log House E N C
134 Mohawk School Road, 16102
(724) 667-8444
Winter: TuThFSa 11-5, W 11-8;
Summer: TuThSa 11-5, W 11-8

New Cumberland

Half Moon Handwerks Q E N C
214 3rd Street, 17070
(717) 774-3020
Tu-F 10-5, Sa 10-3 (See website for expanded seasonal hours.)
www.halfmoonhandwerks.com

New Enterprise

Zimmerman's Bernina Sewing Shop* Q E M
208 Flitch Road, 16664
(814) 766-9942

New Holland

Cedar Lane Dry Goods* Q
204 Orlan Road, 17557
(717) 354-0030

Twin Hill Shoppe* Q
914 Centerville Road, 17557
(717) 445-8153

New Hope

Gazebo Plus E Y N C
7 Village Row, 18938
(215) 862-0740

Newburg

Esh's Store Q E
16285 Cumberland Highway, 17240
(717) 530-5305
Winter: (Oct 1- Apr 30) M-Sa 8-5;
Summer: (May 1-Sept 30) MWThF 8-7, TuSa 8-5

Newtown

Echo Valley Fiber Y W S
2310 Second Street Pike
Front Porch, 18940
(267) 396-6938

Knit LLC Y
10 S. State Street, 18940
(267) 685-0794

Knitting To Know Ewe PA, LLC* Y W S
247 N. Sycamore Street, 18940
(215) 598-9276

Newtown Square

Slip Knot Y
3715 W. Chester Pike, 19073
(610) 359-9070

North East

Calico Patch Quilt Shop Q
107 Clay Street, Suite 3, 16428
(814) 725-2275

Super Stitch Sewing and Vacuum Center Q E M
10429 W. Main Road, 16428
(888) 525-9724 or (814) 725-9724

Oakdale

Tonidale Yarn & Needle Craft Y C
7231 Steubenville Pike, 15071
(412) 788-8850

Oley

All Things Ewesful Ⓨ
3240 W. Philadelphia Avenue, 19547
(484) 491-1330

Ladyfingers Sewing Studio ⓆⓂ
6375 Oley Turnpike Road, 19547
(610) 689-0068

Palmerton

The Quilted Crow Ⓠ
413 Delaware Avenue, 18701
(610) 900-4700

Paradise

Farmhouse Memories* Ⓠ
148-A Harristown Road, 17568
(717) 442-1907

Philadelphia

Gaffney Fabrics* ⓆⒺ
5401 Germantown Avenue, 19144
(215) 849-8180

Handcraft Workshop* ⓆⒺⒸ
7224 Germantown Avenue, 19119
(215) 247-1440

Hidden River Yarns Ⓨ
4358-B Main Street, 19127
(215) 920-2603

Loop Ⓨ
1914 South Street, 19146
(215) 893-9939

Rittenhouse Needlepoint ⒺⓃⒸ
1216 Arch Street, Suite 2A, 19107
(215) 563-4566 or (877) 764-6880

Yarnphoria* Ⓨ
1020 Pine Street, 19107
(215) 923-0914

Phoenixville

Purls of Wisdom* ⓎⓈ
2208 Kimberton Road, 19460
(610) 933-5010

Pine Grove Mills

Stitch Your Art Out ⓆⓎ
235 E. Pine Grove Road, 16868
(814) 238-4151

Pittsburgh

Dyed in the Wool ⓎⓌⓈ
3458 Babcock Blvd., 15237
(412) 364-0310
TuWTh 10-7, FSa 10-4
www.ditwpa.com

Gloria Horn Sewing Studio ⓆⒺⓂ
300 Castle Shannon Blvd., 15234
(412) 344-2330
MTuWFSa 10-5, Th 10-8
www.sew412.com

Airport Sewing Center ⓆⒺ
13 W. Prospect, 15205
(412) 922-1000

Beehive NeedleArts ⓃⒸ
650 Washington Road, Suite 100, 15228
(412) 343-4630

Knit One* Ⓨ
2721 Murray Avenue, 15217
(412) 421-6666

Loom Exquiste Textiles Ⓠ
2124 Penn Avenue, 15222
(412) 586-4346

Needle Point Breeze Ⓝ
6734 Reynolds Street, 15206
(412) 361-6380

Piecing it Together Ⓠ
3458 Babcock Blvd., 15237
(412) 364-2440

Quilters Depot ⓆⒺⓎⓃⒸⓂ
4160 Library Road, 15234
(412) 308-6236
Handi Quilter® Authorized Retailer
Designed by a Quilter, for Quilters.®

Pittsburgh (Bridgeville)

Kid Ewe Knot Ⓨ

➡ SEE AD BELOW
429 Washington Avenue, Suite 4
Bridgeville Plaza, 15017
(412) 257-2557
TuThFSa 10-5, W 10-2; Su 12-4 (Aug.-March)
www.kideweknot.com

Knitting and crochet supplies

Also featuring a full class calendar with a knowledgeable and helpful staff

Tuesday 10-5pm, Wednesday 10-2pm
Thurs-Sat 10am-5pm,
Sunday (Aug-March) 12-4

Bridgeville Plaza, 429 Washington Ave
Bridgeville PA 15017
(412) 257-2557
www.kideweknot.com
Follow us on facebook

Pittsburgh (Oakmont)

Yarns By Design PA ⓎⓌ

➡ SEE AD BELOW
622 Allegheny River Blvd., 15139
(412) 794-8332
TuThF 10-7, WSa 10-4
www.yarnsbydesignpa.com

Pottstown

Pottstown Sewing* ⓆⓂ
142 Shoemaker Road, 19464
(610) 326-5055

Prospect Park

Finely the Knitting Party Ⓨ
1124 Lincoln Avenue, 19076
(610) 328-7210

Quarryville

Good's Store* Ⓠ
333 W. 4th Street, 17566
(717) 786-9028

Reading

Stitch N' Stuff Ⓒ
3646 Pottsville Pike, 19605
(610) 929-2464 or (800) 730-2464

Rebersburg

Main Street Yarn* ⓎⒸ
121 E. Main Street, 16872
(814) 349-2611

Red Lion

Grim Hollow Stitchery Ⓔ Ⓨ Ⓒ
1040 Grim Hollow Road, 17356
(717) 244-3220

Roaring Spring

Country Beefers Ⓠ
125 Lock Mountain Road, 16673
(814) 224-4818

Ronks

Dutchland Quilt Patch Ⓠ
2851 Lincoln Highway E, 17572
(717) 687-0534 or (800) 411-3221

Family Farm Quilt* Ⓠ
3511 W. Newport Road (Route 772), 17572
(717) 768-8375

Rydal

Renee's Knitwear Ⓨ
911 Crosswicks Road, 19046
(215) 376-0505

Saegertown

The Needleworks Ⓠ Ⓔ Ⓨ
16408 State Highway 86, 16433
(814) 783-0040

Sayre

Friendship Star Quilt Shop Ⓠ Ⓜ
131 Center Street, 18840
(570) 886-2296

Schaefferstown

Good's Store* Ⓠ
2499 Stiegel Pike, 17088
(717) 949-2663

Seneca

Quilters Cupboard Ⓠ
3344 PA 257, 16346
(814) 657-4542

Sewickley

Sewickley Yarns Ⓨ
435 Beaver Street, 15143
(412) 741-8894

The Porcupine Needlepoint Shop Ⓝ
404 Beaver Street, 15143
(412) 741-3380

Sharon

Never Enough Yarn* Ⓨ
142 E. State Street, 16146
(724) 347-0800

Shippensburg

Rocky Turf General Store* Ⓠ
949 Mud Level Road, 17257
(717) 532-3977

ShippenStitch Ⓠ Ⓨ Ⓒ Ⓜ
45 W. King Street, 17257
(717) 477-6938

Shiremanstown

The Colonial Yarn Shop Ⓨ
7 Front Street, 17011
(717) 763-8016
M-Th 11-5, F 11-8, Sa 10-4
www.colonialyarn.com

Skippack

Yarnings Ⓨ Ⓝ
4007 Skippack Pike, 19474
(610) 584-6216

Smicksburg

SuzyB Knits* Ⓨ
52 Clarion Street, 16256
(814) 257-8326

Somerset

The Sewing Box Quilt Shop Ⓠ Ⓜ
311 Georgian Place, 15501
(814) 701-2635
MTuWSa 10-5, ThF 10-6
www.sewingboxquiltshop.com

Spring Grove

Painted Spring Farm Alpacas* Y W S
280 Roth Church Road, 17362
(717) 891-8060

Spring Mills

Weaver's Store, Inc* Q E Y N C
108 Market Drive, 16875
(814) 349-2650

State College

Frye's / Moyer's Sweeper & Sewing Center* Q M
1011 E. College Avenue, Suite C, 16801
(814) 237-0089

Stroudsburg

American Ribbon's Quilt Shop Q Y N
925 Ann Street, 18360
(570) 421-7470

Pocono Sew & Vac Q M
567 Main Street, 18360
(570) 421-4580 or (800) 442-8227

Sweet Valley

118 Fabrics & More Q
1205 State Route 118, 18656
(570) 477-3166

Tamaqua

Summershanty Fiber Arts Y W
10 W. Broad Street, 2nd Floor, 18252
(570) 778-7711

Towanda

Shores Quilt Stop* Q
1003 Golden Mile Road, 18848
(570) 265-4444

Troy

Penny's Patches & Calico Cottage Retreat Center* Q
6789 Fallbrook Road, 16947
(570) 297-3697

Perry's Patches & Quilting* Q
29 Painter Lick Drive, 16947
(570) 297-4558

Union City

Bee Happy Quilting Q
16412 State Highway 8, 16438
(814) 694-2126

Uniontown

Sew Special* Q M
73 W. Main Street, 15401
(724) 438-1765

Wampum

Stramba Farm & Fiber Mill Y W S
2331 Chewton Wurtemburg Road, 16157
(724) 752-4146

Warren

Dreamboat Hobbies E Y N C
21690 US 6, 16365
(814) 723-8052

Wayne

Stitch Haus N
110 S. Wayne Avenue, 19087
(610) 688-2726

Waynesboro

Itchin' 2 Stitch Q
204 S. Potomac Street, 17268
(717) 749-0285 or (888) 492-3719

The Knitting Cottage Y
6810 Iron Bridges Road, 17268
(717) 762-1168

Waynesburg

Pine Tree Quilt Shop Ⓠ
175 Wade Street, Suite D, 15370
(724) 833-9147

West Reading

Yarn Gallery Ⓨ
628 Penn Avenue, 19611
(610) 373-1622

Williamsport

Our Generations Quilt Shop* Ⓠ Ⓔ
1307 Park Avenue, Studio 6-108, 17701
(570) 363-2500

Willow Street

Legacy Yarn Company* Ⓨ
2611 Willow Street Pike N, 17584
(717) 464-7575

The Makers Cottage Ⓠ Ⓨ Ⓦ Ⓢ
1327 Byerland Church Road, 17584
(717) 371-4195

Womelsdorf

In Stitches Quilt & Fabric Ⓠ
4017 Conrad Weiser Parkway, 19567
(610) 589-2625

Wyalusing

Patchwork Garden Ⓜ
3137 South Hill Road, 18853
(570) 744-2523

York

Ewe and Me Ⓨ Ⓢ
36 N. Beaver Street, 17401
(717) 848-9276
M 3-8, TuThSa 10-5, F 10-8,and Su 10-3,
http://www.facebook.com/EweandMeYork

Snyder's Sewing Center* Ⓠ Ⓜ
1550 Kenneth Road, 17408
(717) 755-5833

Uncommon Threads Ⓨ
2375 Eastern Blvd., 17402
(717) 699-1600

York Haven

Red Stone Glen Fiber Arts Center Ⓨ Ⓦ Ⓢ
435 Popps Ford Road, 17370
(717) 212-9022

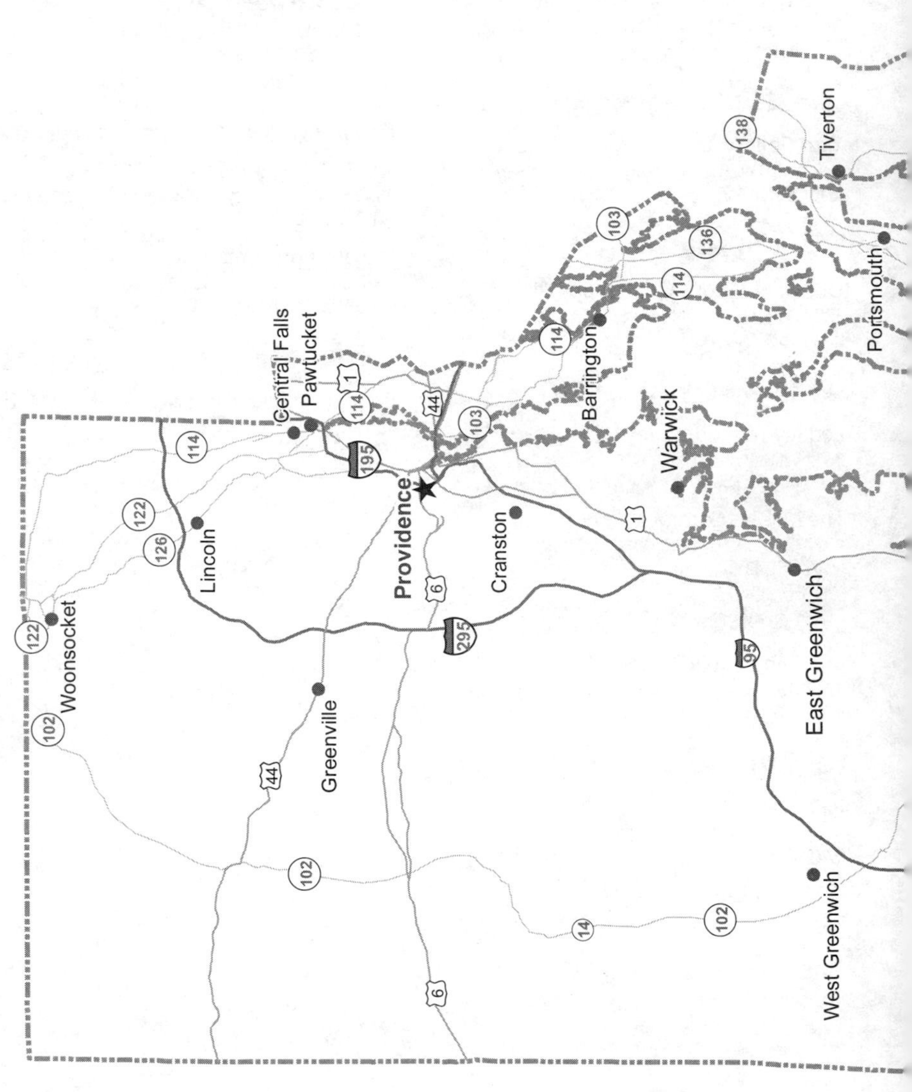
Central Falls
Pawtucket
Barrington
Warwick
Tiverton
Portsmouth
Providence
Cranston
Lincoln
Woonsocket
Greenville
East Greenwich
West Greenwich

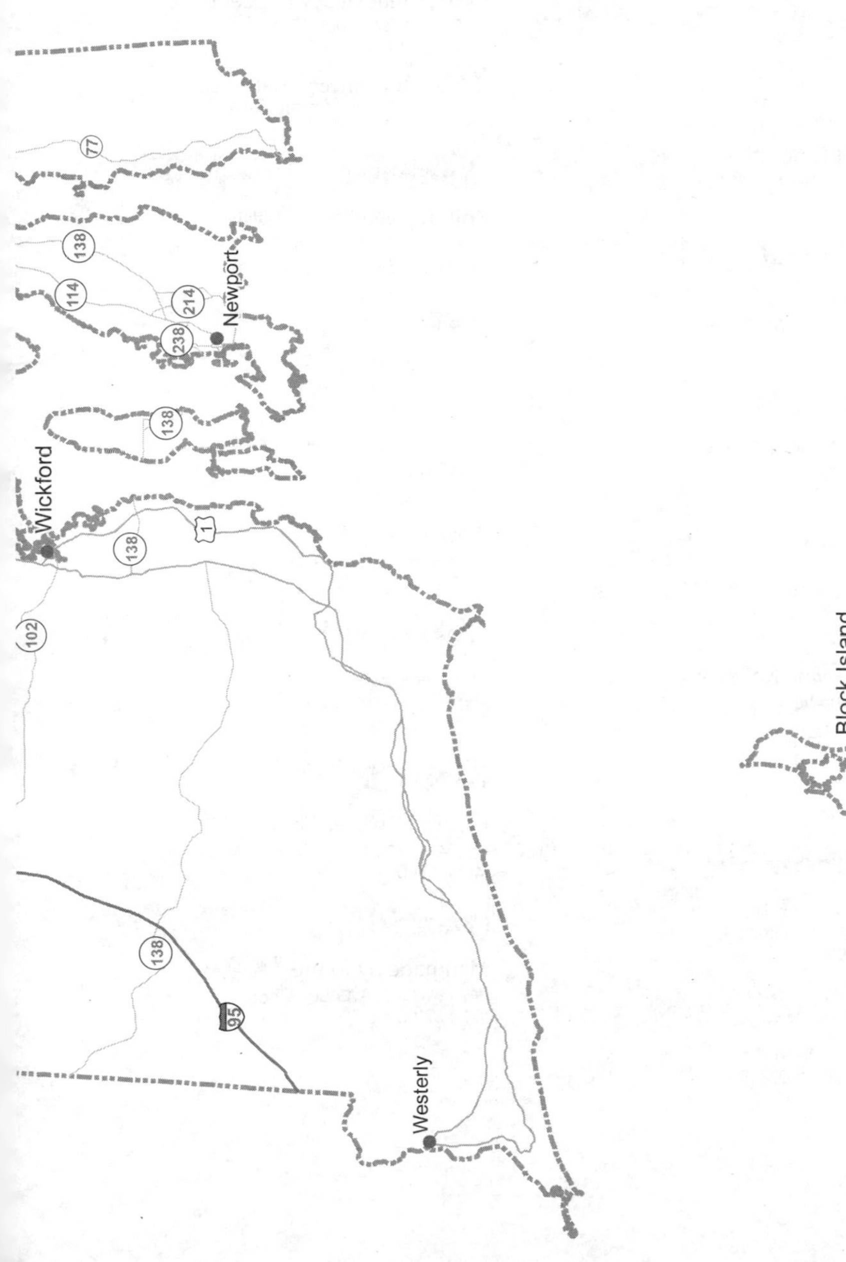
77
138
114
214
Newport
238
138
Wickford
138
1
102
Block Island
138
95
Westerly

Rhode Island

Barrington

Knit One Quilt Too Q E Y W S C
10 Anoka Avenue, 02806
(401) 337-5578

The Picket Fence N
24 Bosworth Street, 02806
(401) 245-0484

Block Island

North Lights Fibers LLC Y W S
129 Spring Street, 02807
(401) 466-2050

Central Falls

Peter Patchis Yarns* Y W
174 Cross Street, 02863
(401) 723-3116

Cranston

Blaine's Sewing Machine Center* Q M
1280 Oaklawn Avenue, 02920
(401) 463-8824

Divines Sewing Nook* Q E
689 Oaklawn Avenue, 02920
(401) 228-7831

Just Fabrics* Q
310 Atwood Avenue, 02920
(401) 383-6286

East Greenwich

Love 2 Knit* Y W S
5600 Post Road, Suite 123, 02818
(401) 398-7939

Greenville

Wood Items & More Q Y
576 Putnam Pike, 02828
(401) 949-3550

Lincoln

Ryco's Creative Sewing Center Q
25 Carrington Street, 02865
(401) 725-1779

Newport

Knitting Needles* E Y N C
555 Thames Street, 02840
(401) 841-5648

Pawtucket

Lorraine Fabrics* Q
593 Mineral Spring Avenue, 02860
(401) 722-9500

The Yarn Outlet* Y
50 Division Street, 02860
(401) 722-5660

Wayland Yarn Shoppe* Y
112 Raleigh Avenue, 02860
(401) 726-4696

Portsmouth

Sew Nice Fabrics* Q
3001 E. Main Road, 02871
(401) 683-9238

Tiverton

Perfectly Twisted Yarn LLC* Y
651 Main Road (rear), 02878
(401) 816-0043

Warwick

Manmade by Jonne Y W S
247 Pawtuxet Avenue, 02888
(401) 829-0015

West Greenwich

Piecing with Poppers Quilting Center Ⓠ
74 Nooseneck Hill Road, 02817
(401) 385-3090

Westerly

Just Fabrics* Ⓠ
105 Franklin Street, 02891
(401) 315-5300

Wickford

The Mermaid's Purl ⒺⓎⓌⓈ
68 Brown Street, 02852
(401) 268-3899

Woonsocket

Yarnia* ⓎⓌⓈ
285 Main Street, 02895
(401) 762-0671

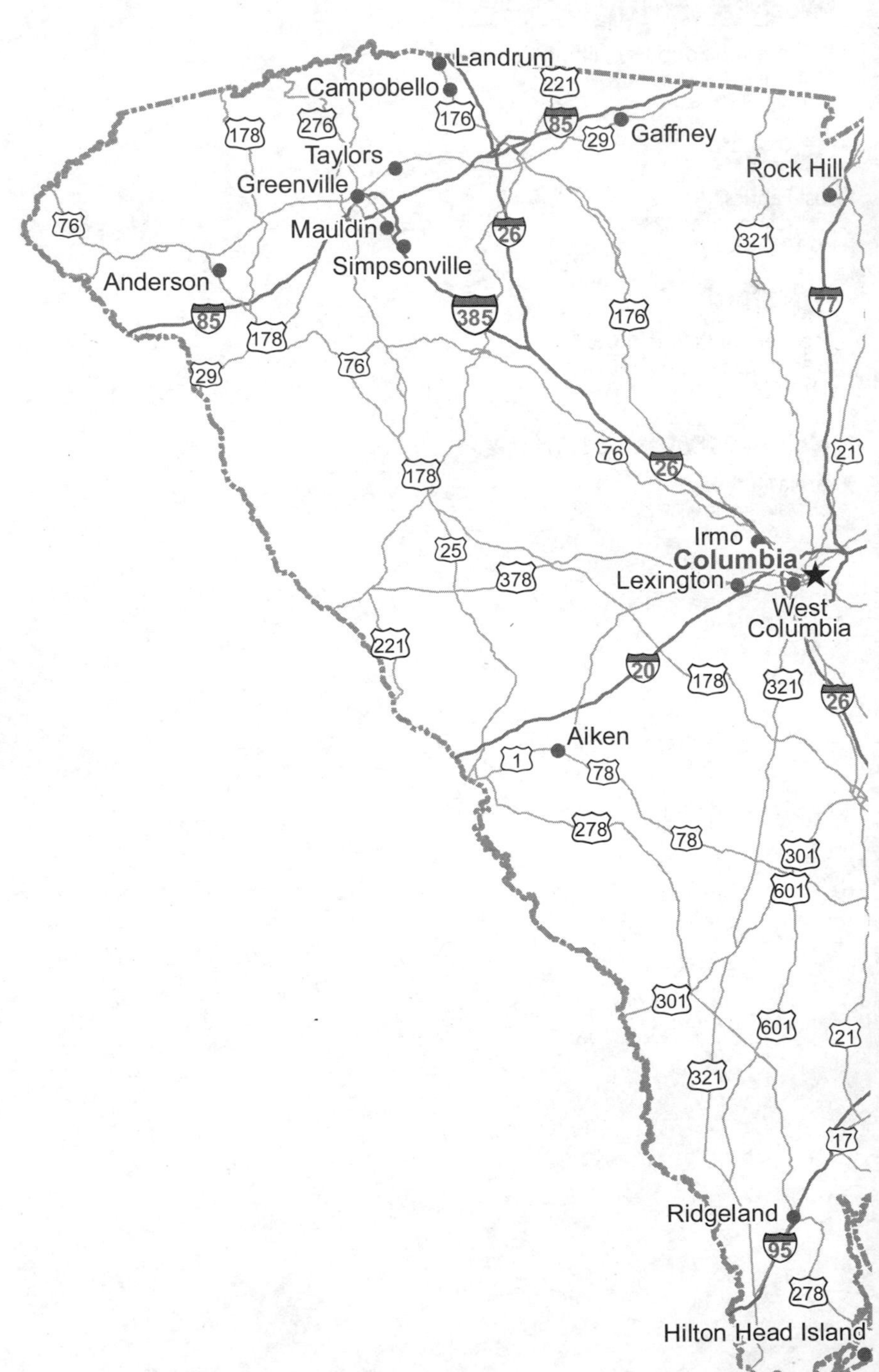
Landrum
Campobello
221
178
276
176
85
29
Gaffney
Taylors
Rock Hill
Greenville
76
Mauldin
26
321
Simpsonville
Anderson
77
176
85
385
178
76
29
76
26
21
178
Irmo
Columbia
25
378
Lexington
West
Columbia
221
20
178
321
26
Aiken
1
78
278
78
301
601
301
601
21
321
17
Ridgeland
95
278
Hilton Head Island

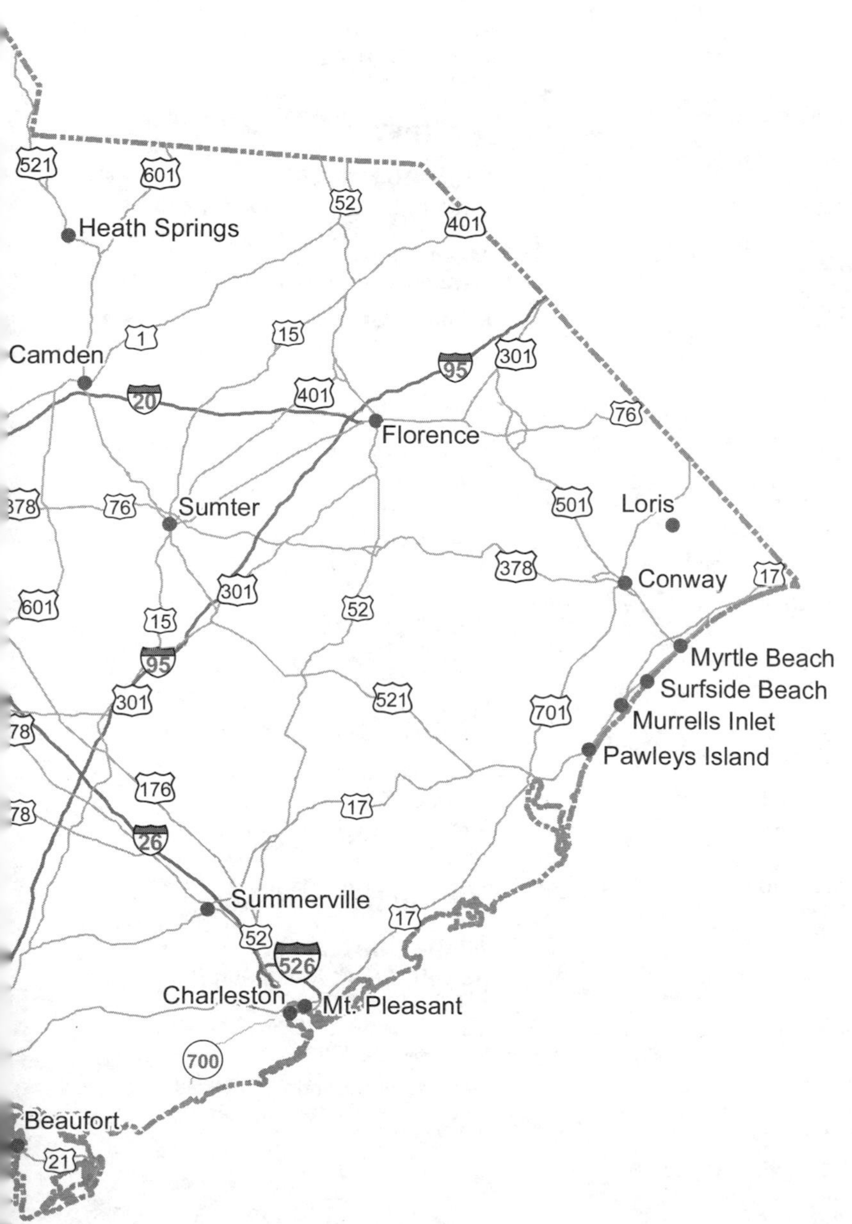

521
601
52
401
Heath Springs
1
15
Camden
20
401
95
301
Florence
76
378
76
Sumter
501
Loris
378
Conway
17
601
15
301
52
95
Myrtle Beach
Surfside Beach
301
521
701
Murrells Inlet
78
Pawleys Island
176
17
78
26
Summerville
17
52
526
Charleston
Mt. Pleasant
700
Beaufort
21

South Carolina

Aiken

Barbara Sue Brodie Needleworks* Y N
345 Hayne Avenue SW, 29801
(803) 644-0990

Anderson

Sew It Goes Quilt Studio* Q M
2406 N. Main Street, 29621
(864) 906-8910

Beaufort

Coastal Knitting* Y W
900 Port Republic Street, 29902
(843) 470-0148

Camden

Emmie's Q E
405 B Rutledge Street, 29020
(803) 272-0051
M-F 10-5:30,Sa 10-4
www.emmiesdesigns.com

Campobello

Palmetto Yarn Shoppe* Y
221 N. Main Street, 29322
(864) 468-1122

Charleston

Cabbage Row Shoppe N C
13 Broad Street, 29401
(843) 722-1528

Five Eighth Seams LLC Q
1942 Sam Rittenberg Blvd., 29407
(843) 225-3958

Columbia

Luna Lola* E Y W S C
3000 Rosewood Drive, Suite 3, 29205
(803) 500-0485

Conway

Sew Many Common Threads Q
2300 Highway 544, 29526
(843) 347-6000

Florence

Ole South Yarnworks Y
1434 S. Floyd Circle, 29501
(843) 615-7654

The Stitch Makers* N
3129 Claussen Road, 29505
(843) 669-7869

Gaffney

Quilting Sew Easy Q M
1231 N. Limestone Street, 29340
(864) 649-1313
M-F 10-5, Sa 10-1
www.quiltingseweasy.com

Greenville

Bernina...We're In Stitches* Q E M
2310 E. North Street, Suite A, 29607
(864) 235-5031

The NeedleTree, Inc. Y N
22 Tindal Avenue, 29605
(864) 235-6060

Yarn & Y'all Y W S
3795 E. North Street, #9, 29615
(864) 239-2222

Heath Springs

The White House Gifts, Fabrics & Quilting Cottons* Q E
426 N. Main Street, 29058
(803) 273-0123

Hilton Head Island

Island Quilters Q
33 Office Park Road, Suite B, 29928
(843) 842-4500
Tu-F 10-5, Sa 10-2
www.islandquilters.com

Needlepoint Junction E Y N W C
1000 William Hilton Parkway, Suite J7E, 29928
(843) 842-8488

Irmo

Copious Fibers* Ⓨ Ⓦ Ⓢ
7325 St. Andrews Road, Suite B, 29063
(803) 466-7949

Landrum

Elaine's Attic* Ⓠ Ⓔ
227 E. Rutherford Street, 29356
(864) 457-1242

Lexington

Beads and Yarn Ⓨ
117 E. Main Street, 29072
(803) 358-2323

Sew Suite Studio Ⓠ Ⓜ
120 Ellis Avenue, Suite A, 29072
(803) 957-0677

Loris

Nancy Bandel Quilts LLC / Long Arm Quilting Services Ⓠ
3438 Alton Road, 29569
(843) 756-9528 or (843) 333-6868
M-F 9-4
www.facebook.com/pg/NancyBandelQuilts/about/?ref=page_internal

Mauldin

Panda's Crossing Ⓔ Ⓒ
400 S. Main Street, Suite G, 29662
(864) 963-0600

Viking Sew 'n Quilt Ⓠ Ⓜ
113 W. Butler, 29662
(864) 286-9507

Mt. Pleasant

Fashion Fabrics Ⓠ Ⓔ Ⓜ
280 W. Coleman Blvd., Suite C, 29464
(843) 884-5266

Stitch n' Sew Fabrics Ⓠ
1212 Chuck Dawley Blvd., 29464
(843) 881-5588

Murrells Inlet

Accent Sewing, Inc. Ⓠ Ⓔ Ⓜ
4410 Highway 17 Bypass S, Unit B7, 29576
(843) 357-3228

Myrtle Beach

Quilting At The Beach Ⓠ Ⓜ
➡ SEE AD BELOW
3246 Waccamaw Blvd., 29579
(843) 742-5854
M-Sa 9:30-5
www.facebook.com/Quilting-At-The-Beach-213809641974910/

European Treasures Ⓒ
701 Kennoway Court, 29579
(412) 600-7033

Knit-N-Purl* Ⓨ
4811B N. Kings Highway, 29577
(843) 945-9484

Pawleys Island

Natasha's Needlepoint* Ⓝ
11378 Ocean Highway, Unit 2, 29585
(843) 235-9219

Ridgeland

Granny's Quilt Fabrics And More* Ⓠ
1108B Argent Blvd., 29936
(843) 645-9002

Rock Hill

The Stitch And Frame Shop Ⓒ
1627 Celanese Road, 29732
(803) 366-6341 or (800) 636-6341

Two's Company Ⓝ
351 E. Main Street, 29730
(803) 327-2967

Uncommon Thread ⓆⒺⒸ
2342C Ebenezer Road, 29732
(803) 327-8866 or (866) 829-7235

YLI ⒺⓃ
1439 Dave Lyle Blvd., Suite 16C, 29730
(800) 296-8139 or (803) 985-3100

Simpsonville

Marietta's Quilt & Sew ⓆⒺⓂ
3421 N. Industrial Drive, 29681
(864) 962-5353
M-F 9:30-6, Sa 9:30-4
www.mariettasquiltandsew.com

Freehaven Farm Ltd. ⓎⓌⓈ
349 Woodside Road, 29680
(864) 862-4802

Summerville

People, Places, & Quilts ⓆⒺⓂ
129 W. Richardson Avenue, 29483
(843) 871-8872

Sew Suite Studio ⓆⓂ
81 Old Trolley Road, 29485
(843) 900-5440

The Village Knittery* ⓎⓌ
219 S. Cedar Street, 29483
(843) 261-9276

Sumter

Heirloom Child Ⓠ
532 Bultman Drive, 29150
(803) 305-1545

Treadle Pushers Quilting Ⓠ
860B W. Liberty Street, 29150
(803) 464-4403

Surfside Beach

Homespun Craft & Antique Mall* Ⓠ
114A Highway 17 N, 29575
(843) 238-3622

Taylors

Judy's Sewing* ⓆⓂ
13 W. Lee Road, 29687
(864) 268-6237

West Columbia

Creative Sewing Machine Center* ⓆⒺⓂ
519 12th Street, 29169
(803) 936-1251

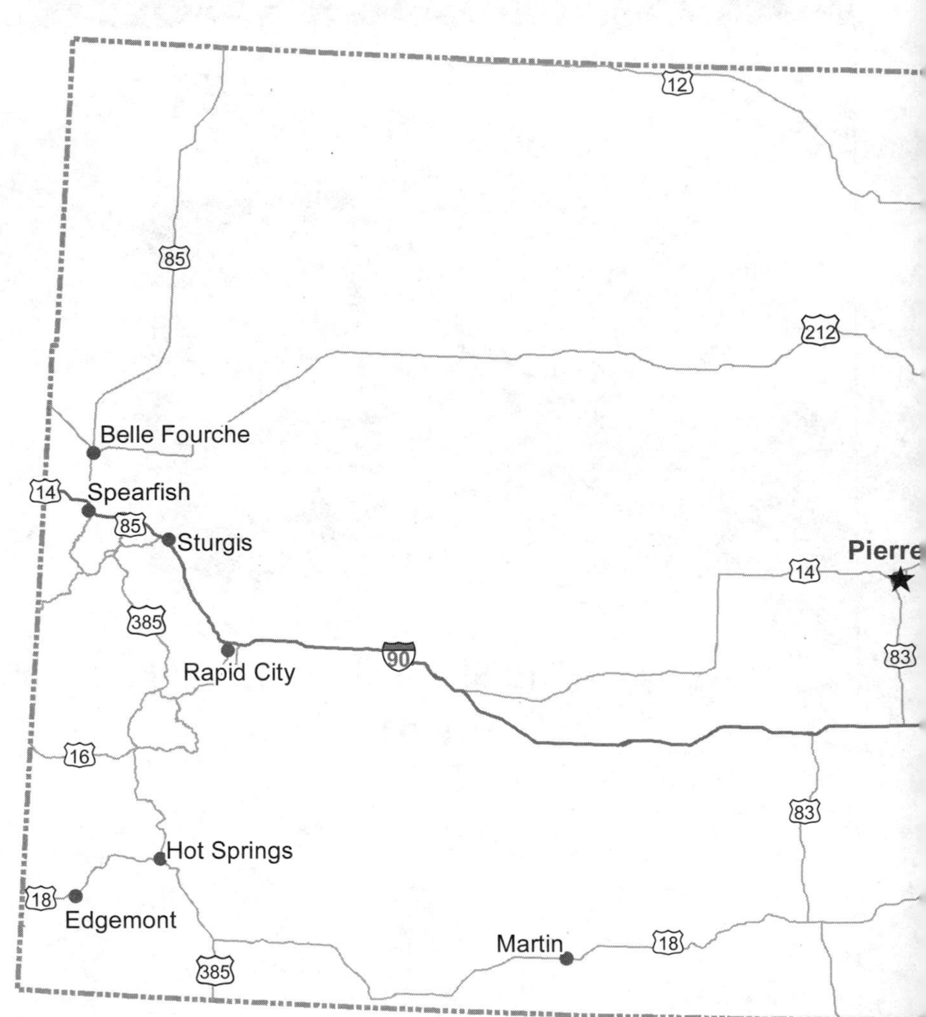
12
85
212
Belle Fourche
14
Spearfish
85
Sturgis
Pierre
14
385
Rapid City
90
83
16
83
Hot Springs
18
Edgemont
Martin
18
385

37
Aberdeen
Groton
12
12
83
Faulkton
212
281
Watertown
212
77
Miller
81
29
14
Huron
37
50
Dell Rapids
Mitchell
Chamberlain
90
Sioux Falls
183
115
50
281
81
Gregory
18
18
46
Beresford
281
Yankton
50

South Dakota

Aberdeen

The Fabric Bin and Sander's Sew-N-Vac Q E M
111 & 113 S. Main Street, 57401
(605) 225-4203
Winter: M-F 9-5:30, Sat 9-4; Summer: M-F 9-5:30
http://www.thefabricbin.com

Belle Fourche

The Bakery Fabrics Q E
705 State Street, 57717
(605) 723-2188

Beresford

The Shanty Stitchers Q E C
104 N. 3rd Street, 57004
(605) 661-4258

Chamberlain

The Quilt Shop* Q
315 N. Main Street, 57325
(605) 234-5739

Dell Rapids

Always Your Design, Inc. Q E
335 E. 4th Street, 57022
(605) 428-4545

Edgemont

Nuts & Bolts Fabric Shop Q E C M
401 2nd Avenue, 57735
(605) 662-5758 or (605) 890-2300

Faulkton

Quilter's Corner Q M
148 8th Avenue S, 57438
(605) 598-4425

Gregory

B & F Variety Q Y N C
613 Main Street, 57533
(605) 835-9415

Quilt Stitchery* Q
515 Main Street, 57533
(605) 835-9050

Groton

Natural Colored Wool Studio Y W S
109 N. 2nd Street, 57445
(605) 397-4504

Hot Springs

Fall River Fibers Y W S
631 N. River Street, 57747
(605) 890-2750

HeartSong Quilts* Q
345 N. River Street, 57747
(605) 745-5330

Huron

Java Hut Quilts & More* Q
2375 Dakota Avenue S, Suite 102, 57350
(650) 352-6598 or (650) 554-0505

Martin

Badlands Quilting* Q
211 Main Street, 57551
(605) 685-1209

Miller

Thread Expressions* Q
21999 SD Highway 45, 57362
(605) 853-3917 or (605) 871-9023

Mitchell

The Pin Cushion* Q E
117 N. Lawler Street, 57301
(605) 996-0947

Pierre

Quilt Yard Q E
209 W. Dakota Avenue, Suite 101, 57501
(605) 945-1195

The Quilt Locker* Q
102 W. Pleasant Drive, 57501
(605) 220-2666

Rapid City

Quilt Connection Etc. Q M
522 St. Joseph Street, 57701
(605) 355-0178
M-F 9-5:30, Sa 9-5
www.quiltconnectionsd.com

The Sewing Center / Fabric City* Q E
120 Knollwood Drive, 57701
(605) 348-1010 or (605) 348-2050

Sioux Falls

Athena Fibers Y W S
3915 S. Hawthorne Avenue, 57105
(605) 271-0741

Barbara's Needlepoint N
401 E. 8th Street, Suite 105, 57103
(605) 367-9050

Fonder Sewing Machine Co. M
2130 W. 41st Street, 57105
(605) 332-3821

Quilters Headquarters Q E
3705 S. Grange Avenue, 57105
(605) 334-1611

The Dutch Rose Quilt Shop Q E
5107 W. 41st Street, Suite 2, 57106
(605) 362-1650 or (877) 362-1650

Spearfish

Dakota Quilt Company* Q
1004 N. Main Street, 57783
(605) 642-2939

The Knothole* Q E Y C
947 E. Colorado Blvd., 57783
(605) 717-5668

Sturgis

Fabric Junction Q M
1609 Junction Avenue, 57785
(605) 347-2235

Watertown

Dakota Quilt Shop* Q
21 1st Avenue SE, #101, 57201
(605) 753-6922

Expressions Gallery / Knit Nook* E Y N C
201 E. Kemp Avenue, 57201
(605) 886-9251

Klein's* Q E Y N C
112 E. Kemp Avenue, 57201
(605) 886-6499

Yankton

Ewe Knit It Y S
909 Broadway Avenue, Suite 3, 57078
(605) 689-3999

Four Seasons Fabric* Q M
909 Broadway Avenue, Suite 4, 57078
(605) 665-3406

Sassy Cat Quilting Company* Q
101 Sky Ranch Drive, 57078
(605) 660-1612

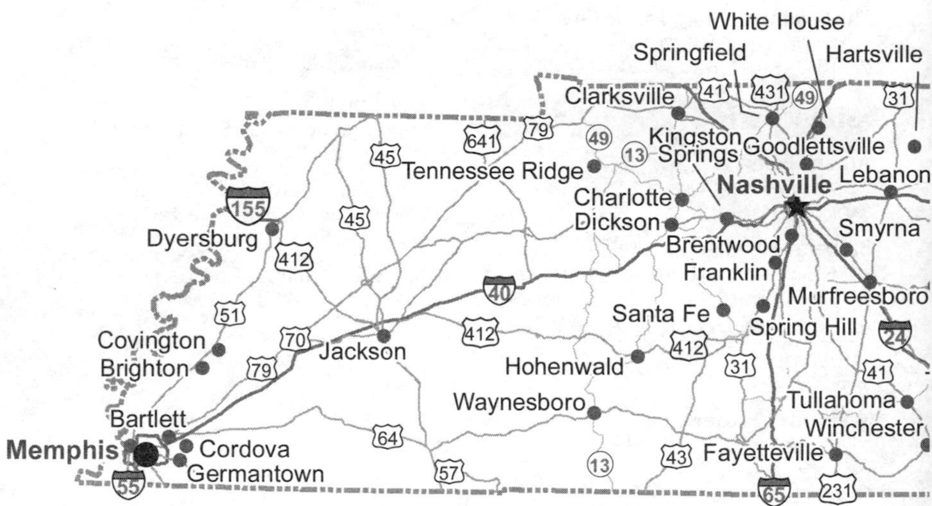
White House
Springfield
Hartsville
Clarksville
41
431
49
31
79
641
49
13
45
Kingston Springs
Goodlettsville
Tennessee Ridge
Nashville
Lebanon
155
Charlotte
Dickson
45
Smyrna
Dyersburg
412
Brentwood
Franklin
40
Murfreesboro
51
Santa Fe
Covington
70
412
Spring Hill
24
Jackson
412
Brighton
79
Hohenwald
31
41
Waynesboro
Tullahoma
Bartlett
Winchester
Memphis
Cordova
64
Germantown
13
43
Fayetteville
57
55
65
231

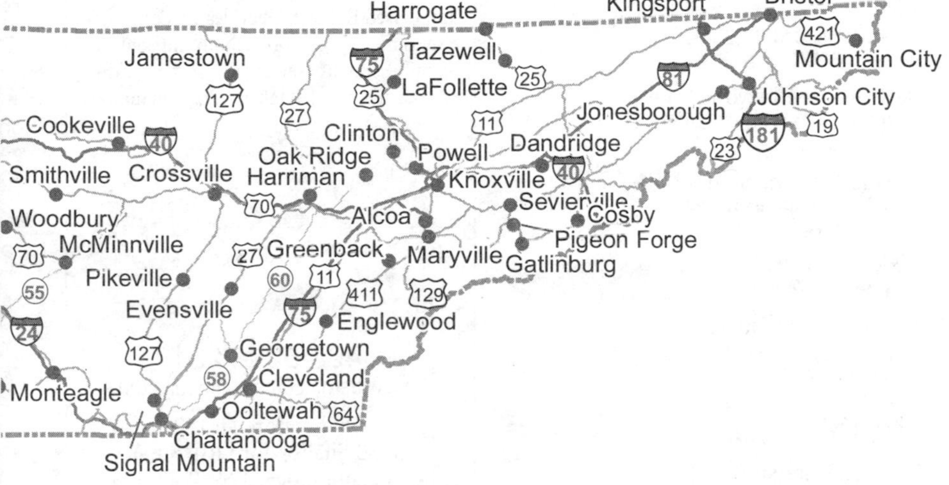
Harrogate
Kingsport
Bristol
Jamestown
Tazewell
Mountain City
LaFollette
Johnson City
Jonesborough
Cookeville
Clinton
Oak Ridge
Powell
Dandridge
Smithville
Crossville
Harriman
Knoxville
Sevierville
Woodbury
Alcoa
Cosby
McMinnville
Greenback
Maryville
Pigeon Forge
Gatlinburg
Pikeville
Evensville
Englewood
Georgetown
Cleveland
Monteagle
Ooltewah
Chattanooga
Signal Mountain
75
25
127
27
11
81
421
19
181
23
40
70
60
411
129
55
24
127
58
64

Tennessee

Alcoa

Twisted Sisters Quilt Shop, LLC Q
240 Gill Street, 37701
(865) 980-0950

Bartlett

Klassy Katz Quilts* Q E M
6022 Stage Road, 38134
(901) 213-0099

Authorized Retailer

Brentwood

Bliss Yarns* Y
127 Franklin Road, 37027
(615) 370-8717

Nashville Needleworks* N
7020 Church Street E, #5, 37027
(615) 377-6336

Sewing Machine Station* Q M
91 Seaboard Lane, #102, 37027
(615) 373-1600

Brighton

The Discerning Quilter* Q
1700 Old Highway 51 S, Suite 242H, 38011
(901) 837-6938

Bristol

Skeins & Things* Y
311 Lark Street, 37620
(423) 764-2144

Charlotte

Butterfly Girl Designs* Q E
3411 Highway 48N, 37036
(615) 789-9194

Three Creeks Farm* S
365 Peabody Road, 37036
(615) 789-5943

Chattanooga

Bernina Sew N Quilt Studio Q M
➡ SEE AD BELOW
5950 Shallowford Road, Suite A, 37421
(423) 521-7231
M-F 10-6, Sa 10-4
www.berninaofchattanooga.com

Handi Quilter® Authorized Retailer
Designed by a Quilter, for Quilters.

Genuine Purl E Y N W
140 N. Market Street, 37405
(423) 267-7335

Pins & Needles Quilt Shop* Q
6503 Hixson Pike, Suite C, 37343
(423) 668-8734

Ready Set Sew!* Q E M
3444 Ringgold Road, 37412
(423) 629-6411

Tennessee Valley Fibers* Y W S
410 Broad Street, 37402
(423) 266-0501

Clarksville

Yarn Asylum Ⓨ
2535 Madison Street, Suite A, 37043
(931) 919-5171
TuWThF 10-6, Sa 10-5
www.yarnasylum.com

Absolutely Fun Sewing & Embroidery ⓆⒺⓂ
2068-C Wilma Rudolph Blvd., 37040
(931) 802-5800

Cleveland

Hyderhangout: Quilt Fabric & More ⓆⒺⓎⓃⒸⓂ
219 1st Street NE, 37311
(423) 715-2908
June-Aug MTuWFSa 10-5, Th 12-7; Sept-May TuWFSa 10-5, Th 12-7 and by appt.
www.hyderhangout.com

Betty's Quilt Shop* ⓆⓂ
102 Keith Street SW, Suite 10, 37311
(423) 559-2458

Lana's Quilts and Sew Much More* Ⓠ
189 Godfrey Lane SE, 37311
(423) 715-1880

Time To Sew ⓆⒺⒸ
2221 Dalton Pike #2, 37311
(423) 310-6117

Clinton

Sew Unique Fabric ⓆⒺⒸⓂ
403 Hillcrest Street, 37716
(865) 457-5070

The Clinch River Yarn Company ⓎⓌⓈ
725 N. Charles G. Seivers Blvd., 37716
(865) 269-4528

Cookeville

Country Patchworks* Ⓠ
283 S. Lowe Avenue, 38501
(931) 526-7276

Spring Creek Quilts & Fabrics* ⓆⒺ
3900 Cookeville Highway, 38506
(931) 498-3473

T's Yarn Barn* Ⓨ
1435 S. Jefferson Avenue, Suite G, 38506
(931) 526-6410

Cordova

QuiltSmiths Ⓠ
1150 Dexter Lane, Suite 103, 38016
(901) 624-9985

Cosby

Deerfoot Quilts* ⓆⒺ
3020 Cosby Highway, 37722
(423) 487-5798

Holloway's Country Home* Ⓠ
3892 Cosby Highway, 37722
(423) 487-3866

Covington

The Stitching Store ⓆⒺⓎⓂ
887 Highway 51 S, 38019
(901) 476-2030

Crossville

Little Blessings Quilt Shop ⓆⓂ
4351 Highway 127 N, 38571
(931) 707-7724

The Yarn Patch ⓎⓌⓈ
1771 Peavine Road, #102, 38571
(931) 707-1255

Dandridge

Mom & Megg Quilt Shop ⓆⒺ
808 Valley Home Road, 37725
(865) 940-1447

Dickson

Granny B's Quilt Shop ⓆⒺⒸⓂ
189 Beasley Drive, 37055
(615) 441-3884

Yarn Frenzy* Ⓨ
107 Myatt Street, 37055
(615) 446-3577

Dyersburg

Stitchery Quilt Shoppe Ⓠ
2675 Lake Road, Suite D, 38024
(731) 285-2332

Englewood

Katy's Fabric* Ⓠ
17 Main Street, 37329
(423) 887-5725

Evensville

The Sewing Shop* ⓆⒺⒸ
14002 Rhea County Highway, Unit 5, 37332
(423) 775-0882

Fayetteville

Hooked On Quilting* ⓆⒺⒸ
8 Elkton Pike, 37334
(931) 433-1886 or (877) 867-1853

Sir's Fabrics* Ⓠ
110 Elk Avenue N, 37334
(931) 433-2487

Franklin

Stitcher's Garden* ⓆⒺⒸ
209 S. Royal Oaks Blvd., Suite 223, 37064
(615) 790-0603

The Quilting Squares Quilt Shop* Ⓠ
1911 Columbia Avenue, 37064
(615) 794-4769 or (877) 794-4769

Gatlinburg

Smoky Mountain Spinnery ⓎⓌⓈ
➡ SEE AD BELOW
466 Brookside Village Way, Suite 8, 37738
(865) 436-9080
M-Sa 9-5, Su 10:30-4
www.smokymountainspinnery.com

Mountain Stitches by Susan Ⓠ
601 Glades Road, Suite 13, 37738
(865) 436-0077

Georgetown

R & M Yarns Ⓨ Ⓦ Ⓢ
8510 Highway 60, 37336
(423) 961-0690

Germantown

Rainbow Yarn & Fibres Ⓨ Ⓦ Ⓢ
1980 Exeter Road
In Farmington Centre, 38138
(901) 753-9835
Winter: TuWF 11-6, Th 11-8, Sa 10-5; Summer (May, June, July): WF 11-6, Th 11-8, Sa 10-5
http://www.rainbowfibres.com

Bumbletees Fabrics* Ⓠ
2219 S. Germantown Road, 38138
(901) 755-9701

Lace Cottage Ⓠ Ⓔ
2024 Exeter Road, Suite 1, 38138
(901) 308-1964

Goodlettsville

Accomplish Quilting TN Ⓠ Ⓜ
855 Springfield Highway, Suite 109, 37072

Sewing Machines Etc.* Ⓠ Ⓜ
808 Meadowlark Lane, 37072
(615) 859-9900

Greenback

Mountain Creek Quilt Shop* Ⓠ Ⓔ
6588 US Highway 411 S, 37742
(865) 856-0805

Harriman

Loose Threads* Ⓠ Ⓔ Ⓨ Ⓒ Ⓜ
1211 S. Roane Street, # 5, 37748
(865) 882-5588

Harrogate

Cosby's Fabric & Crafts Ⓠ Ⓔ Ⓒ
662 Patterson Road, 37752
(423) 869-5599

Hartsville

My Place Quilt Shop* Ⓠ
111 River Street, 37074
(615) 680-8029

Hohenwald

Main Street Fabric And Flowers* Ⓠ Ⓔ Ⓨ Ⓒ
101 E. Main Street, 38462
(931) 796-3451

Quilter's Shack Ⓠ
1220 Columbia Highway, 38462
(931) 306-3204 or (931) 628-9003

Jackson

Sew Carefree Ⓠ Ⓔ Ⓜ
2078 Hollywood Drive, Suite A, 38305
(731) 736-3996

Sew Many Ideas Ⓠ Ⓔ Ⓜ
405 Vann Drive, Suite D, 38305
(731) 668-8099

Jamestown

Fabrics N Quilts Ⓠ Ⓔ Ⓜ
847 Old Highway 127 S, 38556
(931) 752-7539

Weston's Quilt Shop* Ⓠ
230 Billy Ridge Road, 38556
(931) 879-3440

Johnson City

Bernina In Stitches Ⓠ Ⓜ
408 S. Roan Street, Suite 100, 37601
(423) 283-0456

Cross Stitch & Crafts* Ⓝ Ⓒ
240 E. Main Street, Suite 200, 37604
(423) 610-0441

Yarntiques Ⓨ Ⓝ Ⓦ Ⓢ
410 E. Watauga Avenue, 37601
(423) 232-2933

Jonesborough

Tennessee Quilts Ⓠ
➡ SEE AD AT RIGHT
114 Boone Street, 37659
(423) 753-6644 or (877) 385-0934
M-F 9:30-5:30, Sa 9:30-5
www.tennesseequilts.com

Sewing Bee* ⓆⓂ
107 E. Jackson Blvd., Highway 11 E, 37659
(423) 753-7399

The Yarn Asylum ⓎⓈⒸ
144 E. Main Street, 37659
(828) 553-7545

Kingsport

Ben Franklin ⓆⒺⓎⒸ
1001 Waterman Private Road, 37660
(423) 246-1323

Carriage House Ⓨ
505 E. Center Street, 37660
(423) 247-9091

Heavenly Stitches Quilt Shoppe ⓆⒺⓂ
4219 Fort Henry Drive, Suite 100, 37663
(423) 406-1401

Kingston Springs

Ewe & Company Ⓨ
407 N. Main Street, 37082
(615) 952-0110

Knoxville

Loopville Ⓨ
5204 Kingston Pike, Suite 1, 37919
(865) 584-9772
MWFSa 10-5, TuTh 10-8
www.loopvilleyarn.com

MidSouth Sewing & Fabric ⓆⒺⓂ
7240 Kingston Pike, Suite 108, 37919
(865) 249-6381
M-F 10-6, Sa 10-3
www.midsouthsewingcenter.com

Dizzy Divas Fabric Shop Ⓠ
4752 Centerline Drive, 37917
(865) 474-9921

Gina's Bernina Sewing Center ⓆⓂ
10816 Kingston Pike, Suite 100, 37934
(865) 966-5941

Sewing Machines Etc.* ⓆⓂ
8419 Kingston Pike, 37919
(865) 690-7770

The Yarn Haven ⓎⓌⓈ
464 N. Cedar Bluff Road, 37923
(865) 694-9900

LaFollette

The Quilt Patch* ⓆⓂ
2221 Jacksboro Pike, Suite C4, 37766
(423) 562-4420

Lebanon

Grandma's Quilting* Ⓠ
2314 N. Commerce, 37090
(615) 449-0706

Lebanon Vacuum & Sewing Center* ⓆⓂ
1411 W. Main Street, Suite D, 37087
(615) 443-7644

Maryville

The Hook And Needle* ⓎⓈ
113 W. Harper Avenue, 37801
(865) 268-5003

McMinnville

B J's Custom Quilting & Fabric* Ⓠ
1202 Sparta Street, 37110
(931) 473-8141

Memphis

Amy's Golden Strand Ⓝ
3808 Summer Avenue, 38122
(901) 458-6109

Stitchers, Inc. ⒺⓃⒸ
5498 Poplar Avenue, Suite 4, 38119
(901) 681-9276

Yarniverse Ⓨ
709 S. Mendenhall Road, 38117
(901) 818-0940

Monteagle

Mooney's Market & Emporium Ⓨ Ⓢ
1265 W. Main Street, 37356
(931) 924-7400

Mountain City

Mink Crafts Ⓠ Ⓨ Ⓒ
430 S. Church Street, 37683
(423) 557-8918

Murfreesboro

MidSouth Sewing Center Ⓠ Ⓔ Ⓜ
266 River Rock Blvd., 37128
(615) 893-1800
MTuThF 9-5, W 9-4, Sa 9-3
www.midsouthsewingcenter.com

Absolutely Fun Sewing And Embroidery Ⓠ Ⓔ Ⓜ
2705 Old Fort Parkway, Suite L, 37128
(615) 295-2998

Country Cupboard Ⓒ
325 N. Front Street, 37130
(615) 895-1632

Quilt Connection* Ⓠ
1011A Memorial Blvd., 37129
(615) 867-0210

Nashville

Children's Corner Store* Ⓠ
718 Thompson Lane, Suite 104, 37204
(615) 292-1746

Craft South* Ⓔ Ⓨ Ⓜ
2516 12th Avenue S, 37204
(615) 928-8766

Haus of Yarn Ⓨ Ⓢ
265 White Bridge Road, 37209
(615) 354-1007

Textile Fabric Store* Ⓠ
471 Craighead Street, 37204
(615) 297-5346

Oak Ridge

Atomic Fibers Ⓠ Ⓨ Ⓦ Ⓢ
103 W. Tennessee Avenue, 37830
(865) 272-5263

Ooltewah

Chattanooga Quilts Ⓠ
5711 Main Street, 37363
(423) 648-2842

Pigeon Forge

Dixie Darlin Ⓔ Ⓝ Ⓒ
3355 Butler Street, 37863
(865) 453-3104

Pikeville

The Loom* Ⓠ Ⓔ
406 Cumberland Avenue, 37367
(423) 447-2610

Powell

Stitches 'N' Stuff Fabric Shoppe* Ⓠ
7553 Barnett Way, 37849
(865) 512-9109

Santa Fe

The Quilting Frame Ⓠ
5990 Leipers Creek Road, 38482
(931) 682-3746

Sevierville

Iva's Machine Quilting & Sewing Center* Ⓠ Ⓜ
1020 Old Knoxville Highway, 37862
(865) 365-1408

Terri's Yarns & Crafts* Ⓔ Ⓨ Ⓒ
927 Dolly Parton Parkway, 37862
(865) 453-7756

The Cherry Pit Ⓠ
115 Bruce Street, 37862
(865) 453-4062

Signal Mountain

Quilt Shop on Signal* Q
5329 Taft Highway, 37377
(423) 718-4439

Smithville

Country Lane Quilts & Gifts Q
1070 Vaughn Lane, 37166
(615) 215-8696

Smyrna

MidSouth Crafting Supplies Q
1080 Courier Place, Suite 601, 37167
(615) 462-5918
M-F 9-5:30
www.midsouthcraftingsupplies.com

Stitcher's Playhouse Q E
540 Rock Springs Road, 37167
(615) 355-1309

Spring Hill

The Dancing Bobbin Quilt Shop* Q
5326 Main Street, Suite D, 37174
(931) 486-2380

Springfield

Fabric & Fibers - Formerly The Fabric Shop Q W S
508 S. Main Street, 37172
(615) 382-5600

Tazewell

Beckie's Sewing Center Q E Y M
2030 Old Highway 25 E, 37879
(423) 626-5337

Handi Quilter® Authorized Retailer
Designed by a Quilter, for Quilters.®

Mountain Hollow Farm Y S
553 Vancel Road, 37879
(423) 869-8927

Tennessee Ridge

Yards N Yarns* Q E Y
2235 S. Main Street, 37178
(931) 721-4008

Tullahoma

Quilting Dreams Q
114 SW Atlantic Street, 37388
(931) 393-3870

Threaded Needle Q E C M
209 SE Atlantic Street, 37388
(931) 455-8543

Waynesboro

Fabrik Emporium* Q
2014 Old Beech Creek Road, 28485
(931) 676-3253

White House

The Quilting Studio Q
127 Edenway Drive, 37188
(615) 285-7255

Winchester

Hammers Dept. Store* Q
1415 Dinah Shore Blvd., 37398
(931) 967-2886

Woodbury

Treasure Chest Antiques & Quilts* Q E
111 N. Cannon Street, 37190
(615) 563-1484

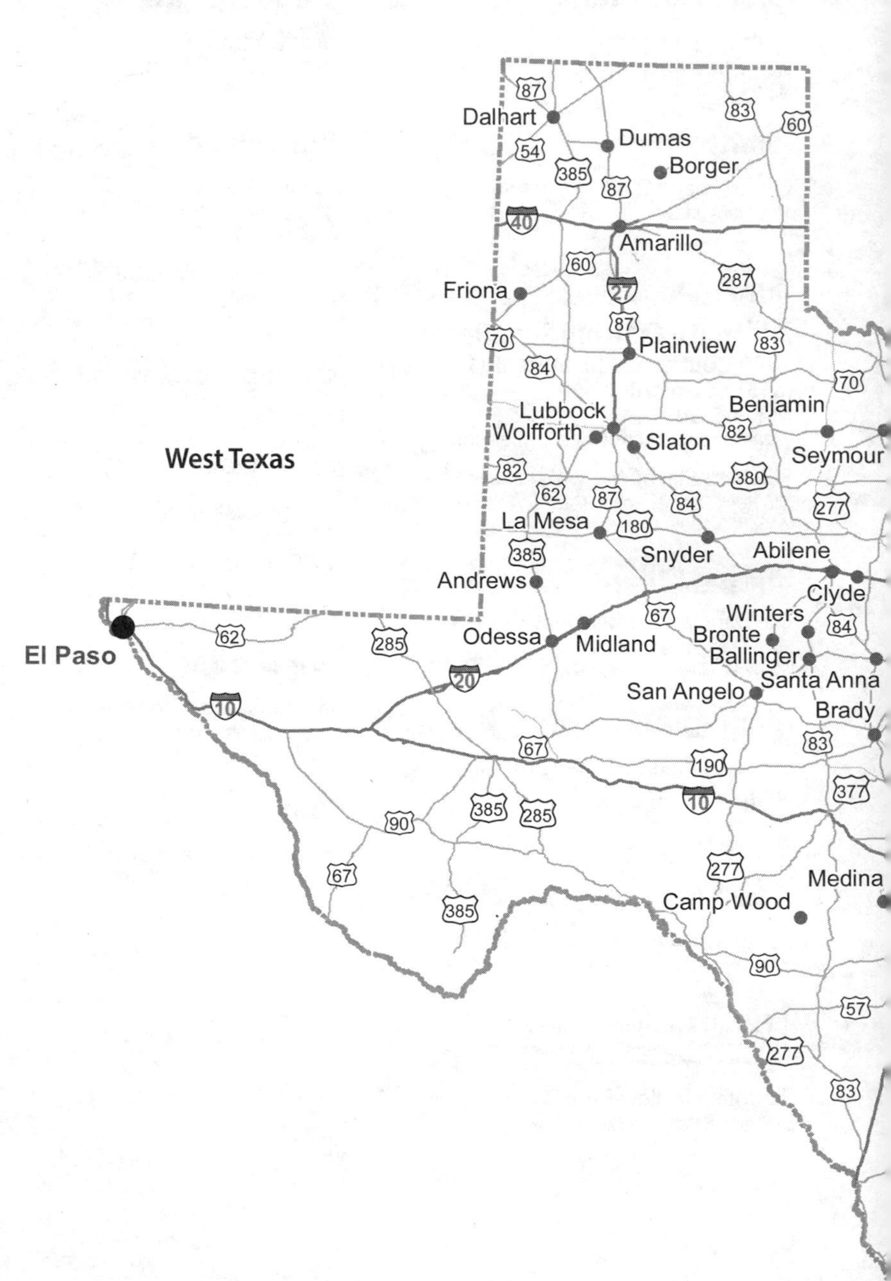
West Texas
87
Dalhart
83
60
Dumas
54
Borger
385
87
40
Amarillo
60
287
Friona
27
87
70
Plainview
83
84
70
Lubbock
Benjamin
Wolfforth
82
Slaton
Seymour
82
380
62
87
84
277
La Mesa
180
385
Snyder
Abilene
Andrews
Clyde
67
Winters
84
62
285
Odessa
Midland
Bronte
El Paso
Ballinger
20
Santa Anna
San Angelo
10
Brady
83
67
190
377
10
90
385
285
277
Medina
67
Camp Wood
385
90
57
277
83

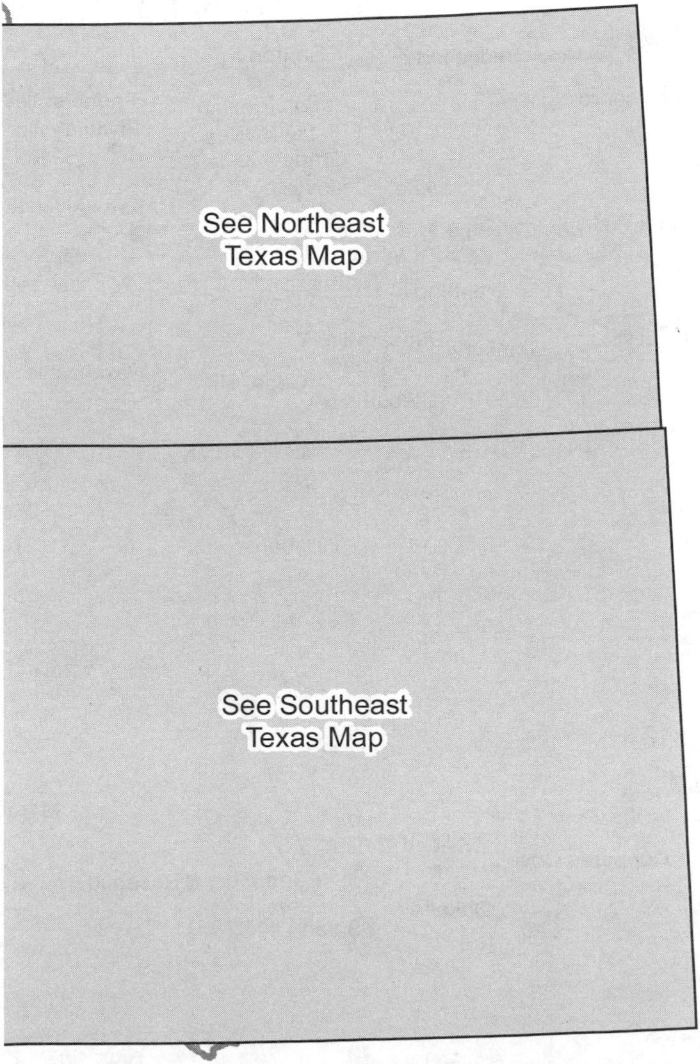

See Northeast Texas Map

See Southeast Texas Map

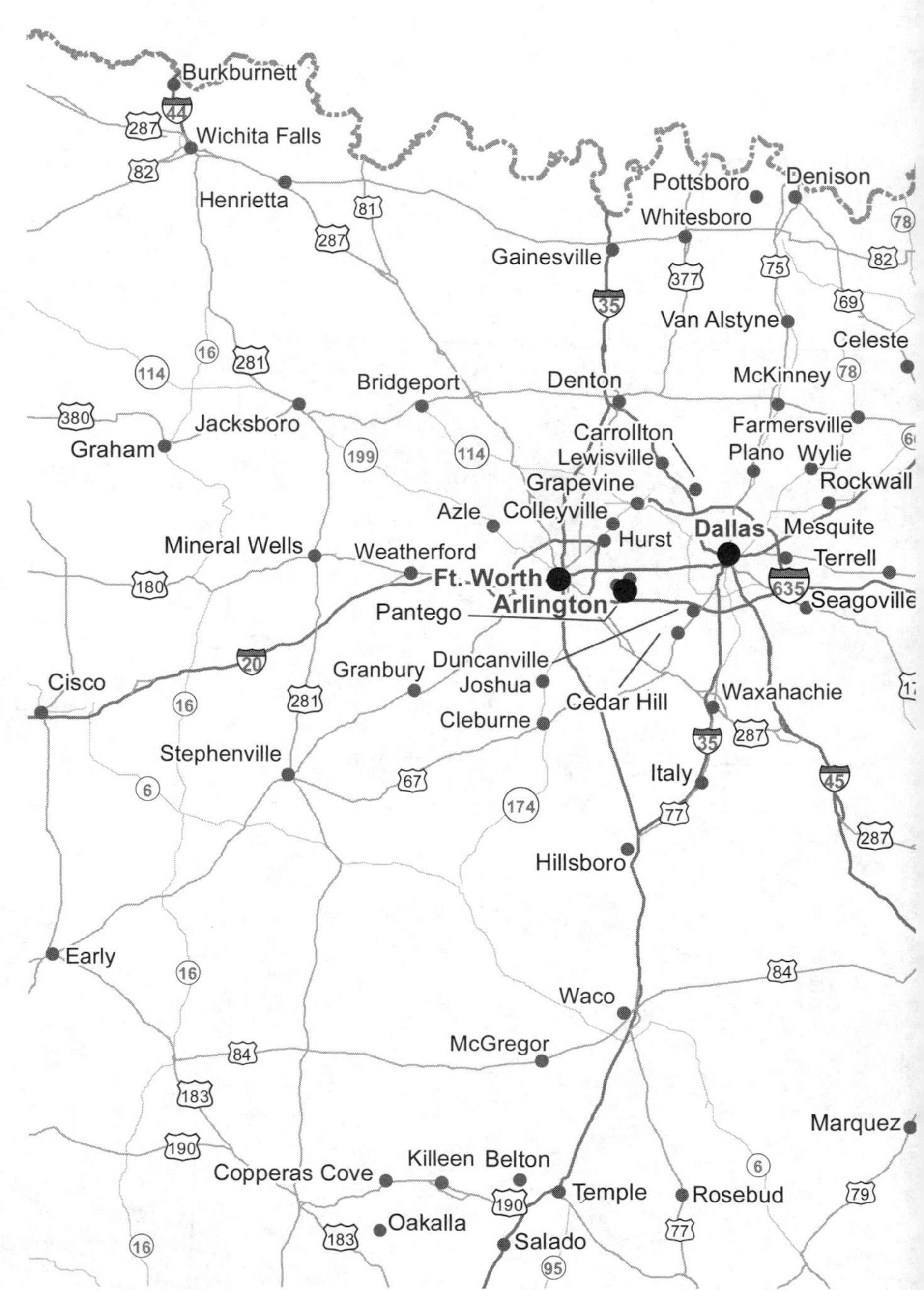

Burkburnett
Wichita Falls
Henrietta
Pottsboro
Denison
Whitesboro
Gainesville
Van Alstyne
Celeste
McKinney
Denton
Bridgeport
Jacksboro
Graham
Farmersville
Carrollton
Lewisville
Plano
Wylie
Grapevine
Rockwall
Azle
Colleyville
Dallas
Mesquite
Hurst
Mineral Wells
Weatherford
Terrell
Ft. Worth
Arlington
Seagoville
Pantego
Duncanville
Granbury
Joshua
Cisco
Cedar Hill
Waxahachie
Cleburne
Stephenville
Italy
Hillsboro
Early
Waco
McGregor
Marquez
Killeen
Belton
Copperas Cove
Temple
Rosebud
Oakalla
Salado

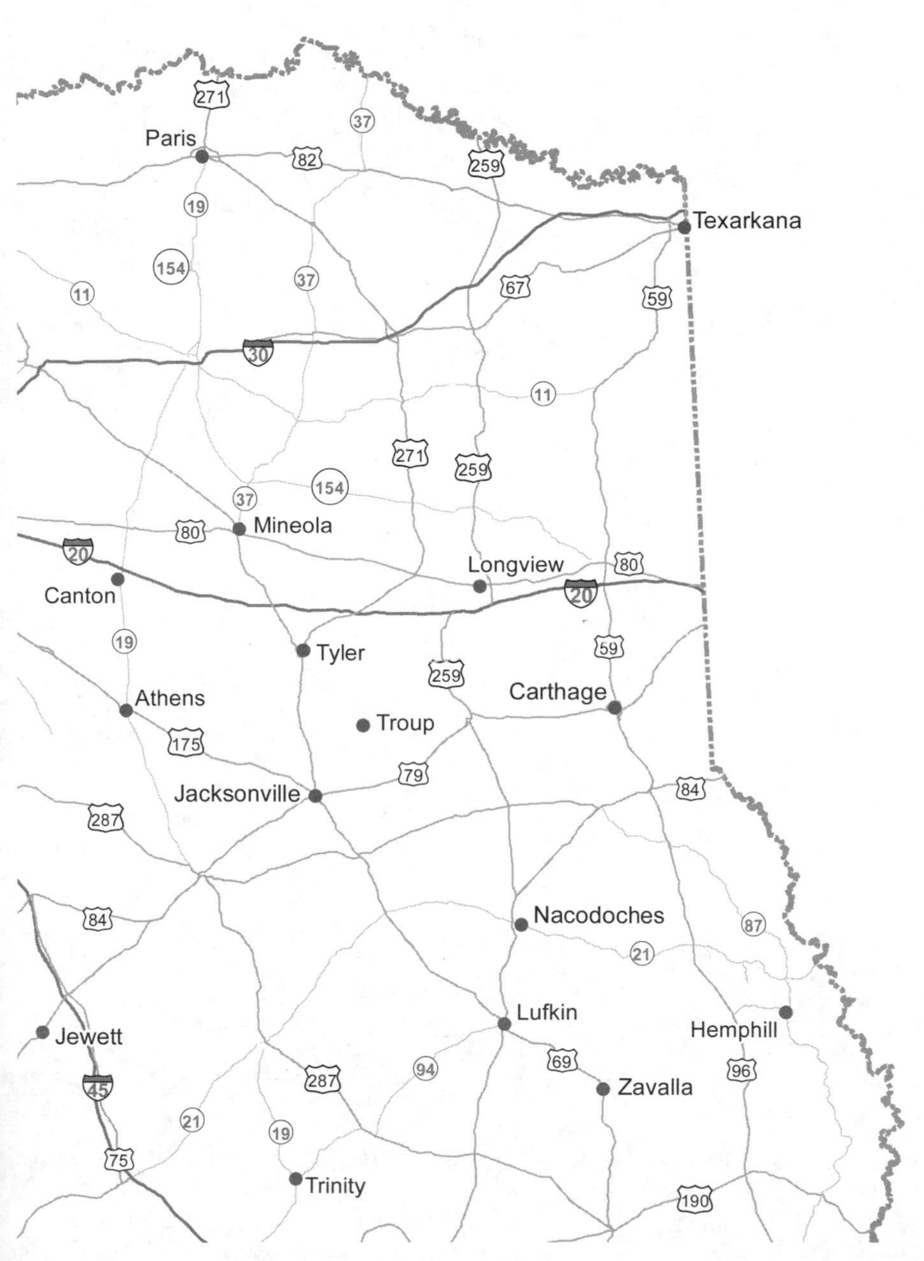
271
37
Paris
82
259
19
Texarkana
154
37
67
11
59
30
11
271
259
154
37
80
Mineola
20
Longview
80
Canton
20
19
Tyler
59
259
Carthage
Athens
Troup
175
79
Jacksonville
84
287
84
Nacodoches
87
21
Lufkin
Hemphill
Jewett
69
96
94
287
Zavalla
45
21
19
75
Trinity
190

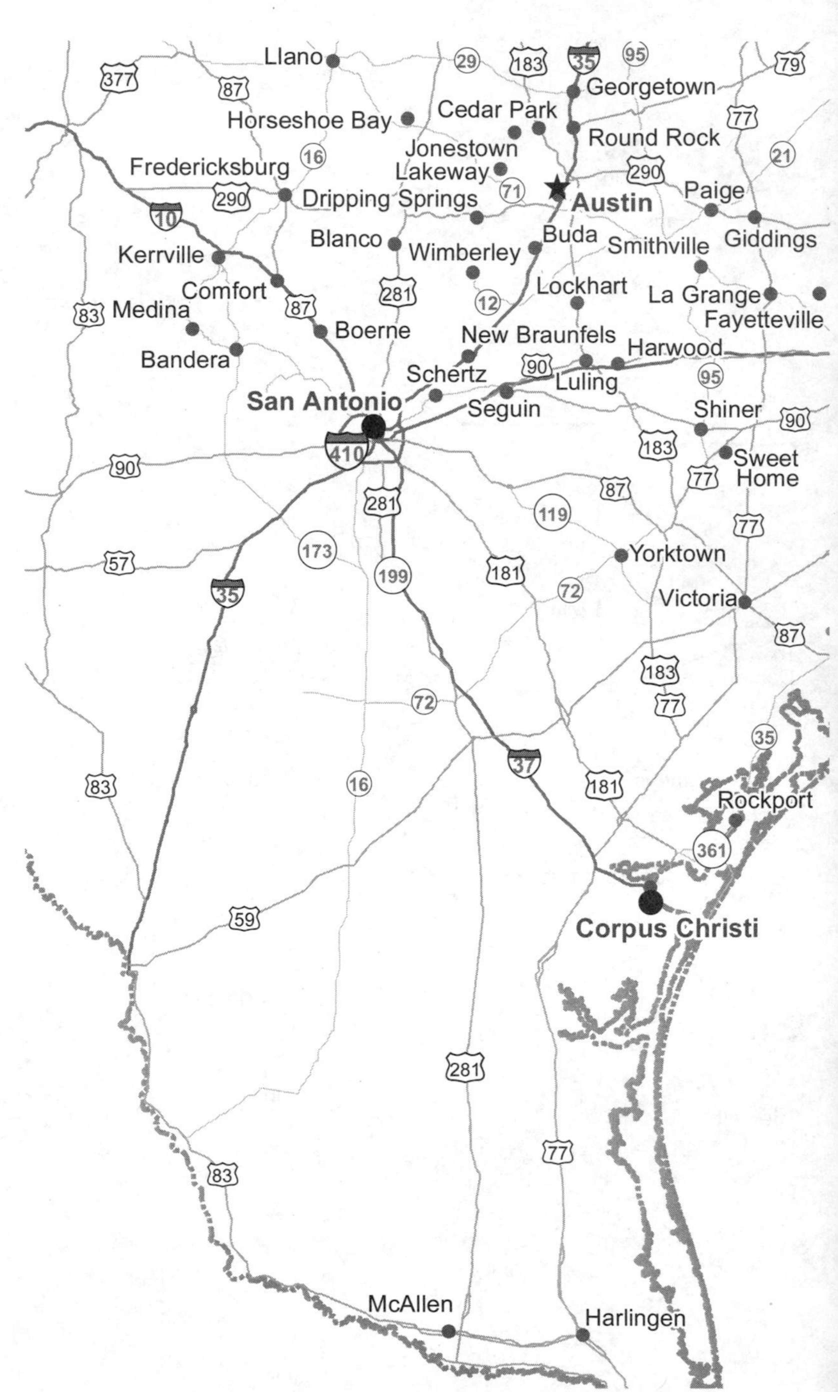
Llano
Georgetown
Horseshoe Bay
Cedar Park
Round Rock
Jonestown
Lakeway
Fredericksburg
Dripping Springs
Austin
Paige
Blanco
Buda
Smithville
Giddings
Kerrville
Wimberley
Comfort
Lockhart
La Grange
Medina
Fayetteville
Boerne
New Braunfels
Bandera
Harwood
Schertz
Luling
San Antonio
Seguin
Shiner
Sweet Home
Yorktown
Victoria
Rockport
Corpus Christi
McAllen
Harlingen

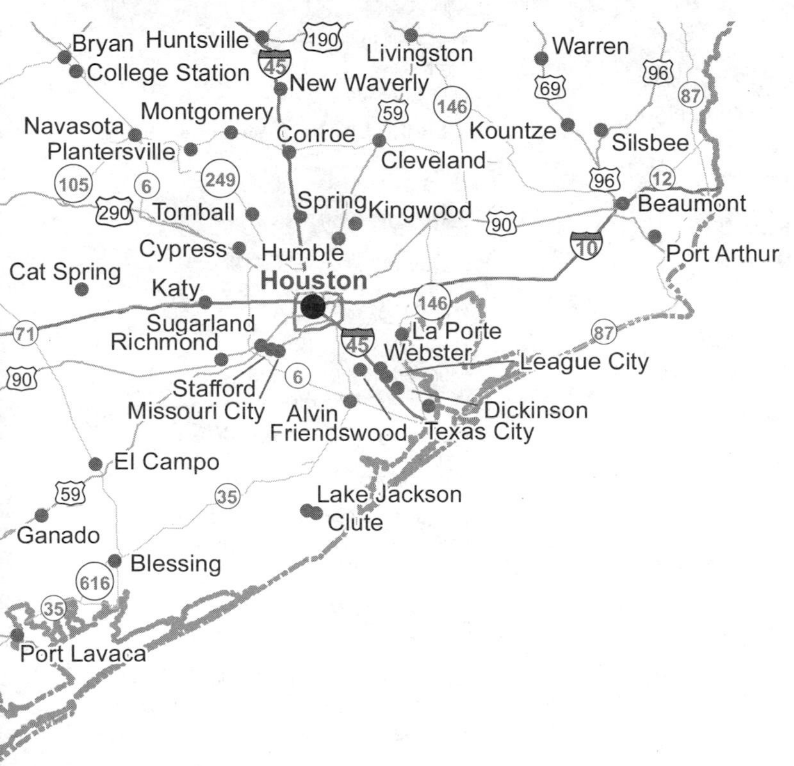
Bryan
Huntsville
College Station
Livingston
Warren
New Waverly
Montgomery
Navasota
Conroe
Kountze
Silsbee
Plantersville
Cleveland
Tomball
Spring
Kingwood
Beaumont
Cypress
Humble
Port Arthur
Cat Spring
Katy
Houston
Sugarland
Richmond
La Porte
Webster
League City
Stafford
Missouri City
Alvin
Dickinson
Friendswood
Texas City
El Campo
Lake Jackson
Clute
Ganado
Blessing
Port Lavaca

Texas

Abilene

Quilt Shop in the Oaks/B-Still Designs Q E
3301 S. 14th Street, Suite 45, 79605
(325) 665-2254

R' Quilt Haven Q E M
3814 N 1st Street, 79603
(325) 232-8761

Sew Q M
736 S. Leggett Drive, 79605
(325) 268-0466

Alvin

Quilter's Corner Q
218 W. House Street, 77511
(281) 489-4925

Amarillo

Pam's Quilting Corner Q E
204 S. Western Street, 79106
(806) 373-7777

Sisters' Scraps Quilt Shop* Q E
6018 SW 33rd Avenue, 79106
(806) 372-0660 or (877) 727-8458

Andrews

The Sewing Cottage Q M
102 S. Main Street, 79714
(432) 524-7409

Arlington

The Stitch Niche C
2425 W. Arkansas Lane, Suite C, 76013
(817) 277-4281
TuW 10-6, Th 12-8, FSa 10-4
www.arlingtonstitchniche.com

Quilt Among Friends Q
2238 Michigan Avenue, Suite A, 76013
(817) 795-0900

Athens

The Needle Niche Q E
905 E. Tyler Street, 75751
(903) 670-3434

Austin

A Quilter's Folly, LLC Q M
8213 Brodie Lane, Suite 100, 78745
(512) 899-3233

Gauge Knits* Y S
5406 Parkcrest Drive, 78731
(512) 371-9300

Hill Country Weavers Y W S
4102 Manchaca Road, 78704
(512) 707-7396

Honey Bee Quilt Store Q E
9308 Anderson Mill Road, Suite 300, 78729
(512) 257-1269

Juniper Tree-Austin Waldorf School Store* Q E Y N W S C M
8702 South View Road, 78737
(512) 288-5106

Me & Ewe* Q Y
4903 Woodrow Avenue, 78756
(512) 220-9592

Northwest Sewing Center Q E M
5448 Burnet Road, #1, 78756
(512) 459-3961

Sew Much More Q E M
3010 W. Anderson Lane, Suite J, 78757
(512) 452-3166

The Needle Works N
4401 Medical Parkway, 78756
(512) 451-6931

Walker Hall Design Q
904 W. 12th Street, Suite D, 78703
(512) 499-0484

Yarnbow Y
1310 Ranch Road 620 S, Suite B202, 78734
(512) 777-1703

Azle

Ladybug Quilt Fabric Ⓠ

217 W. Main Street, 76020
(817) 455-8983
M-F 10-5, Sa 10-4
www.facebook.com/pages/Ladybug-Quilt-Fabric/228740540616368?sk=info

Ballinger

The Quilt Shop In Ballinger Ⓠ
712 Hutchings Avenue (Highway 67), 76821
(325) 365-3230

Bandera

Gone Quiltin', LLC Ⓠ

➡ SEE AD BELOW
1115 Cedar Street, 78003
(830) 796-4360
M-F 9-5, Sa 10-4
www.gonequiltinintexas.com

Lavender & Sage Stitchery ⒺⓎⓃⒸ
331 Main Street, 78003
(830) 796-3272

Suzoo's Wool Works & The Sheepwalk ⓎⓌⓈ
584 Highway 16 S, 78003
(949) 400-4225

Beaumont

Strings and Things* Ⓨ
229 Dowlen Road, Suite 12B, 77706
(409) 225-5185

Belton

Handmade Saori Weaving Studio ⓎⓌⓈ

12866 Stonegate Trail, 76513
(256) 542-8363
Studio open: Tu-F 10-4, Classes available Tu-Sa 9-5
http://www.handmadesaori.com

Benjamin

Front Porch Quilts Ⓠ
111 E. Hays Street (Highway 82), 79505
(940) 454-2000

Blanco

Uptown Blanco Textiles* ⓆⓎⓌ
317 Main Street, 78606
(830) 833-1579

Blessing

Quilt Fabric & More ⓆⒺ
688 Avenue B (FM 616), 77419
(361) 588-6500

Boerne

Sew It Fabulous ⓆⓂ
111 Parkway Drive, Suite 101, 78006
(830) 331-2886 or (830) 377-7502

Borger

Material Girlz* Ⓠ
101 Broadmoor Street, 79007
(806) 273-2311

Brady

Serenity Quilts of Many Colors Q
2018 S. Bridge Street, 76825
(325) 597-3102

Bridgeport

A & K Quilting & Fabric Q
12103 FM 2210 E, 76426
(940) 748-2060

Bronte

The Wool 'N' Cotton Shop Q
105 W. Main Street, 76933
(325) 659-2000

Bryan

Lone Star Quiltworks Q E M
4301A S. Texas Avenue, 77802
(979) 595-1072

Buda

B&B Quilting Q E
410 E. Loop Street, 78610
(512) 312-2299

Burkburnett

The Stitching Depot Quilt Shop* Q
316 E. 3rd Street, 76354
(940) 569-0804

Camp Wood

Suzie Q Quilts Q
105 Mockingbird Lane, 78833
(830) 597-6310

Canton

Sew N Sew* Q E
22390 State Highway 64, 75103
(903) 567-4640

Carrollton

The Old Craft Store* Q E
1110 W. Main Street, 75006
(972) 242-9111

Carthage

The Whistling Chicken Q
450 W. Panola Street, 75633
(903) 690-9992

Cat Spring

Sky Loom Weavers* Y W S
1444 New Ulm Road, 78933
(979) 733-8120

Cedar Hill

Corner Square Quilts* Q M
702 Cedar Street, 75104
(972) 293-0088

Cedar Park

Over The Top Quilting Studio* Q
200 Buttercup Creek Blvd., Suite 111, 78613
(512) 358-4605

Sew Crazy Q
1625 N. Bell Blvd., Suite B, 78613
(512) 259-2988

Celeste

Quilt Mercantile Q M
215 Highway 69 N, 75423
(903) 568-8739

Cisco

JT Ranch Quilt Shop Q M
706 Conrad Hilton, 76437
(254) 442-1940

Cleburne

Fancy Stitches N C
106 N. Pendell Avenue, 76033
(817) 641-4761

Cleveland

Sew & Sew Quilt Shop Q
216 Hubert Street, 77327
(281) 592-2021

Clute

So And Sew Quilting & Fabric Shop* Q
88 Flag Lake Drive, 77531
(979) 299-3445

Clyde

Feathered Star Q
107 Oak Street, 79510
(325) 893-4699

Cold Spring

Sweet Magnolia Fabric Shoppe Q
30 TX 150 E, 77331
(281) 259-1999

College Station

Pruitt's Fabric And Quilt Shop Q C
318 George Bush Drive, 77840
(979) 693-9357

Colleyville

Quilter's Dream Q E
6409 Colleyville Blvd., 76034
(817) 481-7105 or (888) 282-0623

Comfort

The Tinsmith's Wife Y N C
405 7th Street, 78013
(830) 995-5539
W-Sa 10-5, Su 12-5
www.tinsmithswife.com

Artisans Gallery at Comfort Crockery / The Loom Room Y W S
402 7th Street, 78013
(830) 995-5299

Conroe

Quilter's Quarters Q M
3500 W. Davis, Suite 270, 77304
(936) 756-7200

Handi Quilter® Authorized Retailer
Designed by a Quilter, for Quilters.®

Sewing & Vacuum Warehouse Q M
2014 I-45 North, 77301
(281) 469-5377

Handi Quilter® Authorized Retailer
Designed by a Quilter, for Quilters.®

Copperas Cove

Nedlewerkes E N C
➡ SEE AD BELOW
100 Cove Terrace Shopping Center
Highway 190, 76522
(254) 542-6335
MTuWFSa 9:30-5:30, Th 9:30-7
www.nedlewerkes.com

A full-service Cross Stitch and Embroidery Shop

We specialize in:
- Counted Cross Stitch
- Peyote Stitch Beading
- Counted Thread Canvas
- Embroidery, and so much more!

You are always welcome to come sit and stitch with us anytime at our stitching table.

We also offer Hug Me Bags, the complete line of Rolaframe Scroll Frames and Stands, Lumenaris Wool Felt Kits, overdyed threads, silks and fabrics. Hundreds of patterns in stock at all times!

Mon. - Sat. 9:30-5:30, Thurs. till 7:00

254-542-6335
100 Cove Terrace, Hwy 190
Copperas Cove, TX 76522

Corpus Christi

Heirloom Elegance Q
4343 Kostoryz Road, 78415
(361) 852-4247

Knotty Girl Fiber Arts Studio* Y N
3230 Reid Drive, Suite C, 78404
(361) 906-9276

Cypress

Thread Art* Q E
16333 Mueschke Road, Suite B, 77433
(281) 373-5058 or (800) 504-6867

We Longarm Quilt Q
9212 Fry Road, 77433
(405) 658-5342

Dalhart

Sew-It-Seams* Q
221 Denrock Avenue, 79022
(806) 244-8429

Dallas

Holley's Yarn Shoppe Y
5211 Forest Lane, Suite 115, 75244
(972) 503-5648
MTuThF 10-6, W 10-9, Sa 10-4
www.holleysyarn.com

Needlepoint This! N
4420 Lovers Lane, 75225
(214) 363-6377
MTuThF 10-5, W 10-8, Sa 10-3:30
www.needlepointthis.com

Sew Let's Quilt It Q
7989 Belt Line Road, Suite 142, 75248
(972) 661-0044
M-Sa 10-5
http://www.sewletsquiltit.com

Creative Stitches & Gifts, Carol Eix Design* N C
12817 Preston Road, Suite 137, 75230
(214) 361-2610

Fleece Y
6464 E. Northwest Highway, Suite 330, 75214
(214) 238-3820

Golden D'or Fabrics Q
10795 Harry Hines Blvd., 75220
(214) 351-2339

Rocking Bobbin Quilt Shop Q M
9090 Skillman Street #166A, 75243
(972) 803-8400

Urban Spools Sewing Lounge* Q M
1152 N. Buckner Blvd., Suite 121, 75218
(214) 324-5755

White Rock Weaving Center LLC Y W S
9533 Losa Dr., Suite 2, 75218
(214) 320-9276

Yarn And Stitches* Y
15615 Coit Road, #206, 75248
(972) 239-9665

Denison

Home a la mode, LLC* Q
611 W. Main Street, 75020
(214) 542-5159 or (903) 786-7099

Denton

Material Girl Quilt Shop Q E
1800 N. Carroll Blvd., #102, 76201
(940) 484-2500

Minding My P's & Q's Quilt Shop Q
5800 135N, Suite 401, 76207
(940) 365-5933

Quilter's Consignment* Q
3923 Morse Street, Suite 109, 76208
(940) 435-9450

Dickinson

Teo's Treasures Q
1837 FM 517 E, 77539
(832) 794-3795
M-F 9:30-5, Sa 9:30-4
http://www.teostreasures.com/

Pinwheels and Posies Q
3335 Gulf Freeway, 77539
(281) 337-1213

Dripping Springs

The Sated Sheep Y W
100 Commons Road, Suite 5, 78620
(512) 829-4607

Valli And Kim, LLC* Q M
700 W. Highway 290, 78620
(512) 858-4433

Dumas

Down Home Quilts Q
102 E. 7th Street, Suite A, 79029
(806) 934-4041

Duncanville

Ben Franklin Apothecary* Q Y
302 N. Main Street, 75116
(972) 298-1147

Early

Quilter's Hide Out Q Y
413 Garmon Drive, 76802
(325) 643-2800

El Campo

Cedar Chest Quilt Shoppe Q
121 S. Mechanic, 77437
(979) 578-8929

El Paso

Made with Love Quilt Store & More* Q E
6324 Edgemere Blvd., 79925
(915) 270-9028

Mundo De Papel* Y
3417 Alameda Avenue, 79905
(915) 351-0250

Owensville Quilting & Country Store* Q E
10117 Dyer Street, 79924
(915) 751-8887

Farmersville

Fiber Circle Y S
200 McKinny Street, 75442
(972) 782-6630
MTu by appt, W 10-2, Th-Sa 9:30-5
www.fibercircleyarn.com

Fancy Fibers Studio Y W S
406 McKinney Street, 75442
(972) 616-3276

Fayetteville

Blue Mule Fiber/Blue Mule Winery Y
8127 N FM 1291, 78940
(832) 372-3979

Fredericksburg

Fredericksburg Pie Company And Quilts* Q
108 E. Austin Street, 78624
(830) 990-6992

One Quilt Place Q E M
648 Post Oak Road, 78624
(830) 990-4140

Sandy Jenkins Designs E N
203 E. Austin Street, 78624
(830) 997-9863

Things in a Room* Q Y
239 E. Main Street, 78624
(830) 997-3388

Friendswood

Marie's Yarn Shop* Y
210 Dawn Street, 77546
(281) 482-8546

Friona

Malouf's Fabrics* Q M
503 W. 11th Street, 79035
(806) 250-3575

Ft. Worth

Berry Patch Fabrics* Q M
4913 S. Hulen Street, 76132
(817) 346-6400 or (866) 273-1234

Cabbage Rose Quilting & Fabrics Q E
3905 W. Vickery Blvd., 76107
(817) 377-3993

Suddenly Sewing* Q M
3529 Heritage Trace Parkway, Suite 173, 76244
(817) 741-5400

The French Knot N
4706 Bryce Avenue, 76107
(817) 731-3446 or (877) 731-3446

Gainesville

Cynthia's Corner Ⓨ Ⓦ Ⓢ
201 N. Commerce Street, 76240
(972) 880-3667

Pass Time Fabrics Ⓠ Ⓔ
105 W. California Street, 76240
(940) 668-1747

Ganado

Two Chicks Quilting* Ⓠ Ⓜ
8936 Highway 59, 77962
(361) 771-3978

Georgetown

A Sheep At The Wheel Yarn Co. Ⓨ Ⓦ Ⓢ
3010 Williams Drive, Suite 174, 78628
(737) 444-6969
MTh 10-7, TuF 10-5, W 10-9, Sa 10-4
www.sheepatthewheel.com

Fire Ant Ranch Fiber Arts* Ⓨ Ⓦ Ⓢ
170 Young Ranch Road, 78633
(512) 868-8695

Poppy Quilt N Sew Ⓠ
3010 Williams Drive, Suite 156, 78628
(512) 863-6108

The Knitting Cup Ⓨ Ⓦ Ⓢ
708 S. Rock Street, 78626
(512) 869-2182

Giddings

All Around the Block Quilt Shop Ⓠ
979 N. Leon Street, 78942
(979) 542-2782

Meme's Quilts* Ⓠ
1695 Country Road 119, 78942
(979) 540-8162

Graham

Frances' Fabrics* Ⓠ
506 Oak Street, 76450
(940) 549-4244

The Quilt Box* Ⓠ Ⓒ
1033 4th Street, 76450
(940) 282-9406

Granbury

Patti's Last Resort Quilt Shop & Retreat Center Ⓠ Ⓔ
6495 Smoky Hill Court, 76049
(817) 326-3287

Sew KraZee Quilt Shop* Ⓠ Ⓔ Ⓒ
1804 Acton Highway, 76049
(817) 573-3070

Grapevine

Must Love Fabric Ⓠ Ⓔ Ⓜ
1451 State Highway 114 W, Suite 502, 76051
(817) 488-6764

Harlingen

GOB Quilts* Ⓠ
102 S. Third Street, 78550
(956) 648-9709

Harwood

Omi'z Quilting Haus* Ⓠ
1097 County Road 234, 78632
(210) 865-5823

Hemphill

Six Mile Quilting* Ⓠ
203 Worth Street, 75948
(409) 579-1119

Henrietta

Aunt Pam's Closet Ⓠ
101 W. Gilbert Street, 76365
(940) 631-7101

Hillsboro

Elaine's Fabric Shop* Ⓠ
106 S. Covington, 76645
(903) 851-0968

Hockley

Robin's Birdhouse of Quilts and Fabric Q
24331 Walnut Hill Drive, 77447
(832) 326-2533

Horseshoe Bay

Nan's Needleworks* Y
100 Bunny Run Lane, Suite 200, 78657
(830) 598-4560

Houston

Tea Time Quilting Q
➜ SEE AD BELOW
1046 Tulane Street, 77008
(713) 861-7743
M-F 10-5:30, Sa 10-4
www.teatimequilting.com

Tea Time Quilting
Beautiful Fabric, Precuts, Patterns, Kits, Long Arm Quilting Services Available
713-861-7743
1046 Tulane St., Houston, TX 77008
www.teatimequilting.com • info@teatimequilting.com
Monday-Friday 10:00am-5:30pm • Saturday 10:00am-4:00pm

ABC Stitch Therapy E N C
14405 Walters Road, Suite 950, 77014
(281) 205-7507
Call for hours
http://www.abcstitch.com

Chandail Needlework E N C
2400 Mid Lane, Suite 340, 77027
(713) 524-6942
M 10-8, TuW 10-6, ThF 10-5, Sa 10-3
www.chandailneedlework.com

Illusionsha Q E
11722 S. Spicewood Lane, 77044
(409) 434-3361 or (832) 298-9335
Available 24 hours, call first

AllBrands.com / Sew Contempo Q E M
18203 Egret Bay Blvd., 77058
(281) 333-5322 or (800) 739-7374

Buttons 'n' Bows Q E
14070 Memorial Drive, 77079
(281) 496-0170

Chaparral Needlework N
3701 W. Alabama, Suite 300, 77027
(713) 621-7562

High Fashion Fabric Center* Q
3101 Louisiana Street, 77006
(713) 528-7299

Lone Star Loom Room Y W
Please call for location, 77077
(281) 497-3997 or (888) 562-7012

Merribee Needlearts* E Y N C
12682 Shiloh Church Road, 77066
(281) 440-6980

Nancy's Knits Y
5300 N. Braeswood Blvd., #30, 77096
(713) 661-9411

Needle House* N
2422 Tangley Street, 77005
(713) 522-9704

Nimblefingers* Y N
12456 Memorial Drive, 77024
(713) 722-7244

Sew Houston Q M
7710 Cherry Park Drive, Suite F, 77095
(832) 427-6349

Sewing & Vacuum Warehouse Q M
18351 State Highway 249, 77070
(281) 469-5377

Stitches In Time N
2421 Tangley, Suite 100, 77005
(713) 975-9778

Thimble Fingers Sewing Studio Q
14505 Memorial Drive, 77079
(281) 493-1941

Humble

Cupcake Quilts Ⓠ Ⓜ
➡ SEE AD AT RIGHT
9574 FM 1960 Bypass, 77338
(281) 446-4999
M-F 10-5:30, Sa 10-5
www.CupcakeQuilts.com

Handi Quilter® Authorized Retailer
Designed by a Quilter, for Quilters®

Huntsville

Fabric Carousel* Ⓠ Ⓜ
1101 12th Street, 77340
(936) 295-8322

Hurst

Quilter's Stash Ⓠ
848 W. Pipeline Road, 76053
(817) 595-1778

Richland Sewing Center* Ⓠ Ⓜ
850 W. Pipeline Road, 76053
(817) 590-4447

Handi Quilter® Authorized Retailer
Designed by a Quilter, for Quilters®

Sew It Up Bernina* Ⓠ Ⓜ
740 Grapevine Highway, 76054
(817) 514-6061

Italy

Suzzett's Fabric, Quilts & More LLC Ⓠ
200 Hamrock Road, 76651
(214) 797-0393

Jacksboro

Seams Sew Right Quilt Shop Ⓠ
409 N. Main Street, 76458
(940) 507-5040

Jacksonville

Options Custom Creations Quilt Shop Ⓠ Ⓔ
102 E. Commerce Street, 75766
(903) 586-9546

Jewett

A Cowgirl Quilt Shop Ⓠ
299 LCR 915, 75846
(903) 626-4808

Jonestown

Happy Ewe* Ⓨ Ⓦ Ⓢ
18360 FM 1431, Suite B, 78645
(512) 284-7408

Joshua

Batiks Galore Ⓠ
7301 CR 912, 76058
(817) 556-2200

Sandy's Quilt Shop Ⓠ Ⓜ
613 N. Broadway, 76058
(817) 447-1233

Katy

Quilt N Sew Studio Ⓠ Ⓔ Ⓜ
829 S. Mason Road, #224, 77450
(281) 398-0670

Sew Special Quilts Ⓠ
21800 Katy Freeway, Suite 100, 77449
(281) 717-8033

Kerrville

Hometown Crafts and Gifts Ⓠ Ⓔ Ⓨ Ⓝ Ⓦ Ⓢ Ⓒ
841 Junction Highway, 78028
(830) 896-5944
M-Sa 9-7, Su 12-6
www.facebook.com/hometowncraftsandgifts

Creations Ⓠ Ⓔ
1013 Main Street, 78028
(830) 896-8088

Killeen

Killeen Sew and Quilt Store Q M
➡ **SEE AD BELOW**
2201 South W. S. Young Drive, Suite 107C, 76543
(254) 616-2200
M-F 10-6, Sa 10-4
http://www.sewandquiltstore.com

Kingwood

Quilts & Creations Q E M
23858 Highway 59 N, 77339
(832) 644-5696

Kountze

Stone Creek Quilts* Q
2918 Haynes Loop, 77625
(409) 926-1222

La Grange

The Quilted Skein Q Y
126 W. Colorado Street, 78945
(979) 968-8200
W-F 10-5:30, Sa 10-5, Su 12-4
www.thequiltedskein.com

La Mesa

Sew Jo's Q
407 S. 1st Street, 79331
(806) 872-2411

La Porte

And Sew It Began Q
211 S. First Street, 77571
(713) 828-9800

Painted Pony 'n Quilts Q M
1015 S. Broadway Street, 77571
(281) 471-5735

Lake Jackson

Calico Cat Sewing Center* Q E M
107 West Way, Suite 5, 77566
(979) 285-9277

Lakeway

The Cotton Cupboard* Q E
1607 Ranch Road 620 N, Suite 100, 78734
(512) 294-2776

League City

Park Avenue Yarns Q E Y N W S C
260 Park Avenue, 77573
(832) 932-0300

Lewisville

Quilt Country Q
701 S. Stemmons Freeway, Suite 90, 75067
(972) 436-7022
M-Sa 10-5, Su 1-5
http://www.quiltcountry.com

Fiberlady's Fine Fibers and Yarns* Y W S
438 S. Fork Drive, Suite 200, 75057
(469) 571-9276

Livingston

Jean's Corner Q M
712 N. Jackson Avenue, 77351
(936) 327-8817

Llano

Buckaroo Blankets Q
103 E. Main Street, 78643
(409) 673-2837

The Country Quilt Shop Q
100 Exchange Place, 78643
(325) 248-0300

Lockhart

Calico Crossing* Q E
215 W. Market Street, 78644
(512) 398-2422

Simple Sewing Solutions* Q E C
111 W. San Antonio Street (Highway 142), 78644
(512) 398-3930 or (512) 227-4596

Longview

Stitches 'n Stuff Y N C
7793 N. Highway 259, 75605
(903) 663-3840 or (800) 708-4417
Tu-Sa 10-5
www.stitchesnstufflongview.com

Sharman's Sewing Center* Q M
112A Johnston Street, 75601
(903) 753-8014

Lubbock

Pattys Heart Q
4249 34th Street, 79410
(806) 368-7805

Pocket Full Of Stitches E N C
4523 50th Street, 79414
(806) 792-1761 or (800) 234-1761

RahRah's Fabrics & Quilting Q
6015 82nd Street
Ste 2, 79424
(806) 792-1885

The Sewing Studio* Q M
4601 S. Loop 289, Suite 14, 79424
(806) 792-3863

Lufkin

Machine Quilting Magic Quilt Shop Q
806 Jefferson Avenue, 75904
(936) 632-7050
Tu & Sa 10-4
https://www.facebook.com/pg/Machine-Quilting-Magic-725896144141124/

Bove Sewing Center Q M
501 E. Lufkin Avenue, 75901
(936) 634-5323 or (936) 634-2146

Luling

HollyDee Quilts Q
405 E. Davis Street, 78648
(830) 875-5432

Marquez

Country Living Quilts* Q
1816 CR 427, 77865
(936) 396-2889

McAllen

A Block Away Quilt Shop Q M
2706 N. 10th Street, 78501
(956) 638-1961

Handi Quilter® Authorized Retailer
Designed by a Quilter, for Quilters®

Bela's Needleworks* E N C
10916 N. Bentsen Road, 78504
(956) 287-9882

The Lamb's Loom Y
1102 Tamarack Avenue, 78501
(956) 607-6855

McGregor

Mary Ann's Needleworks, Inc. E N C
309 W. 4th Street, 76657
(254) 840-9797

McKinney

Happiness Is...Quilting! Q E M
153 S. Central Expressway, 75070
(972) 542-8839

McKinney Knittery Y S
107 W. Louisiana Street, 75069
(469) 714-4002

Stitched With Love Q M
500 N. Custer Road, Suite 110, 75071
(972) 540-5355

Handi Quilter® Authorized Retailer
Designed by a Quilter, for Quilters®

Medina

Little Cottage Quilt Shop Q E C M
14076 State Highway 16 N, 78055
(830) 589-2502
Tu-Sa 10-4
http://www.littlecottagequiltshop.com

Mesquite

Pieced Together Studio Q
205 W. Main Street, 75149
(972) 270-0961

Thomas Sewing Center, Inc.* Q E M
18775 LBJ Freeway, Suite 200, 75150
(972) 681-3996 or (877) 682-3996

Watt A Find* Q E Y M
910 W. Kearney Street, Suite D, 75149
(972) 896-4088

Midland

Patches & Scraps Q E M
2420 W. Illinois Avenue, 79701
(432) 695-9961

Mineola

Stitchin' Heaven Q
1118 N. Pacific Street, 75773
(800) 841-3901 or (903) 638-6915

Mineral Wells

Hen House Quilts Q E
339 Millsap Highway, 76067
(940) 325-5858

Missouri City

Little Stitches Sewing Center Q E M
3340 FM 1092 Road, 77459
(281) 403-1564

Montgomery

Montgomery Quilt Company Q E
301 Prairie Street, 77356
(936) 597-4885

Nacogdoches

Yarnia-TX Y
321 E. Main Street, 75961
(936) 205-3233

Navasota

WC Mercantile Y W S
201 E. Washington Avenue, 77868
(936) 825-3378
W-Sa 10-5, Su 12-5
www.wcmercantile.com

New Braunfels

Lucky Ewe Yarn Y W S
647 S. Seguin Avenue, 78130
(830) 620-0908

Sew Little Time - Bernina* Q M
625 W. San Antonio Street, 78130
(830) 626-8463

The Quilt Haus* Q
651 N. Business IH 35, Suite 510-529, 78130
(830) 620-1382

New Waverly

Mohair And More Y W S
231 Gibbs Street, Highway 150, 77358
(936) 661-8022

Oakalla

Threadheads* Q
28625 FM 963, 78608
(512) 556-4739

Odessa

Wooden Spool Boutique Q
1601 N Grandview, 79761
(432) 614-8873
https://www.facebook.com/pages/category/Shopping---Retail/Wooden-Spool-Boutique-145977342709538/

Betty's Bobbin Box* Q M
2734 N. Grandview Avenue, 79762
(432) 550-0093 or (800) 249-9791

Paige

Yarnorama Y W S
130 Gonzales Street, 78659
(512) 253-0100
W-Sa 10-5, Su 1-4
www.yarnorama.com

Pantego

Peggy's Quilt Studio Q
2410 Superior Drive, Suite C, 76013
(817) 275-4155

Sew Fabricated Q
2899 W. Pioneer Parkway, 76013
(817) 795-1925

Paris

Sew Always QEM
1709 Clarksville Street, 75460
(903) 784-6342
M-F 10-5, Sa 9:30-3
www.sewalways.com

Plainview

Cindy's Country Quilt Shoppe Q
633 N. Ash Street, 79072
(806) 296-5888

Plano

Best of Bernina Plano QM
340 Coit Road, Suite 500, 75075
(972) 578-9227

Fabric Fanatics* Q
642 Haggard Street, Suite 706, 75074
(972) 881-7750

Not Your Mama's Quilt Store Q
4152 W. Spring Creek Parkway, #156, 75024
(972) 612-2641

Plantersville

Sweet Magnolia Fabric Shoppe* Q
17029 Village Circle, 77363
(281) 259-1999

Port Arthur

Sew it Seams QECM
7600 Twin City Highway, Suite B, 77642
(409) 729-7397

Port Lavaca

Beefore It's A Quilt & Gifts QE
119 E. Main Street, 77979
(361) 552-1350

Pottsboro

Quilt Republic Q
321 W. FM 120, 75076
(903) 327-4504

Richmond

Quilter's Cottage Q
920 FM 359 Road, 77406
(281) 633-9331

Rockport

Sew by the Bay QM
701 N. Allen Street, 78382
(361) 729-7873

Rockwall

Texas Quiltworks* QM
212 E. Rusk Street, Suite B, 75087
(972) 771-9952 or (800) 275-9436

Rosebud

The Fabric Barn QEW
413 W. Main Street,, 76570
(254) 583-0050

Round Rock

Austin Sewing Machines QM
1601 S. Interstate 35, Suite 300, 78664
(512) 310-7349

Salado

A Sewing Basket QEC
74 Van Bibber Road, 76571
(254) 947-5423

San Angelo

The Fiber Co-op* QE
7024 Orient Road, 76905
(325) 262-5447

San Antonio

Grome's Sewing Machine Company Q M
4719 Manitou, 78228
(210) 684-0376
M-F 9-5, Sa 9-1
www.gromes.com

AllBrands.com / Creative Sewing Center Q E M
11777 West Avenue, 78216
(210) 344-0791

Authorized Retailer

InSkein Yarns Y S
8425 Bandera Road, Suite 128, 78250
(210) 334-0200

Las Colchas Q E
110 Ogden Street, 78212
(210) 223-2405

Memories By The Yard* Q E
8015 Mainland Drive, 78250
(210) 520-4833

Mesquite Bean Fabrics Q
6708 N. New Braunfels Avenue, 78209
(210) 281-1256

Patty's Sewing Center* Q E M
12721 Mountain Air, #101, 78249
(210) 734-5515

Sew Special Quilts - Bernina Q E M
5139 N. Loop 1604W, Suite 110, 78249
(210) 698-6076

Stitches From The Heart C
5123 N. Loop 1604W, Suite 109, 78249
(210) 479-2600 or (877) 479-2620

Unraveled - The Chic Yarn Boutique* Y
815 E. Rector, Suite 104, 78216
(210) 251-4451

Yarn Barn of San Antonio* Y N W C
1615 McCullough Avenue, 78212
(210) 826-3679

Yarnivore* Y W S
2357 NW Military Highway, 78231
(210) 979-8255

Santa Anna

Country Quilting & More* Q
803 Avenue B, 76878
(325) 348-3771

Schertz

Scrappy Quilter Q E M
1196 FM 78, Suite 4, 78154
(210) 281-8667
M-F 9:30-5:30, Sa 9:30-3:30
www.scrappyquilter.com

Cotton Boll Quilting* Q
457 Silver Buckle, 78154
(210) 288-8205

Seagoville

Fabrics-4-You Q
1501 N. Kaufman Street, 75159
(972) 287-3800

Seguin

You're So Crafty* E Y W S
208 S. Austin Street, 78155
(830) 379-0730

Seymour

Mrs. Sew 'n Sew Q
713 N. Charles Street, 76380
(940) 256-2017

Shiner

The Square Quilter* Q E
807 N. Avenue D, 77984
(361) 594-8022

Silsbee

In The Loop* Y
130 East Avenue H, 77656
(409) 373-2144

The Vintage Owl Q M
110 East Avenue H, 77656
(409) 373-2069

Slaton

Quilts-N-More* Q
121 S. 9th Street, 79364
(806) 828-3222

Smithville

Making Memories Quilt Shop Q E
1004 Nichols Street, 78957
(512) 575-7040

Snyder

Nana Bear's Notions* Q
2513 College Avenue, 79549
(325) 436-0211

Sour Lake

Quilts etc Q
1028 Highway 326 S, 77659
(409) 287-3032
W-F 10-6, Sa 10-2
https://mobile.facebook.com/Quilts-etc-1702772293109944/

Spring

Cupcake Quilts Q E M
➡ SEE AD PAGE 521
219 Gentry Street, 77373
(281) 528-2929
Tu-Sa 10-5, Su 12-5
www.cupcakefabricsandquilts.com

Handi Quilter® Authorized Retailer
Designed by a Quilter, for Quilters.®

Cupcake Quilts Q M
➡ SEE AD PAGE 521
2311 Sciaaca Road, 77373
(281) 288-0220
Tu-Sa 10-4
www.cupcakequilts.com

Handi Quilter® Authorized Retailer
Designed by a Quilter, for Quilters.®

GRS Creations and Fabrics Q
302 Main Street, 77373
(281) 528-9898
Tu-Sa 10-5, Su 1-5
www.grsfabrics.com

3 Stitches E N C
7822 Louetta Road, 77379
(281) 320-0133

The Social Knitwork* Y S
26511 Keith Street, 77373
(281) 630-4144

Twisted Yarns Y W S
702 Spring Cypress Road, Suite A, 77373
(281) 528-8664

Yarn Store Boutique Y W
8900 Eastloch Drive, Suite 300, 77379
(713) 249-7311

Stafford

Quilter's Emporium Q E M
11925 SW Freeway, Suite 11, 77477
(281) 491-0016 or (800) 395-7794

Stephenville

Deb's Flying Needle Q E Y C
1495 W. South Loop, 76401
(254) 965-7577

Sugarland

It Seams To Be Sew Q M
1039 Eldridge Road, 77478
(281) 302-6059

Handi Quilter® Authorized Retailer
Designed by a Quilter, for Quilters.®

Sweet Home

Sweet Home Stitching Post* Q
7159 FM 531, 77987
(361) 293-6733

Temple

Temple Sew And Quilt Store* Q M
1510 S. 31st Street, 76504
(254) 774-9797

Terrell

Quilter's Apprentice Q M
1100 E. Moore Avenue, 75160
(972) 563-3830 or (855) 563-3830

Texarkana

The Yarn Garden* Y
3423 New Boston Road, 75501
(903) 223-9276

Texas City

Cactus Quilts Q E M
1811 6th Street N, 77590
(409) 965-9778

Tomball

Quilters Crossing Q M
1006 W. Main Street, 77375
(281) 516-7515

Trinity

Heavenly Threads Quilt Shop Q
334 Prospect Drive, 75862
(936) 594-1237

Troup

All Those Quilts Q M
159 County Road 4924, 75789
(903) 842-2044

Tyler

A Nimble Thimble Q E M
1813 Capital Drive, Suite 300, 75701
(903) 581-4926

Crafts & Quilting, Etc. Q E Y W
715 S. College Avenue, 75701
(903) 533-1771

Sharman's Sewing Center* Q M
6005 S. Broadway Avenue, 75703
(903) 581-5470

Van Alstyne

Apple Leef Farm* Y
7454 FM 121, 75495
(903) 482-5128

Victoria

Quilters Patch Q E
205 North Star, Suite Q, 77904
(361) 578-0380

Silver Threads * Q
104D Kelly Drive, 77904
(361) 703-5032

Waco

Homestead Fiber Crafts Y W S
608 Dry Creek Road, 76705
(254) 300-2436
M-Sa 10-6
www.homesteadfibercrafts.com

PHD Quilts, LLC Q E M
921A Lake Air Drive
, 76710
(254) 741-6988

Simply Fabrics Q E
6408 Gholson Road, 76705
(254) 829-7119

Waco Sew And Quilt Store* Q
4300 W. Waco Drive, Suite B, 76710
(254) 772-2887

Warren

Hall To Wall Quilts & More* Q
957 County Road 1220, 77664
(409) 547-0026

Waxahachie

Common Threads Quilting* Q
315 S. Rogers Street, 75165
(972) 935-0510

Weatherford

Quilting Around Q
806 Palo Pinto Street, 76086
(817) 599-7810

Webster

Fabrics Etcetera Q M
571 W. Bay Area Blvd., 77598
(281) 338-1904

Whitesboro

Kaleidoscope Quilt Shop* Q
114 E. Main Street, 76273
(903) 564-4681

Quixotic Fibers* Ⓨ Ⓦ Ⓢ
116B E. Main Street, 76273
(903) 564-3740

Wichita Falls

Ace Sewing Center Ⓠ Ⓔ Ⓜ
2400 Kemp Blvd., 76309
(940) 766-4633 or (800) 242-4506

The Enchanted Quilt Ⓠ Ⓔ
1813 9th Street, 76301
(940) 689-0990

Wimberley

Ply Yarn Ⓨ
101 Henson Road, 78676
(512) 648-0160

Wimberley Stitch Studio Ⓠ Ⓔ
704 FM 2325, 78676
(512) 808-0490

Winters

Bee's Quilting & Gifts Ⓠ
106 S. Main Street, 79567
(325) 754-4624

Wolfforth

Red Barn Retreat & Quilting Center Ⓠ Ⓔ
18311 County Road 1640, 79382
(806) 863-2276

Scarborough Fabrics and Designs Ⓠ
8905 CR 7500, 149th and Kirksey (GPS), 79382
(806) 441-9341

Wylie

Blue Ribbon Quilt Shoppe Ⓠ Ⓔ Ⓝ
102C N. Ballard Avenue, 75098
(972) 941-0777

Yorktown

Seams Like Home, A Little Fabric Store* Ⓠ
441 W. 5th Street, 78164
(361) 564-9455

Zavalla

Ross Fabric & Crafts Ⓠ
502 Pickard Road, 75980
(936) 404-0643

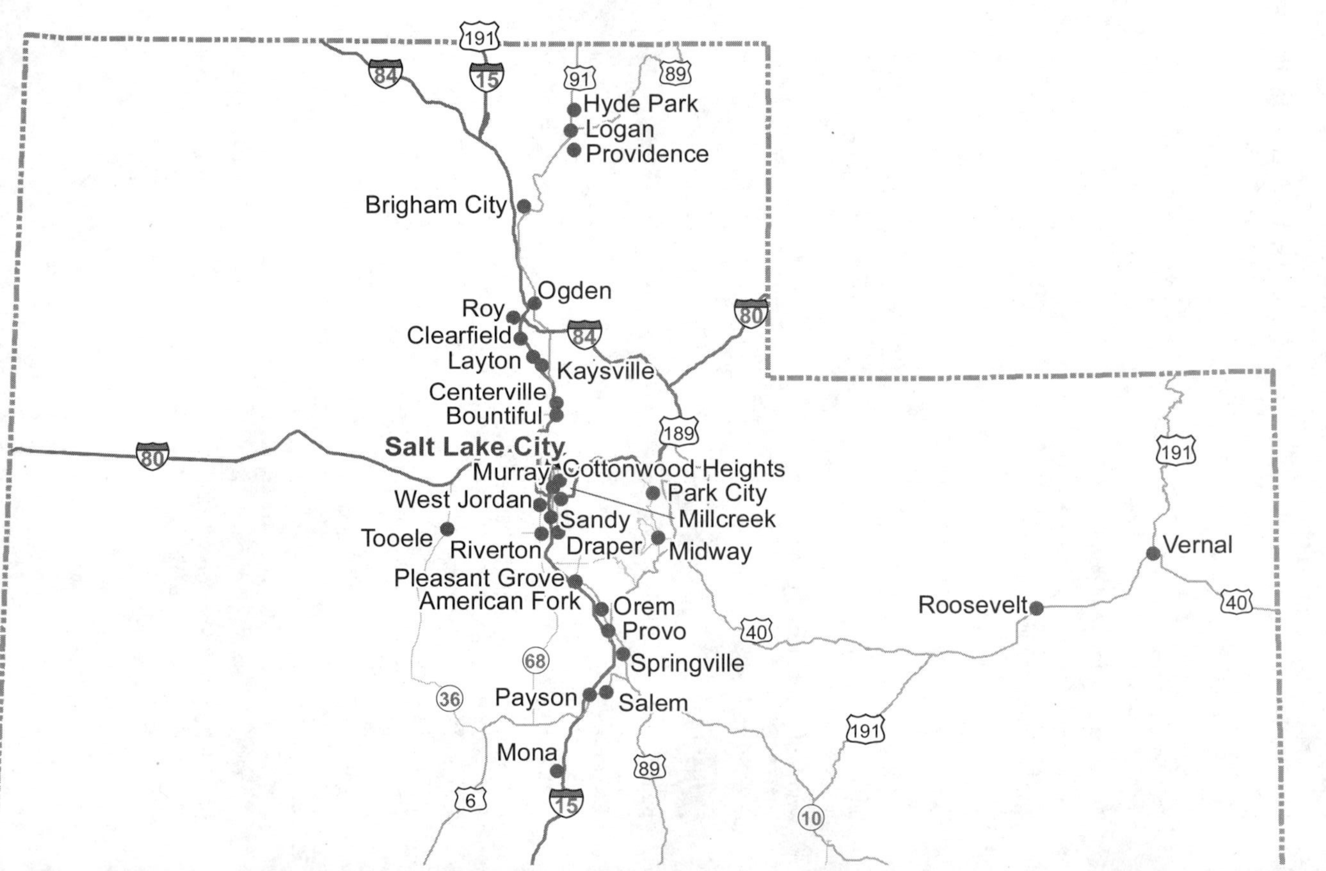
191
84
15
91
89
Hyde Park
Logan
Providence
Brigham City
Ogden
Roy
Clearfield
84
80
Layton
Kaysville
Centerville
Bountiful
189
80
Salt Lake City
Murray
Cottonwood Heights
Park City
West Jordan
Sandy
Millcreek
Tooele
Riverton
Draper
Midway
191
Vernal
Pleasant Grove
American Fork
Orem
Roosevelt
40
Provo
40
68
Springville
36
Payson
Salem
191
Mona
89
6
15
10

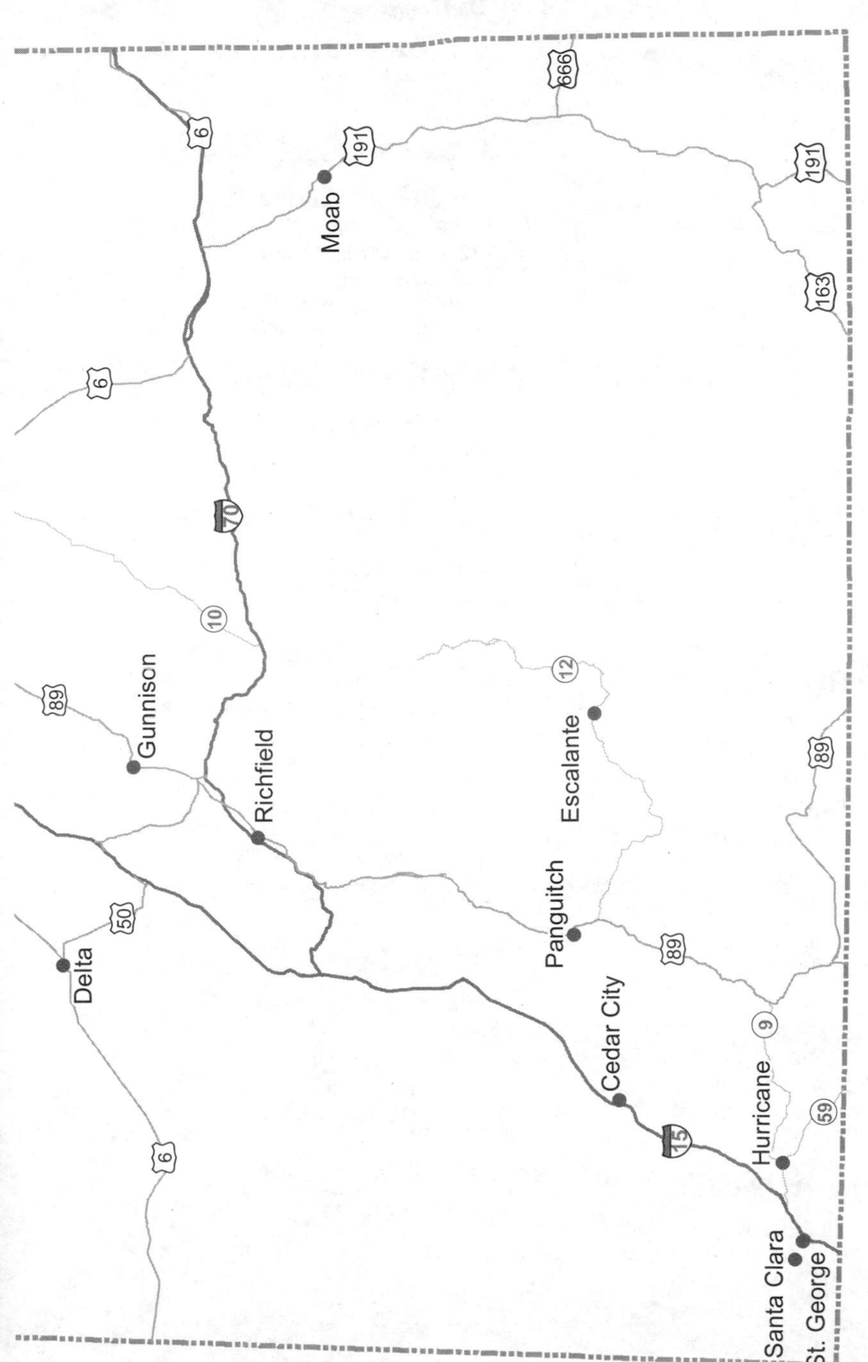
Moab
Gunnison
Richfield
Escalante
Panguitch
Delta
Cedar City
Hurricane
Santa Clara
St. George
6
191
666
163
70
10
12
89
50
9
59
15

Utah

American Fork

The Sewing Basket Q E
51 S 100th E, 84003
(801) 980-9150

Bountiful

Hemstitched Heirlooms Y
585 W 2600 S, 84010
(801) 298-8212

Jewel's Fabric Stash Q M
575 W 2600 S, 84010
(385) 777-2957

Quilter's Attic Q
2155 S. Orchard Drive, #102, 84010
(801) 292-1710

Brigham City

Village Dry Goods Q E
92 S. Main Street, 84302
(435) 723-1315

Cedar City

Stitching It Up Q E C M
117 N. Main Street, 84720
(435) 586-6300

Centerville

Judy's Novelty Wool Y S
1035 N. Main Street, 84014
(801) 298-1356

Clearfield

Sew N Save Q
1475 S. State, Suite A, 84015
(801) 825-2177

Cottonwood Heights

Elaine's Quilt Block Q
6970 S 3000 E, 84121
(801) 947-9100

Delta

Mom's Crafts and Fabrics Q Y
313 S 100 W, 84624
(435) 864-3325

Draper

The Quilter's Lodge Q
➜ SEE AD AT RIGHT
12214 S 900 E, 84020
(801) 576-0390
MWFSa 10-6, TuTh 10-8
www.quilterslodge.com

Escalante

Cross Stitch & More E N C
55 S 200 E, 84726
(435) 826-4628

Gunnison

Quilt S'More Q M
98 S. Main Street, 84634
(435) 528-5393

Hurricane

Main Street Quilt Cottage Q
130 S. Main Street, 84737
(435) 635-4748

Hyde Park

ADORNit With Carolee Q E
3419 N. US Highway 91, 84318
(435) 563-1100

Kaysville

Bennion Crafts and Frames Q Y
354 N. Main, 84037
(801) 444-1177

K & H Quilt Shoppe Q
250 W 200 N, #4, 84037
(801) 444-4375

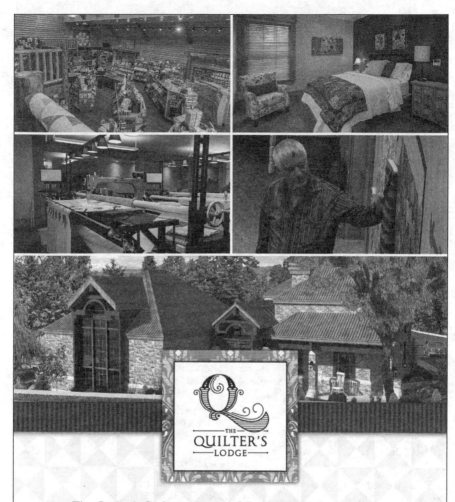

Layton

Nuttalls Bernina & Fabrics Q M
78 S. Fairfield Road, 84040
(801) 444-0203 or (801) 773-6625

Wimmer's Sewing Q E M
1078 E. Gentile Street, 84041
(801) 546-4906

Logan

My Girlfriend's Quilt Shoppe Q E M
1115 N 200 E, Suite 230, 84341
(435) 213-3229
M-Sa 10-6
www.mygirlfriendsquiltshoppe.com

Clover Patch Quilt Shop Q
1 N. Main Street, 84321
(435) 258-9728

Stylish Fabrics Q E M
138 N. Main Street, 84321
(435) 752-4186

Handi Quilter
Designed by a Quilter, for Quilters.
Authorized Retailer

Midway

My Girlfriend's Quilt Shoppe* Q M
6 S 200 W, 84049
(435) 654-2844

Millcreek

The Wool Cabin Y
3295 S. 2000 E, Suite B, 84109
(801) 466-1811

Moab

Desert Thread LLC Y W S
29 E. Center Street, 84532
(435) 259-8404

It's Sew Moab LLC Q E
40 W. Center Street, 84532
(435) 259-0739

Mona

E-Z P-Z Quilt & Sew LLC Q
327 W 300 S, 84645
(435) 655-5356

Murray

Daines Cotton Shops Q M
6100 S. State Street, 84107
(801) 266-6942

Handi Quilter Authorized Retailer
Designed by a Quilter, for Quilters.

Nuttall's Bernina & Fabrics Q M
4742 S 900 E, 84117
(801) 262-6665 or (800) 262-7607

Ogden

Bennion Crafts and Frames Q Y
4335 Harrison Blvd., 84403
(801) 475-7400

Knit Craft Studio E Y N C
432 27th Street, 84401
(801) 394-9304

My Heritage Fabrics Q E
1843 Valley Drive, 84401
(801) 621-2202

Needlepoint Joint E Y N W S
241 Historic 25th Street, 84401
(801) 394-4355 or (800) 660-4355

Shepherd's Bush* E C
220 24th Steet, 84401
(801) 399-4546

Wimmer's Sewing & Vacuum* Q M
309 W. 12th Street, 84404
(385) 244-1199

Orem

American Quilting Q
426 W 800 N, 84057
(801) 802-7841

Fabric Mill Q Y
414 E 1400 S, 84058
(801) 225-3123

Panguitch

Panguitch Home Center* E Y C
24 E 100 N, 84759
(435) 676-8836

Park City

Wasatch and Wool Yarns* Ⓨ Ⓢ
1635 W. Redstone Center Drive, Suite G130, 84098
(435) 575-0999

Payson

Frames & Sew Forth Ⓠ
51 S. Main Street, 84651
(801) 465-9133

Pleasant Grove

Nuttall's Bernina Sewing Center Ⓠ Ⓜ
518 N 2000 W, 84062
(801) 763-1669 or (801) 756-2223

Providence

The Quilt House* Ⓠ
135 S 100 E, 84332
(435) 752-5429

Provo

Dave's Bernina Ⓠ Ⓔ Ⓜ
2017 N 550 W, 84604
(801) 374-5520
M-F 10-6, Sa 9-5
http://www.davesbernina.com

Daines Cotton Shops* Ⓠ Ⓔ Ⓜ
164 W 500 N, 84601
(801) 373-6210

Harmony Ⓠ Ⓨ Ⓦ Ⓢ
315 E. Center Street, 84606
(801) 615-0268

Heindselman's Yarn and Needlework Ⓔ Ⓨ Ⓝ Ⓦ Ⓢ Ⓒ
176 W. Center Street, 84601
(801) 373-5193

Richfield

Christensen's Fabric Department* Ⓠ
39 N. Main Street, 84701
(435) 896-6466

Julia's Shoppe* Ⓨ Ⓦ Ⓢ
350 S 100 E, 84701
(435) 896-1821

Knit N Craft* Ⓔ Ⓨ Ⓒ
5 N. Main Street, 84701
(435) 896-8133

Lora Lee's Rather Bee Quilting* Ⓠ
25 N. Main Street, 84701
(435) 896-8354

Riverton

My Sister's Quilts Ⓠ
12544 S. Pasture Road (4000 W), 84096
(801) 810-3999
M 10-5, Tu-Th 10-9, F 10-7, Sa 9-5
www.mysistersquilts-utah.com

Nuttall's Bernina & Fabrics Ⓠ Ⓜ
12538 S. Doreen Drive 1960 W, 84065
(801) 446-7958

Roosevelt

Miss Annie's Quilt Shoppe* Ⓠ
165 E 100 S, 84066
(435) 722-3111

Roy

Rea's Fabrics Ⓠ Ⓨ
2081 W 3775 S, 84067
(801) 731-2862

Salem

Gracie Lou's* Ⓠ Ⓔ
446 N. State Road 198, 84653
(801) 423-1339

Salt Lake City

...and sew on, Millcreek Q M
2037 E 3300 S, 84109
(801) 467-6465

...and sew on, Rose Park Q
1625 W 700 N, Suite H, 84116
(801) 355-0553

Blazing Needles Y
1365 S 1100 E, 84105
(801) 487-5648

Craft Center of Fine Stitchery* E N C
1920 E. Fort Union Blvd., 84121
(801) 944-4994 or (877) 833-9990

Sandy

Daines Cotton Shops* Q Y M
9441 S 700 E, 84070
(801) 572-1412

Handi Quilter Authorized Retailer
Designed by a Quilter, for Quilters.

Gingerbread Antiques and Yarn Y
8540 S 700 E, 84070
(801) 255-5666

Heartfelt Hobby & Craft* Q
407 W 9000 S, 84070
(801) 233-9028

Quilt Etc. Q M
11 E. Main Street, 84070
(801) 255-2666 or (877) 422-6765

Quilts on the Corner* Q M
208 E. Main Street, 84070
(801) 503-7012

The Handmaiden* Q E Y
11 E. Main Street, 84070
(801) 566-6350

Santa Clara

Clover Patch Quilt Shop* Q
2721 Santa Clara Drive, 84765
(435) 986-9070

The Knitting Post* Y
2305 Santa Clara Drive, 84765
(435) 610-1488

Springville

Corn Wagon Quilt Co.* Q E
303 E 400 S, 84663
(801) 491-3551

Utah Valley Quilting Q
1190 Spring Creek Place, Suite D2, 84663
(801) 310-7714

St. George

A Passion For Painting (Sewing Studio) Q M
310 Tabernacle Street, 84770
(435) 628-5890

Hurst General Store* Q E Y
160 N. Bluff Street, 84770
(435) 673-6141

Mother Superior's FAB Fabrics Q
87 E 2580 S, 84790
(435) 256-6420

Quilted Works, Inc. Q E M
140 N 400 W, #A7, 84770
(435) 674-2500

Scrap Apple Quilts* Q
144 W. Brigham Road, #23, 84790
(435) 628-8226 or (800) 994-0097

The Sewing and Quilting Center Q M
779 South Bluff Street, 84790
(435) 628-4069

Handi Quilter Authorized Retailer
Designed by a Quilter, for Quilters.

Tooele

Yard Sale Fabrics & Gifts* Ⓠ Ⓔ Ⓨ
60 S. Main Street, 84074
(435) 843-0139

Vernal

Quilted Hens* Ⓠ
38 S 600 W, 84078
(435) 789-2411

West Jordan

Fabric Center Ⓠ
9135 S. Redwood Road, 84088
(801) 561-8726

Floyd and Lizzies* Ⓠ Ⓔ Ⓜ
2263 W 7800 S, 84088
(801) 255-4130

Knittin Pretty* Ⓨ Ⓢ
1393 W 9000 S, 84088
(801) 676-9933

Pine Needles* Ⓠ Ⓔ Ⓒ
1100 W 7800 S, #29, 84088
(801) 233-0551

Willow Hill Yarn Company Ⓨ
1100 W 7800 S, Suite 6, 84088
(801) 282-0477

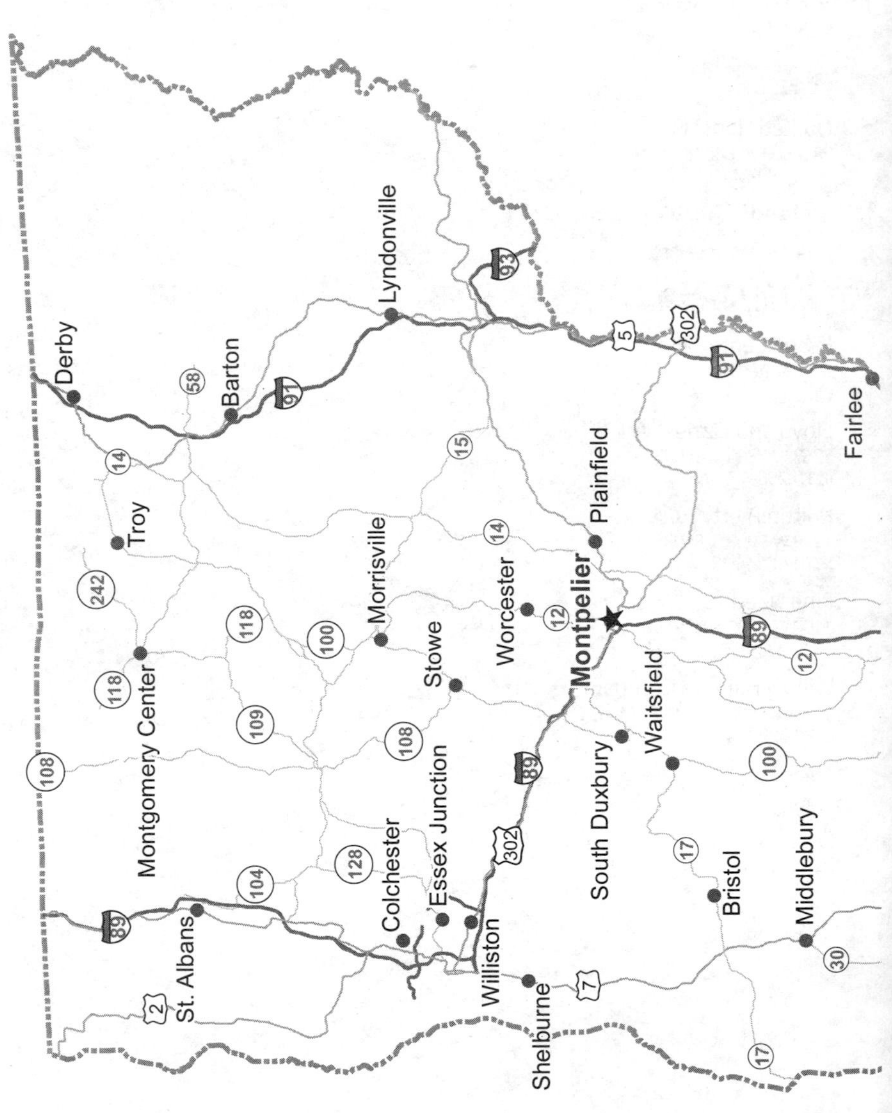
Derby
Barton
Lyndonville
Troy
Morrisville
Montgomery Center
Stowe
Worcester
Montpelier
Plainfield
Fairlee
Waitsfield
South Duxbury
Essex Junction
Colchester
St. Albans
Williston
Shelburne
Bristol
Middlebury
91
93
5
302
58
14
15
242
118
100
12
89
109
108
104
128
2
7
17
30

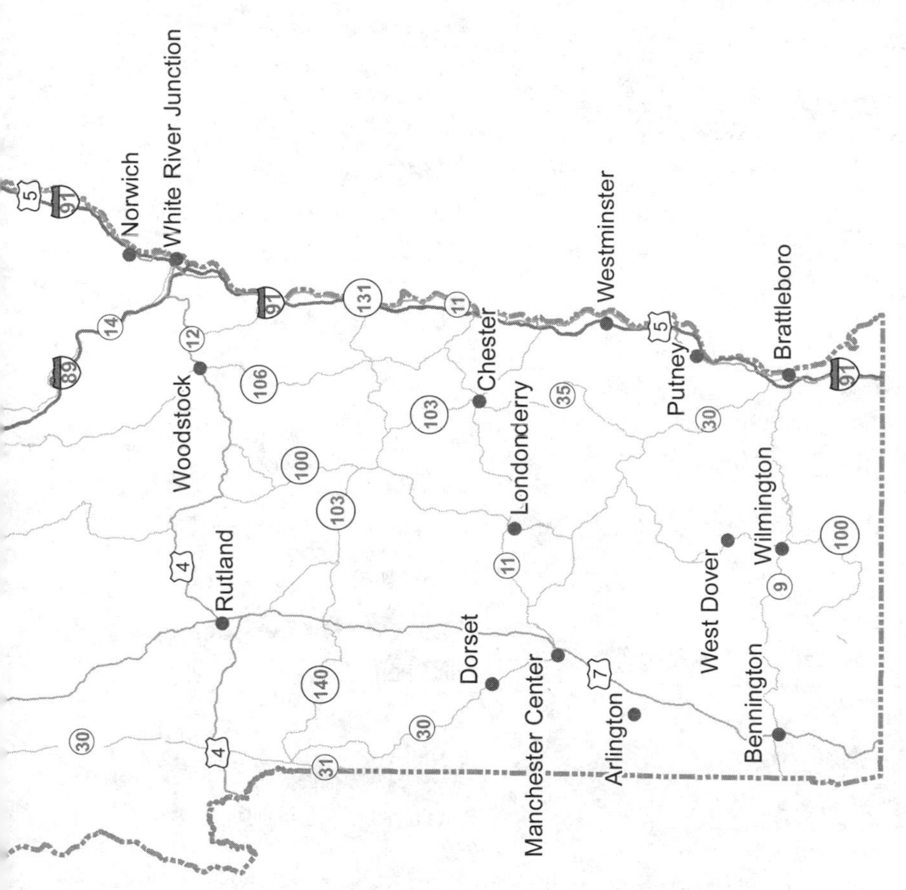
Norwich
White River Junction
Woodstock
Rutland
Chester
Londonderry
Westminster
Putney
Brattleboro
Wilmington
West Dover
Dorset
Manchester Center
Arlington
Bennington
5
91
89
14
12
106
131
11
103
100
35
30
4
140
31
7
9

Vermont

Arlington

Battenkill Stitchery N C
6350 VT Route 7A, 05250
(802) 362-0654

Barton

Sheep to Shawl, LLC Y
315 Elm Street, 05822
(802) 731-1091

Bennington

The Scarlett Creation Q E Y C
626 Main Street, 05201
(802) 447-3794

Brattleboro

HandKnits Y W S
56 Elliot Street, 05301
(802) 579-1799

Bristol

Yarn & Yoga Y W S
25A Main Street, 05443
(802) 453-7799

Chester

Country Treasures Q
12 The Commons, 05143
(802) 875-4377

Six Loose Ladies Yarn & Fiber Y W S
287 Main Street, 05143
(802) 875-7373

Colchester

Sunny Laurel Sisters LLC* Q
3424 Roosevelt Highway, 05446
(802) 872-5363

Derby

Country Thyme Vermont Q E Y
60 Route 111, 05829
(802) 766-2852

Dorset

In Stitches Fine Needlepoint N
3041 Route 30, 05251
(802) 867-7031

Essex Junction

Yankee Pride Quilts* Q
9 Main Street, 05452
(802) 872-9300

Fairlee

Barnyard Quilting* Q
232 US Route 5N, 05045
(802) 333-3566

Londonderry

Waterwheel House Quilt Shop Q E M
6795 Route 100, 05148
(802) 824-5700

Lyndonville

Ewe-Forium Y
646 Peak Road, 05851
(802) 274-3521

God's Little Acres Alpaca Farm* Y S
45 Chamberlain Bridge Road, 05851
(802) 522-6741

Sewin' Love Fabric Shoppe* Q Y
101 Depot Street, 05851
(802) 427-3070

Manchester Center

Knit 1 Purl 1 Y
4783-2 Main Street, 05255
(802) 362-3918

Middlebury

Ben Franklin* Q E Y N C
63 Main Street, 05753
(802) 388-2101

Cacklin' Hens: A Vermont Yarn, Beads & Gift Emporium* Y
383 Exchange Street, Suite B, 05753
(802) 388-2221

The Quilters' Corner at Middlebury Sew-N-Vac Q M
1428 Route 7S, 05753
(802) 388-3559

Handi Quilter Authorized Retailer
Designed by a Quilter, for Quilters.

Monkton

Kits by Carla Q
2433 Boro Hill Road, 05469
(802) 377-0361

Montgomery Center

The Mountain Fiber Folk Cooperative* Y S
188 Main Street, 05471
(802) 326-2092

Montpelier

A Quilter's Garden, Inc. Q E M
342 River Street, Route 302, 05602
(802) 223-2275

Yarn Y
112 Main Street, 05602
(802) 229-2444

Morrisville

Bailey House Floral* Y N
853 Brooklyn Street, 05661
(802) 888-7909

Norwich

Northern Nights Yarn Shop* Y
289 Main Street, 05055
(802) 649-2000

Plainfield

Vermont Yarn Shop at Plainview Farm Y
858 E. Hill Road, 05667
(802) 454-1114

Putney

Green Mountain Spinnery Y
7 Brickyard Lane, 05346
(800) 321-9665

Rutland

Green Mountain Fibers Yarn Store* Y W S
259 Woodstock Avenue, (US Route 4E), 05701
(802) 775-7800

Shelburne

Must Love Yarn Y S
2438 Shelburne Road, Suite 2, 05482
(802) 448-3780

South Duxbury

Singing Spindle Spinnery Y W S
701 VT Route 100, 05660
(802) 244-8025

St. Albans

What A Yarn & Antiques Y
54 N. Main Street, 05478
(802) 393-0121

Stowe

Stowe Fabric & Yarn Q Y S
37 Depot Street, 05672
(802) 253-6740
MWThF 10-5, Sa 9-5, Su 10-4
http://www.facebook.com/pages/Stowe-Fabric-Yarn/136563569700757

The Wooden Needle E N C
56 Park Street, 05672
(802) 253-3086

Troy

Vermont Quilter's Schoolhouse Q
6529 Vermont Route 100, 05868
(802) 744-4023

Waitsfield

Shades of Winter Yarn E Y N C
5121 Main Street, Suite 9, 05673
(802) 496-9040

West Dover

Ugly Duckling Yarn* Y
114 Route 100, 05356
(802) 464-6300

Westminster

Quilt-a-Way Fabrics Ⓠ Ⓔ
190 Back Westminster Road, 05159
(802) 722-4743

White River Junction

Hen House Fabric Ⓠ
246 Holiday Drive, #2, 05001
(802) 295-4436

Savage Hart Farm* Ⓨ
2514 Jericho Road, 05001
(802) 281-5850

Williston

Northeast Fiber Arts Center Ⓨ Ⓢ
7531 Williston Road, 05495
(802) 288-8081

Quilting With Color* Ⓠ
21 Taft Corners Shopping Center, 05495
(802) 876-7135

Wilmington

Norton House, A Quilter's Paradise Ⓠ Ⓔ Ⓝ Ⓒ
30 W. Main Street, 05363
(802) 464-7213

Woodstock

Whippletree Yarn Shop Ⓨ
7 Central Street, 05091
(802) 457-1325
M-Sa 10-5, Su 11-4
www.whippletreeyarnshop.com

Worcester

Wool Shed At Frostbite Falls Farm* Ⓨ Ⓢ
3 Hancock Brook Road, 05682
(802) 223-2456

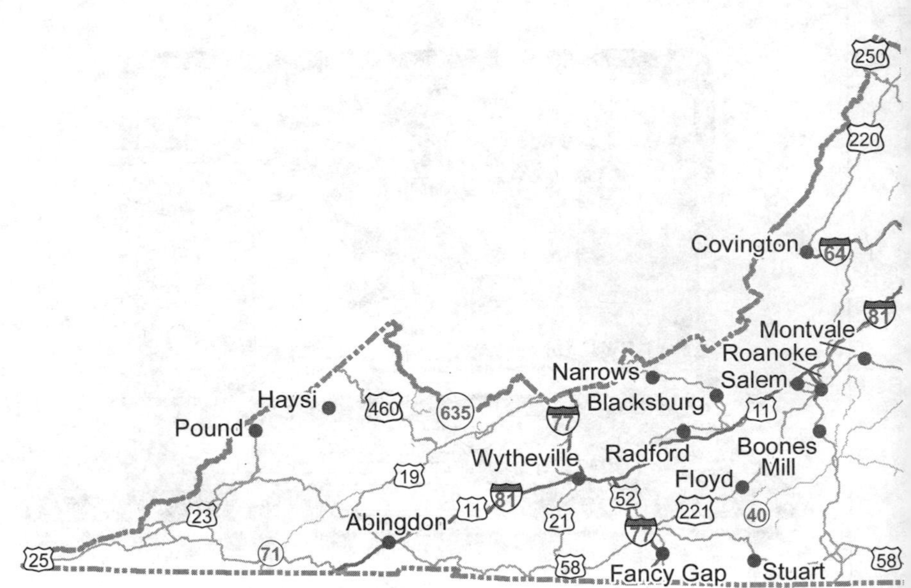

250
220
Covington
64
81
Montvale
Roanoke
Salem
Narrows
Blacksburg
Haysi
460
635
77
11
Pound
Radford
Boones
Mill
Wytheville
19
Floyd
81
52
23
11
221
40
Abingdon
21
77
25
71
58
Fancy Gap
Stuart
58

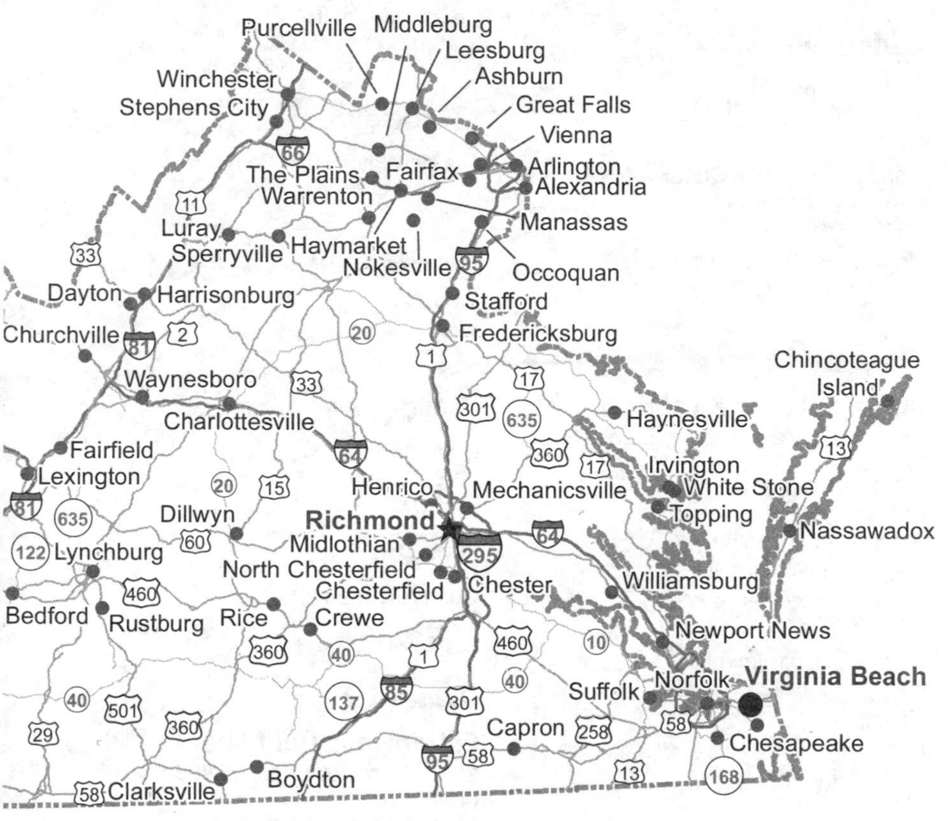
Purcellville
Middleburg
Leesburg
Ashburn
Winchester
Stephens City
Great Falls
Vienna
The Plains
Fairfax
Arlington
Warrenton
Alexandria
Manassas
Luray
Sperryville
Haymarket
Nokesville
Occoquan
Dayton
Harrisonburg
Stafford
Churchville
Fredericksburg
Chincoteague Island
Waynesboro
Charlottesville
Haynesville
Fairfield
Lexington
Irvington
White Stone
Henrico
Mechanicsville
Topping
Dillwyn
Richmond
Nassawadox
Midlothian
Lynchburg
North Chesterfield
Chesterfield
Chester
Williamsburg
Bedford
Rustburg
Rice
Crewe
Newport News
Norfolk
Virginia Beach
Suffolk
Capron
Chesapeake
Clarksville
Boydton

Virginia

Abingdon

A Likely Yarn Ⓨ Ⓨ Ⓦ Ⓢ
213 Pecan Street, 24210
(276) 628-2143

Jeannine's Fabrics & Quilt Shop Ⓠ Ⓔ Ⓝ Ⓒ Ⓜ
414 W. Main Street, 24210
(276) 628-9586

Virginia Highlands Quilt Shop* Ⓠ Ⓔ
25066 Lee Highway, 24211
(276) 628-6442

Alexandria

Bonny's Sewing & Fabric Ⓠ Ⓔ Ⓜ
5515 Cherokee Avenue, Suite 101, 22312
(703) 451-8480
M-F 10-6, Sa 10-4
www.bonnysews.com

Artistic Artifacts Ⓠ Ⓔ Ⓜ
4750 Eisenhower Avenue, 22304
(703) 823-0202

Fabric Place Basement Ⓠ
6660 Richmond Highway, 22306
(703) 660-6661

Fibre Space Ⓨ Ⓦ Ⓢ
1319 Prince Street, 22314
(703) 664-0344

Hollin Hall Variety Store Ⓠ Ⓨ
7902 Fort Hunt Road, 22308
(703) 765-4110

In Stitches Needlework Ⓔ Ⓝ Ⓒ
8800F Pear Tree Court, 22309
(703) 360-4600

Arlington

Waste Knot Needlepoint Ⓝ
2100 N. Glebe Road, 22207
(703) 807-1828

Ashburn

Sew Magarbo* Ⓠ Ⓔ Ⓜ
44933 George Washington Blvd., Suite 130-135, 20147
(703) 375-9739

Bedford

Hearthside Quilts* Ⓠ
207 E. Depot Street, 24523
(540) 587-4165 or (800) 451-3533

Blacksburg

The New River Fiber Company Ⓠ Ⓨ Ⓢ
102 Roanoke Street E, 24060
(540) 382-8245

Boones Mill

Boone's Country Store Ⓠ Ⓔ
2699 Jubal Early Highway, 24065
(540) 721-2478

Boydton

Quilter's Nook* Ⓠ
129 Bank Street, 23917
(434) 265-6150

Capron

Quilters N Friends* Ⓠ
17293 Pinopolis Road, 23829
(434) 658-4564

Charlottesville

Cottonwood Quilt Shop Ⓠ Ⓔ Ⓜ
2035 Barracks Road, 22903
(434) 244-9975
M-Sa 10-6, Su 12-4
www.cottonwoodquiltshop.com

EWE Fine Fiber Goods Ⓨ Ⓦ Ⓢ
617 W. Main Street, 22903
(434) 409-9095

Laughing Sheep Yarns Ⓨ
188 Zan Road, 22901
(434) 973-0331

Magpie Knits Ⓔ Ⓨ Ⓝ Ⓦ
111 W. Main Street, 22902
(434) 296-4625

Mangham Wool and Mohair Farm Ⓠ Ⓔ Ⓨ Ⓦ Ⓢ
901 Hammocks Gap Road, 22911
(434) 882-2222

Threads Ⓝ
2246 Ivy Road, Suite 9, 22903
(434) 295-3575

Chesapeake

A Different Touch Q M
1107 S. Military Highway, 23320
(757) 366-8830

Chester

The Busy Bea LLC Q
➡ SEE AD BELOW
11934 Centre Street, 23831
(804) 748-4951
MWThF 10-5:30, Tu 1-5:30, Sa 10-4
www.facebook.com/pages/The-Busy-Bea/1493493530882785

Chesterfield

Stitch By Stitch Quilt Shop Q E
6501 Centralia Road, 23832
(804) 318-9575

Chincoteague Island

Carodan Farm Wool Shop Y W
7151 Horseshoe Drive, 23336
(800) 985-7083 or (757) 336-0536

Churchville

Cestari Sheep & Wool Company Y W S
3581 Churchville Avenue, 24421
(540) 337-7270

Clarksville

Frames & Stitches E Y C
317 Virginia Avenue, 23927
(434) 374-5949

Covington

Sew Many Quilts Q
431 W. Main Street, 24426
(540) 962-0023

Crewe

Rose Patch Creations Q
125 W. Carolina Avenue, 23930
(434) 645-7780

Dayton

Patchwork Plus Q M
17 Killdeer Lane, 22821
(540) 879-2505

Handi Quilter® Authorized Retailer
Designed by a Quilter, for Quilters.®

Dillwyn

Yarn Barn Y
5077 Andersonville Road, 23936
(434) 983-1965 or (800) 850-6008

Fair Lawn

Sew Biz Q E Y C M
7327 Peppers Ferry Blvd. Ste A, 24141
(540) 639-1138
MTuWFSa 10-6, Th 10-7:30
www.sewbiz.com

Fairfax

The Quilters Studio Q E M
9600 Main Street, Unit L, 22031
(703) 261-6366

Handi Quilter® Authorized Retailer
Designed by a Quilter, for Quilters.®

Fairfield

The Quiltery LLC Q
5499 N. Lee Highway, 24435
(540) 377-9191

Fancy Gap

Fancy Gap Pottery and Fabric Outlet Ⓠ Ⓔ Ⓨ
350 Pottery Drive, 24328
(276) 728-9524

Floyd

Woolly Jumper Yarns Ⓨ
202 S. Locust Street, 24091
(540) 745-5648
W-F 12-5, Sa 10-5
www.woollyjumperyarns.com

Schoolhouse Fabrics Ⓠ Ⓔ Ⓨ Ⓒ
220 N. Locust Street, 24091
(540) 745-4561

Fredericksburg

The Crazy Cousin Ⓠ Ⓔ Ⓜ
4131 Plank Road, 22407
(540) 786-2289

Untangled Purls Ⓨ
2561 Cowan Blvd., 22401
(540) 479-8382

Great Falls

Jinny Beyer Studio Ⓠ
776-E Walker Road, 22066
(703) 759-0250 or (866) 759-7373

Harrisonburg

Sew Classic Fabrics Ⓠ
121 Carpenter Lane, 22801
(540) 421-3309
M-Sa 10-6
www.sewclassicfabrics.com

Ragtime Fabrics Ⓠ Ⓔ
926 W. Market Street, 22801
(540) 434-5663

Haymarket

Needles In The Haymarket Ⓔ Ⓨ Ⓝ Ⓢ Ⓒ
15125 Washington Street, Suite 108, 20169
(703) 659-1062

Oh Sew Persnickety Fabrics and Threads Ⓠ
15125 Washington Street, Suite 116, 20169
(571) 222-7759

Haynesville

Franklin Sewing Machine Ⓠ Ⓔ Ⓜ
11051 Richmond Road, 22472
(804) 333-3533

Haysi

Jan's Fabrics Ⓠ
26531 Dickenson Highway, 24256
(276) 865-4108

Henrico

Quilting Adventures Ⓠ Ⓔ Ⓒ
6943 Lakeside Avenue, 23228
(804) 262-0005
Tu-Th 10-8, FSa 10-6, Su 12-5
www.quiltingadventures.com

Blue Crab Quilt Co. / Bernina Of Richmond Ⓠ Ⓔ Ⓜ
3991 Deep Rock Road, 23233
(804) 755-4499

Irvington

Sewlovelee Ⓠ Ⓜ
4504 Irvington Road, 22480
(804) 438-5800

Village Needlepoint Of Irvington Ⓝ
4395 Irvington Road, 22480
(804) 438-9500

Leesburg

Finch Knitting and Sewing Studio Ⓠ Ⓨ Ⓜ
102 Loudoun Street SW, 20175
(703) 777-8000

Lexington

House Mountain Yarn Co. Ⓨ
117 S. Main Street, 24450
(540) 462-2931

Luray

Shenandoah Moon Ⓨ
58 W. Main Street, 22835
(540) 743-5810

Lynchburg

Backstitches Ⓨ
100 Wayne Drive, 24502
(434) 385-0185

Friends on a Limb Ⓨ
1415 Kemper Street, 24502
(434) 426-1305

Quilted Expressions Ⓠ Ⓜ
3622 Old Forest Road, 24501
(434) 385-6765

Sew Simple of Lynchburg LLC Ⓠ Ⓜ
2414 Wards Road, 24502
(434) 239-6708

Manassas

Suzzie's Quilt Shop Ⓠ Ⓔ
10404 Portsmouth Road, 20109
(703) 368-3867

Mechanicsville

Millstone Quilts Ⓠ
8074 Flannigan Mill Road, 23111
(804) 779-3535

Middleburg

Stitch Ⓝ
103 W. Federal Street, 20117
(540) 687-5990

Midlothian

Quilter's Corner Ⓠ Ⓔ Ⓜ
➡ SEE AD BELOW
1245 Sycamore Square, 23113
(804) 794-1990
M-Sa 10-5
www.quilterscornerva.com

Dances With Wool, LLC Ⓨ
1229 Sycamore Square, 23113
(804) 594-5849

Montvale

Bargain Barn Fabrics Ⓠ Ⓔ
11600 W. Lynchburg-Salem Turnpike, 24122
(540) 947-2894
Tu-F 10-5, Sa 10-3
www.bargainbarnfabrics.com

Narrows

Ms. Audre's Fabric-n-Fellowship Ⓠ Ⓔ Ⓨ Ⓝ Ⓒ
206 Main Street, 24124
(540) 921-2042

Nassawadox

Teresa's Quilts Ⓠ
7401 Railroad Avenue, 23413
(757) 710-0644

Newport News

Nancy's Calico Patch Ⓠ Ⓜ
896 J Clyde Morris Blvd., 23601
(757) 596-7397

Village Stitchery Ⓔ Ⓨ Ⓝ Ⓒ
97 Main Street, Suite 100, 23601
(757) 599-0101

Nokesville

Daffodil Quilts & Fibers Ⓠ
13059 Fitzwater Drive, 20181
(703) 594-0386
Tu-F 10-6, Sa 10-5, Su 12-5
www.daffodilquilts.net

Norfolk

Baa Baa Sheep LLC Ⓨ Ⓦ Ⓢ
754 W. 22nd Street, 23517
(757) 802-9229
Tu 10-8, W-F 10-6, Sa 10-4
www.baabaasheepllc.com

Fabric Hut Ⓠ Ⓔ Ⓨ Ⓒ Ⓜ
828 E. Little Creek Road, 23518
(757) 588-1300 or (877) 4FA-BHUT

North Chesterfield

Material Things Ⓠ Ⓔ
9930 Hull Street Road, 23236
(804) 276-3689

Occoquan

Yarn Cloud Ⓨ Ⓢ
➡ SEE AD BELOW
204 Washington Street, 22125
(571) 408-4236
TuWFSa 10-5, Th 10-7, Su call first
www.yarncloud.com

Attic Treasures & Sew Easy Sewing Studio Ⓜ Ⓠ Ⓔ
203 Washington Street, 22125
(703) 490-1536
Tu-F 10:30-5:30, Sa 10:30-4:30
www.seweasysewing.com

Handi Quilter® Authorized Retailer
Designed by a Quilter, for Quilters.®

Pound

Fabric House* Ⓠ Ⓔ
8424 W. Main Street, 24279
(276) 796-4500

Purcellville

Two Rivers Yarns Ⓨ Ⓢ
500 E. Main Street, Suite 100, 20132
(240) 457-0410
WF 11-5, Th 12-7, Sa 11-4, Su 12-4
www.tryans.com

Web Fabrics Ⓠ Ⓔ
116 N. Bailey Lane, 20132
(540) 751-2069 or (866) 932-3227

Rice

Lib's Place LLC Ⓠ Ⓔ Ⓨ Ⓝ Ⓒ
23147 Prince Edward Highway, 23966
(434) 392-5427

Richmond

Chadwick Heirlooms Ⓠ Ⓔ
12501 Patterson Avenue, 23238
(804) 285-3355

Jermies Ⓝ
5706 Patterson Avenue, 23226
(804) 282-8021

Knitting B Ⓨ
8801 Three Chopt Road, Suite L, 23229
(804) 484-6005

The Stitching Studio and Gift Boutique Ⓝ
5615 Patterson Avenue, 23226
(804) 269-0355

Roanoke

Wool Workshop Ⓨ Ⓢ
2130 Colonial Avenue, 24015
(540) 685-2285

Yarn Explosion Ⓨ Ⓝ
5227 Airport Road NW, 24012
(540) 206-2638

Rustburg

Threads Run Thru It, Inc. Ⓠ Ⓜ
40 Exchange Drive, 24588
(434) 821-3000

Salem

Quilting Essentials Ⓠ
405 Apperson Drive, 24153
(540) 389-3650

Sperryville

Knit Wit Yarn Shop Ⓨ Ⓢ
45 Main Street, 22740
(540) 987-8251
MTh 12-5, F 12-6, SaSu 10-6
www.knitwityarns.com

Stafford

Bonny's Sewing & Fabric Ⓠ Ⓔ Ⓜ
2789 Jefferson Davis Hwy., Suite 107, 22554
(540) 288-2022
M-F 10-6, Sa 10-4
www.bonnysews.com

Stephens City

Cloth Peddler* Ⓠ
5330 Main Street, 22655
(540) 868-9020

Stuart

Quilted Colors Ⓠ
107 N. Main Street, 24171
(276) 694-3020

Suffolk

Stitch Please Yarn Arts Ⓨ
5501 Bennett's Pasture Road, Suite G, 23435
(757) 880-5546

The Plains

Hunt Country Yarns Ⓨ Ⓝ Ⓢ
6482 Main Street, 20198
(540) 253-9990

Topping

2 B's Quilt Shop Ⓠ
2324 Grey's Point Road, 23169
(804) 758-2642

Vienna

Red Fox Yarn, LLC Ⓨ Ⓢ
421 Church Street NE, Suite D, 22180
(703) 865-6343

Virginia Beach

Dyeing to Stitch Ⓔ Ⓒ
5312 Kemps River Drive, Suite 102, 23464
(757) 366-8740
Tu-F 10-4, Sa 11-5
www.dyeing2stitch.com

Sarah's Thimble Ⓠ
2245 W. Great Neck Road, Suite 5, 23451
(757) 481-1725
M-Sa 10-5
www.sarahsthimble.com

The Yarn Club, Inc. Ⓨ Ⓦ Ⓢ
2448 Virginia Beach Blvd., 23454
(757) 486-5648

Warrenton

Kelly Ann's Quilting Ⓠ Ⓔ
9 S. 5th Street, 20186
(540) 341-8890

Yarnia of Old Town Ⓨ Ⓦ Ⓒ
92 Main Street, Suite 101, 20186
(540) 878-2039

Waynesboro

Cross Stitch Station Ⓒ
1500 W. 11th Street, 22980
(540) 943-7742

Stitch Amour* Ⓨ
112 S. Wayne Avenue, 22980
(540) 942-9022

White Stone

Dirt Woman Fiber Arts* Ⓨ Ⓦ Ⓢ
577 Rappahannock Drive, 22578
(804) 725-7525

Williamsburg

Haus Tirol, Inc. Ⓔ Ⓒ
1915 Pocahontas Trail, Suite E6, 23185
(757) 220-0313

The Flying Needles Ⓨ Ⓦ Ⓢ
5251 John Tyler Highway, Suite 11, 23185
(757) 345-3655

Yarn Matters Ⓨ
7437 Richmond Road, 23188
(757) 585-4344

Winchester

Knit 1, Purl 2 Ⓨ
20 W. Boscawen Street, 22601
(540) 662-6098

The Scrappy Apple, Quilts & More* Ⓠ
1206 Valley Avenue, 22601
(540) 665-1770

Wytheville

Batiks Etcetera & Sew What Fabrics Ⓠ Ⓜ
460 E. Main Street, 24382
(276) 228-6400 or (800) 228-4573

Wythe Yarn Ⓨ
175 A-B Tazewell Street, 24382
(276) 223-4459

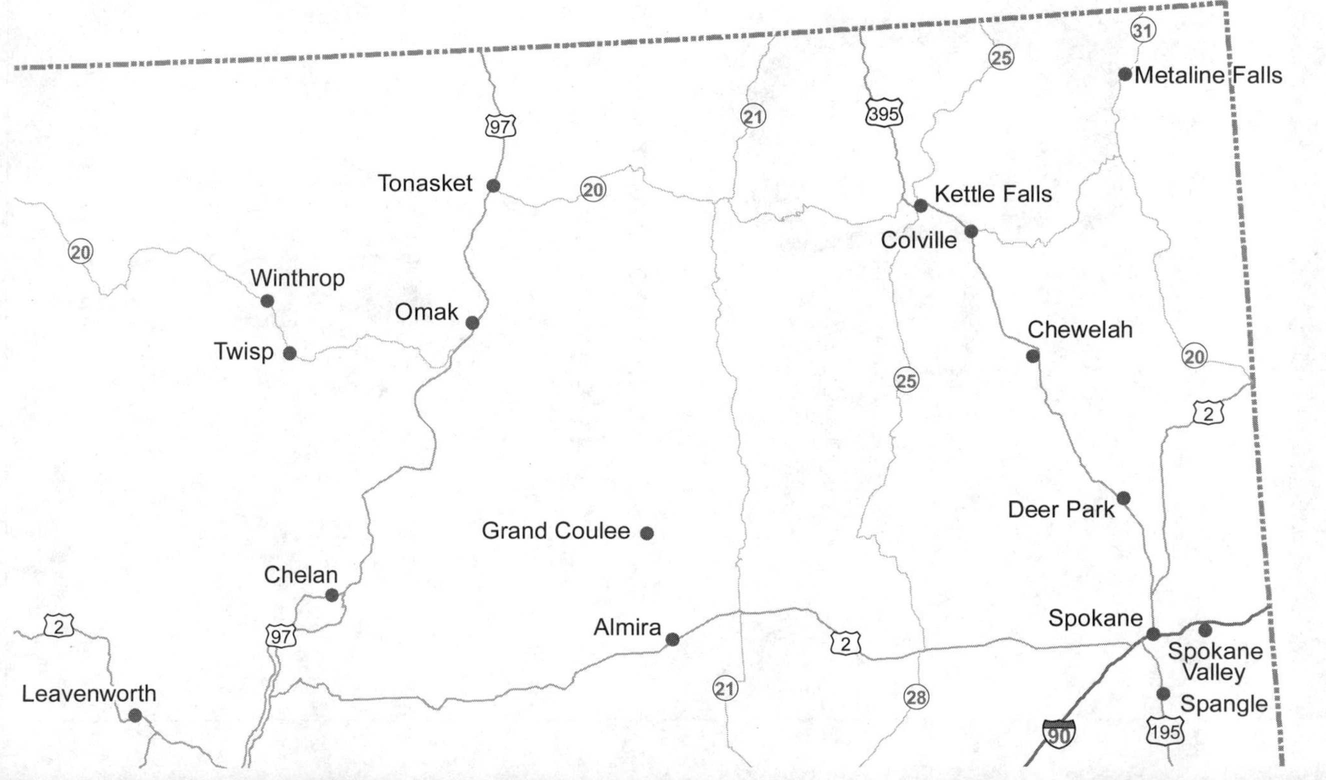

31
Metaline Falls
25
21
395
97
Tonasket
20
Kettle Falls
Colville
20
Winthrop
Omak
Twisp
Chewelah
20
25
2
Deer Park
Grand Coulee
Chelan
Almira
Spokane
2
97
2
Spokane Valley
Leavenworth
21
28
Spangle
90
195

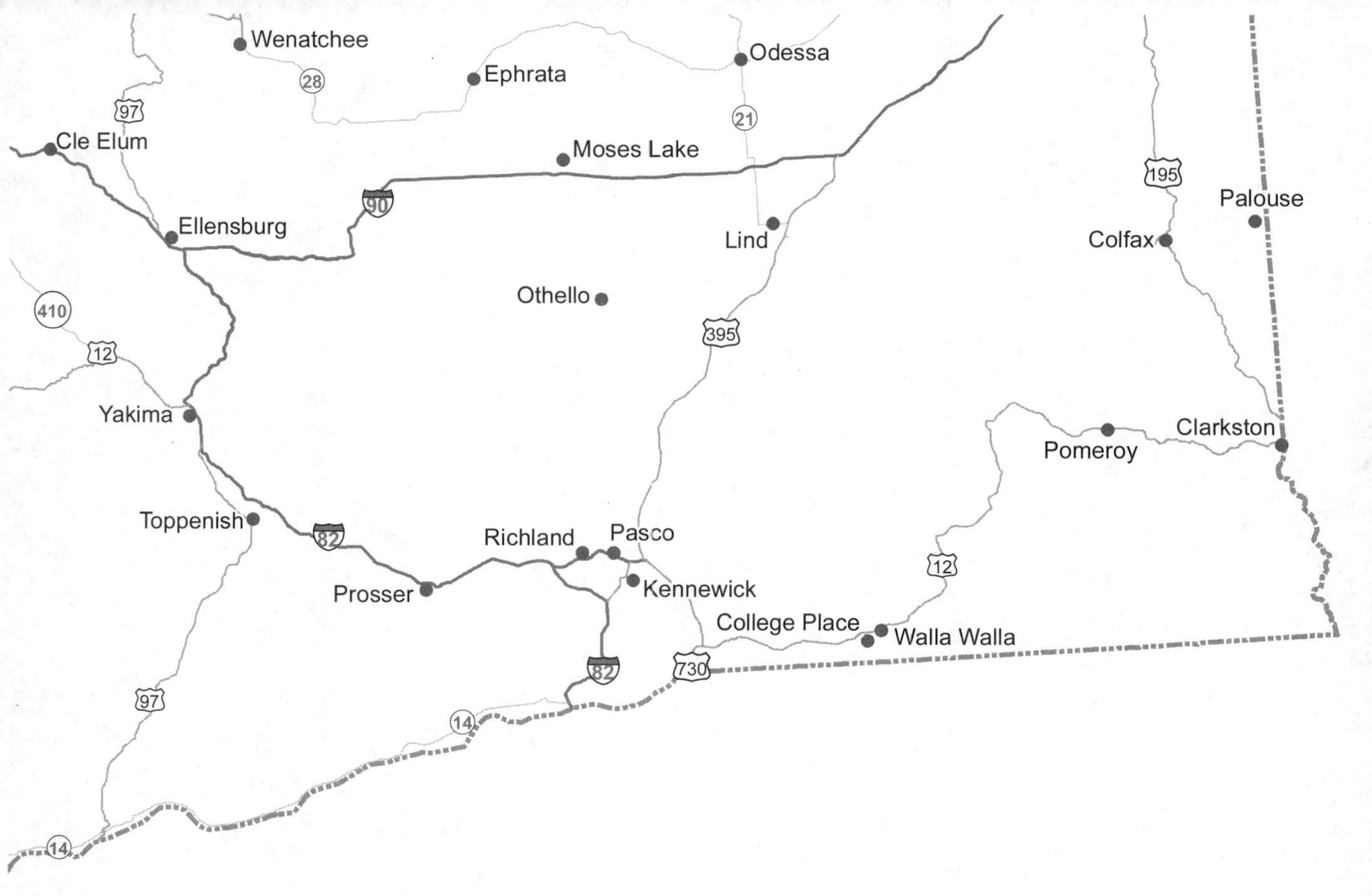
Wenatchee
28
Ephrata
Odessa
97
21
Cle Elum
Moses Lake
195
Palouse
90
Ellensburg
Lind
Colfax
Othello
410
395
12
Yakima
Clarkston
Pomeroy
Toppenish
82
Richland
Pasco
12
Prosser
Kennewick
College Place
Walla Walla
82
730
97
14
14

Port Angeles
101
Forks
101

Lynden
539
9
Bellingham
5
Orcas Island
Anacortes
20
Friday Harbor
20
Sedro-Woolley
Lopez Island
Mt. Vernon
La Conner
20
9
Oak Harbor
530
530
Camano Island
Stanwood
Coupeville
Arlington
Port Townsend
Sequim
525
116
Langley
20
Freeland
Everett
525
101
104
Snohomish
9
Port Gamble
Edmonds
Monroe
2
Woodinville
Lake Forest Park
Poulsbo
Duvall
3
Redmond
Kirkland
Bainbridge Island
Silverdale
Seattle
Carnation
3
Bellevue
203
405
Issaquah
509
167
16
Burien
Renton
18
Vashon
169
3
5
90

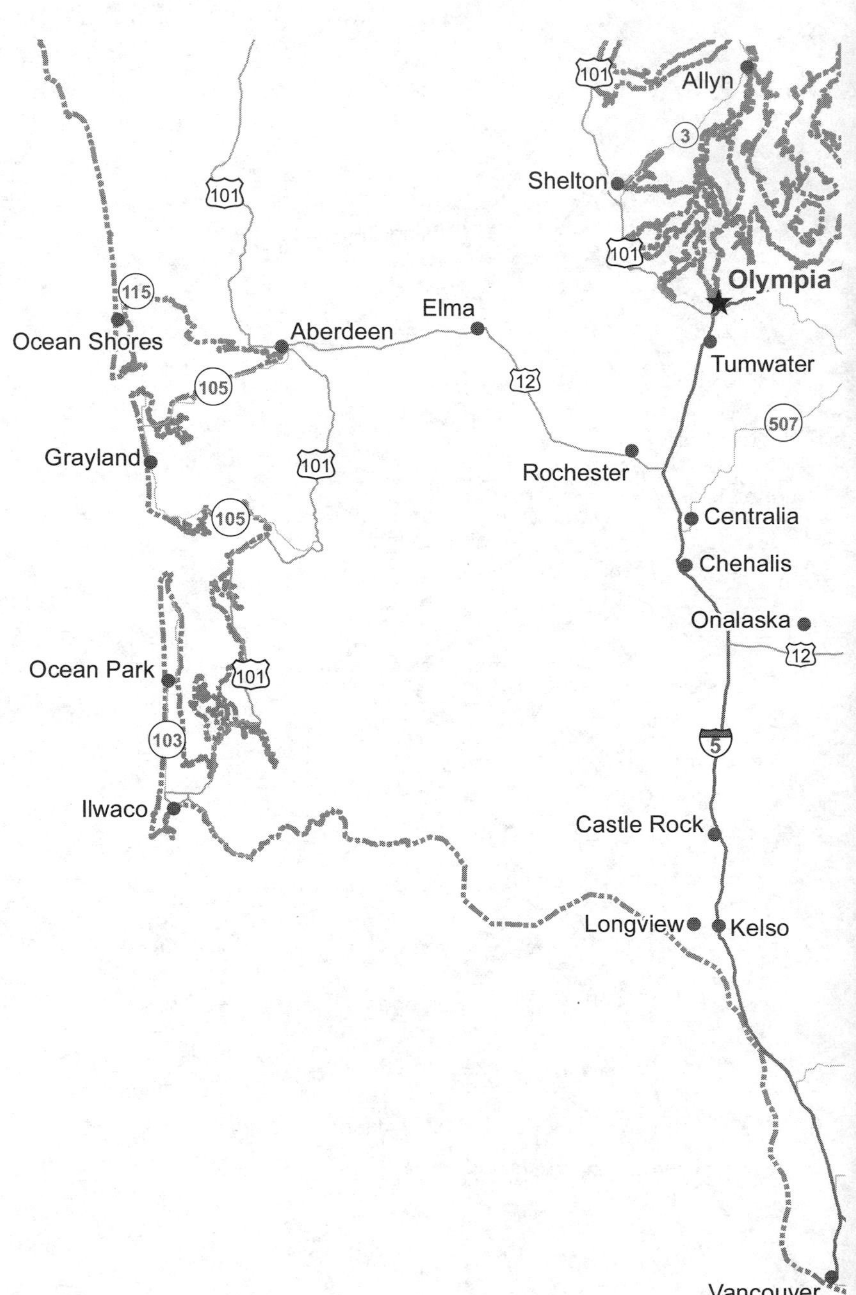
101
Allyn
3
Shelton
101
101
Olympia
115
Elma
Aberdeen
Ocean Shores
Tumwater
105
12
101
507
Grayland
Rochester
105
Centralia
Chehalis
Onalaska
12
Ocean Park
101
103
5
Ilwaco
Castle Rock
Longview
Kelso
Vancouver

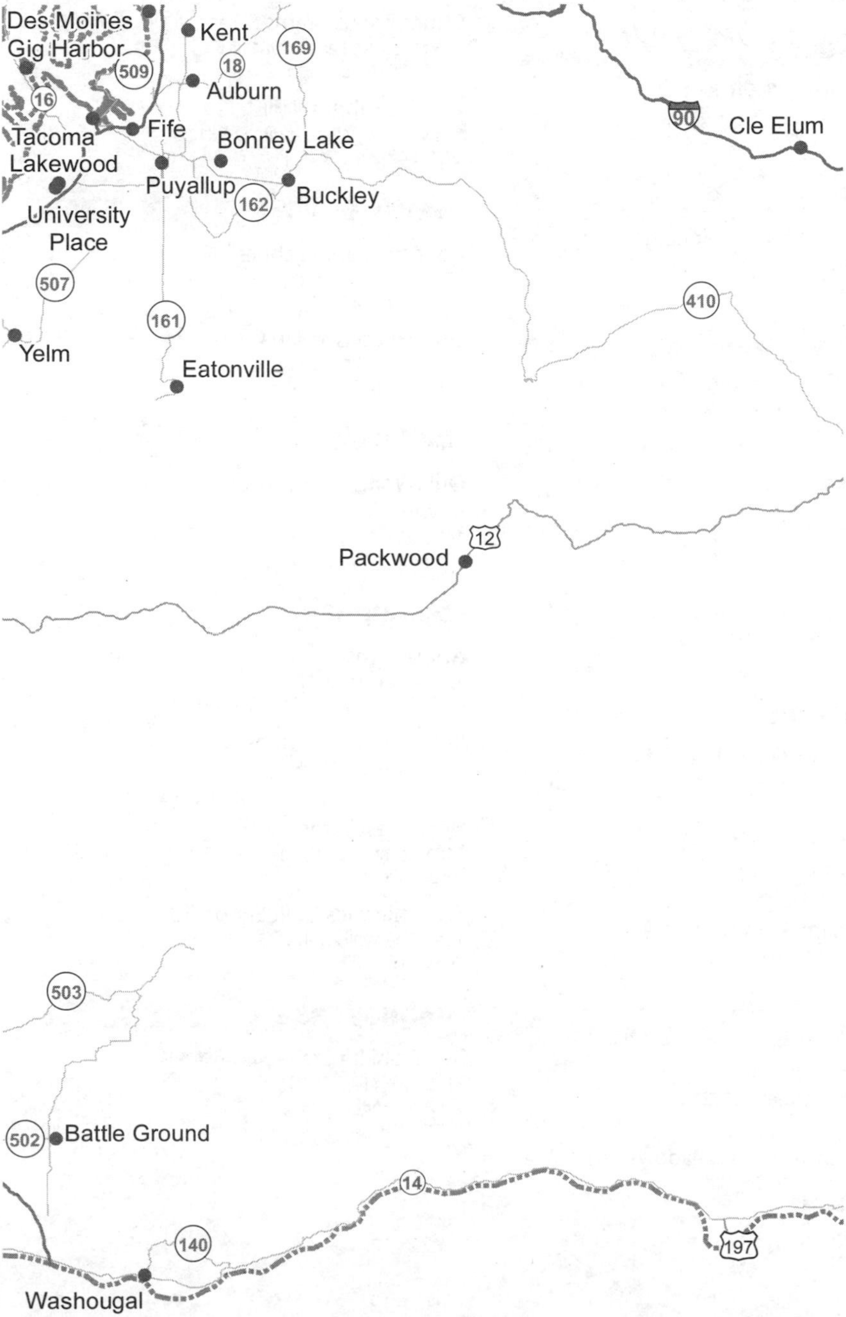

Des Moines
Gig Harbor
Kent
169
18
509
Auburn
16
Fife
Tacoma
Bonney Lake
Lakewood
Puyallup
Buckley
162
University
Place
507
161
Yelm
Eatonville
90
Cle Elum
410
12
Packwood
503
502
Battle Ground
14
140
197
Washougal

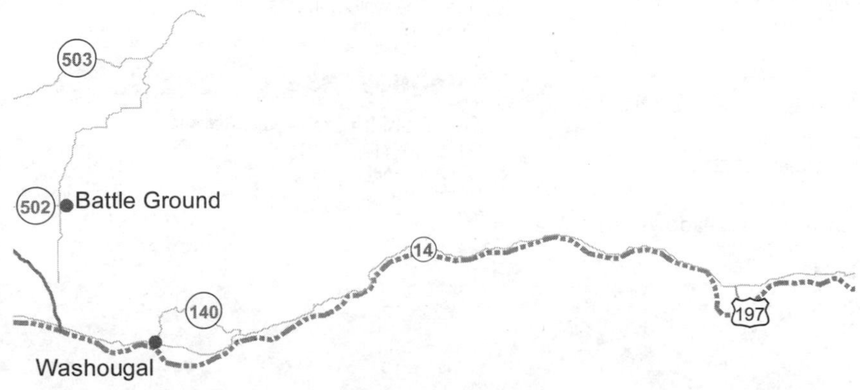

Washington

Aberdeen

Quilt Harbor Q E Y M
208 S. Broadway Street, 98520
(360) 532-1200

Allyn

Allyn Knit Shop & Spinning Supply Y W S
16590 E. State Route 3, 98524
(360) 275-4729

Almira

Nana's Quilts & More* Q
318 W. Maple Avenue, 99103
(509) 639-2648

Anacortes

Fabrics Plus Q E
608 Commercial Avenue, 98221
(360) 293-7641

Fidalgo Artisan Yarn & Clothing Y W S
711 Commercial Avenue, 98221
(360) 293-7377

Arlington

Aunt Mary's Quilt Shop Q E
17306 Smokey Point Drive, Suite 20A, 98223
(360) 657-1116

Perfectly Knotty Y
310 N. Olympic Avenue, 98223
(425) 273-5563

The Quiltmaker's Shoppe Q E
315 N. Olympic Avenue, 98223
(360) 435-3993

Auburn

A Little Knitty Y
218 E. Main Street, 98002
(206) 659-5987

Spin Alpaca at Fair Meadows Farm* Y S
4131 53rd Street SE, 98092
(253) 833-0113

Bainbridge Island

Churchmouse Yarns & Teas Q E Y N W S C
118 Madrone Lane N, 98110
(206) 780-2686

Esther's Fabrics Q E C
181 Winslow Way E, Suite D, 98110
(206) 842-2261

Battle Ground

Country Manor Fabrics * Q
7702 NE 179th Street, 98604
(360) 573-6084

Urban Basics Q E Y C
209 E. Main Street, 98604
(360) 666-5331

Bellevue

QuiltWorks Northwest and Beads & Beyond Q M
145 106th Avenue NE, 98004
(425) 453-6005 or (877) 295-7222

Bellingham

Apple Yarns Y W S
1780 Iowa Street, 98229
(360) 756-9992 or (855) 850-9276

Kori's Fabric Creations Q
4300 Alice Street, 98226
(360) 671-7570

Northwest Yarns Y W S
1401 Commercial Street, 98225
(360) 738-0167

Two Thimbles Quilt Shop* Q E
1805 Cornwall Avenue, 98225
(360) 715-1629

Bonney Lake

Ben Franklin Crafts Q E Y N W C
21121 SR 410 E, 98391
(253) 862-6822

Buckley

Front Porch Quilts Q
832 Main Street, 98321
(360) 761-7185
M 12-5, Tu-Sa 10-5
www.facebook.com/frontporchquilts

Elizabeth's Fiber and Yarns Q Y W S
24912 112th Street E, 98321
(253) 267-9870

Burien

Town Square Fabric and Yarn Y
445 SW 152nd Street, Suite 100, 98166
(206) 246-9276

Camano Island

Over the Rainbow Q
740 Michael Way, 98282
(360) 387-2366
Open Daily 9-12, Closed Su
www.overrainbow.com

Carnation

Tolt Yarn and Wool LLC* Y S
4509 Tolt Avenue, 98014
(425) 333-4066

Castle Rock

The Quilt Nest & Yarn Boutique Q Y
105 Cowlitz Street W, 98611
(360) 274-4663
M-F 10-5, Sa 10-4
www.thequiltnest.com

Centralia

Whalen Quilt Works Q E
404 S. Tower Avenue, #5, 98531
(360) 807-1255

Chehalis

Ewe and I LLC Y W S
566 N. Market Blvd., 98532
(360) 345-1506

Sister's Quilt Shop Q
476 N. Market Blvd., 98532
(360) 748-9747

Chelan

3 Wild Sheep Y
210 E. Woodin Avenue, 98816
(509) 888-0285

Woven Threads Q E
136 E. Woodin Avenue, 98816
(509) 682-7714

Chewelah

Akers United Drug Q E Y N
406 N. Park Street, 99109
(509) 935-8441

Clarkston

Patrick's Craft Shoppe Q E Y C
840 6th Street, 99403
(509) 758-2110

Cle Elum

Ruby's Q E Y N C M
➡ SEE AD BELOW
116 E. 1st Street, 98922
(509) 674-2296
MSa 10-4:30, Tu-F 10-5
www.rubysstore.com

Colfax

Palouse River Quilts* Q E
101 S. Main Street, 99111
(509) 397-2278

College Place

Alpine Cottage Quilting* Q
505 SW Bade Avenue, 99324
(509) 301-1658 or (210) 379-1828

Colville

E Z Knit Fabrics Q E Y C M
165 N. Main Street, 99114
(509) 684-2644

Coupeville

Whidbey Isle Yarns, Gifts and Teas Q E Y N W S
12 NW Front Street, 98239
(360) 632-4200

Deer Park

Sew-Into-Quilts & Sew-Fix-It LLC Q M
110 W. Crawford Street, 99006
(509) 276-2035
M-F 9-5, Sa 9-4
www.sew-into-quilts.com

Ed & Jean's Quilt Shop Q
22 S. Vernon Street, Suite 4, 99006
(509) 276-6678

Des Moines

All Points Yarn Y W
21921 Marine View Drive S, 98198
(206) 824-9276

Carriage Country Quilts Q E
22214 Marine View Drive S, 98198
(206) 878-9414

Duvall

Quintessential Knits Y
26331 NE Valley Street, Suite 4, 98019
(425) 890-6756

Eatonville

Reflection Farm Sheep & Wool Products Y S
31801 79th Avenue, Court E, 98328
(253) 380-5511

The Country Mouse Q E Y N C
755 Eatonville Highway W, 98328
(360) 832-8065

Edmonds

All Wound Up Yarn Shop Y
18521 76th Avenue W, Suite 109, 98026
(425) 245-5104 or (602) 605-7062

The Needlepointer N
22811 100th Avenue NW, 98020
(425) 252-2277 or (888) 252-9733

Ellensburg

Purple Door Fabric* Q
180 Range View Road, 98926
(509) 607-3951

Yarn Folk Y
304 N. Pearl Street, 98926
(509) 304-4588

Elma

Elma Variety Q E Y N C
325 W. Main Street, 98541
(360) 482-2411

Ephrata

The Fabric Patch Q E M
220 10th Avenue SW, 98823
(509) 754-8280
M-F 9:30-5:30, Sa 9-5
www.fabricpatch.net

Everett

Great Yarns! Y
4023 Rucker Avenue, 98201
(425) 252-8155

Quilter's Roost Q E
11623 11th Place W, 98204
(425) 355-8705

Fife

Firwood Farm Alpacas Y S
8002 48th Street E, 98424
(253) 926-2582

Forks

Chinook Pharmacy & Variety Q E Y N C
11 S. Forks Avenue, 98331
(360) 374-5030

Freeland

Island Fabric & Sewing Center Q E
1592 Main Street, 98249
(360) 331-7313

Friday Harbor

Island Wools Y
278 A Street, 98250
(360) 370-5648

Gig Harbor

Rainy Day Yarns Y
3200 Tarabochia Street, 98335
(253) 514-6890
M-F 11-5, Sa 10-5
www.rainydayyarns.com

Nancy's Quilt Shop & Longarming Q E
7716 Pioneer Way, Suite C&D, 98335
(253) 358-3856

Grand Coulee

KISSED Quilts Q
301 Main Street, 99133
(509) 386-5715

Grayland

Yarn N Darn Things* Y
2172 State Road 105, 98547
(360) 267-0281

Ilwaco

Purly Shell Fiber Arts Y S
157 Howerton Street, Suite B, 98624
(360) 642-3044

Issaquah

Gossypium Quilt Shop Q
355 NW Gilman Blvd., Suite 102, 98027
(425) 557-7878
Winter: MWFSa 10-6, TuTh 10-8;
Summer: MTuWFSa 10-6, Th 10-8
www.gossypiumquilt.com

APQS Northwest Q M
1315 NW Mall Street, Suite 4, 98027
(425) 243-3502

Issaquah Sewing & Vacuum Q M
1180 NW Gilman Blvd., 98027
(425) 392-9868

The Nifty Knitter Y W S
317 NW Gilman Blvd., Suite 1, 98027
(425) 369-3098

Threadneedle Street E N C
485 Front Street N, Suite B, 98027
(425) 391-0528

Kelso

LaFavorites Y W
204 S. Pacific Avenue, 98626
(360) 575-9305

Paisley Duck Quilting and Design Q E
404 S. Pacific Avenue, Suite E, 98626
(360) 703-3279

Kennewick

Discount Vac and Sew 2 Q
115 W. 1st Avenue, 99336
(509) 586-1680

Fabric 108* Q
1108 E. 44th Avenue, 99337
(509) 586-1741

Sandy's Fabrics & Machines Q M
24 N. Benton Street, 99336
(509) 585-4739

Sheep's Clothing Y S
3311 W. Clearwater Avenue, Suite B120, 99336
(509) 734-2484

Kent

Makers' Mercantile Q E Y N W S C
18437 E. Valley Highway, #102, 98032
(425) 251-1239

Running Stitch Fabrics* Q E
213 1st Avenue S, 98032
(253) 277-2248

Kettle Falls

Primitive Daisy* Q
475 Meyers Street, 99141
(509) 675-8104

Red Rooster Quilt Shop Q E
41 Enzyme Lane, 99141
(509) 690-1779 or (509) 690-1779

Kirkland

Serial Knitters Yarn Shop Y W S
8427 122nd Avenue NE, 98033
(425) 242-0086
MTuSa 10-6, WTh 10-8, F 10-9, Su 11-5
www.serialknitters.com

Quality Sewing & Vacuum Centers Q M
13501 100th Avenue NE, 98034
(425) 215-1563

La Conner

Jennings Yarn & Needlecrafts E Y N C
612 S. 1st Street, 98257
(360) 466-3177

Lake Forest Park

Mad Cow Yarn Y S
17171 Bothell Way NE, #A013, 98155
(206) 397-4898

Lakewood

The Sock Peddlers, LLC Y
6122 Motor Avenue SW, 98499
(253) 267-0148
MTuWThSa 11-6, F 11-8
www.facebook.com/thesockpeddlers/

Misty's Gifts and Things Q
11004 Gravelly Lake Drive SW, 98499
(253) 503-3093

Langley

Casey's Crafts Q E Y C
14485 SR 525, 98260
(360) 321-0577

Knitty Purls* Y
210 1st Street, 98260
(360) 331-2212

Leavenworth

Leavenworth Quilt Co. Q Y
11007 Highway 2, 98826
(509) 888-8807

Solbakken Fiber Studio Y W S
19995 Shugart Flats Road, 98826
(509) 679-6633

Lind

Crazy Quilter & Retreats Q E C
119 N. I Street, 99341
(509) 677-3335
M-F 10-3, Evenings & Sa by appt.
www.quiltingretreat.info

Longview

Longview Sewing and Fabric Q M
1113 Vandercook Way, 98632
(360) 578-2628

Lopez Island

Island Fibers Y W S
4208 Port Stanley Road, 98261
(360) 468-2467

Lynden

Calico Country* Q
1722 Front Street, 98264
(360) 354-4832

Folktales* Q E
1885 Kok Road, 98264
(360) 354-0855

Tangled Threads Quilt Shop Q
202 6th Street, 98264
(360) 318-1567

Metaline Falls

Sweet Creek Creations Q
219 E. 5th Avenue, 99153
(509) 446-2429

Monroe

Ben Franklin Crafts Q E Y N C
19505 Highway 2, 98272
(360) 794-6745

Moses Lake

Country Fabrics Q M
711 N. Stratford Road, Suite B, 98837
(509) 764-4706

Mt. Vernon

Calico Creations Q
400 S. 1st Street, 98273
(360) 336-3241

WildFibers Y
706 S. 1st Street, 98273
(360) 336-5202

Oak Harbor

Quilter's Workshop Q E Y C
601 SE Pioneer Way, 98277
(360) 675-7216

Ocean Park

Tapestry Rose Yarn Shop* E Y N W S C
1401 Bay Avenue, 98640
(360) 665-6050

Ocean Shores

Beach Tyme Quilts Q E C
873 Point Brown Avenue NW, #2, 98569
(360) 289-7917

Odessa

Experience Quilts! Q E
4 W. 1st Avenue, 99159
(509) 982-2012

Olympia

Jorstad Creek* Y S
414 1/2 Legion Way SE, 98501
(360) 451-4146

The Black Sheep Yarn Boutique Y W S
2615 Capital Mall Drive SW, Suite 3B, 98502
(360) 350-0470

Omak

Needlelyn Time Q E M
9 N. Main Street, 98841
(509) 826-1198

Onalaska

Heavenly Quilts and Fabrics Redeemed Q
266 Carlisle, 98570
(360) 978-6300

Orcas Island

Warm Valley Orchard* Y W S
124 Warm Valley Lane, 98280
(360) 376-4386

Othello

The Old Hotel Art Gallery* Q
33 Larch Street, 99344
(509) 488-5936

Packwood

Packwood Spirits and Quilts Q
13042 US Highway 12, 98361
(360) 494-5781
MTuWThSa 11-6, F 11-7, Su 11-5
www.spiritsandquilts.com

Palouse

Grammy G's Quilt Shop Q
124 E. Main Street, 99161
(509) 878-1660

Pasco

Janean's Bernina Q M
6303 Burden Blvd., 99301
(509) 544-7888

Pomeroy

Rather-Be's Quilt Shop and Retreat Center Q
382 Highway 12E, 99347
(509) 843-6162

Port Angeles

Cabled Fiber and Yarn Y W S
➡ SEE AD BELOW
125 W. 1st Street, 98362
(360) 504-2233
Tu-F 11-6, Sa 10-5
www.cabledfiber.com

Sleepy Valley Quilt Co.* Q
1107 E. Front Street, 98362
(360) 452-5227

Port Gamble

Quilted Strait Q E
➡ SEE AD AT RIGHT
32280 Puget Way NE, 98364
(360) 930-8145 or (855) GOQ-UILT
Every Day 10-5
www.quiltedstrait.com

The Artful Ewe Y W S
32180 Rainier Avenue NE, 98364
(360) 643-0183

Port Townsend

Bazaar Girls Yarn Shop E Y S
126 Quincy Street, 98368
(360) 379-9273

Creative Union Fabrics* Q
112 Kala Square Place, Suite 1, 98368
(360) 379-0655

Diva Yarn Q E Y S
940 Water Street, 98368
(360) 385-4844

Poulsbo

Amanda's Art-Yarn Y W S
Call for location, 98370
(360) 779-3666

The Quilt Shoppe Q E N C
19020 Front Street NE, 98370
(360) 697-7475

Prosser

The Sewing Basket Q
1108 Wine Country Road, 99350
(509) 786-7367

Puyallup

The Quilt Barn Q
2102 E. Main, Suite 102, 98372
(253) 845-1532
Handi Quilter® Authorized Retailer
Designed by a Quilter, for Quilters®

The Quilting Fairy LLC Q
13507 Meridian E, Suite O, 98373
(253) 845-0462

Redmond

Ben Franklin Crafts Q E Y N C
15756 Redmond Way, 98052
(425) 883-2050

Renton

Knittery Y
601 S. Grady Way, Suite C, 98057
(425) 228-4694 or (800) 742-3565

Sewing Machine Service Co M
315 Main Avenue S, 98057
(425) 255-8673 or (800) 432-8673
Handi Quilter® Authorized Retailer
Designed by a Quilter, for Quilters®

Richland

Badger Mountain Yarns Ⓨ Ⓢ Ⓒ
114 Keene Road, 99352
(509) 579-0090

Needful Needlecrafts Ⓔ Ⓒ
1515 Wright Avenue, Suite D, 99354
(509) 539-4918

Quiltmania Ⓠ Ⓔ
1442 Jadwin Avenue, Suite C, 99354
(509) 946-7467

Rochester

Cathy's Classy Quilts Ⓠ Ⓜ
6835 183rd Avenue SW, 98579
(360) 339-2120
MTu by appt. only; W-Sa 10:30-5, call first
www.cathysclassyquilts.com
Handi Quilter® Authorized Retailer
Designed by a Quilter, for Quilters.®

Seattle

Acorn Street Shop Ⓨ
2818 NE 55th Street, 98105
(206) 525-1726

Drygoods Design Ⓠ
301 Occidental Avenue S, 98104
(206) 535-6950

Okan Arts Ⓠ
315 NW 52nd Street, Lower Level, 98107
(206) 795-1010

Seattle Yarn Ⓔ Ⓨ Ⓒ
5633 California Avenue SW, 98136
(206) 935-2010

So Much Yarn Ⓨ
1525 First Avenue, Suite 4, 98101
(206) 443-0727 or (866) 443-0727

Stitches Ⓠ Ⓔ Ⓨ Ⓒ
711 E. Pike Street, 98122
(206) 709-0707

The Fiber Gallery Ⓨ Ⓦ Ⓢ
8212 Greenwood Avenue N, 98103
(206) 706-4197

The Tea Cozy Yarn Shop Ⓨ
5816 24th Avenue NW, 98107
(206) 783-3322

Tricoter Ⓨ
3121 E. Madison Street, Suite 103, 98112
(206) 328-6505

Undercover Quilts from the USA Ⓠ
98 Virginia Street, 98101
(206) 622-6382

Sedro-Woolley

Cascade Fabrics Ⓠ
824 Metcalf Street, 98284
(360) 855-0323

Sequim

Karen's Quilt Shop ⓆⒺⓂ
271 S. 7th Avenue, #26, 98382
(360) 681-0820

Shelton

Annie's Quilt Shoppe ⓆⒺⓂ
2505 Olympic Highway N, #220, 98584
(360) 427-6164

Silverdale

Knit2gether Ⓨ
9234 Bayshore Drive NW, 98383
(360) 979-0120

Snohomish

Country Yarns* ⓎⓌⓈ
119 Avenue B, 98290
(360) 568-7611

Quilting Mayhem ⓆⒺ
1011 2nd Street, 98290
(425) 533-2566

Spangle

KnitKnit - The Studio Ⓨ
13919 S. Stentz Road, 99031
(509) 496-8051

Spokane

Regal Fabics & Gifts ⓆⒺ
5620 S. Regal Street, #8, 99223
(509) 242-3731
M-Sa 9:30-5:30, Th 9:30-6:30, one Su per month 11-3 (check website)
www.regalfabricsandgifts.com

The Hook & Needle Nook LLC ⓎⓌⓈ
1508 N. Monroe Street, 99201
(509) 368-9527
Tu 11-8, W-Sa 11-6
https://www.thehookandneedlenook.com

Paradise Fibers ⓎⓌⓈ
225 W. Indiana Avenue, 99205
(509) 536-7746

Quilt Patch Lane* Ⓠ
413 W. Hastings Road, 99218
(509) 467-0133

Quilted Posies Quilt Shop* Ⓠ
6412 N. Monroe Street, 99208
(509) 474-9394

Sew E-Z Too ⓆⒺⓎⓃⒸⓂ
603 W. Garland Avenue, 99205
(509) 325-6644

Sew Uniquely You* Ⓠ
11402 N. Newport Highway, Suite C, 92218
(509) 467-8210

The Quilting Bee ⓆⒺⓂ
16002 E. Broadway Avenue, 99037
(509) 928-6037 or (888) 928-6037

Spokane Valley

Hattie's Quilt Shop* Ⓠ
13817 E. Sprague Avenue, Suite 4, 99216
(509) 279-2150

Heartbeat Quilting ⓆⓂ
16909 E. Sprague Avenue, 99037
(509) 465-0344

Stanwood

Cotton Pickins Ⓠ
8718 270th Street NW, 98292
(360) 629-4771

PinchKnitter Yarns Ⓨ
8712 271st Street, 98292
(360) 939-0769

Stilly River Yarns* Ⓨ Ⓦ Ⓢ
9913 271st Street NW, Suite A, 98292
(360) 631-5801

Tacoma

Artco Crafts Ⓠ Ⓔ Ⓨ
5401-401 6th Avenue, 98406
(253) 759-9585
M-F 9-8, Sa 9-6, Su 10-5:30
www.artcocrafts.com

Fibers Etc.* Ⓨ Ⓦ Ⓢ
705 Opera Alley, 98402
(253) 572-1859 or (253) 531-3257

Trains & Fabrics Etc.* Ⓠ
1315 S. 23rd Street, 98405
(253) 779-0219

Tonasket

WOW World of Wool Ⓠ Ⓨ Ⓦ Ⓢ
315 S. Whitcomb Road, 98855
(509) 771-7777

Toppenish

Hope Chest Crafts Ⓠ Ⓔ Ⓨ Ⓒ
508 W. 2nd Avenue, 98948
(509) 865-5666

Tumwater

Ruby Street Quiltworks Ⓠ Ⓔ
100 Ruby Street SE, 98501
(360) 236-0596

Twisp

The Quilting Hive* Ⓠ Ⓔ Ⓨ
309 N. Methow Valley Highway 20, 98856
(509) 997-7020

University Place

Shibori Dragon Ⓠ
7025 27th Street W, Suite 1, 98466
(253) 582-7455

Vancouver

Blizzard Yarn and Fiber Ⓨ Ⓦ Ⓢ
6924 NE 4th Plain Blvd., Suite A, 98661
(360) 991-5350

Fiddlesticks Quilt Shop Ⓠ
2701 NE 114th Avenue, Suite 1, 98684
(360) 718-7103

Just For Fun Quilting Ⓠ
6918 NE 4th Plain Blvd., #110, 98661
(360) 882-9101

Quilted Treasures* Ⓠ Ⓔ
6400 NE Highway 99, Suite N, 98665
(360) 606-9812

Vashon

Vashon Pharmacy Ⓔ Ⓨ Ⓢ
17617 Vashon Highway SW, 98070
(206) 463-9118

Walla Walla

Grandma's Sewing Room Ⓠ
901 W. Rose Street, 99362
(509) 240-2425

Purl2* Ⓨ
27 W. Main Street, 99362
(509) 876-8600

Stash Ⓠ Ⓔ Ⓝ Ⓒ Ⓜ
25 W. Main Street, 99362
(509) 526-5141

Thread and Bolts Ⓠ
326 Newtown Road, 99362
(509) 386-4289

Walla Walla Sew & Vac Ⓠ Ⓜ
900 W. Rose Street, 99362
(509) 529-7755

Washougal

Wooly Wooly Wag Tails Yarns Ⓨ
982 E Street, 98671
(360) 835-9649 or (800) 676-2302

Wenatchee

K1P2 Yarn Ⓨ Ⓦ Ⓢ
1012 Springwater Avenue, 98801
(509) 888-0337

Sew-Creative Ⓠ Ⓜ
1139 Princeton Ave N, Ste A, 98801
(509) 663-5516

Winthrop

3 Bears Cafe & Quilts Ⓠ Ⓔ
414 Riverside Avenue, 98862
(509) 996-8013

Woodinville

Gathering Fabric Quilt Shop Ⓠ
14450 Woodinville-Redmond Road NE, 98072
(425) 402-9034

Yakima

Ann's Quilts and Things Ⓠ
3504 Ahtanum Road, 98903
(509) 965-2313

Sandy's Sewing Center* Ⓠ Ⓔ
404 W. Chestnut Avenue, 98902
(509) 901-7792

Stitch n Quilt* Ⓠ Ⓔ
8405 Ahtanum Road, 98903
(509) 945-2560

The Quilters Cafe Ⓠ Ⓜ
910 Summitview Avenue, Suite 1A, 98902
(509) 452-8666

Viking Pfaff Sewing Center Ⓠ Ⓔ Ⓜ
5643 Summitview Avenue, 98908
(509) 966-3430

Yelm

Gee Gee's Quilting, Inc. Ⓠ Ⓔ Ⓨ Ⓒ
601 W. Yelm Avenue, 98597
(360) 458-5616

NeedleTravel

Download our App!

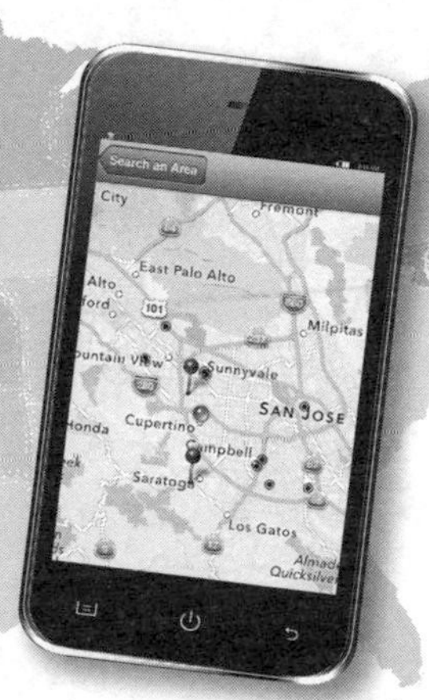

Find Shops From Your Phone

It's Free!

Check us out on:

www.facebook.com/Needletravel

http://www.pinterest.com/needletravel

https://twitter.com/Needletravel

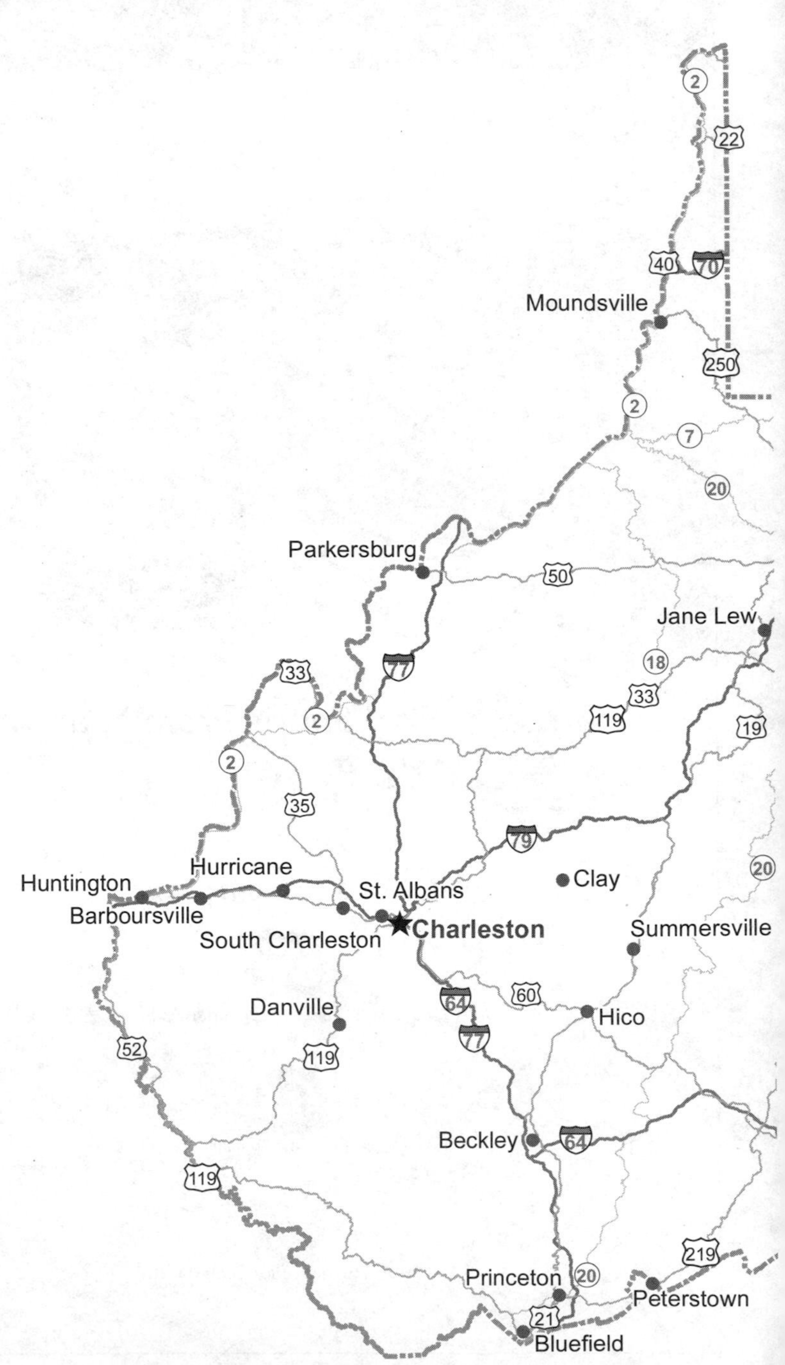
2
22
40
70
Moundsville
250
2
7
20
Parkersburg
50
Jane Lew
18
33
77
33
119
2
19
2
35
79
Hurricane
Huntington
St. Albans
Clay
20
Barboursville
Charleston
South Charleston
Summersville
60
64
Danville
Hico
77
52
119
Beckley
64
119
219
Princeton
20
Peterstown
21
Bluefield

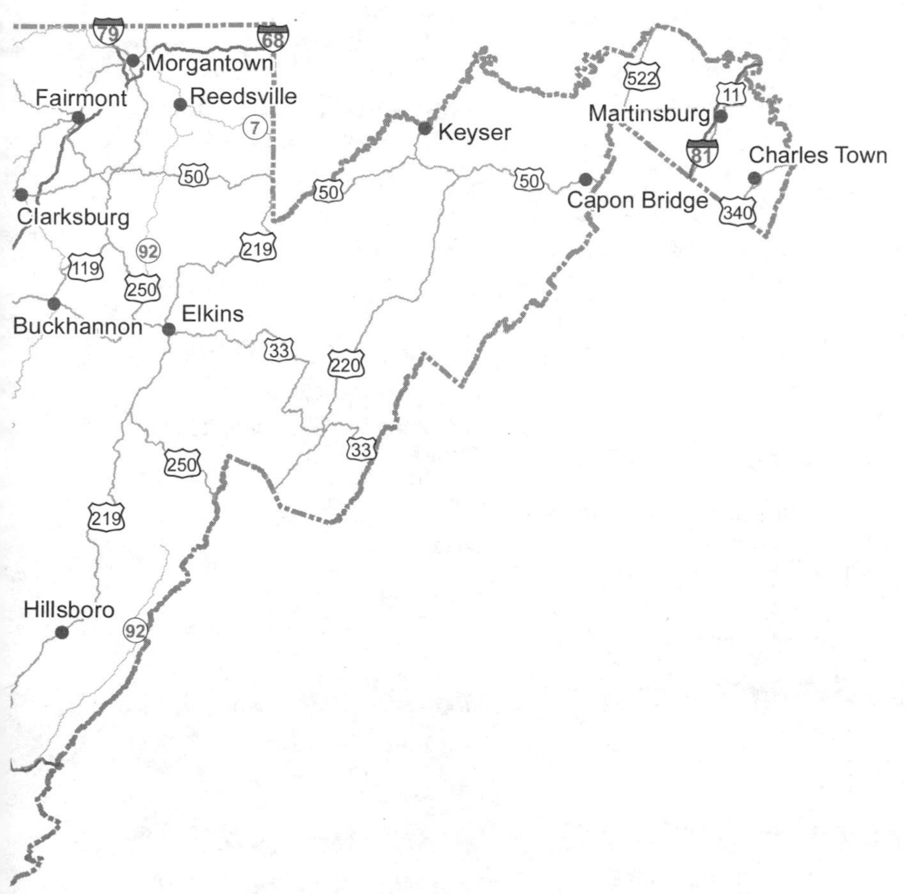
79
68
Morgantown
Fairmont
Reedsville
7
Keyser
522
11
Martinsburg
81
Charles Town
50
Clarksburg
50
50
Capon Bridge
340
219
92
119
250
Buckhannon
Elkins
33
220
33
250
219
Hillsboro
92

West Virginia

Barboursville

WV Quilt Ⓠ Ⓜ
642 Main Street, Suite 101, 25504
(304) 302-5400

Beckley

Itchin' 2 Be Stitchin' Ⓠ
612 N. Eisenhower Drive, 25801
(304) 252-4575

Bluefield

Bluefield Yarn Company Ⓨ
313 Federal Street, 24701
(304) 800-4229

Buckhannon

Helen's Hen House Ⓠ Ⓔ Ⓨ Ⓒ
34 E. Main Street, 26201
(304) 472-1723

Stitching House and Sew Much More* Ⓠ Ⓔ Ⓜ
255 King Schoolhouse Road, 26201
(304) 472-8188

Capon Bridge

Liberty View Quilt Shop & Gifts Ⓠ
2886 Northwestern Pike, 26711
(304) 856-2234
TuThSaSu 11-5, W 12:30-6, F 11-6, classes available
www.LibertyViewQuiltShop.com

Charles Town

Yarnability* Ⓨ
130 W. Washington Street, 25414
(304) 876-8081

Charleston

Kanawha City Yarn Company Ⓨ Ⓦ Ⓢ
5132A MacCorkle Avenue, 25304
(304) 926-8589

Clarksburg

Classic Quilt Shop Ⓠ
1236 E. Pike Street, 26301
(304) 326-6969

Clay

Rene's Fabric and Gift Shop Ⓠ Ⓔ Ⓨ Ⓒ
594 Main Street, 25043
(304) 587-7411

Danville

Town Square Fabrics & Crafts Ⓠ
28 Town Square, 25053
(304) 369-6269

Elkins

Elkins Sewing Center Ⓠ Ⓔ Ⓒ Ⓜ
300 Davis Avenue, 26241
(304) 636-9480
MTuWThSa 9-5, F 9-7
www.elkinssewingcenter.com

Yarn and Company* Ⓨ
RR 4 Box 242, 26241
(304) 636-3760

Fairmont

Sew Chic Ⓠ Ⓔ Ⓜ
348 Meadowdale Road, 26554
(304) 366-4135
M-F 10-5, Sa 10-2
www.sewchic.com

Hico

Sew Simple Hobbie House* Ⓠ
112 Baughan Road, 25854
(304) 658-5900

Hillsboro

Deb Ann's Fabrics Ⓠ
37 Hill Street, 24946
(304) 653-4150

Huntington

Sew Many Blessings Ⓠ Ⓔ Ⓜ
1925 Adams Avenue, 25704
(304) 429-0050
MW 10-5, TuTh 10-8, F 10-6, Sa 10-3
www.sewmanyblessingsquiltshop.com

Hurricane

Quilts By Phyllis, Inc. Q
2943 Putnam Avenue, 25526
(304) 562-7404
Tu-Sa 9-5
www.quiltsbyphyllis.com

Jane Lew

Quilter's Garage Q
6385 Main Street, 26378
(304) 805-2140

Keyser

Quaint Acres Alpacas Y
11071 Knobley Road, 26726
(304) 813-5443

Martinsburg

All About Fabric Q
248 N. Queen Street, 25401
(304) 263-6800

Morgantown

Country Roads Quilt Shop Q
709 Beechurst Avenue, Suite 27, 26505
(304) 241-5645

Stitch Morgantown Q E C
22 Commerce Drive, 26501
(304) 943-7137

Moundsville

Theresa's Fabrics Q E Y N C
264 Jefferson Avenue, 26041
(304) 845-4330

Parkersburg

Bolts & Quarters Quilt Shop Q E
1809 Dupont Road, Suite 1
(GPS 1050 Division Street), 26101
(304) 428-4933

Market Street Yarn and Crafts Q Y W S
615 Market Street, 26101
(304) 865-9276

Sew Creative Q Y W S M
615 Market Street, 26101
(304) 422-6454

Peterstown

Quilting Essentials* Q
Route 2, Box 515, 24963
(304) 753-5832

Princeton

Granny's Sewing Room Q E Y C M
1119 Mercer Street, 24740
(304) 425-6554

Sewing Gallery LLC Q E C
431 Rogers Street, 24740
(304) 487-6700

Reedsville

Eleanor's Quilts & Fabrics Q E Y N C
399 N. Robert Stone Way, 26547
(304) 864-6330

South Charleston

Cranberry Needlecrafts C
230 6th Avenue, 25303
(304) 744-6390

English Cottage Q
45 MacCorkle Avenue SW, 25303
(304) 744-7564

St. Albans

Village Sampler - Since 1987 E N C
86 Olde Main Plaza, 25177
(304) 722-0123

Summersville

The Quilt Shoppe LLC Q E C
521 Main Street, 26651
(304) 872-0959

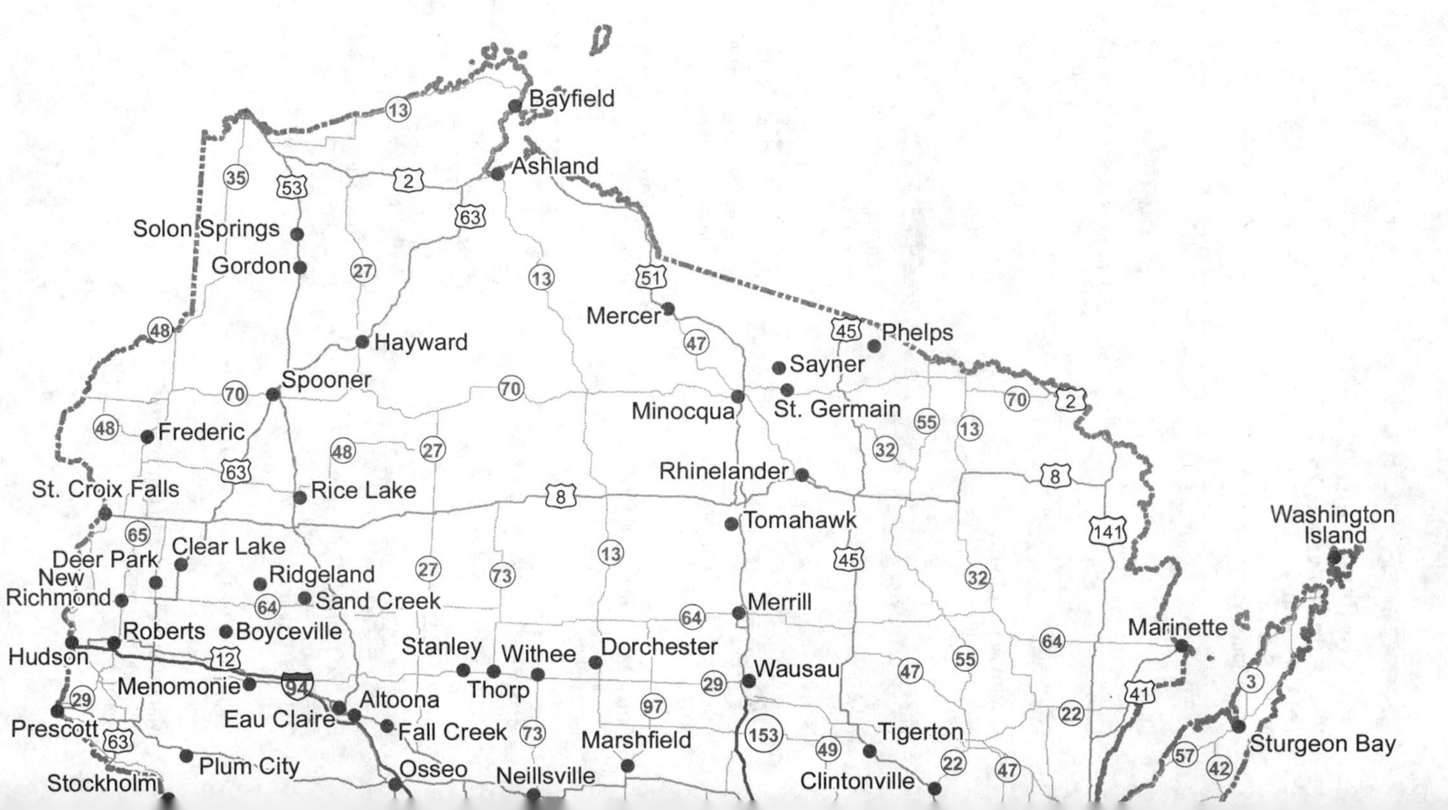
Bayfield
Ashland
Solon Springs
Gordon
Hayward
Mercer
Phelps
Sayner
Spooner
Minocqua
St. Germain
Frederic
Rhinelander
St. Croix Falls
Rice Lake
Tomahawk
Washington Island
Clear Lake
Deer Park
New Richmond
Ridgeland
Sand Creek
Merrill
Roberts
Boyceville
Hudson
Stanley
Withee
Dorchester
Marinette
Wausau
Menomonie
Thorp
Altoona
Eau Claire
Fall Creek
Marshfield
Tigerton
Sturgeon Bay
Prescott
Plum City
Osseo
Neillsville
Clintonville
Stockholm
13
35
53
2
63
27
51
47
45
70
55
48
32
8
65
141
73
64
12
29
94
97
153
49
22
41
3
57
42

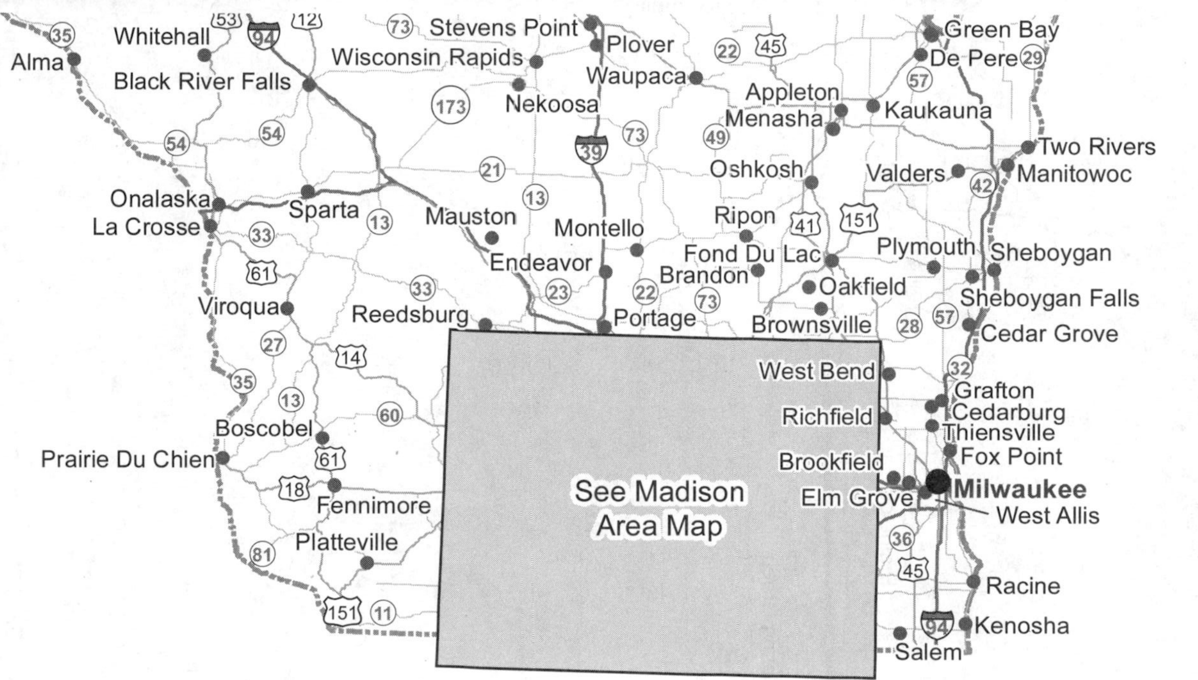
Alma
Whitehall
Black River Falls
Stevens Point
Wisconsin Rapids
Nekoosa
Plover
Waupaca
Appleton
Menasha
Kaukauna
Green Bay
De Pere
Two Rivers
Manitowoc
Valders
Oshkosh
Onalaska
La Crosse
Sparta
Mauston
Montello
Endeavor
Ripon
Fond Du Lac
Brandon
Oakfield
Plymouth
Sheboygan
Sheboygan Falls
Cedar Grove
Viroqua
Reedsburg
Portage
Brownsville
West Bend
Grafton
Cedarburg
Thiensville
Richfield
Fox Point
Brookfield
Milwaukee
Elm Grove
West Allis
Boscobel
Prairie Du Chien
Fennimore
Platteville
See Madison
Area Map
Racine
Kenosha
Salem

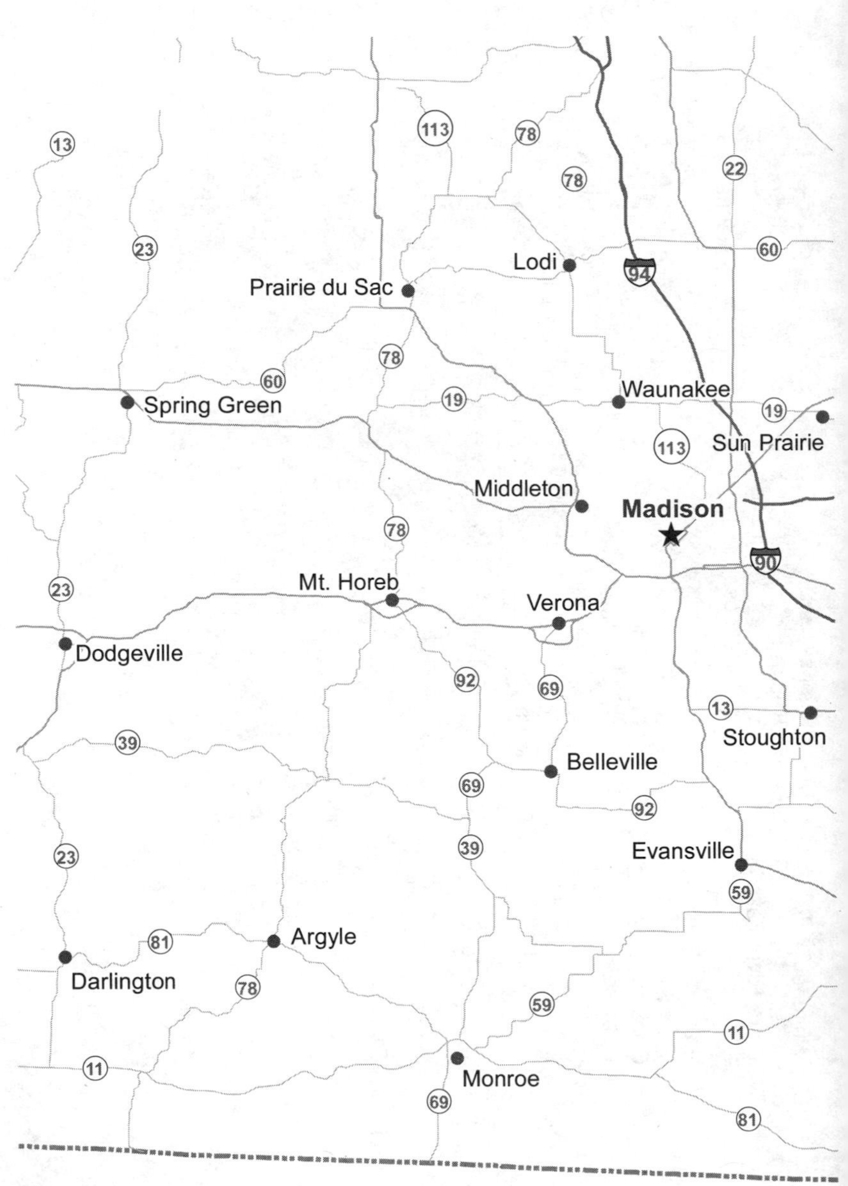
113
78
78
13
22
60
23
Lodi
94
Prairie du Sac
78
60
Waunakee
Spring Green
19
19
113
Sun Prairie
Middleton
Madison
78
90
23
Mt. Horeb
Verona
Dodgeville
92
69
13
Stoughton
39
Belleville
69
92
39
Evansville
23
59
81
Argyle
Darlington
78
59
11
11
Monroe
69
81

Mayville
Beaver Dam
73
33
Juneau
26
67
41
83
Columbus
60
Hartford
151
167
19
16
67
83
94
Oconomowoc
73
Delafield
Cambridge
18
Jefferson
90
12
Waukesha
59
Ft. Atkinson
51
26
59
Mukwonago
59
Whitewater
Milton
20
14
Janesville
Burlington
11
Delavan
36
67
Lake Geneva
51
43
50
Clinton
14
12
Beloit
81
67

Wisconsin

Alma

The Burlington Hotel Quilt Shop Q
809 N. Main Street, 54610
(608) 685-3636

Altoona

Stitch Supply Co. Q Y
913 S. Hillcrest Parkway, 54720
(715) 829-7824

Appleton

Ana's Sewing Studio / Julie's Sewing Center Q M
1230 W. College Avenue, Suite B, 54914
(920) 734-8262
MTuWF 10-5, Th 10-7, Sa 10-4
www.anasewstudio.com

Going To Pieces Quilt Company Q E
1017 W. Northland Avenue, 54914
(920) 882-6430

KK Sew & Vac II Q M
N9654 County Highway N, 54915
(920) 380-0667

Sew 'n Sew Q M
1881 N. Silverspring Drive, 54915
(920) 830-9372

Argyle

Argyle Fiber Mill Y S
200 E. Milwaukee Street, 53504
(608) 543-3933

Ashland

Northwoods Dyeworks Y S
417B Main Street W, 54806
(715) 682-0588

Quilt Elements Q E M
222 Main Street W, 54806
(715) 292-6524

The Craft Connection E Y C
205 E. Main Street, 54806
(715) 682-6454

Bayfield

Brownstone Centre Y
121 Rittenhouse Avenue, 54814
(715) 779-5571

Beaver Dam

Firefly Fibers E Y
114 Front Street, 53916
(920) 356-8859

Nancy's Notions Q E M
333 Beichl Avenue, 53916
(920) 887-7321 or (800) 725-0361

Belleville

Patches & Petals Q M
13 W. Main Street, 53508
(608) 424-1516

Beloit

At The Heart Of Quilting Q M
1621 E. Gale Drive, 53511
(608) 313-3322

Black River Falls

Fiber Garden Y W S
N5095 Old Highway 54, 54615
(715) 284-4590

Quilt N Sew Haven* Q
222 Armstrong Avenue, 54615
(715) 896-1090

Boscobel

The Paisley Star Q
903 Elm Street, 53805
(608) 375-2556

Boyceville

The Grain Bin Market & Bakery Q
E4548 County Road FF, 54725
(715) 632-2444

Brandon

RagSpun Studio* Q
172 E. Main Street, 53919
(920) 346-5684 or (920) 904-5684

Brookfield

Cream City Yarn Y W
15565 W. North Avenue, 53005
(262) 923-7014

Brownsville

Quilt and Loom Q
W6249 County Road Y, 53006
(920) 948-7469

Burlington

Artistic Fibers Y
324 N. Pine Street, 53105
(262) 757-0960

Cambridge

Kaleidoscope Fibers Y S
131 W. Main Street, 53523
(920) 342-0496

Cedar Grove

Bahr Creek Llamas & Fiber Studio Y W S
N1021 Sauk Trail Road, 53013
(920) 668-6417

Cedarburg

Ye Olde Schoolhouse Q E
318 Green Bay Road, 53012
(262) 377-2770

Clear Lake

Quilter's Corner Q
510 3rd Avenue NW, 54005
(715) 263-3440

Clinton

Twin Turtle Quilts Q E
244 Allen Street, 53525
(608) 676-6196

Clintonville

The Copper Llama LLC Y W S
E8558 Steenbock Road, 54929
(715) 460-6468

Columbus

Susan's Fiber Shop Y W S
N250 County Road A, 53925
(920) 623-4237
MTuWF 10-4, Sa 10-5, Su 12-5, or call ahead
www.susansfiber.com

Darlington

Pins & Pieces Quilt Shop Q
242 Main Street, 53530
(608) 776-2116

De Pere

KK Sew & Vac III Q M
815 Main Avenue, 54115
(920) 403-7490

Life's A Stitch Q M
124 N. Broadway, 54115
(920) 338-1381

De Pere (Green Bay)

Icon Fiber Arts Y W S
1876 Dickinson Road, 54115
(920) 338-0505
M-F 9-6, Sa 9-4, Su 11-3
www.iconfiberarts.com

Deer Park

Knot Sew Perfect Quilting Q
131 Main Street N, 54007
(715) 269-5444
WF 10-5, Th 10-7, Sa 9-2
www.facebook.com/pages/knot-sew-perfect-quilting

Delafield

Knitch Y S
608 Milwaukee Street, 53018
(262) 646-9392

Delavan

Needles 'n Pins Yarn Shoppe Ⓨ
W9034 County Road A, 53115
(608) 883-9922
MWFSa 9-5, Su 1-5
www.needlesnpinsyarnshoppe.com

Studio S Fiber Arts ⓎⓌⓈ
W8903 County Road A, 53115
(608) 883-2123

The Stitchery Ⓠ
N2482 County Road O, 53115
(262) 728-6318

Dodgeville

White Rose Silver Thread Ⓠ
101 1/2 W. Leffler Street, 53533
(608) 935-5564

Dorchester

Creative HideAway Ⓠ
640 E. Business County Road A, 54425
(715) 654-5250

Eau Claire

Blue Boxer Arts ⒺⓎⓌⓈⒸ
416 S. Barstow Street, 54701
(715) 577-3199

Quilting & More Ⓠ
E10070 190th Avenue, 54701
(715) 832-9800

Sew Complete ⓆⓂ
1408 S. Hastings Way, 54701
(715) 832-3343 or (800) 924-4075

The Calico Shoppe ⓆⒺ
214 S. Barstow Street, 54701
(715) 834-9990

Elkhorn

The Quilting Connection, LLC* Ⓜ
21 Adams Street, 53121
(262) 723-6775

Elm Grove

Bigsby's Sewing Center ⓆⒺⓂ
13200 Watertown Plank Road, 53122
(262) 785-1177

Patched Works, Inc. Ⓠ
13330 Watertown Plank Road, 53122
(262) 786-1523

Endeavor

Homespun Fabrics Ⓠ
N149 County Road T, 53930
(608) 742-6400

Evansville

Sew Many Threads Ⓠ
801 Brown School Road, 53536
(608) 882-0287

The Dancing Lamb ⓎⓌⓈ
217 W. Main Street, 53536
(608) 882-0267

Fall Creek

Yard Work Fabrics* ⓆⒺⓎ
133 S. State Street, 54742
(715) 877-3885

Fennimore

The Quilt Peddler ⓆⒺⓎⓂ
4420 US Highway 18E, 53809
(608) 822-6822

Fond Du Lac

The Knitting Room ⒺⓎ
28 N. Main Street, 54935
(920) 906-4800

The Woolgatherers ⒺⓎⓌⓈⒸ
25A N. Main Street, 54935
(920) 907-0510

Fox Point

Knitting Knook Yarn & Needlepoint ⓎⓃ
6858 N. Santa Monica Blvd., 53217
(414) 540-4080

Frederic

Fibre Functions Yarns Y W S
2628 68th Street, 54837
(715) 472-8276

Ft. Atkinson

The Quilt Patch LLC Q
W3352 Lower Hebron Road, 53538
(262) 593-8462

Gordon

Kunert Kreations Q Y W S
9586 E. County Road Y, 54838
(715) 376-4722

Grafton

Grafton Yarn Store Y
1300 14th Avenue, 53024
(262) 377-0344

Green Bay

Ana's Sewing Studio / Julie's Sewing Center Q M
933 Anderson Drive, Suite D, 54302
(920) 965-0680
MTuWF 10-5, Th 10-7, Sa 10-4
www.anasewstudio.com

Quilting Divas Sewing Boutique LLC Q
445 Cardinal Lane, Suite 108, 54313
(920) 434-9980
MWF 10-5, TuTh 10-8, Sa 9-4
www.quiltingdivassew.com

My Favorite Quilt Shop Q
1550 Dousman Street, 54303
(920) 965-2085

Silver Thimble Quilt & Yarn Shoppe Q Y
2475 University Avenue, 54302
(920) 468-1495

The Stitching Bee E C
2304 Velp Avenue, 54303
(920) 434-6884

Hartford

Esa's Fabric & Custom Framing Q
37 N. Main Street, 53027
(262) 670-6364

Main St. Yarn Shop Y
59 N. Main Street, 53027
(262) 673-2203

Hayward

Farmstead Creamery & Cafe Y W S
11077 N. Fullington Road, 54843
(715) 462-3453

Michelle's Crafts E Y N C
10578 Main Street, 54843
(715) 699-1569

River's Edge Antiques & Quilt Loft Q E
10103 State Road 27, 54843
(715) 634-0706

Hudson

Yarn Nook at Thunderwillow* Y
1615 Maxwell Street, 54016
(715) 808-8034

Janesville

Quilt Barn Studio Q M
5139 S. Reid Road, 53546
(608) 960-7797
Tu-F 10-4, Sa 10-1:30
www.quiltbarnstudio.com

A Quilt Lovers Shoppe Q
1604 S. Crosby Avenue, 53546
(608) 754-6497

Quilt Central Q M
1800 Humes Road, Suite 120, 53545
(608) 563-4415

The Dragonfly Yarn Shop Y S
1327 N. Wright Road, 53546
(608) 757-9228

Jefferson

Tea and Textiles Quilt Shop Q
107 S. Main Street, 53549
(920) 674-9017

Juneau

J & A Stitches* Q M
N3914 Welsh Road, 53039
(920) 696-3827

Kaukauna

Kaukauna Vacuums & Sewing Center* Q M
132 W. Wisconsin Avenue, 54130
(920) 766-3657

Make.Do at KC&T Y
127 W. Wisconsin Avenue, 54130
(920) 766-4038

Kenosha

Fiddlehead Yarns Y
7511 26th Avenue, 53143
(262) 925-6487

La Crosse

Fitting Knit Shop* Y
533 Main Street, 54601
(608) 784-4920

River Road Quilt Shop* Q
2501 South Avenue, 54601
(608) 788-2990 or (800) 458-4838

Unwound* Y S
413 Jay Street, 54601
(608) 519-3722

Lake Geneva

Sign Of The Unicorn* E N C
233 Center Street, 53147
(262) 248-1141

Lodi

Village Creek LLC Q
123 S. Main Street, 53555
(608) 592-5793

Madison

Electric Needle* Q M
4281 W. Beltline Highway, 53719
(608) 422-5449

Knitcircus Yarns Y
582 Grand Canyon Drive, 53719
(608) 841-1421

Lynn's E N C
5928 Odana Road, 53719
(608) 274-1442

Quintessential Quilts Sewing Center Q E M
4261 Lien Road, 53704
(608) 242-8555

The Knitting Tree* Y
2636 Monroe Street, 53711
(608) 238-0121

Wisconsin Craft Market* Y C
148 Westgate Mall, 53711
(608) 271-6002

Manitowoc

Fabric Creations* Q
912 S. 8th Street, 54220
(920) 482-0545

Lucky Rose Fibers Y W S
826 York Street, 54220
(920) 320-9855

Marinette

Pine Street Quilts* Q
801 Marinette Avenue, 54143
(715) 735-9806

Marshfield

Quilt Kits & Beyond Q
S549 W. Mann Road, 54449
(715) 384-8004

Mauston

Mielke's Fiber Arts LLC* W S
N4826 21st Avenue, 53948
(608) 350-0600

Mayville

Knitty Gritty Shop Y
48 N. Main Street, 53050
(920) 214-2050

Loose Ends Yarn Shop LLC Y
40 S. Main Street, 53050
(920) 210-8726

Menasha

Primitive Gatherings Quilt Shop* Q E C
850 Racine Street, 54952
(920) 722-7233

Menomonie

Woodland Ridge Retreat Q
➡ SEE AD PAGE 320
E4620 County Road C, 54751
(715) 664-8220
By Appointment and open to guests
www.woodlandridgeretreat.com

Thread Lab Q E Y
301 Main Street E, Suite A, 54751
(715) 578-9050

Mercer

Cheri's Fabric To Quilt Q N C
5244 N. Highway 51, 54547
(715) 476-0111

Merrill

The Woolgathering LLC* Y
W4168 County Road C, 54452
(715) 370-4600

Middleton

Blue Bar Quilts Q M
6333 University Avenue, Suite 105, 53562
(608) 284-9299

Milton

Loose Threads* Q
8005 N. Milton Road, Business 26, 53563
(608) 868-7912

Milwaukee

Fiberwood Studio Y W S
2709 N. 92nd Street, 53222
(414) 302-1849

Fischberger's Variety* Q E Y
2445 N. Holton Street, 53212
(414) 263-1991

Planet Bead* Y

710 N. Milwaukee Street, 53202

Yarn Junkie and Gifts* Y
5400 N. Lovers Lane, 53225
(414) 269-8941

Minocqua

The 13th Colony / Elizabeth's Woolery Q E Y
7735 Highway 51S, 54548
(715) 358-6600 or (866) 926-5669

Monroe

Orange Kitten Yarns* Y
1620 11th Street, 53566
(608) 328-4140

Montello

Teapot Quilt Cottage Q E Y W S
505 Main Street, 53949
(608) 297-7849
Everyday 10-5
www.teapotquiltcottage.com

Mt. Horeb

Blackberry Ridge Woolen Mill Y S
3776 Forshaug Road, 53572
(608) 437-3762

The Cat and Crow Y W S
205 E. Main Street, 53572
(608) 437-1771

Witchery Stitchery N C
103 E. Front Street, 53572
(608) 437-8635

Mukwonago

Quilt-agious Q
109 Lake Street, 53149
(262) 363-3066

Neillsville

Christie Country Quilts Q
432 Hewett Street, 54456
(715) 819-1299

Nekoosa

Knitwise Yarns and Fiber Arts Gallery LLC Y
421 County Road G, 54457
(715) 886-1030

New London

The Quilting Connection, LLC* M
200 W. North Water Street, 54961
(262) 723-6775

New Richmond

A Little Piece Of Mind Quilt Shop Q E Y
1027 N. Knowles Avenue, 54017
(715) 246-7314

Doyle's Farm & Home Q E Y C
560 Deere Drive, 54017
(715) 246-6184

Oakfield

Quilter's Finishing Touch LLC Q
W7791 Highbridge Road, 53065
(920) 583-6110

Stitches 'N Tyme Quilt Shoppe Q E M
203 S. Main Street, 53065
(920) 583-2625

Oconomowoc

Ben Franklin Crafts Q E Y N C
1083 Summit Avenue, 53066
(262) 567-0271
M-F 9-9, Sa 9-6, Su 10-5
www.benfranklincraftswi.com

Onalaska

Olive Juice Quilts Q E M
1258 County Road PH, 54650
(608) 782-3257

Oshkosh

It's Sew Rite Q E M
1821 Harrison Street, 54901
(920) 230-7397

Quilt Essentials* Q
1928 S. Washburn Street, 54904
(920) 230-3680

Osseo

the Quilting Nook & More LLC Q E
13712 7th Street, 54758
(715) 864-0742

Phelps

Sheeping Beauty Fibre Arts Y W S
2429 Highway 17, Box 5, 54554
(262) 623-0244

Platteville

Hidden Quilts LLC Q E
85 W. Main Street, 53818
(608) 348-4977

Plover

Antoinette's Quilt Shop Q E
3046 Village Park Drive, 54467
(715) 544-6076
MTuThFSa 10-5, W 10-8
www.antoinettesquiltshop.com

Plum City

Designs By Dianne Q
408 1st Street, 54761
(715) 647-5050

Plymouth

The Sewing Basket Q E M
426 E. Mill Street, 53073
(920) 892-4751

Portage

The Welcome Home Sewing Center Q E M
118 E. Cook Street, 53901
(608) 566-1663

Prairie Du Chien

Front Porch Quilts Q
216 N. Marquette Road, 53821
(608) 326-4371

The Pickett Fence Q E Y M
100 W. Blackhawk Avenue, 53821
(608) 326-4593

Prairie du Sac

DMarie Knit and Fiber, LLC Y N
422 Water Street, 53578
(608) 370-2414

Prescott

Two Meandering Ladies* Q E
220 Broad Street, 54021
(715) 262-2032

Racine

Sew 'n Save Q Y M
3701 Durand Avenue, 53405
(262) 554-8708
MW 10-8, TuThF 10-6, Sa 9:30-3
www.sewnsaveofracine.com

Reedsburg

Quintessential Quilts LLC Q E M
940 E. Main Street, 53959
(608) 524-8435

Rhinelander

Sew Creative Q M
30 West Davenport Street, 54501
(715) 420-1818

Handi Quilter® Authorized Retailer
Designed by a Quilter, for Quilters.®

Sew Smart LLC* Q M
2193 Lincoln Street, 54501
(715) 362-8321

Rice Lake

Busy Bobbin Q M
234 N. Wilson Avenue, 54868
(715) 234-1217

Twisted Ewe Yarns* Y
304 Phipps Avenue, 54868
(715) 651-6333

Richfield

Sew Many Pieces Q
1717 Wolf Road, Suite A, 53076
(262) 628-9505

Ridgeland

Blueberry Line Quilting Q
101 Diamond Street S., 54763
(715) 949-0050

Ripon

Bungalow Quilting & Yarn* Q Y
646 W. Fond du Lac Street, 54971
(920) 748-2905

Roberts

Color Crossing* Y W S
201 N. Vine Street, 54023
(715) 749-3337

Salem

Buttons and Bolts Fabric & Quilting Supply Q E N M
27642 75th Street, 53168
(262) 586-2522

Handi Quilter® Authorized Retailer
Designed by a Quilter, for Quilters.®

Sand Creek

Heart Blossom Design Q E
N13430 County Road I, 54765
(715) 658-1333

Sayner

Plum Lake Quilts* Q
3019 Highway 155, 54560
(715) 542-4888

Sheboygan

Lost Sheep Yarn Shop Y
808 Pennsylvania Avenue, 53081
(920) 453-0316

Sheboygan Falls

Magpie's Cottage* Q Y W S
507 Broadway Street, 53085
(920) 467-9978

Solon Springs

The Little Gift House* Q E Y
9234 E. Main Street, 54873
(715) 378-4170

Sparta

Quilt Corner Ⓠ Ⓔ
219 N. Water Street, 54656
(608) 269-1083

Yarn Stash Ⓨ
103 W. Oak Street, 54656
(608) 269-5648

Spooner

Northwind Book & Fiber Ⓨ
205 Walnut Street, 54801
(715) 635-6811
M-F 9-5:30, Sa 9-5, Su (May-Dec) 11-3
www.northwindbook.com

Spring Green

Country Sampler Ⓠ Ⓒ
133 E. Jefferson Street, 53588
(608) 588-2510

Nina, Inc. Ⓔ Ⓨ
143 E. Jefferson Street, 53588
(608) 588-2366

St. Croix Falls

Pins N Needles Ⓠ Ⓔ
126 N. Washington Street, 54024
(715) 483-5728

St. Germain

Just Yarnin' LLC Ⓨ
446 Highway 70E, 54558
(715) 479-9276

Sutter's Gold 'n Fleece Ⓨ
9094 County Highway O, 54558
(715) 479-7634

Stanley

Pine Hollow Store Ⓠ Ⓜ
N14085 Fernwall Avenue, 54768
(715) 644-3591
M-F 8-6, Sa 8-4
www.pine-hollow-quilting-variety-store.business.site

Sew N Sew Quilts & Fabrics Ⓠ Ⓔ Ⓢ
36360 County Highway MM, 54768
(715) 644-5563

The Woolen Shoppe Ⓔ Ⓨ
7444 345th Street, 54768
(715) 644-5814

Stevens Point

Herrschners, Inc. Ⓠ Ⓔ Ⓨ Ⓝ Ⓦ Ⓒ
2800 Hoover Avenue, 54481
(715) 341-4554 or (800) 441-0838

Wisconsin Wool Exchange Ⓨ Ⓦ Ⓢ
1009 1st Street, 54481
(715) 295-0975

Stockholm

Black Cat Farmstead Ⓨ Ⓦ Ⓢ
N3049 Nelson Lane, 54769
(612) 599-9047

Hugga Bugga Yarns Ⓨ
W12103 State Highway 35, 54769
(612) 308-1714

Stoughton

Spry Whimsy Fiber Arts Ⓨ Ⓢ
168 W. Main Street, 53589
(608) 239-0688

Sturgeon Bay

Barn Door Quilt Shop Ⓠ
154 N. 3rd Avenue, 54235
(920) 746-1544

Sun Prairie

J.J. Stitches Ⓠ
221 E. Main Street, 53590
(608) 837-2266

Prairie Junction LLC / Prairie Quiltworks LLC* Q Y C
227-229 E. Main Street, 53590
(608) 837-8909

Thiensville

My Material Matters Q M
221 N. Main Street, 53092
(262) 292-8218 or (262) 292-8218

Thorp

Bolts of Fun Q
102 E. Stanley Street, 54771
(715) 773-0652

Tigerton

Pinery Patches LLC Q
N4647 Highway 45, 54486
(715) 535 2277

Tomahawk

Sew Pieceful Quilting Q
118 W. Wisconsin Avenue, 54487
(715) 453-7126

Tomahawk Sew N Vac M
214 W. Wisconsin Avenue, 54487
(715) 224-3401

Two Rivers

Intertwined Yarn Shop E Y W C
1623 Washington Street, 54241
(920) 629-9011

The Quilt Shop of Two Rivers Q
1603 Washington Street, 54241
(920) 657-1999

Valders

Hidden Valley Farm & Woolen Mill Q Y W S
14804 Newton Road, 54245
(920) 758-2803

Verona

The Sow's Ear Y W S
125 S. Main Street, 53593
(608) 848-2755
M-F 6:30am-8:30pm (1st & 3rd Friday open until 10 pm), SaSu 7am-5pm
www.knitandsip.com

Viroqua

Ewetopia Fiber Shop Y S
102 S. Main Street, 54665
(608) 637-3443

Quilt Basket 'n' Creations Q E Y
117 FS Drive, 54665
(608) 637-7002

Washington Island

Sievers School Of Fiber Arts Q Y W S
986 Jackson Harbor Road, 54246
(920) 847-2264

Waukesha

Sew Much More Q E Y M
2140 W. St. Paul Avenue, Suite L, 53188
(262) 547-7774

Waunakee

Mill House Quilts Q E M
100 Baker Street, 53597
(608) 849-6473

Waupaca

Sew 'n Sew Q E M
112 S. Main Street, 54981
(715) 256-1071

Wausau

Needle Workshop / Quilting Workshop Q E C
312 & 314 S. 1st Avenue, 54401
(715) 848-5546

Sew Smart LLC Q M
2907 Rib Mountain Drive, 54401
(715) 845-9675

Wausau (Rib Mountain)

Ana's Sewing Studio / Julie's Sewing Center Ⓠ Ⓜ
4505 Rib Mountain Drive, 54401
(715) 355-1511
MTuWF 10-5, Th 10-7, Sa 10-4
www.anasewstudio.com

West Allis

Coins & Quilts Ⓠ
11037 W. Oklahoma Avenue, 53227
(414) 546-3233

West Bend

Royce Quilting Ⓠ Ⓔ Ⓜ
840 S. Main Street, 53095
(262) 338-0597

Xpressions Yarn & Bead Boutique Ⓨ
264 N. Main Street, 53095
(262) 306-1300

Whitehall

Pammy's Patchwork Playhouse Ⓠ
18453 Scranton Street, 54773
(715) 797-4882

Whitewater

Kari's Sew Unique Ⓠ Ⓜ
12524 E. County Road N, 53190
(262) 473-2049

Woodland Quilts LLC Ⓠ
147 W. Main Street, 53190
(262) 473-2978

Wisconsin Rapids

The Cotton Thimble Ⓠ
540 Daly Avenue, 54494
(715) 424-1122

Withee

Brubaker Sewing & Furniture Ⓠ Ⓔ Ⓒ Ⓜ
N14590 County Highway O, 54498
(715) 229-2851
M-Th 8-6, F 8-8, Sa 8-4

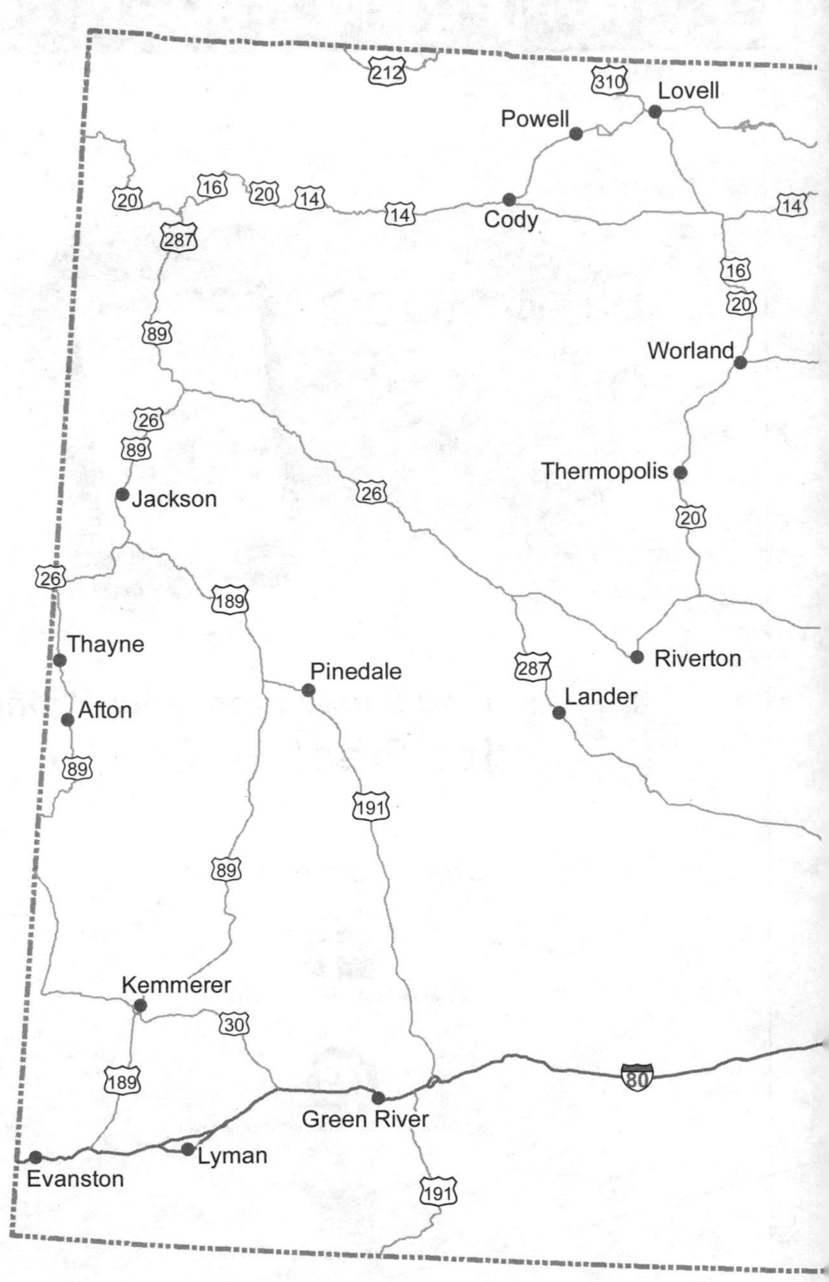

212
310
Lovell
Powell
20
16
20
14
14
Cody
14
287
16
20
89
Worland
26
89
Thermopolis
Jackson
26
20
26
189
Thayne
Pinedale
287
Riverton
Afton
Lander
89
191
89
Kemmerer
30
189
80
Green River
Lyman
Evanston
191

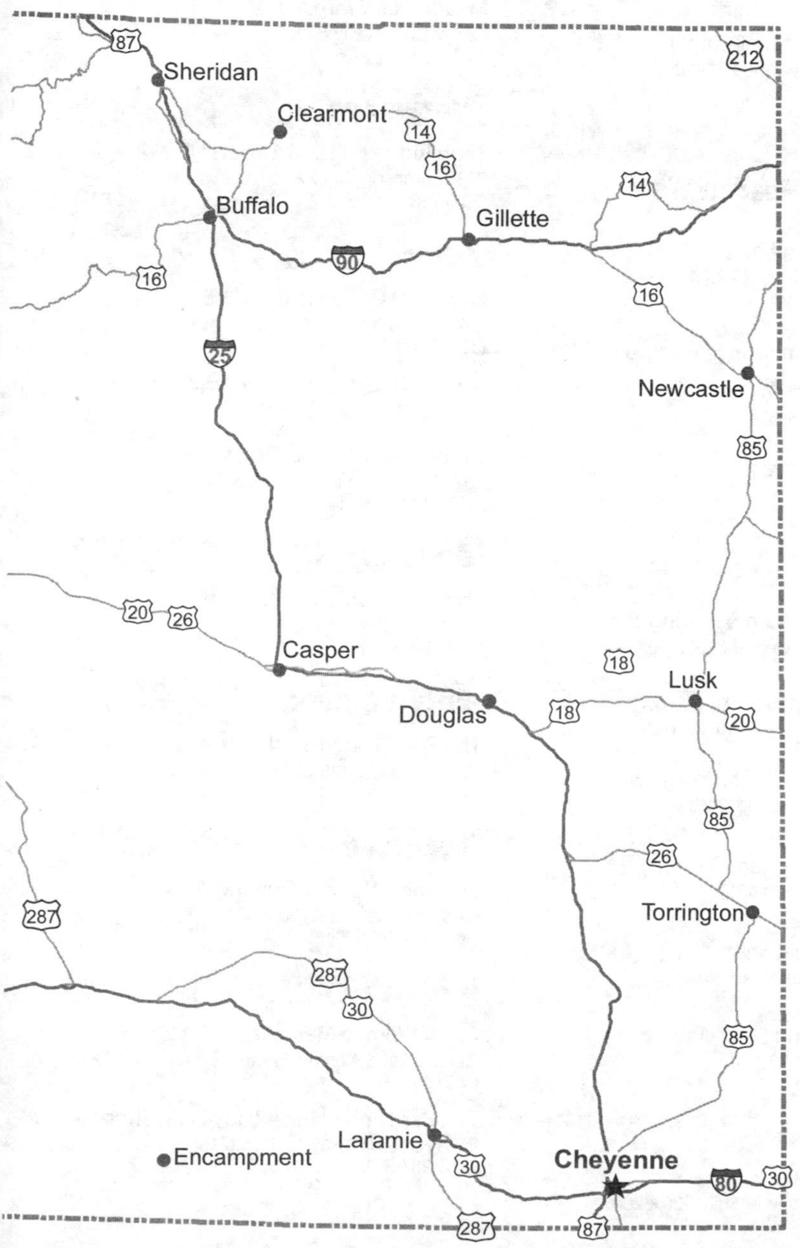
87
212
Sheridan
Clearmont
14
16
14
Buffalo
Gillette
90
16
16
25
Newcastle
85
20
26
Casper
18
Lusk
Douglas
18
20
85
26
287
Torrington
287
30
85
Laramie
Encampment
Cheyenne
30
80
30
287
87

Wyoming

Afton

Jenny M's Quilting Company Q E N C
419 Washington Avenue, 83110
(307) 885-2522

Buffalo

Mountain Meadow Wool Mill Y N W S
➡ SEE AD PAGE 344
22 Plains Drive, 82834
(307) 684-5775
M-F 9-5
www.mountainmeadowwool.com

DJ's Grocery & Variety Q Y
895 Fort Street, 82834
(307) 684-2518

E.T. Quilts* Q E N C
80 S. Main Street, 82834
(307) 684-9006 or (877) 387-8458

Casper

Blakeman Vacuum & Sewing Q M
275 S. Montana Avenue, 82609
(307) 234-4581
Handi Quilter® Authorized Retailer
Designed by a Quilter, for Quilters.®

Cottontales Quilt Company* Q
299 Country Club Road, 82609
(307) 337-4200

Dancing Sheep Yarn & Fiber* Y S
120 E. 2nd Street, 82601
(307) 265-6173

Kalico Kat Quilt Shop Q
1239 S. Elk Street, 82601
(307) 237-8458

Prism Quilt and Sew* Q
114 E. 2nd Street, 82601
(307) 234-4841

Cheyenne

Around the Block Q E
453 Vandehei Avenue, Suite 120, 82009
(307) 433-9555

Ewe Count E Y N C
819 Randall Avenue, 82001
(307) 638-1148

Meadowlark Yarns* Y S
220 W. Lincolnway, 82001
(307) 369-4371

Clearmont

Sage Ridge Mill and Critters* Y W S
239 Thompson Creek Road, 82835
(307) 758-4616

Cody

Friends & Co. Quilt Shop Q M
402 Warren Avenue, 82414
(307) 527-7217
Handi Quilter® Authorized Retailer
Designed by a Quilter, for Quilters.®

Grand Loop Yarns & Fibers Y S C
2522 Mountain View Drive, 82414
(307) 250-8499

Douglas

The Prairie Stitcher* Q E Y M
120 N. 3rd Street, 82633
(307) 358-5571

Encampment

The Sheep Shed Studio* Y W S
421 Lomax Avenue, 82325
(307) 327-5568

Evanston

Common Threads Quilting Q
1029 Main Street, 82930
(307) 444-1675

Gillette

Crazy Woman Mercantile* E Y C
214 S. Gillette Avenue, 82716
(307) 682-3152

The Barn and Blanket Lady Quilt Shop* Q
8506 N. US Highway 14-16, 82716
(307) 257-3912

Green River

A Little Country Character* Q M
1740 Uinta Drive, 82935
(307) 875-7172

Handi Quilter® Authorized Retailer
Designed by a Quilter, for Quilters.®

Keama's Quilts* Q E Y
91 W. Flaming Gorge Way, 82935
(307) 875-5461 or (888) 875-5461

Jackson

Knit On Pearl E Y N C
145 W. Gill Avenue, 83001
(307) 733-5648

Kemmerer

Ace Hardware Fabric & Gifts Q E Y C
709 Pine Avenue, 83101
(307) 877-6956 or (800) 837-6957

Lander

Wyoming Quilts* Q
305 Main Street, 82520
(307) 332-4123

Laramie

Cowgirl Yarn Y W S
119 E. Ivinson Avenue, 82070
(307) 755-9276

Quilt Essentials Q
314 S. 2nd Street, 82070
(307) 742-6156

Snowy River Quilts Q E
216 E. Custer Street, 82070
(307) 721-3160

Lovell

Mayes Fabrics Q
435 Oregon Avenue, 82431
(307) 548-7715

Lusk

Lickety Stitch Quilts Q M
206 S. Main Street, 82225
(307) 334-9963

Lyman (Urie)

Valley Fabric Shop Q E
102 Mountain Meadow Street, 82937
(307) 786-2653

Newcastle

Strawberry Patch Quilt Shop Q
210 W. Main Street, 82701
(307) 746-3116

Pinedale

Heritage Quilts & Fabric Shoppe Q E Y C
21 E. Pine Street, 82941
(307) 367-7397

Powell

Cut & Sew Fabrics Q E Y N W S C
217 N. Bent Street, 82435
(307) 754-7247

Riverton

Country Cottage Quilt Shoppe Q M
710 E. Washington Ave, 82501
(307) 463-0237

Sheridan

The Fiber House Y W S
146 Coffeen Avenue, 82801
(307) 673-0383
MWThF 10-5, Tu 10-7, Sa 10-4
www.thefiberhouse.com

The Quilter's Fix Q
1135 N. Main Street, 82801
(307) 674-0558
M-F 10-6, Sa 9-4
www.quiltersfix.com

Ben Franklin Q E Y N C
1447 Coffeen Avenue, 82801
(307) 672-5889

Thayne

Beyond Bolts Ⓠ Ⓔ Ⓨ Ⓒ
120 Petersen Parkway, 83127
(307) 883-2464

Handi Quilter® Authorized Retailer
Designed by a Quilter, for Quilters.®

Thermopolis

Gooseberry Garden Quilt Shop Ⓠ Ⓨ
521 Broadway Street, 82443
(307) 864-3503
M-F 10-5, Sa 10-4
www.gooseberrygardenquiltshop.com

Torrington

The Covered Wagon Quilt Shop Ⓠ Ⓜ
2006 Main Street, 82240
(307) 532-1077

Worland

Colors & Crafts Ⓨ
325 N. 11th Street, Suite C, 82401
(307) 431-7296

Heart-N-Home Ⓠ Ⓔ Ⓨ Ⓒ
1201 Big Horn Avenue, 82401
(307) 347-4954